100 YEARS AT The Hawthorns

100 YEARS AT The Hawthorns

A celebration of West Bromwich Albion's home since 1900

by Tony Matthews

Express & Star

The Breedon Books
Publishing Company
Derby

First published in Great Britain by
The Breedon Books Publishing Company Limited
Breedon House, 44 Friar Gate, Derby, DE1 1DA.
1999

ISBN 1 85983 158 3

Printed and bound by Butler & Tanner Ltd, Selwood Printing
Works, Caxton Road, Frome, Somerset.

Colour separations and jacket printing by GreenShires Group Ltd,
Leicester.

Contents

Acknowledgements

This book would not have been possible but for the dedicated and kind co-operation of my good friend and fellow statistician Colin Mackenzie.

I would also like to to say a big thank you to the following, many of whom have loaned photographs for use in this publication: former players Ronnie Allen, Ray Barlow, Wilf Carter, Glyn Hood, Harry Kinsell, Jimmy Sanders and Dave Walsh; former Albion chairman and now ppresident Sir Bert Millichip; former Albion trainer-physiotherapist Fred Pedley; amateur photographers and avid Albion fans Kevin Grice, Barry Marsh and Laurie Rampling; Paul Leddington; Baggies' newspaper editor Glenn Willmore; Albion supporters' club chairman Alan Cleverley; Lee Grice and Michael Reynolds; and my wife Margaret. Also the *Express & Star* editor Warren Wilson and his staff, and Anton Rippon and his staff at Breedon Books. Finally, to anyone who I have inadvertantly missed, my apologies and sincere thanks

Introduction

ON 3 September 2000, The Hawthorns – home of West Bromwich Albion Football Club – will celebrate its 100th birthday.

Since 1900 more than 4,000 matches (not including friendlies) have been played there involving various Albion teams. The first XI have played in over 2,000 competitive matches including 1,662 in the Football League, 131 in the FA Cup and 60 in the League Cup.

Derby County were Albion's first visitors to the ground – drawing 1-1 in a Football League match almost a century ago – and since then over 150 other different teams have ventured to West Bromwich to compete against the Baggies, including club sides from Austria, Belgium, France, Germany, Holland, Italy, Malta, Portugal, Romania, Russia, Spain, Switzerland, Turkey and Yugoslavia as well as representative sides from Canada and China.

The Hawthorns has staged three major internationals (1922, 1924 and 1945) and played host to both FA Cup and League Cup semi-finals. Some of the game's greatest players have performed on the Hawthorns' pitch – among them Ivor Allchurch, Gordon Banks, Cliff Bastin, Jim Baxter, George Best, Danny Blanchflower, Steve Bloomer (scorer of the first goal on the ground back in 1900), Rainer Bonhoff, Billy Bremner, Charlie Buchan, Roger Byrne, Raich Carter, John Charles, Bobby Charlton, Kenny Dalglish, Dixie Dean, Jimmy Dickinson, Peter Doherty, Ted Drake, Duncan Edwards, Tom Finney, Trevor Ford, Neil Franklin, Hughie Gallagher, Jimmy Greaves, Johnny Haynes, Glenn Hoddle, Eric Houghton, David Jack, Alex James, Pat Jennings, Bryn Jones, Kevin Keegan, Fred Keenor, Mario Kempes, Denis Law, Tommy Lawton, Jimmy McIlroy, Wilf Mannion, Stanley Matthews, Billy Meredith, Bobby Moore, Stan Mortensen, Ian Rush, Len Shackleton, Peter Shilton, Neville Southall, Ronnie Starling, Frank Swift, Tommy Taylor, and Billy Wright. And of course there have been many star players who have donned the famous navy blue and white striped shirts of Albion, including Ronnie Allen, Jeff Astle, Ray Barlow, Sid Bowser, Tony Brown, Fred Buck, Joe Carter, Clive Clark, Jimmy Cookson, Laurie Cunningham, Stan Davies, Jimmy Dudley, Jimmy Dugdale, Billy Elliott, Doug Fraser, Johnny Giles, Tommy Glidden, Frank Griffin, Asa Hartford, Bobby Hope, Don Howe, Willie Johnston, Harry 'Popeye' Jones, John Kaye, Mario Kempes, Joe Kennedy, Derek Kevan, George Lee, Bobby McNeal, Tommy Magee, Len Millard, Fred Morris, Jimmy Murphy, Johnny Nicholls, John Osborne, Bob Pailor, Harold Pearson and his father Hubert Pearson, Jesse Pennington, Cyrille Regis, Bill Richardson, Sammy Richardson, 'W. G.' Richardson, Stan Rickaby, Ally Robertson, Bobby Robson, Bryan Robson, Reg Ryan, Jimmy Sanders, Teddy Sandford, Maurice Setters, George Shaw, Chippy Simmons (scorer of Albion's first goal at The Hawthorns), Joe Smith, Derek Statham, Jack Vernon, Dave Walsh, John Wile, Billy Williams, Graham Williams and Stuart Williams…and we can't leave out strikers Don Goodman, Lee Hughes, Andy Hunt and Bob Taylor.

The Everiss family – Fred and his son Alan – have been associated with Albion and The Hawthorns for well over 100 years. Alan is now a life member and shareholder and he first set foot inside The Hawthorns back in 1933, when he worked as an office clerk under his father who was secretary-manager of Albion from 1902 to 1948 – a Football League record in terms of service with one club.

Managers have come and gone – Jack Smith, Vic Buckingham, Gordon Clark, Archie Macaulay, Jimmy Hagan, Alan Ashman, Johnny Giles, Ron Atkinson, Ron Saunders, Ron Wylie, Nobby Stiles, Ossie Ardiles, Keith Burkinshaw, Alan Buckley, Ray Harford and Denis Smith along with ex-players Don Howe, Ronnie Allen, Brian Talbot and Bobby Gould. Some did Albion proud, others failed.

Albion have won the League Championship, the FA Cup and the Football League Cup during their time at The Hawthorns. Now they want to get into the Premiership.

The ground itself, the facilities therein, the supporters are all there – let's hope Albion will soon be entertaining the likes of Manchester United, Arsenal and Liverpool and, indeed, competing with the best teams in Europe.

Tony Matthews
Summer 1999

The Hawthorns

THE HAWTHORNS, home of West Bromwich Albion Football Club, was the first Football League ground built in the 20th century (or the last in the 19th century depending on your view of when one finished and the other began), with work commencing on a large site situated on the border of Handsworth, Smethwick and West Bromwich in mid-May 1900.

It was virtually completed within four months – in readiness for the official opening on 3 September 1900.

The lease on Albion's previous ground in Stoney Lane expired in 1899, and at the time it was one of the worst grounds in the Football League. However, being unable to finalise details on a new ground, the management renewed the lease for a further 12 months, thus allowing enough time for the ground committee, with Harry Keys a key figure, to search for a suitable site to build Albion's new stadium.

After lengthy negotiations, on 5 December 1899 a letter was written by Benjamin Karliese, the secretary of the Sandwell Park Colliery, to the Albion club which sparked off the eventual move to The Hawthorns.

It read: 'My board direct me to offer you a lease of the piece of land forming the corner of Halford's Lane and the Birmingham Road, about ten acres (less sufficient land next to the 'Oaklands' to make a road across, 40 to 50 feet wide) for 14 years at a rental of £750 per annum for the first seven years and £80 per annum for the second seven years. The West Bromwich Albion Football Club Company to have option of terminating the lease at the end of the first seven years on giving such notice as may be mutually agreed. The Football Club Company to pay to the Company one-third of the revenue that my be derived from any hoarding that may be erected by the Club on the land in question during the existence of the lease, the Club retaining two-thirds of the revenue for the cost of erecting and maintaining the hoarding and collecting the revenue arising therefrom. My board will reserve full powers for working the mines under and adjacent to the land, without being liable for damage to surface or erections thereon, and would require the covenants usual in their leases to be embodied in this. It is understood that this offer is left open for your acceptance till 1 February 1900, but if practicable my Board would be glad of a decision earlier.'

The land referred to was a meadow owned at one time by an ancient Coventry charity. Just two days before the Sandwell Park Colliery Company's offer was due to expire, the Albion board passed a crucial resolution: '...that we accept the offer of Sandwell Park Colliery and take the ground at the corner of Halford's Lane and Birmingham Road on a 14-year lease upon the terms mentioned in their letter of 5 December 1899.'

On 14 May 1900 it was resolved by the directors that the lease for the ground be signed and sealed with the seal of the company, and the club's seal was duly affixed to a 14-year lease of the field that was to become known as The Hawthorns.

Why The Hawthorns? Well, on the surveyor's map, the area surrounding the 'ground' was referred to as 'Hawthorns Estate' and hawthorn bushes had flourished there at one time. Therefore, it seemed an appropriate and obvious choice of name.

The land itself had a marshy look about it when building work commenced in late February, and there was a brook flowing nearby which formed the boundary between the towns of Smethwick, Handsworth and West Bromwich. But this did not deter the workie force and in no time at all the ground was ready for use.

Initially, the field of play sloped dramatically from the Halford's Lane/Birmingham Road corner, across and down towards the Smethwick End/now Rainbow Stand corner. The slope was measured up to seven feet at one time.

But over the years, the playing area itself has been built-up and now there is a gradual slope of approximately 2ft 4ins.

Bearing this in mind, there haven't been too many waterlogged pitches at The Hawthorns over the years. In fact, only three League games have been abandoned owing to the state of the pitch – those against Bury in 1925, Luton Town in 1958 and Aston Villa in 1965 (all in the old First Division). There have been other matches called off through fog, poor light and falling snow.

Hawthorns Calendar

1900

Ground officially opened on Monday, 3 September 1900 for the First Division game between West Bromwich Albion and Derby County. At the time The Hawthorns could house around 35,500 fans, and there were 20,104 present on the opening day to see Steve Bloomer (Derby) score the first goal with 'Chippy' Simmons equalising to become the first player to find the net for Albion. The game ended all square at 1-1.

transferred to The Hawthorns, burned down on Guy Fawkes' Night. Reports say that the blaze was caused by a spectator leaving a lighted cigarette in the stand.

1904

The old Stoney Lane stand, known as 'Noah's Ark' which had been

1905

A half-time scoreboard was installed for the first time.

Albion players and officials pictured at the official opening of The Hawthorns on 3 September 1900. Back row (left to right): I. Whitehouse (president, Birmingham League), W. Heath (secretary, Staffordshire FA), J. C. Orr (secretary Birmingham FA), D. I. Pitt (director, WBA), T. H. Sidney (vice-president, Football League), H. Lockett (secretary, Football League). Second row: H. Powell (director, WBA), T. H. Spencer (director, WBA), H. Radford (committeeman, Football League), C. E. Sutcliffe (committeeman, Football League), D. Haigh (vice-president, Football League), J. J. Bentley (president, Football League), H. Keys (chairman, WBA), W. W. Hart ((committeeman, Football League), W. McGregor (founder, Football League), C. Perry (director, WBA), J. Lones (director, WBA). Seated: Frank Heaven (secretary, WBA), C. Keys (auditor, WBA), Pickering, Wheldon (captain), Simmons, Jones, Dunn, Adams, J. Paddock (trainer, WBA). On ground: J. M. Bayliss (director, WBA), Chadburn, Roberts, Reader, Williams, Hadley.

The Hawthorns on the left of Halford's Lane about 1910. The Hawthorns Hotel on the right was previously known from 1661 as Street House and when it was rebuilt in 1846 was the residence of local ironmaster, Mr H. H. Halford. Straighthouse Lane was probably the original name for Halford's Lane and 'Street House' therefore a corruption. Just after Albion moved from Stoney Lane to The Hawthorns in 1900, the public house was granted a licence for the refreshment of football spectators. Street House Farm and the barn in the centre of the picture survived for two and half centuries.

1906
A new stand was constructed at the Smethwick End of the ground.

1911
The main Halford's Lane stand was completely overhauled and the returfed.

1912
Following a mini subsidence, the Hawthorns pitch was completely returfed.

banking was increased on the Handsworth side.

1913
Albion purchased the freehold of The Hawthorns for £5,350.

1914
The Halford's Lane stand was extended.

1920
Concrete terracing was installed and a concrete wall was constructed to replace the wooden fencing surrounding the playing area.

1922
The first international match was staged at The Hawthorns: England 2 Ireland 0.

1923
The embankment on the Handsworth side (opposite the main stand) was extended further back and the roof heightened.

1924
The Hawthorns ground capacity was officially put at 65,000 and a second international took place there, England defeating Belgium 4-0.

The plaque at The Hawthorns commemorating the visit of the Prince of Wales after Albion had achieved a unique double of FA Cup and promotion to Division One.

1931
Terracing all round the ground was finally completed and tip-up seats were installed in the wing-stands. The nearby Hawthorns Halt railway station, on the Great Western Line, was opened on Christmas Day.

1934
A new stand with 750 extra seats, was completed at the Smethwick/Halford's Lane corner of the ground. This brought the capacity of The Hawthorns up to nearly 66,000.

1935
A new oak-panelled tea-room was constructed in the Halford's Lane stand.

Poster advertising an athletics meeting at The Hawthorns in May 1908.

HAWTHORNS CALENDAR

The Halford's Lane Stand in 1954 before it was redeveloped in 1982.

1939

The wooden roof over the Halford's Lane stand was dismantled and replaced by some asbestos sheeting which rested on five giant steel stanchions. The roof was also extended outwards to the front of the terraces.

1940-46

Owing to the war very little work was carried out on the ground but in 1945 England played Wales in a Victory International which drew a 54,610 crowd.

1947

A new block of turnstiles was erected on the Handsworth side of the ground, behind the Woodman Corner.

1949

The wooden terraces in front of the main Halford's Lane stand were replaced by concrete and 750 extra seats were installed in the stand itself. The first electronic turnstile aggregator to be installed on a Football League ground in Britain was put in at The Hawthorns.

1950

A new Directors' Box was provided and the club's offices and dressing rooms were completely re-modernised.

1951

Eight new turnstiles were installed at the Smethwick End.

1957

Floodlights were erected at the ground for the first time at a cost of £18,000. The first game under the 'new' lights saw Albion draw 1-1 with Chelsea in a League Division One fixture on 18 September. Soon afterwards – on 29 October – the Russian Red Army team (CDSK from Moscow) came over to officially open the lights. Albion beat them 6-5 in a classic friendly in front of a 52,805 crowd.

1958

A wing stand at the West Bromwich/Birmingham Road End, was

In 1951-52, a season ticket for the Halford's Lane end cost £5 5s (£5.25).

The Birmingham Road end before the start of a First Division game in 1958.

The famous Throstle at The Hawthorns.

1961

A new car park with spaces for some 600 vehicles, was opened just off Middlemore Road (behind the Handsworth Road stand). And by 1964 there were four car parks with-in 800 yards of the ground.

1964

The Rainbow Stand, costing £40,000, was erected on the Hands-worth side. It contained 4,100 tip-up

The Smethwick end pictured in 1962.

added to the main Halford's Lane stand.

seats and was paid for with funds from the Development Association. The 'old' Handsworth stand was transferred across to cover the ter-racing behind the Birmingham Road goal.

1965

The first Throstle Club (for Albion supporters) was opened next to The Hawthorns on the Birmingham Road. Two left-backs and former skippers, England international Jesse Pennington and Welshman

1976

Fourteen executive boxes were installed in front of the Rainbow Stand and an extra 750 paddock seats were also inserted in front of the boxes themselves.

1977

The Executive box complex was completed, while the terracing was

1967

The buffet bars situated inside the ground were all renovated at a cost of £20,000.

1968

The Hawthorns Halt railway station was closed down.

1969

The first-ever 'Open Day' for sup-porters was held at The Hawthorns and around 10,000 fans turned up to look behind the scenes.

1970

The Hawthorns' floodlighting sys-tem was renovated four-fold to fall in line with colour TV transmis-sions.

Graham Williams, attended the opening ceremony.

HAWTHORNS CALENDAR

The Halford's Lane Stand in 1977.

reconstructed at the Smethwick and Birmingham Road Ends with several new crush-barriers also being erected.

1979

Work started on the new £2.5 million Halford's Lane stand which would accommodate 4,500 spectators. This was built in two phases over a three-year period:1979-82, and included some more Executive boxes.

1983

The Hawthorns Throstle Club (built next to the ground in 1964) was closed. A large electronic scoreboard was erected on the front of the stand at the Smethwick End (but this was removed in 1985).

1985

A completely new roof was fitted over the terracing at the Smethwick End of the ground and new safety measures were installed at the ground.

1986

A up-to-date, state-of-the-art crowd control video system was installed at the ground.

1988-92

Major safety work was carried out all over the ground following the

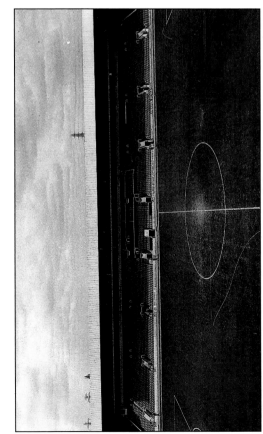

Between 1979 and 1982 the Halford's Lane Stand was rebuilt at a cost of £2.5 million.

100 YEARS AT THE HAWTHORNS

View from the Halfords Lane executive boxes which came into use in the early 1980s.

The Hawthorns in 1981-82 showing the Birmingham Road end-Rainbow Stand corner.

HAWTHORNS CALENDAR

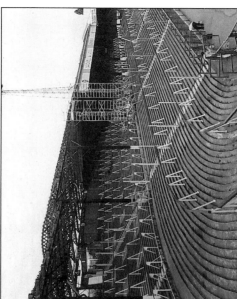

Work under way on the Smethwick end in the wake of the Taylor Report.

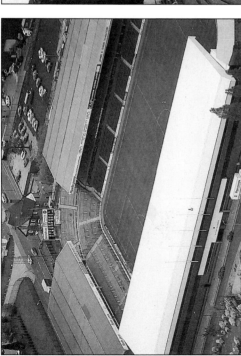

An elevated view of the same Birmingham Road end-Rainbow Stand corner in1990.

Aerial view of The Hawthorns in 1993-94.

The Apollo 2000 Stand at the Birmingham Road end in 1997.

The Halfords Lane Stand pictured in 1992.

tragedies at both the Valley Parade and Hillsborough stadiums.

1989

A smart new Sponsors' Lounge was opened in the corner of the Halford's Lane stand, next to the Birmingham Road terraces.

1990

The Hawthorns pitch was complete-

ly returfed for only the second time in 90 years. Sods of turf were then sold to supporters as souvenirs.

1991

In February a major pipe-burst caused thousands of pounds worth of damage in the Halford's Lane complex. In December, television pictures of Albion's away FA Cup-tie with Leyton Orient were beamed

back to The Hawthorns on two giant screens which were erected in front of the main stand.

1992

The roof was removed from above the Smethwick End terracing as plans were put into operation to redevelop the ground and make it into an all-seater stadium.

A view familiar to all Albion fans, the Smethwick end pictured in 1997.

1994

In the close season the pitch was relaid with enhanced drainage in the summer and the Birmingham Road terracing was dug up as work continued on the redevelopment of The Hawthorns. Albion kicked-off the 1994-95 season with five away League games as the ground was not declared ready when the League programme was due to commence.

The combined cost of refurbishing the stadium came to £4.15 million, of which the club received £2,097,000 from the Football Trust in 1995. The 'new' modernised Hawthorns was officially opened for the First Division visit of Bristol City on Boxing Day, a game Albion won 1-0.

1995

The Hawthorns Museum was officially opened by manager Alan Buckley, vice-chairman Clive Stapleton and curator Tony Matthews. The Hawthorns railway station was re-opened after 27 years and the capacity of ground was cut to 27,000.

1996

The club offices were moved from The Hawthorns to the newly erected and more substantial Tom Silk Building situated on the opposite side of Halford's Lane, some 300 yards away. A new club shop was also opened.

1997

The Hawthorns ground was now officially an all-seater stadium with a capacity of 25,296.

1998

In the summer The Hawthorns pitch was completely dug up again, and returfed for only the fourth time in 98 years, following similar exercises in 1912, 1990 and 1994. Undersoil heating was installed.

1999

Albion played their 2,000th home game in the Football League at The Hawthorns on Saturday, 17 April, drawing 2-2 with Portsmouth in front of 12,750 spectators.

2000

The Hawthorns officially celebrated its 100th birthday on 3 September.

Facts and Figures

- The Hawthorns is the highest League ground above sea level in the UK – 551 feet. (Non-League Tow Law's ground in the north-east of England is said to be 998 feet above sea level).

- The never-to-be-beaten attendance record of 64,815 at The Hawthorns was set in March 1937 when Arsenal were the visitors for a sixth-round FA Cuptie.

- A breakdown on The Hawthorns seating arrangements, including box-holders, is:

Rainbow Stand	6,084
Halford's Lane Stand	5,110
Smethwick End	5,816
Birmingham Rd. End	8,286
Total	25,296

- There have been three major internationals played on the ground: England 2 Ireland 0 in 1922, England 4 Belgium 0 in 1924 and England 0 Wales 1 (Victory International) in 1945.

- In 1914, the Football League played the Irish League at The Hawthorns, and there have also been three other representative games played on the ground: England v The South in 1920 and England v The Rest in 1928 and 1935.

- There have been a number of schoolboy and youth internationals staged at The Hawthorns.

Action from the England v Wales Victory international at The Hawthorns in 1945.

plus a handful of non-League Cup Finals and a League Cup Final (Albion v West Ham, second leg, 1965-66), the 1971 Watney Cup Final (Albion v Colchester United) and the first leg of the 1995-96 Anglo-Italian English Final, Albion v Port Vale. There have also been two FA Cup semi-finals: Derby County v Sheffield United in 1901-02 and Aston Villa v Wolverhampton Wanderers in 1959-60; one other League Cup semi-final: Burnley v Swindon Town replay in 1968-69. (Albion themselves have appeared in four League Cup semi-finals on their own ground: 1965-66,

- 'W. G.' Richardson scored more goals at The Hawthorns than any other player: a total of 216 in all first team matches.

final: Albion v Swansea City second leg, 1992-93.

- The size of The Hawthorns pitch in 1999-2000 is 115 yards long by 75 yards wide (it used to be 118 x 79).

- Tony Brown played in a record 282 Football League games for Albion at The Hawthorns. He made 361 first-team appearances all told on the ground and scored 173 goals (132 in the League).

- Well over 4,000 matches (at various levels) have now been staged at The Hawthorns in the 100 years since 1900.

- Albion's 1,000th home game in the Football League was staged at The Hawthorns against Manchester United on 29 November 1952 – and this was also their 2,000th in the competition (home & away).

1966-67, 1969-70 and 1981-82.) And one Second Division Play-off semi-final: Albion v Swansea

FACTS AND FIGURES

- The 1,000th Football League game at The Hawthorns was between Albion and Leeds United on 10 October 1970 when over 37,000 fans witness the 2-2 draw. And in April 1999 Albion's 2,000th home match in the Football League attracted a crowd of 12,750 to The Hawthorns to see the 2-2 draw with Portsmouth. This fixture was marred however, when a supporter raced on to the pitch and assaulted a linesman.

- In November/December 1919 Wolverhampton Wanderers played two Second Division League games at The Hawthorns v Barnsley (lost 4-2) and Stockport County (2-2) because their home ground at Molineux had been closed following crowd disturbances.

- Walsall played Brighton & Hove Albion in a Third Division game at The Hawthorns in February 1970 because the Saddlers' Fellows Park ground was waterlogged. Brighton won 3-0.

- On 11 May 1931, HRH The Prince of Wales (later King Edward VIII and the Duke of Windsor) visited The Hawthorns to offer his congratulations to Albion on their unique 'double' achievement.

- On 7 August 1944, the American and Canadian armies staged a baseball match at The Hawthorns before a 5,000 crowd.

- Immediately before World War One an athletics meeting, staged over two days, took place at The Hawthorns, and there was also a boxing tournament held there featuring the great Jimmy Wilde.

- On 29 July 1977 a limited over cricket match was staged at The Hawthorns between the Indian and Pakistan Test sides. The Indians won by four wickets and 2,641 attended. The proceeds went towards a children's charity and Imran Khan's benefit.

- On 15 October 1980, the first floodlight cricket match was played at The Hawthorns when Ian Botham's XI (which included David Gower) played Warwickshire CCC in a 30 overs match, the proceeds going towards Alistair Robertson's testimonial fund.

- The Albion v Liverpool Coca-Cola Cup-tie at The Hawthorns on Wednesday 15 October 1997 realised record gate receipts for the club (League and Cup matches) of £264,127.50.

- Albion's average home League attendance at The Hawthorns is 19,765. The average FA Cup attendance is 31,618, and in the League Cup (under its various guises) it is 16,788. The best seasonal League average is 38,819 in 1953-54. The lowest is 4,884 in 1904-05.

FA Cup					
P	W	D	L	F	A
131	76	30	25	268	123

European Fairs, UEFA & Cup-winners' Cup					
P	W	D	L	F	A
11	6	1	4	21	13

Anglo-Italian Cup					
P	W	D	L	F	A
10	3	3	4	16	13

Autoglass Trophy					
P	W	D	L	F	A
4	3	0	1	10	2

Anglo Scottish Cup					
P	W	D	L	F	A
2	1	1	0	4	2

Full Members Cup					
P	W	D	L	F	A
2	1	1*	0	4	3

* lost on penalties

Watney Cup					
P	W	D	L	F	A
1	0	1*	0	4	4

* Lost on penalties

Texaco Cup					
P	W	D	L	F	A
5	3	1	1	8	3

Wartime Football					
P	W	D	L	F	A
136	87	20	29	421	216

Totals					
P	W	D	L	F	A
2024	1131	491	402	4170	2125

Albion's record at The Hawthorns (competitive level):

Football League

P	W	D	L	F	A
1661	917	419	325	3299	1678

Football League Play-off

P	W	D	L	F	A
1	1	0	0	2	0

Football League Cup (inc CCC, LC & WC)

P	W	D	L	F	A
60	33	14	13	113	68

Hawthorns Firsts (1900-2000)

- The first Football League game at The Hawthorns took place on 3 September 1900 when Albion drew 1-1 with Derby County.

- Derby's Steve Bloomer (born in the Black Country town of Cradley Heath and 'missed' by Albion) scored the first goal in the above fixture after 23 minutes.

- The first Albion goal was the equaliser, netted by Chippy Simmons in the 78th minute.

- The attendance for this first competitive match was 20,104.

- The match referee was Mr R. J. Corbett (Walsall).

- Albion's first defeat at The Hawthorns was a 1-0 reverse at the hands of Aston Villa on 8 September 1900, when, for the first time, the attendance was 35,000.

- Albion's first League victory at The Hawthorns was a 3-2 League success over Manchester City on 6 October 1900.

- Grenville Morris of Nottingham Forest became the first opposing player to score a hat-trick at The Hawthorns in his side's 6-1 League defeat of Albion on 20 October 1900.

- On 29 October 1900 the first benefit match was staged at The Hawthorns when a crowd of 5,000 saw Albion held to a 3-3 draw by Wolves. The proceeds from the game went to Billy Richards. This was also the first friendly fixture at the ground.

- The first Albion player to score a hat-trick at The Hawthorns was left-winger Dick Roberts in the League game v Bolton Wanderers (won 7-2) on 8 December 1900.

- Albion's Fred Wheldon recorded the first penalty miss at The Hawthorns in the League game v Preston North End on 22 December 1900.

- On 9 February 1901 the first FA Cup-tie was staged at The Hawthorns when Albion entertained Manchester City. This tie was postponed from 26 January.

- A crowd of 10,026 saw Ben Garfield score the first Cup goal on the ground in the above tie to give Albion their first Cup victory (1-0).

- The first Second Division League game at The Hawthorns was that involving Albion and Glossop on 2 September 1901. This was also Albion's first defeat in this Division (0-1) and the official attendance was given as 5,064.

- Fred Crump of Glossop scored the first Second Division goal on the ground in the 43rd minute of that game (above).

- Albion's first Second Division victory was 3-1 v Preston North End on 7 September 1901.

- Right-winger Jimmy McLean scored Albion's first Second Division goal in the 30th minute of the above match.

- The first penalty to be scored at The Hawthorns was by Albion's Chippy Simmons v Chesterfield in a Second Division match on 9 September 1901.

- On 19 October 1901, a crowd of 7,829 witnessed the first Second Division draw at The Hawthorns when Albion were held 2-2 by Bristol City.

- The first Second Division hat-trick on the ground was netted by Albion's Chippy Simmons for Albion v Blackpool in a League game on 22 February 1902.

- The Stoke goalkeeper Leigh Richmond Roose became the first Doctor to play in a senior game at The Hawthorns where he lined up in a League game

HAWTHORNS FIRSTS

against Albion on 6 December 1902.

- This first FA Cup goal scored by an opponent at The Hawthorns was by Vivian Woodward of Tottenham Hotspur in a first-round replay on 11 February 1903 – and it this was also Albion's first Cup defeat on the ground.

- The first 3-3 League draw at the ground followed three days later when Albion were held by Sheffield United on 14 February 1903 (Division 1).

- The first FA Cup semi-final took place at The Hawthorns on 15 March 1902 when Derby County drew 1-1 with Sheffield United in front of 33,603 supporters.

- The first FA Cup draw at The Hawthorns was that between Albion and Nottingham Forest (1-1) on 10 February 1904.

- The first official *Albion News* was produced for the home League game with Burnley on 2 September 1905.

- The first opposing player to score two hat-tricks at The Hawthorns was Charlie Millington of Aston Villa – in a Birmingham Cup-tie on 4 September 1905 and in a Staffordshire Cup match on 2 October 1905.

- The first player to be sent-off at The Hawthorns was Jimmy Conlon of Bradford City in a Second Division League game v Albion on 11 November 1905.

- On 24 February 1906 Albion registered their first 6-0 League win at The Hawthorns v Glossop (Division 2).

- Albion recorded their first 5-0 League win at The Hawthorns on 10 March 1906 v Blackpool (Division 2).

- On 5 October 1906 the first players' social club room was opened at The Hawthorns.

- Albion's Fred Shinton was the first four-goal hero at The Hawthorns in his side's 5-0 victory over Clapton Orient (Division 2) on 6 October 1906.

- 19 January 1907 saw the first abandonment of a competitive game at The Hawthorns when the Albion-Barnsley Second Division clash was called off after 80 minutes through failing light.

- The first representative match held at The Hawthorns was a Junior International between England and Scotland on 4 April 1908. England won 4-0.

- The first player to score a hat-trick on his debut for Albion at The Hawthorns was Billy Jordan v Gainsborough Trinity (League) on 16 February 1907. Jordan was also the first Reverend to play in a senior game at The Hawthorns.

- The first recorded own-goal at The Hawthorns was scored by Fulham's Leslie Skene v Albion in a Second Division match on 12 September 1908.

- Albion's first 7-0 League victory at The Hawthorns was against Grimsby Town (Division 2) on 2 January 1909.

- The first player to score from the penalty spot in an FA Cup-tie at The Hawthorns was Albion's George Harris v Bolton Wanderers on 16 January 1909.

- On 30 September 1911, the first 40,000 crowd assembled at The Hawthorns – 45,203 fans watching the League game with Aston Villa.

- Hubert Pearson became the first goalkeeper to score at The Hawthorns when he netted a penalty for Albion in a 2-0 win over Bury on 26 December 1911.

- The first wartime game at The Hawthorns was played on 24 April 1916 when Albion defeated Aston Villa 3-1 in a friendly in front of 8,221 fans.

- On 27 September 1919 Sid Bowswer became then first Albion defender to score a hat-trick in a senior game – doing so against Bradford City at The Hawthorns in a Division One match.

- Albion's first 8-0 League win at The Hawthorns was against Notts County (Division 1) on 25 October 1919. In this same game Fred Morris also became the first player to score five goals.

- A League game – not involving Albion – was staged at The Hawthorns for the first time on 29 November 1919 when Wolves were beaten 4-2 by Barnsley in a Second Division encounter. This was because Wolves were made to play two 'home' games away on a neutral ground following crowd trouble at Molineux.

- Albion won the League Division One championship for the first (and so far only) time in season 1919-20, clinching the title at

100 YEARS AT THE HAWTHORNS

- The Hawthorns on 10 April with a 3-1 home win over Bradford. This same season saw the average League attendance at The Hawthorns rise above the 30,000 mark for the first time (30,532).

- The first full international at The Hawthorns was played on 21 October 1922 when England beat Ireland 2-0 in front of 20,173 spectators.

- On 3 February 1923 the first 50,000 plus attendance was recorded at The Hawthorns when Albion met Sunderland in an FA Cup-tie in front of 56,474 fans.

- Len Davies (Cardiff City) was the first opposing player to score four goals at The Hawthorns in a League game, doing so v Albion on 10 November 1923.

- Two years later, on 21 February 1925, the first 60,000 crowd assembled at The Hawthorns – 64,612 spectators watching Albion play Aston Villa in an FA Cup-tie.

- The first player to score a double hat-trick (six goals) at The Hawthorns was Albion's Jimmy Cookson in a 6-3 Second Division win over Blackpool on 17 September 1927.

- The first ten-goal League match at The Hawthorns saw Albion beat Wolverhampton Wanderers 7-3 in a Second Division encounter on 28 December 1929.

- Joe Carter became the first Albion player to be sent-off at The Hawthorns when he took an early bath in the League game with Blackburn Rovers on 19 September 1931.

- The first game at The Hawthorns during World War Two was a friendly between Albion and Wolves on 23 September 1939. The visitors won 5-3.

- The first 'competitive' World War Two game on the ground saw Albion beat Luton Town 3-1 in a Midland Regional League fixture on 21 October 1939 before a crowd of 5,424.

- Eddie Connolly (Albion) and John Snape (Coventry City) were the first players to be sent-off at The Hawthorns in wartime soccer – dismissed together for fighting on 23 March 1940.

- On 1 November 1941 the first foreign visitors came to The Hawthorns when the Czechoslovakian Army side were beaten 3-1 by Albion in a wartime friendly.

- 'W. G. Richardson was the first and only player to score at The Hawthorns 16 years running – from 1929 to 1944 inclusive.

- *The first and only time two players from the same team scored a hat-trick against Albion at The Hawthorns was on 19 February 1944 when Freddie Steele and Tommy Sale netted three goals apiece for Stoke City in a wartime fixture.

- On 22 June 1948 Albion's directors appointed their first ever official team manager when Jack Smith took over the hot-seat at The Hawthorns (from Fred Everiss).

- On 12 May 1951, SC Wacker (Austria) were the first foreign visitors to win at The Hawthorns when they beat Albion 4-3 in a Festival of Britain game.

- The first FA Youth Cup at The Hawthorns was played on 25 October 1952 when Albion defeated Stoke City 7-0.

- The first part-floodlit game at The Hawthorns took place on Wednesday 18 September 1957 when Albion drew 1-1 with Chelsea in a League Division One encounter. Jimmy Greaves (Chelsea) scored first in the 17th minute; Ronnie Allen equalised with a penalty in the 40th minute. The lights were switched on for the second half of this match.

- The first game played entirely under lights was the friendly between Albion and the CDSA (Red Army) club from Russia on 29 October 1957. Albion won 6-5 in front of 52,805 fans – a record at the time for a non-competitive game at The Hawthorns.

- The first goal under the Hawthorns lights was scored in the above game by the visiting centre-forward Vasily Busenov in the 17th minute. Don Howe with a 20-yard drive on 28 minutes, netted Albion's first 'floodlit' goal.

- Albion scored nine goals for the first and only time at The Hawthorns in a Division One game v Manchester City on 21 September 1957 (won 9-2). Frank Griffin scored his first hat-trick in this game.

- On 12 September 1964, Bobby Cram became the first Albion full-back ever to score a hat-trick – achieving the feat in a

League Division One game v Stoke City.

- The first former Albion player to score a hat-trick at The Hawthorns was Derek Kevan (then of Manchester City) who netted three times for a past Baggies' XI in Graham Williams' Testimonial match on 28 April 1965.

- The first League Cup-tie at The Hawthorns saw Albion beat neighbours Walsall 3-1 in a second-round tie on 22 September 1965. Albion's Tony Brown scored the first League Cup goal on the ground while the first visitors' goal was netted by Colin Taylor.

- Gerry Howshall was the first Albion substitute to come on at The Hawthorns – replacing John Kaye in the League game with Nottingham Forest on 5 February 1966.

- The first Albion 'sub' to score at The Hawthorns was Dick Krzywicki v Manchester City in a League Cup-tie on 5 October 1966.

- The first competitive European game took place at The Hawthorns on 9 November 1966 when Albion defeated the Dutch side D.O.S. Utrecht 5-2 in a second round, second leg tie of the Fairs Cup to go through 6-3 on aggregate. Tony Brown scored Albion's first 'home' European goal in this game; he also netted Albion's first European penalty and the Baggies' first European hat-trick – all in front of a 19,170 crowd.

- Albion suffered their first 'European' home defeat when they went down 3-1 to the Italian side Bologna in a third round, second leg clash on 8 March 1967.

- The first European Cup-winners' Cup game at The Hawthorns was between Albion and the Belgium side RFC Brugge on 2 October 1968 when Albion won 2-0 with goals by Asa Hartford and Tony Brown to go through to the second round on the away goal rule.

- Albion's first home defeat in the Cup-winners' Cup came on 19 February 1969 when Dunfermline Athletic won a third round, second leg encounter 1-0 in freezing conditions.

- Albion's first home League Cup defeat occurred v Tottenham Hotspur, who won 1-0 on 8 September 1971.

- The first Hawthorns League Cup draw followed on 3 October 1972 when Albion were held 1-1 by Liverpool in round three.

- Willie Johnston (Albion) and Archie Styles (Everton) were the first two players to be sent-off in the FA Cup at The Hawthorns – dismissed for fighting in a third-round replay on 30 January 1974.

- On 19 June 1975 Albion appointed their first-ever player-manager at The Hawthorns when Johnny Giles joined the club from Leeds United.

- Willie Johnston was also the first player to be sent-off in a League Cup-tie at The Hawthorns v Brighton & Hove Albion on 22 September 1976.

- In season 1977-78 Cyrille Regis scored in his first home games for Albion in the League Cup (v Rotherham United), in the First Division (v Middlesbrough) and in the FA Cup (v Blackpool).

- The first UEFA Cup game at The Hawthorns was played on 27 September 1978 when Albion defeated the Turkish side Galatasaray 3-1 in a first round, second leg clash. Bryan Robson scored the first goal.

- Albion's first UEFA Cup home defeat was suffered at the hands of Carl Zeiss Jena on 3 October 1979, the East German side winning a second round, second leg encounter 2-1. At half-time in this match Albion's Ally Brown became the first player to be sent-off in a European game at The Hawthorns.

- John Deehan (Ipswich Town) was the first ex-Albion player to score a hat-trick in a competitive match at The Hawthorns – doing so in a Division Two League game on 13 September 1986.

- In 1988-89 defender Stacy North became the first Albion player to appear in 46 League games in a single season.

- The first former Albion player to score a 'Cup' goal at The Hawthorns was Ian Banks of Barnsley – in a Zenith Data Systems Cup encounter on 21 November 1990.

- The first Third Division match at The Hawthorns was between Albion and Exeter City on 17 August 1991. Albion won 6-3 (their first Third Division win) and Albion's Craig Shakespeare netted the first goal in this Division from the penalty spot.

100 YEARS AT THE HAWTHORNS

- Mario Bortolazzi became the first Italian to play in a League game for Albion at The Hawthorns when he appeared as a substitute in the 4-1 win over Sheffield United on 15 August 1998.

- In season 1998-99 Adam and James Chambers became the first twins ever to play for an Albion team and also for an England side, achieving international recognition at under 18 level in the Nigerian soccer tournament in April 1999.

- Miss Amy Rayner became the first female 'official' to be involved in an Albion first team game at The Hawthorns when she was named as the reserve official for the home League match with Crewe Alexandra on Monday 5 April 1999.

- Miss Amy Rayner became the first female 'official' to be involved in an Albion first team game at The Hawthorns when she was named as the reserve official for the home League match with Crewe Alexandra on Monday 5 April 1999.

Hawthorns Diary

1900-01

Unfortunately Albion's first season at The Hawthorns ended in bitter disappointment when relegation was suffered for the first time in the club's history; Albion finished bottom of the League table with only 22 points out of a possible 68.

Under secretary-manager Frank Heaven, Albion drew their opening game on 3 September with Derby County (1-1) in front of a 20,104 crowd, and after that the team's performances, at home and away, were inconsistent to say the least, and, in fact, they lost 19 of their 34 League games, nine in front of their own supporters. They failed to win two games in a row and recorded only seven victories during the whole campaign, one of them a crushing

7-2 success over mid-table Bolton Wanderers in early December.

Of the many defeats, the heaviest were those of 6-1 at home to Nottingham Forest and 5-0 at Liverpool, Bury and Derby.

Some of the more established players, including three England internationals – the legendary goalkeeper Joe Reader, right-half Tom Perry and inside-forward Fred Wheldon – were coming to their end of their respective careers, while another England star, full-back Billy Williams, was forced to quit the game through injury at the age of 24. In all 24 players were utilised during the course of the season, with only Amos Adams and Harry Hadley ever-presents. Fred Buck played the first of his 319 senior

games for the club and scored the first of his 94 goals.

Despite their dismal League form Albion had a good run in the FA Cup and reached the semi-final stage before losing 4-0 to Tottenham Hotspur at Villa Park. Albion also lost in the Final of the Birmingham Charity Cup to Aston Villa.

Home League attendances in 1900-01 averaged almost 12,000, around 6,500 up on the previous season. The top crowd was that of 35,417 which saw the local derby with Aston Villa on 8 September 1900.

1901-02

During the 1901 summer break several new players were signed as Albion's directors and management

Albion line-up in 1901-02, Second Division champions. Back row (left to right, players only): J. Stevenson. A. Adams, I. Webb J. Kifford, H. Hadley. Front: A. Smith, W. Lee, D. Nurse, C. Simmons, T. Worton. On ground: J. McLean, G. Dorsett.

decided unanimously on re-organisation. Pick of the bunch were right-half Dan Nurse and inside-left Tom Worton, who were both acquired from neighbouring Wolves. Nurse was immediately handed the captaincy. Goalkeeper Ike Webb arrived from nearby Small Heath (now Birmingham City) to replace Reader and full-back Jack Kifford was brought in to take over from the unfortunate Billy Williams.

Scot Jimmy Stevenson was bedded in at centre-half in place of the overweight Abe Jones; little Jimmy McLean came in on the right-wing after playing well for neighbours Walsall and soon after the start of the season centre-forward Billy Lee was added to the front-line to partner Chippy Simmons.

In January, a sparkling left-winger from Brownhills Albion, George 'Sos' Dorsett, made his debut and kept his place in the side for the rest of the season.

After an opening day set-back against Glossop, Albion quickly got into their stride and they went on to play some scintillating football, running up some high-scoring wins in the process: 4-0 v Chesterfield, 7-0 v Gainsborough, 4-1 v Lincoln City, 7-2 v Blackpool and 4-0 v Newton Heath (now Manchester United).

The key to all this was a settled side and a record sequence of 17 undefeated games (from 7 December to 22 March) took them deservedly to the championship and rapid promotion back into the First Division. Sadly, attendances were poor, the average falling to 7,822, and only rarely did the fans turn out in force (almost 23,700 saw the Boxing Day game with Stockport). Even a 5-1 defeat at Bury in the FA Cup didn't upset Albion's romp towards the title, which they took in fine style with 55 points, four ahead of runners-up Middlesbrough. And they even won the Staffordshire

Cup, beating Stoke 3-0 in the Final, but lost to Aston Villa 1-0 in the Final of the Birmingham Charity Cup. The second XI also got in on the act, winning the Birmingham & District League with 54 points, scoring 126 goals in the process.

Simmons, Worton and Lee netted 56 League goals between them for the first team and eight players made 30 appearances or more.

In March 1902 The Hawthorns staged the FA Cup semi-final between Derby County and Sheffield United which finished level at 1-1 before a 33,603 crowd.

1902-03

In May 1902, Frank Heaven was asked to resign and Albion immediately appointed his assistant, 18-year-old Fred Everiss, as his successor.

He had been with the club since 1896 and today his son, Alan, who also became secretary as well as a director, is still associated with West Bromwich Albion as a Life Member, meaning that the Everiss family has had links with the club for some 104 years.

Fred Everiss's early days were fraught with difficulties. There were internal quarrels about policy and directors resigned with regularity. The club's bank balance was at a very low ebb (despite promotion) and it was plain to see that there was an overall lowering of standards. But out on the field the team battled on and over the first half of the season played exceptionally well, picking up 32 points out of 44 up to mid-January, actually topping the table at one stage. There were some hand-some wins – 6-1 over Newcastle, 3-0 at Villa Park, 5-3 at home to Blackburn and 2-0 at Liverpool – and the attendances were on the increase as well (the season's average was 15,657). While George Dorsett was doing the business on the left-

wing, while Simmons and Co. were scoring freely in attack. But all of a sudden it went horribly wrong and after losing to Spurs in the FA Cup, Albion's form slumped dramatically. Out of their last 12 League games they won only once (the final match of the season), losing eight on the bounce in the process. They eventually finished seventh, just six points fewer than the champions Sheffield Wednesday. Albion also lost to Aston Villa in the Birmingham Cup Final and Wolves in the Final of the Birmingham Charity Cup, but they did defeat Stoke to retain the Staffordshire Cup. It was all so frustrating…and not the greatest of games for Fred Everiss.

Harry Hadley became the first Albion player to win a full cap this century – for England v Ireland in February 1903 at Molineux. And Dan Nurse represented the Football League v the Irish League.

1903-04

This was a disastrous season all round for Albion. They were relegated for the second time since moving to The Hawthorns and again they finished bottom of the table with just 24 points out of a possible 68. It was the defence which took most of the blame with 60 goals conceded. They only won seven of their 34 matches, two early on – and, in fact, they registered just three victories from the turn of the year to the season's end; they also crashed out of the FA Cup to Nottingham Forest in the first round. One new face to appear on the scene was a player who in years to come would prove to be one of the greatest defenders in the country – full-back Jesse Pennington. He went on to play in almost 500 League and FA Cup games for Albion and won 25 caps for England. Another newcomer to come forward during this sad season was right-half Arthur Randle. He took the place of Dan Nurse and went on to play 143 times for the club up to 1908. Harry Brown was installed in the forward-line to accompany Simmons, but he found it hard going and scored only three goals in 21 games.

With poor performances on the field, it was no surprise to see the average attendance fall by 3,000, down to 12,651.

Fred Everiss and his directors knew that there was a lot of work to be done if Albion were to climb back into the top flight – and at the AGM in the summer, positive moves were forthcoming in this respect – although it must be said there wasn't a great deal of money around to buy new players.

1904-05

Back in the Second Division with problems mounting all the time, Albion began with Jack Manners at centre-half and a trio of new faces in the forward-line – Lawrie Bell, Walter Jack and Albert Lewis, and indeed, Lewis got off to a flying start, scoring all his side's goals in an inspired 4-1 victory at Burnley. After that Albion's on-the-field performances were rather mixed despite the introduction of more new players, such as brothers Arthur and Llewellyn Davies (a future Welsh international), Fred Haycock, tall goalkeeper Jimmy Stringer (another former Wolves man) and centre-half Tom Hayward. But for long periods the team was well below par, although occasionally they did produce the goods, beating Doncaster Rovers 6-1, Burton United 4-0, Blackpool 4-2 and Barnsley 4-1 before Christmas. To make matters worse (regarding money) the old stand ('Noah's Ark') which had been transferred from Stoney Lane, burned down on Bonfire Night (the cause being put down to a lighted cigarette being left in the stand).

More signings were made, including Ted Pheasant, a robust defender from Wolves, but his presence did not make all that much difference and as 1904 gave way to 1905, the players found themselves hovering in a mid-table position. Bumped out of the FA Cup by Leicester Fosse who won a preliminary-round tie at The Hawthorns by 5-2, Albion failed to make much headway in the League and after recording a mere seven more wins they ended up a poor tenth – a massive 28 points behind the champions Liverpool, but only three away from having to apply for re-election. Half-backs Manners and Randle were the mainstays of the team; of the forwards Jack top-scored with 13 League goals. The average attendance at The Hawthorns slumped to a disappointing 4,884 – a drop of 7,800 on the previous season… with only 2,072 bothering to turn up for the clash with Gainsborough Trinity in January.

Albion's creditors were hammer-

Albion's first-team squad in 1904-05. Back row (left to right): F. Everiss (secretary), J. Kifford, I. Webb, R. Playfair, J. Pennington, Mr G. Dempster. Middle: W. Barber (assistant trainer), A. Randle, L. Bell, H. Hadley, A. Lewis, J. Manners. On ground: W. Jack, H. Brown, H. Aston, G. Dorsett.

ing on the door for quite some time, consequently, in March 1905, the whole of the board resigned, including chairman and ex-player 'Jem' Bayliss. Harry Keys returned to take the 'chair' (he had previously held office from 1899-1903), former player Billy Bassett became a director along with several local businessmen, a two years' grace was obtained and thankfully Albion carried on.

During the season many stalwarts were sold to keep the club afloat, including Harry Hadley to Aston Villa, 'Ike' Webb to Sunderland, George Dorsett to Manchester City and Harry Brown to Southampton.

1905-06

On the playing side Fred Shinton – signed towards the end of the previous campaign from Hednesford Town – started this season off at centre-forward with Chippy Simmons and Adam Haywood his inside partners. And what an impact Shinton had, scoring 18 goals in 31 League games; Simmons notched 16, while top marksman Haywood, a tiny but astute inside-forward bought from Wolves, netted 21.

Albion's form improved considerably this season; fourth place was achieved, ten points behind runners-up and promoted Manchester United. Everything looked to be going well for the Baggies as they went into the New Year. They had lost just three games (all inside the first five weeks of the campaign) and went 16 matches without defeat from 14 October. But all of a sudden they dropped vital points, slowly slipping off the pace, and they went out of the FA Cup to Everton. Earlier, a seven-goal thriller in the Birmingham Charity Cup Final went Aston Villa's way by 4-3.

Albion did manage some big League wins – Glossop were hammered 6-0 and Blackpool 5-0, both at The Hawthorns – but it was all to no avail and as the curtain came down, home gates had slumped to 4,800, having been as high as 23,000 in late December; nevertheless the season's average was up to 8,637.

Several new players appeared during the second half of the season including former Everton wingers Bruce Rankin and Tom Dilly, who in fact was the last Scotsman to play for Albion for 30 years, and Dudley-born wing-half Eli Bradley while Fred Buck returned to The Hawthorns after spells with Liverpool and Plymouth Argyle.

1906-07

Albion began this season with a new right-back, Dick Betteley, whom they secured from Wolves. The opening two matches were both won and after three months had passed the Baggies were leading the Second Division after amassing 21 points out of a possible 28. The team had a settled look about it with new recruit Tommy Broad playing his part on the right-wing.

Albion maintained their form and continued to lead the pack with some more impressive displays during November and December when the goals rained thick and fast from Shinton, Dilly and Buck. However, early in the New Year the team suffered a slump in League form, allowing Nottingham Forest and Chelsea to take over at the top, but progress was made in the FA Cup. Shinton was injured yet the goals still flowed, with the Reverend Billy Jordan, an Oxford undergraduate, coming in to fill the centre-forward berth. As the season developed, sadly Albion's League challenge floundered, but they remained on course to reach the FA Cup Final after knocking out Stoke, Norwich City, Derby County and Notts County.

Alas, it was not to be, and it all ended in bitter disappointment when Everton won the Cup semi-final showdown at Bolton by 2-1.

Albion finished fourth in the League – 13 points behind the champions Forest and ten adrift of second-placed Chelsea.

Despite missing eight League games, Shinton top-scored with 28 goals with Buck netting 20 plus two in the FA Cup, while right-half Arthur Randle, who had a fine season, was the only ever-present in the side. Full-back Jesse Pennington won the first of his 25 England caps, lining up v Wales and Scotland and he also represented the Football League against the Scottish League.

The average League attendance at The Hawthorns was 12,126 – a rise of almost 3,500 on the previous figure. And on 23 February a record attendance of 35,529 witnessed the FA Cup clash with Derby County.

1907-08

Albion began with a morale-boosting 2-1 win over rivals Wolves at Molineux. Fielding this line-up: Stringer; Betteley, Pennington; Timmins, Pheasant, Manners; George Garratt (signed from Plymouth), Buck, Jordan, Walker and Yorkshireman Joe Brooks (ex-Barnsley) they won well with goals from Buck (penalty) and debutant David Walker, a former 'Wolf' of 1904-05.

There followed five more victories from seven games, including another over Wolves in front of a 30,000 Hawthorns crowd. The Baggies were looking a useful side. Their football was fluent and purposeful and there was a solid look about the defence. As the League programme progressed Albion continued to pocket the points and were handily placed at the turn of the year, having chalked up four wins during December.

At this juncture Harry Wilcox (ex-Leicester) had been introduced to the forward-line, Billy Young was in the middle line and Albert Evans, once of Aston Villa, who broke his leg four times in his career, was challenging Betteley and Pennington for a full-back spot. It was very competitive and despite losing to Southern League Southampton in the FA Cup, Albion continued to do the business in the Second Division, pushing Bradford City, Leicester and Oldham all the way. However, two home defeats against mid-table Gainsborough and Grimsby Town, and crucial reverses at Leicester, Hull City and lowly Chesterfield didn't help matters, and at the end of the day Albion had to settle for fifth place in the table, just seven points adrift of the champions Bradford City.

It was obviously disappointing, but there was a feeling within the camp that the good old days were not too far away.

Buck top-scored in 1907-08 with 18 League goals; Walker in his only season with Albion, netted 15 and early in the New Year Hubert Pearson made the first of 377 senior appearances in Albion's goal. He was to remain at the club until 1926 by which time he had been joined by his son, Harold, also a goalkeeper.

Albion's average League attendance this season was 11,100 – just over 1,000 down on the previous campaign. On 11 January 1908 a new record crowd for The Hawthorns of 36,727 saw the FA Cup-tie with Birmingham.

Pennington added four more England caps to his collection, playing against Ireland, Wales, Scotland and Austria, while Billy Jordan scored six goals for England's amateur side v France.

At the club's AGM Harry Keys was replaced as chairman by former player William 'Billy' Isaiah Bassett, who was to hold this office until his death in 1937.

1908-09

This season saw Albion miss promotion to the First Division by just .0056 of a goal – and the players claimed that they were robbed of that extra goal by a referee's decision at Blackpool. This match at Bloomfield Road on 28 November 1908 resulted in a 2-0 win, but it should have been 3-0 as Charlie Hewitt's effort rebounded from the net support so hard that the referee and his linesman thought that it had hit the crossbar and disallowed the goal. Billy Garraty, who could have put the ball back into the net, walked away towards the centre spot unaware of the furore to follow.

Bolton won the title from Tottenham and neither team beat Albion during the campaign, the Baggies doubling up over the Londoners.

Albion lost only two of their first 22 League games up to 2 January and looked well on course to take the title. But they stuttered with just one win in the next six, and they were also eliminated from the FA Cup by Bradford City. From their next ten fixtures they won six and drew three and required (as it transpired) just two points to gain promotion and three to take the championship. Sadly they could only take a point from a 0-0 draw at Stockport and then blew it all on the very last day by losing 2-1 at Derby.

A 7-0 win over Grimsby was Albion's best League win this term – and they were equally impressive in beating Blackpool 5-1, both at home.

Ten players each made over 25 appearances; goalkeeper Stringer, full-back Pennington, half-backs George Baddeley (who was signed from Stoke at the age of 34 and went on to play for the club until three weeks short of his 40th birthday), Sam Timmins and Jack Manners and forwards Billy Thompson (ex-Sunderland), Welsh international Bill Davies, former Liverpool star Charlie Hewitt, Fred Buck and England international Billy Garraty, who helped Aston Villa win both the League Division One title and FA Cup before transferring to The Hawthorns from Leicester Fosse.

With promotion a strong possibility right up to the last week of the season, Albion's average home attendance went up to 17,845 – their best ever since entering the Football League in 1888. On Boxing Day a record League attendance of 38,049 attended the Albion-Birmingham local derby.

On the international front, Pennington took his total of England caps to 11 with appearances v Wales, Scotland, Hungary (2) and Austria, and winger Bill Davies played for Wales v England.

In May, 1909 Albion went on their first-ever overseas tour, playing seven games in Scandinavia, including friendlies against two English clubs, Hull City and Newcastle United. They recorded four victories, the best coming v Gefle 10-0 and a Stockholm Select XI 8-3.

1909-10

This season saw Albion finish 11th in Division Two – their lowest position in the Football League up to that time.

They started off well enough, winning eight of their first 12 matches. But six defeats from the next seven balanced things out and after that they never really threatened. Indeed, the Baggies ended on a dismal note, suffering four straight defeats as well as playing out a dull goalless draw with Derby. They did a little better in the FA Cup, losing to Barnsley in the third round after overcoming Clapton Orient and Bristol City.

A comfortable 5-0 romp over Gainsborough was Albion's best win of the season, while their heaviest defeat (1-5) came at Hull in late April. There were some other entertaining encounters, including a 4-3 victory over Grimsby Town and a 3-2 win at Burnley, where Billy Garraty netted a fine hat-trick.

Hubert Pearson established himself in goal during the second half of the season, while the former Sheffield Wednesday defender Harry Burton partnered Pennington for most of the time at full-back. Outside-left George Simpson also arrived from Hillsborough, while Welsh international winger Bill Davies was prominent in the forward-line along with Handsworth-born Sid Bowser, who was to go on and gain England recognition while making over 370 appearances for the club in two separate spells at The Hawthorns, the second ending in 1924.

Bob Pailor, who had been signed in October 1908 and was to become a real star turn, scored his first goals for the club in the FA Cup win over Clapton Orient, while his first League goal followed soon after in the 1-1 draw with Oldham Athletic.

A total of 27 players were used this term. There were no ever-presents – Fred Buck missed just one game and George Baddeley five. Buck also ended up as top-scorer with 16 goals. Sadly the average League attendance was down by 1,100 to 11,705.

Pennington was capped twice more by England (v Wales and Scotland) and Bill Davies won another cap for Wales (v Scotland).

At the end of the season Albion found themselves in a parlous financial state. The club's financial advisory committee wrote to Mr Bassett, the chairman, advising him that there was no alternative but to close down. Despite this advice, Fred Everiss and Billy Bassett stood firm and with the help of two other stalwarts, Dan Nurse and Harry Keys, the crisis was averted – but only just.

In July 1910 the early and untimely death was announced of former Albion defender Ted 'Cock' Pheasant.

1910-11

Centre-half Frank 'Puffer' Waterhouse from Wednesbury Old Athletic and tough-tackling left-half Bobby McNeal, a future England international from County Durham, both came to the fore this season, as did wingers Billy Wollaston from Willenhall and Pelsall-born Amos Lloyd, while Jesse Pennington, who thankfully had re-signed for the club after asking for a transfer in February 1910, acquired a new full-back partner in Black Country-born Joe Smith, who was to become a quality player, also winning England honours and amassing a total of 471 appearances for Albion over a period of 16 years. Another newcomer who was to figure prominently over the next few years was inside-forward Harry Wright.

These new faces certainly contributed greatly to the team as Albion at long last regained their place in the First Division. They won eight of their last ten matches, but they had to wait until the very last day of the season before clinching the championship with a hard-fought 1-0 victory over Huddersfield Town, Fred Buck's 30th minute 'straight' penalty doing the trick in front of a 30,135 best-of-season attendance at The Hawthorns.

Albion played well as a unit throughout the campaign, losing only eight matches, one of them in the FA Cup at Derby. They had their bad times, albeit only a few, and realistically speaking they looked promotion material from the word go. In the end they had two points to spare over Bolton Wanderers (53-51) with Chelsea in third place on 49.

The biggest win was a 5-1 demolition job on Leicester on Bonfire Day; Stockport were defeated 4-2 and there were 3-0 victories over Lincoln City, Bradford Park Avenue and Clapton Orient.

Sid Bowser top-scored with 24 League and Cup goals; Pailor netted 12 and Buck ten including five penalties. Bowser and Waterhouse were both ever-present while six other players all made over 30 appearances in a relatively settled side.

The average League attendance at The Hawthorns was an impressive 15,601 – up by almost 4,000 on the previous season's figure.

Pennington played three more games for England (v Ireland, Wales and Scotland) and played for the Football League v the Scottish League.

In the Final of the Birmingham Charity Cup Albion lost 2-1 to arch rivals Aston Villa.

1911-12

Back in the First Division after a seven-year absence, Albion finished ninth, ten points behind the champions Blackburn Rovers, but only five short of third-placed Newcastle United. In fact, it was an excellent run in the FA Cup competition which probably cost Albion a much higher placing – even perhaps the championship – for they had to play no fewer than nine League games in April, five of them in eight days with the Cup Final and a replay sandwiched in between. They battled through to the Final with some splendid performances, only to suffer the huge disappointment of losing to Second Division underdogs Barnsley after a replay at Sheffield. Harry Tufnell scored the game's only goal in the very last minute of

HAWTHORNS DIARY

Albion's 1912 FA Cup Final side: Back row (left to right, players only): G. Baddeley, H. Pearson, S. Bowser, R. Pailor. Seated: A. Cook, J. Pennington, R. McNeal, F. Buck. On ground: C. Jephcott, B. Shearman and H. Wright.

extra-time after Jesse Pennington had refused to 'foul' the Barnsley forward as he broke clear of the Baggies' defence.

Secretary-manager Fred Everiss started the season with Stan Allan (ex-Newcastle United) at centre-forward in place of the injured Bob Pailor and Ben Shearman from Bristol City on the left-wing. Then halfway through the campaign he introduced the speedy Claude Jephcott to the other flank. His career was to end prematurely in 1922 with a broken leg but he went on to serve the club as a director for many years after retiring. Late on Albion debuts were given to two players who were to become vital members of the team after the War – ace goalscorer Fred Morris from Tipton and inside-left Howard Gregory from Aston Manor (Villa territory) who later became,e a star left-winger.

Albion's performances were professional rather than dashing, their

best League win coming early on when they triumphed 3-0 at Villa Park. Pailor top-scored with 13 goals and 'keeper Hubert Pearson, who missed only two League matches, netted with two penalties. The average League attendance at The Hawthorns rose by 2,400 for over 18,000 – the highest in the club's history. On 30 September The Hawthorns attendance record was broken when 45,203 fans watched the League game with Aston Villa.

Again Albion succumbed to Villa in the Final of the Birmingham Charity Cup (0-4).

Pennington's cap tally went up to 19 with games against Ireland, Scotland and Wales, while Fred Buck and Ben Shearman both played twice for the Football League, lining up together in the games against the Southern League and Irish League.

1912-13

This turned out to be a rather moderate season for Albion, who had to

settle for tenth place in the First Division, 16 points below the champions Sunderland and 15 clear of relegated Notts County. They also went out of the FA Cup in the first round,. beaten by Southern League West Ham United at the third attempt.

Albion, in fact, had a useful first-half to their programme, amassing 25 points out of 38, but after Christmas they struggled both at home and away and mustered just 13 more points from their remaining fixtures to finish up rather disappointingly in mid-table. The usual line-up (fitness and availability permitting) was: Pearson (or Moorwood); Smith, Pennington; Waterhouse, Buck, McNeal; Jephcott, Wright/Morris, Pailor/Morris, Bowser and Shearman. Full-back Arthur Cook, George Baddeley and Howard Gregory were the main reserves.

Pailor scored a smart hat-trick early on in an impressive 4-2 win at

Villa Park in front of 55,000 fans, and did the same at Blackburn (in another 4-2 win) in December. The centre-forward top-scored with 16 goals and had another very good season. Jephcott was the only ever-present in the team while seven other players appeared in 30 or more matches. The average League attendance at The Hawthorns was down by a 1,000 to 17,047, with a best of 40,589 attending the return game with Aston Villa.

In the Final of the Birmingham Charity Cup Albion were slaughtered 5-1 at home by the bogey team Aston Villa.

During the summer break Albion recruited hard-shooting centre-forward Alf 'Noddy' Bentley from Bolton Wanderers and re-signed inside-left Albert Lewis from Northampton Town.

In June the freehold of The Hawthorns was purchased for what has proved to be a bargain £5,350.

Prior to obtaining the freehold, the directors were giving serious consideration to obtaining a new ground immediately opposite The Hawthorns on the Birmingham Road.

Pennington passed the 20 cap mark for England with outings against Wales and Scotland. Bobby McNeal played for the Football League v the Southern League and the Irish League and Pennington also lined up against the Irish League.

1913-14

Alf Bentley made a terrific start to his Albion career — scoring all his side's goals in a 4-1 opening day home win over Burnley. Morris, his inside partner, had a helping hand with three of them.

Albion's second XI won the Birmingham & District League for the second time under the stewardship of former goalkeeper Joe Reader.

Again the Baggies did very well during the first half of the season and were well on course for honours. After Christmas they suffered a very indifferent spell — recording just one win in seven and although they recovered somewhat, they eventually ended up in fifth place, only eight points adrift of the champions Blackburn Rovers. They lost some crucial matches and on reflection, it was their poor away form (nine defeats and six draws) which let them down. At The Hawthorns Albion's performances were solid, losing just once to Liverpool and conceding a mere 16 goals in 19 games.

In the FA Cup they were eliminated by arch rivals Aston Villa (away) in the third round in front of a 57,000 plus attendance; earlier in the season Villa were defeated 1-0 in the Final of the Birmingham Charity Cup (Morris the scorer).

Newcomer Bentley top-scored with 17 senior goals; Hubert Pearson was the only-ever present although eight other players all starred in more than 25 matches.

The average League attendance at The Hawthorns topped the 20,000 mark for the first time — a rise of some 3,600 on the previous season's figure. On 4 October a record Hawthorns crowd of 48,057 attended the League game with rivals Aston Villa.

This was Bob Pailor's last season at The Hawthorns. The centre-forward bid farewell and joined Newcastle United after scoring 47 goals in 92 matches for the Baggies. Albion recruited the England Amateur international centre-forward and Cambridge University graduate Harold Bache to replace Pailor and he scored on his debut in that Cup encounter at Villa Park.

Albert Lewis also left The Hawthorns and veteran George Baddeley retired after playing his last game in an Albion shirt (v Sheffield Wednesday) at the ripe old age of almost 40.

That great servant Fred Buck, who had switched from inside-forward to centre-half late in his career, also moved on, to Swansea Town.

Bobby McNeal (v Wales and Scotland) and Jesse Pennington (v Ireland and Scotland) represented England this season and both players also lined up for the Football League, McNeal against the Southern League and Scottish League and Pennington v the Irish League and Southern League. Claude Jephcott also appeared against the Scottish League.

In September 1913, former Albion wing-half Arthur Randle died, aged 32.

1914-15

The Great War broke out in August 1914, but the Football League Management Committee in conjunction with the Government agreed that football should continue for at least another season — and it turned out it be a mixed one for Albion, who finished 11th in the First Division. They gained 40 points, which was only six fewer than the champions Everton. In fact some very mediocre performances during the second half of the campaign contributed to Albion's downfall. They won only six games out of the 18 played between 2 January and 24 April and after being in a position to challenge for honours, they were regarded as 'also rans' when the final curtain came down. They also suffered a first round exit in the FA Cup at the hands of Hull City.

Wolverhampton-born forward Alonzo Poulton, Irishman Louis Bookman, craggy centre-half Fred Reed, Arthur Swift, plus a handful of others, all made their first appearances for Albion this season, with Bookman scoring on his debut.

Albion v. Liverpool on Saturday Last.

PEARSON GOING OUT. THE BALL AT A CRITICAL MO... WITH THE ALBION BACKS IN COA...

Cutting from the *Birmingham Daily Mail* covering the Baggies' First Division match against Liverpool at The Hawthorns in January 1914.

Albion registered only 49 League goals during the season, but conceded just 43, only nine of these at The Hawthorns. They ran up some impressive victories including a 4-0 win over Liverpool and 4-1 victories over Notts County and Bradford (away), but they also lost heavily at Bradford City (0-5), Manchester City (0-4) and Chelsea (1-4), the latter two late on when points were a necessity.

Fred Morris finished up as leading marksman with 11 goals; Bentley netted nine and Swift seven. Howard Gregory, who was slowly getting into his stride, grabbed a superb hat-trick in a 3-2 home win over Tottenham Hotspur.

A total of 26 players were called up for first team action with eight of

them appearing in 28 or more games.

Owing to the circumstances and uncertainty of the War, the average League attendance at The Hawthorns was down by almost half to 10,823 with the best single attendance of 19,492 watching the local derby with Aston Villa in late January. Just 4,410 saw the final League game of the season at home to Bradford City, Albion's lowest for three years.

Harold Bache, McNeal and Hubert Pearson all represented the Football League, the former and Pearson v the Irish League and the latter v the Scottish League.

The Irish League fixture, played on 7 October 1914, in front of 9,250 spectators, was the first representative match to be staged at The Hawthorns, and it was so well organised by Fred Everiss that he received a gold medal from the Football League afterwards.

1915-19

There was no competitive football played by Albion until March 1919. Prior to that the team participated in friendly matches but these were few and far between because the Midlands was a vast munitions centre.

On 15 February 1916 Albion's brilliant unorthodox centre-forward Harold Bache, a Lieutenant in the Army, was tragically killed on a Flanders battlefield. He was only 26.

Although they lost one star player, Albion gained another when 'wee' Tommy Magee was signed in the trenches' after being recommended to the club by an army colleague of his, Tom Brewer. Magee officially joined the club in January 1919 and went on to appear in more than 400 games for the Baggies, helping them win the League championship and FA Cup as well as gaining England recognition. He was to stay at The Hawthorns until May 1934 when he transferred to Crystal Palace.

After peace had been declared in 1918, Albion played in the Midland Victory League during March and April 1919 – and they duly won the title with two victories over Aston Villa, one over Derby County and a draw with Wolves, amassing a total of seven points from their six matches. Derby finished second, Wolves third and Villa fourth.

This highly competitive tournament certainly reunited the players once more and despite such a lengthy break owing to the conflict in Europe, the Albion team looked very useful in those 'Victory' games. The likes of goalkeeper Hubert Pearson, full-backs Joe Smith, Jesse Pennington and Arthur Cook, half-backs Sammy Richardson, Sid Bowser, Fred Reed, Bobby McNeal and Frank Waterhouse and forwards Claude Jephcott, Jack Crisp, Tommy Magee, Andy Smith, Alf Bentley,

34

100 YEARS AT THE HAWTHORNS

Albion, 1915. Back row (left to right): Ernie Shore, Sid Bowser, Hubert Pearson, Ted Bowen, Jim Stevenson (trainer), Len Moorwood. Second row: Bill Barber (trainer), Alonzo Poulton, Billy Hackett, Tommy Newall, Harry Wright, Matt Wood, Sam Richardson, Harry Parkes, Louis Bookman. Seated: Arthur Cook, Arthur Swift, Frank Waterhouse, Bobby McNeal, Jesse Pennington, Ben Shearman, Fred Morris, Howard Gregory. On ground: Alf Bentley, Joe Smith, Claude Jephcott.

Fred Morris and Howard Gregory were all ready, willing and eager to get back into the 'real battle' of First Division League soccer and FA Cup action.

During the War, apart from the passing of Harold Bache, a handful of other players with Hawthorns connections also lost their lives. Frank Costello, an ex-Albion reserve, who also played for West Ham, Bolton and Southampton, was killed in action in December 1914; Billy Vale, once of Langley St Michael's, Wednesbury Old Athletic and Albion was killed in the trenches in November 1916 and Baggies' amateur centre-forward William H. Jackson, was killed while serving with the West Yorkshire Regiment in May 1917.

Former Albion reserve, E.J. Hickman, lost his life in the Dardanelles in October 1915 and just prior to the Armistice another pre-war reserve, George Bell, was killed on active service.

1919-20

All that serious preparation in the Victory League games paid off for success, with an 8-0 home victory over Notts County the highlight. Morris netted five times against the League Division One championship for the first – and so far only – time in the club's history. The Baggies accumulated a record 60 points from their 42 matches. They registered 28 wins and four draws, and scored 104 goals, conceding only 47.

Albion's 65 goals at The Hawthorns was the highest home tally in

the First Division up till then and was not bettered until 1931 by Arsenal.

The title was clinched on Saturday 10 April 1920 when Bradford were beaten 3-1 at The Hawthorns.

They won nine of their first 11 matches, scoring 36 goals in the process. Morris netted five times against the Magpies to create a new club record, while centre-half Sid Bowser banged in a hat-trick (including two penalties) in a 4-1 win over Bradford City. Nine goals went past Everton (with wins of 4-3 and 5-2 in the space of six days) and Bolton were beaten 4-1 and 2-1 as Albion bounded along at the top. After two defeats in early

HAWTHORNS DIARY

Albion, League champions 1919-20. Back row (left to right): W. Barber (trainer), Pearson, T. H. Gopsil (assistant trainer), E. Smith (assistant secretary). Second row: Mr F. Everiss (secretary), Mr D. Nurse, (director), Cook, Mr W. L. Bassett (vice-chairman), Mr H. Keys (chairman), Jephcott, Mr Seymour (director), Lieut-Col Ely (director). Seated: Crisp, A. Smith, McNeal, Pennington, Bowser, Morris, Gregory. On ground: J. Smith, Magee, Bentley, Richardson. The trophies are the League championship and the FA Charity Shield.

November, seven more victories followed in quick succession and despite an early exit from the FA Cup (beaten by Barnsley) Albion powered on with two successive five goal romps over Blackburn. They lost only two of their last 15 League matches and finished up deserving champions with a massive nine points margin over second-placed Burnley. Albion's attacking play at times quite brilliant, inducing rave reports in various newspapers up and down the country.

The League's leading scorer Fred Morris created a new club by netting 37 goals. And between 29 November and 24 January he scored in ten consecutive League games – another record.

He was aided and abetted by Bentley (15) and Gregory (12) while Bowser weighed in with ten (eight penalties). McNeal was the only ever-present, but 11 other players each managed 24 or more League appearances. Bowser (v Ireland), Pennington (v Wales and Scotland),

Joe Smith (v Ireland) and Morris (v Scotland) all played for England, with Pennington taking his final tally of caps to 25, having gained his first in 1906-07. Smith also played in the Victory international v Wales. Wingers Jack Crisp and Claude Jephcott (both v the Irish League) and Pennington (v Scottish League) all represented the Football League.

Crisp, Pennington and Morris all took part in the England v The South international trial at The Hawthorns on 9 February, attended by 14,427 spectators.

Albion's success this term realised a record average home League attendance of 30, 532 – a rise of almost 20,000 on the 1914-15 figure.

Albion also won the FA Charity Shield by defeating Tottenham Hotspur 2-0 at White Hart Lane, Andy Smith claiming both goals.

Albion's second XI also won their respective championship – taking the Birmingham & District League title for the third time… after losing their opening game 5-1.

1920-21

As reigning League champions, Albion began the defence of their crown in unconvincing fashion, drawing their first four games and losing the fifth. In fact, they recorded just two victories in their opening 11 fixtures in their opening 11 fixtures in their opening games and they recorded just two victories in their opening 11 fixtures in their opening 11 fixtures and fell well off the pace. They never recovered and finished in 14th position with 40 points, 19 behind the champions Burnley, who had taken the runners-up spot behind the Baggies the year before.

Fielding practically the same players who had done the club proud in 1919-20, Albion never matched the performances of the previous season and they won only eight home matches, losing six times in front of their own supporters. They had several poor spells during the campaign, the worst coming in December, February and March – and they lost four games on the bounce around Easter time.

They were hammered 5-1 at Blackburn and Huddersfield, crashed 4-0 at Manchester City and 3-0 at Sunderland, Bolton and Chelsea. Arsenal won a thriller by 4-3 at The Hawthorns and perhaps Albion's best display was their 4-1 victory at Old Trafford against Manchester United.

Albion didn't last long in the FA Cup either, losing in the opening round to Second Division Notts County 3-0 at Meadow Lane.

A handful of new signings were made including centre-forward Bob Blood, who was bought from Port Vale for £4,000 in February. He went on to score 26 goals in 53 games for the Baggies before leaving in 1924. And right at the end of the campaign a player who was to become a big favourite at The Hawthorns – Aston-born Joe Carter – arrived from Westbourne Celtic.

Goalkeeper George Ashmore, who went on to win England honours, also made his first appearance for the club, conceding five goals in that heavy defeat at Ewood Park.

Morris again finished up as leading marksmen with 16 goals; Blood netted seven in 15 outings including a penalty on his debut v Spurs. Joe Smith and Sid Bowser made 40 League appearances apiece, while Sam Richardson played in 38.

The average League crowd at The Hawthorns was 27,802 – down by almost 3,000 on the previous season.

Fred Morris was the only Albion player to receive an international call this term, collecting his second England cap v Ireland.

1921-22

In November 1921 Albion's squad was boosted with the signing of the versatile Welsh international Stan Davies and towards the end of the season his fellow countryman Ivor Jones arrived at The Hawthorns from Swansea Town. Inside-forward Charlie 'Tug' Wilson also burst on to the scene, making his League debut at the age of 16 years, 63 days at Oldham in October. But as these three arrived so one great player left – Jesse Pennington decided to retire after 19 years and almost 500 senior appearances for the club. He played his first and last games for Albion against the same team – Liverpool – and skippered the Baggies to the League title in 1920.

Unfortunately 1921-22 was another disappointing season for Albion, who again finished below halfway in 13th position with 40 points, only eight clear of relegation yet 17 behind the champions Liverpool, whom they beat 2-1 at Anfield only to lose the return 4-1 at The Hawthorns in Pennington's farewell match.

Albion had a very poor first half to the campaign, winning only six games before Christmas. Of the ten they lost, two were real hammerings – 6-1 at Manchester City and 5-0 at Sunderland.

Immediately after the festive season Albion's form improved but they quickly faded again, and after crashing out of the FA Cup in the third round to their bogey team Notts County, just five more League victories were registered (out of 15 games).

Changes were made frequently and a total of 29 players were called upon by secretary-manager Fred Everiss.

Consistent right-back Joe Smith was the team's only ever-present. Bobby McNeal missed one game, Richardson and Morris were both absent on four occasions and the only other players to appear in 30 or matches were Sid Bowser and Tommy Magee. Stan Davies top-scored with 17 senior goals; Morris netted 11.

The average League crowd at The Hawthorns dropped again – this time by 6,000 to 21,691.

On the international scene, Stan Davies starred for Wales against Scotland, Ireland and England and Sam Richardson represented the Football League against the Irish League.

Towards the end of the season Albion recruited Tommy Glidden from Sunderland West End. He was to lead Albion in two Wembley Cup Finals and skippered the team to that memorable and unique Cup and promotion double in 1931.

Albion's second XI entered the Central League for the first time this season.

At the end of the season Bill Barber relinquished his training duties. He had been an essential part of The Hawthorns staff since 1900, as groundsman, assistant-trainer and trainer.

1922-23

Albion's overall performances improved considerably this season and they rose to seventh place, only nine points behind runners-up Sunderland but 15 adrift of the champions Liverpool who amassed a total of 60. The Baggies won 12 and drew seven of their 21 home matches but they lost 12 times on their travels.

Billy Adams replaced Pennington at left-back, and Sid Bowser was switched to centre-half. Adams contributed well to Albion's cause, making 40 League appearances. The evergreen Smith, half-backs Magee, Bowser and McNeal and forwards Jones, Davies, Morris and Gregory were the other mainstays, and late on wingers Jimmy Spencer and Tommy Glidden as well as Joe Carter all came and showed great promise.

Albion though had too many hit and miss sequences yet occasionally they played some sparkling football – Arsenal (7-0) and Tottenham (5-1) were both hammered at The Hawthorns before the end of October. After Christmas results continued to fluctuate and they went down heavily at Blackburn (by 1-5) and Huddersfield (1-4) while defeating Nottingham Forest 4-0 away and Sheffield United by the same score at home.

There was nothing doing either in the FA Cup as Charlton Athletic ousted the Baggies in the third round after Stalybridge Celtic and Sunderland had been eliminated early on.

A record crowd of 56,476 saw the Sunderland tie on 3 February at The Hawthorns.

Davies and Morris teamed up well as partners in attack and they netted 37 goals between them, Davies top-scoring with 21.

Nine players appeared in 31 or more League matches with Bowser an ever-present. Smith missed only one game, while Adams, Magee, McNeal and Morris were absentees on two occasions.

HAWTHORNS DIARY

Wing-half Sammy Richardson, a key member of the League championship side and a virtual ever-present in the first three seasons after World War One, lost his place to Tommy Magee in 1923 but returned in 1924-25 and 1925-26.

The average League attendance this season dropped once more – by almost 3,000 to 18,817. In mid-March a meagre 5,520 fans saw the home game with Newcastle United – the lowest at The Hawthorns since April 1915.

Tommy Magee gained the first of his five full caps for England, lining up in two internationals against Wales and Sweden. Joe Smith played for England in their 2-0 win over Ireland at The Hawthorns in front of 20,173 fans; both Stan Davies (v Scotland) and Ivor Jones (v England and Ireland) wore the 'red' of Wales while goalkeeper Hubert Pearson played for the Football League v the Irish League.

Albion's reserve side won the Central League title with 63 points.

They were unbeaten at The Hawthorns, scoring 61 goals in 21 games.

In April 1923 former Hawthorns favourite, centre-forward Fred Shinton died at the early age of 40.

1923-24

Albion began this season with a confident 2-0 home victory over the reigning League champions Liverpool. The players as a whole looked strong and purposeful, remaining unbeaten in their first five matches, but then things started to go wrong and surprisingly only one victory was recorded from the next ten games. The team slipped slowly down the table and when Everton came to The Hawthorns in late November the Baggies were on the edge of the relegation drop-zone.

A 5-0 annihilation of the Merseysiders, when Bob Blood smacked in a superb hat-trick, was quickly followed by a 4-1 victory over Spurs, all the goals coming from Joe Carter. These performances certainly boosted morale but Albion couldn't keep it up and although they made progress in the FA Cup with wins over Millwall, the Corinthians and Wolves, their League form left a lot to be desired. They huffed and puffed throughout March and April, winning only four times – and at the same time went out of the Cup, beaten at home by neighbours Aston Villa. Thankfully, Albion finished the season with two 3-1 home wins over Sunderland and Sheffield United (Blood claiming another hat-trick against the Blades) and in effect those six points gained kept the Baggies in the First Division (they ended up in 16th spot). It was so frustrating for the diehard supporters and the average League crowd dropped yet again to 17,381 (the lowest since the War) with only 8,003 fans witnessing the home game with Notts County.

A shortage of goals was a problem for Albion this term (only 51 obtained in the League and nine in the Cup) and it was Carter who headed the scoring-charts with ten. His colleagues Blood and Davies each netted nine.

Joe Smith was once more as reliable as ever in defence, appearing in all 42 League games. But alas this was the last season at the club for both Sid Bowser, who moved to nearby Walsall, and ace marksman Fred Morris, who joined Coventry City. He had netted 118 goals in 287 appearances for the Baggies.

Making their name now were the raven-haired Charlie Wilson and goalkeeper George Ashmore, while centre-forward George James had also entered the action along with winger Jack Byers, signed from Blackburn Rovers. And at full-back Albion had Arthur Perry, a member of the famous West Bromwich family which had supplied Charlie, Tom and Walter in the late 1800s.

Only one Albion player figured on the international scene this season – Ivor Jones – who was capped for Wales against Scotland.

1924-25

Albion came so close this season to winning the Football League championship for the second time in five years, finishing runners-up to Huddersfield Town, who took the star prize by just two points (58-56).

Albion lost the race for the right at the death, picking up just four points from their last four games following an excellent run of results from late November through to mid-April, when they won 14 matches, six of these on the trot during December and January.

Fielding a settled side, comprising Ashmore; Smith, Perry (Dickie Baugh late on); Magee, Reed and McNeal (Richardson from Boxing Day); Spencer (Glidden from November), Carter, James, Wilson and Byers, Albion started off with two quick defeats, but then began to produce some fine displays as they powered towards the top of the table. George James (in for Stan Davies) was in terrific form, ably assisted by Carter and Wilson. But after losing a fourth-round FA Cup-tie at Sheffield United Albion's League performances became patchy and they missed out on the championship to the team from whom they took three points during the season.

Hot-shot James, a big favourite with the supporters, scored the fastest goal ever recorded at The Hawthorns – netting after five seconds play against Nottingham Forest in a 5-1 win in December. He scored four times in that game and also hit a hat-trick in a 4-1 home

The reserves won the Central League championship again after a pulsating duel with Huddersfield Town which went right to the wire. Albion won on the last day of the season and scored as many as 68 goals in 21 matches at The Hawthorns.

win over Aston Villa. He topped Albion's scoring charts with 30 goals in League and Cup; Carter notched 14 and Wilson 13.

Eight players appeared in 34 or more League games this season, with ever-present Joe Smith again the inspiration. Goalkeeper George Ashmore was absent once (a 2-1 defeat at West Ham) while Magee, skipper Reed and Wilson all had 40 outings apiece.

Albion's average League attendance this term was up by 3,200 to 20,596.

Magee was capped three times by England – v Belgium, Scotland and France. The the match v Belgium was the second international to be staged at The Hawthorns and England won 4-0 on 8 December in front of 15,405 fans. Davies added two more Welsh caps to his tally, playing against Scotland and Ireland and Jimmy Spencer represented the Football League in the annual game against the Irish League.

Albion's second XI, going for a hat-trick of Central League triumphs, could only finish third this time round.

Harold Pearson, son of former goalkeeper Hubert Pearson, joined Albion as an amateur goalkeeper from Tamworth Castle. He was to remain at The Hawthorns until 1937.

In February 1925 Albion's first trainer at The Hawthorns, Jack Paddock passed away and the following month former Hawthorns defender Jim Stevenson died aged 49, following an accident at the Leven Shipyard in Scotland.

1925-26

In this season the fixture list reverted back to pre-war days in that each club no longer met the same opposition on successive Saturdays – a change instigated by Albion.

At the start of the campaign

Albion were listed as one of the favourites to win the League title. But they never responded to the call and ended up having a very moderate campaign, finishing in 13th position with 40 points, 17 behind the champions Huddersfield, who duly retained the trophy for the third successive season.

Albion won only three of their first ten matches then lost two of the next ten; from Boxing Day onwards they were totally inconsistent, conjuring up just seven more victories while suffering 11 defeats.

Practically the same set of players who had performed so well the previous season were still at The Hawthorns, although Magee, James, Byers and Adams all struggled with injury. In fact, up to Christmas, once it had settled down, the team looked very useful, especially when beating Manchester City 4-1, West Ham United 7-1, Bury 4-0, Burnley 5-3, Newcastle 4-0 and Manchester United 5-1, all at home. Messrs. Carter, Davies, Glidden and Wilson were scoring goals, but then, perhaps surprisingly after the New Year had arrived, League results everywhere began to fluctuate and Aston Villa ended Albion's hopes in the FA Cup.

Davies (with 19 goals), Wilson (17), Carter (14) and James (12) were Albion's top League scorers while Carter also netted twice in the FA Cup. Ashmore again did well in goal, making 40 League appearance. His performances between the posts led to his winning an England cap v Belgium. Joe Carter also made his international debut for England in that same match and scored to celebrate the occasion. Stan Davies won three more caps for Wales (v England, Scotland and Ireland) while Ivor Jones also appeared in that latter game.

Tommy Magee played in 15 games on the F.A's. tour of Canada between May and July 1926.

Jones was one of two internationals who left The Hawthorns this season, rejoining his former club, Swansea Town. The other was right-back Joe Smith, who signed for Birmingham after 16 years and 471 first-team games for the Baggies.

Goalkeeper Hubert Pearson, who had missed an international call in 1923 because of injury, also left The Hawthorns after 377 League and Cup appearances.

Bob Finch made his League debut at full-back against Leicester City – the first of 234 appearances for Albion – and Harry Dutton established himself in the senior side at left-half.

The supporters became disillusioned early on and only 8,287 saw the home game with Manchester City in September. After the Yuletide period attendances at The Hawthorns ranged from 10,000 to 19,500 and when the last ball was kicked Albion's average for the season stood at 18,595 – a drop of 2,000 on the previous campaign.

1926-27

In the summer of 1926, Albion recruited left-half Nelson Howarth from Bolton Wanderers and he lined up in the first team on the opening day of the League programme against Sunderland at The Hawthorns. Over 31,000 fans saw the Baggies win that game 3-0, but things didn't go too well out on the park after that.

Out of their next 25 matches, Albion registered just four victories and they they slithered down the Division, falling deep into the relegation zone. Sadly they never recovered from that disastrous spell and although the players battled out of their skins during the latter stages of the campaign, the Baggies eventually went down as wooden spoonists with Leeds United, having lost a record number of matches – 23.

Two new full-backs were introduced halfway through the season – England international Bill Ashurst from Notts County and George Shaw from Huddersfield Town, the latter at a record cost of £4,100 – while Teddy Rooke held down the centre-half berth from December and eager-beaver Sammy Short came into the side at inside-left.

One or two encouraging home wins were registered along the way – 4-2 v Burnley, 5-0 against Tottenham, 6-2 over Aston Villa (in front of more than 50,000 fans) and 4-2 v Newcastle being the best four – but there were far too many poor away performances and this was summed up by 16 defeats, the worst coming at Bury (3-7).

Albion conceded 86 goals while scoring 65 themselves. Joe Carter and Stan Davies each netted 15 while Tommy Magee (an ever-present), Tommy Glidden (41 League appearances), goalkeeper George Ashmore (38), Joe Carter (36), Nelson Howarth (34) and Welsh international Stan Davies (33) were the mainstays of the side.

Albion failed to make much impact in the FA Cup either, losing in the third round by 2-1 away to Hull City of the Second Division.

The average League attendance at The Hawthorns of 21,710, was surprisingly up by more than 3,100 on the previous season's figure.

Albion's only international representative this season was Stan Davies who was capped by Wales against Scotland.

One consolation out on the field of play was that Albion's second string had another successful season, winning the Central League championship for the third time in five years.

The reserves scored 73 goals in their 21 home matches but it was not until the last day of the season that Albion clinched the title, pip-ping Manchester United by a single point.

1927-28

Back in the Second Division for the first time since 1911, Albion's forward-line was boosted by the arrival of Jimmy Cookson from Chesterfield. He was to become a truly magnificent goalscorer and, in fact, went on to claim 92 goals in only103 League outings for Albion in his first three seasons at The Hawthorns, eventually finishing up with a haul of 110 in 131 appearances before leaving to join Plymouth Argyle in August 1933.

He had already scored 85 League goals for Chesterfield and made a great start to his Baggies' career, netting in each of his first two games which unfortunately were lost, away at Oldham and at home to Stoke City.

Cookson, though, continued to hit the net and he set a new club record (which still stands today) by grabbing a double hat-trick (all six goals) when Blackpool were defeated 6-3 at The Hawthorns on 17 September 1927.

Albion's form, however, was mixed and after winning six of their opening 11 League matches they proceeded to win only two of their next 12 and slowly slipped down the table from what was once a promising position.

Changes were made and new faces came in, one being the former England international inside-left Harry Chambers, signed from Liverpool. His presence certainly injected some life into Albion's performances and after losing to Arsenal in the third round of the FA Cup they came back into some good form and eventually settled for eighth spot in the Division, chalking up 46 points, 13 behind the champions Manchester City, and the same number ahead of relegated Fulham.

Albion ran in 17 League wins with a best of 6-0 at Grimsby in early January when Cookson hit a four-timer. Cookson also scored four times in a 5-3 home defeat of Reading the following week.

Their heaviest defeats were suffered at Wolves and Port Vale (both by 1-4) and against Stoke and Preston North End who both won 4-2 at The Hawthorns.

Cookson was in superb form throughout the campaign and ended up as top-scorer with 38 goals in 38 League appearances, breaking Fred Morris' club record of 37 goals, set in 1919-20. He was also the leading Division Two scorer in 1927-28.

George Shaw was the team's only ever-present, playing in all 43 League and Cup games. Magee missed one game and Glidden and Finch three; both Cookson and Joe Carter were absent from four League encounters.

Albion's average home League attendance dropped from 21,710 to 19,596 with the lowest turnout of 8,116 coming against Hull City in mid-November. The reasons for the drop were explained in the directors' report in August 1928: "... with regard to the finances, we cannot trace any season which has produced weather so consistently bad as was experienced in the opening half of the past season in our home games. Attendances at match after match were seriously affected by shocking, climatic conditions."

Stan Davies won another cap for Wales v Scotland but left for nearby Birmingham in November 1927 after scoring 83 goals in 159 competitive games for the Baggies.

Full-back Bob Finch took part in two international trials for The Rest v England, the first of which was played at The Hawthorns on 23 January 1928 in front of 9,345 fans. England won 5-1.

1928-29

In April 1928 Albion secured the service of left-winger Stan Wood from Winsford. He was to become one of the stars of the 1930s and made his debut in the fourth game of this season at home to Notts County.

Albion began this campaign rather disappointingly, losing three of their opening four matches. They picked up and won four of the next five only to fall away again by recording just two more victories in their next ten League outings up to mid-December.

At this juncture Albion were lying nearer the relegation area than challenging for a top six place, but after an unbeaten Christmas period which saw them win three and draw one of their four matches, they commenced a useful run in the FA Cup. They knocked out Grimsby Town, Middlesbrough and Bradford Park Avenue before losing in a replay to Huddersfield Town.

During this excellent Cup campaign, Albion's League performances were poor – only one win in seven – but from 16 March onwards they roared back and collected 18 points from their last 12 matches, registering eight victories, including five in a row.

Jimmy 'Iron' Edwards had gained a regular place in the side at inside-left and Bill Richardson was now firmly established in the middle line. These two players, along with Wood, goalkeeper Harold Pearson, full-back George Shaw, right-half Tommy Magee, skipper Tommy Glidden and inside-right Joe Carter, were to become key members of the side over the next three seasons.

Albion finished the 1928-29 campaign in seventh position with 46 points, only nine fewer than champions Middlesbrough and seven behind runners-up Grimsby Town.

Cookson with 28 goals, was again leading scorer. Glidden netted 23 and Carter 13. The reliable Shaw played in every League game; Glidden missed two and right-back Bob Finch three. But a handful of players moved on – Chambers became player-manager of Oakengates, Howarth was forced to retire through injury and George James signed for Reading after scoring 57 goals in 116 games for the Baggies.

Albion's average League crowd in 1928-29 dropped by over 6,000 to 13,220 – the lowest since 1909-10.

Joe Carter appeared in two internationals for England, scoring in them both against Belgium (one goal) and Spain (2).

In this latter match England led 3-0 in Madrid, but eventually crashed 4-3 amid wild scenes of excitement, and Spain thus became the first continental side to defeat England.

Albion, 1928-29. Back row (left to right): Phil Hunt (assistant trainer), Bill Richardson, Jim Edwards, Arthur Perry, Harold Pearson, Len Darnell, George Ashmore, Joe Carter, Herbert Webster, Joe Evans, Stan Wood, Jim Hudson, Maurice Jones (ground assistant). Second row: Mr Eph Smith (assistant secretary), Mr Fred Everiss (secretary-manager), Ernie Pattison, Mr L. Nurse (director), Mr H. Keys (director), Mr W. I. Bassett (chairman), Mr J. Round (director), Mr W. Hackett (director), Tommy Glidden, Sam Guest (assistant trainer), Fred Reed (trainer). Third row: Reg Fryer, George James, Nelson Howarth, Jack Rix, Dickie Baugh, Sammy Short, Enos Bromage, Francis Corbett, Bertram Cope, Bob Finch. On ground: Fred Leedham, Frank White, Jimmy Cookson, Jimmy Murphy, Arthur Fitton, George Shaw, Griffith A. Taylor, George Bytheway, Tommy Magee.

In January 1929, former Albion and England full-back Billy Williams died at the age of 53.

1929-30

This was a terrific goalscoring season for Albion and it marked the arrival at The Hawthorns of one of the finest marksmen ever to don the famous navy blue and white stripes – 'W. G.' Richardson – who arrived from Hartlepools United in June 1929.

From the word go Albion's forward-line looked sharp and decisive and the goals came thick and fast...20 in the opening seven League matches with Jimmy Cookson in prime form with ten to his name.

Into October and the goals continued to flow – 28 more were bagged up to Christmas Day. At this stage Albion were well placed for promotion and when former bus-driver Richardson was given his debut against Millwall at The Hawthorns on Boxing Day, over 24,000 saw Albion win 6-1 with 'W. G.' scoring to celebrate the occasion. This was the first of more than 320 goals he was to score for Albion in various competitions.

A handsome 7-3 home win over the ten men of Wolves followed two days later and although the team suffered an early FA Cup exit at the hands of Wrexham, Albion powered on in the League, scoring happily along the way. But they had their ups and downs during March and this resulted in them missing out on promotion despite a late flourish which revealed seven straight wins.

Albion ended the season in sixth place on 47 points, eight behind runners-up Chelsea. The team scored a club record 105 goals, 73 at home, and Cookson was once more top-dog with 33 to his credit. Glidden netted 20, Carter 19 and new man Richardson two.

Centre-half Bill Richardson (no relation to 'W. G.') played in every game; George Shaw and Glidden both missed one game and Bob Finch was sidelined from four.

The average League crowd at The Hawthorns rose to 14,023, but only 1,495 fans bothered to watch the March mid-week afternoon League game versus Nottingham Forest – the lowest to this day for a senior match at the ground.

Harold Pearson was now first choice goalkeeper; full-back Bert Trentham had made his senior debut and was soon to become a first team regular, partnering George Shaw; Frank Cresswell played at inside-left for the majority of this season, but he was to move on (to Chester) allowing Wood to be partnered by Jimmy Edwards, who later switched to left-half.

Albion's reserve side was also looking strong after finishing third in the Central League. They scored 128 goals (the previous record was 116) with 'W. G.' Richardson obtaining as many as 50.

Everything was now becoming clear as to what secretary-manager Fred Everiss wanted and soon everyone associated with Albion would be rejoicing in more ways than one.

In August 1929 a great Albion stalwart, Harry Keys, passed away. he had been an Albion 'fanatic' through thick and thin and had given unstinting service to the club as chairman, director and editor of the Albion News for many years. His son, Major H. Wilson Keys, followed him on to the Albion board in August 1930.

1930-31

Albion created unique football history this season when they won promotion from the Second Division and also carried off the FA Cup, beating neighbours Birmingham 2-1 in the Final at Wembley. This feat has still to be equalled.

After a cracking start to the campaign (five wins from their first six matches) Albion steam-rollered on and, in fact, they only lost two of their first 12 Second Division matches.

Everton and Tottenham Hotspur were the other challengers at the head of the Division (with Wolves close by) and when the halfway mark in the League programme arrived Albion were very well placed on 28 points (out of a possible 42).

Surprisingly (to some people) Jimmy Cookson lost his place in the side in November and this is when 'W. G.' Richardson started to blossom. Also, a young local lad, Teddy Sandford was introduced into the inside-left position with Joe Carter switching to the other flank to partner Glidden.

Albion's jigsaw was complete – and they looked a mighty useful side, comprising: Pearson; Shaw, Trentham; Magee, W. Richardson, Edwards; Glidden, Carter, W. G. Richardson Sandford and Wood.

Albion's new line-up began with a thumping 6-1 home win over Nottingham Forest (their biggest triumph of the season) and beat Stoke City 4-0 and Barnsley 5-0 at The Hawthorns, but then they had to battle through a series of three tedious Cup matches with Charlton Athletic before entering the fourth round.

League points were steadily chalked up, although their keenest rivals for promotion, Everton, took the honours at Goodison Park. Progress was made in the FA Cup at the expense of Tottenham Hotspur, Portsmouth and then neighbours Wolves (after a replay), and as Easter approached Albion were right in there, going for glory on both fronts.

A tough FA Cup semi-final win over rivals Everton at Old Trafford

get) and then by narrowly defeating Charlton Athletic 3-2 in a nail-biting encounter in front of a record League attendance of 52,415 on the final day of the season. 'W. G.' headed in the deciding goal at the packed Birmingham Road End midway through the second half.

It was a truly great moment for the players and management – and indeed, the supporters.

Albion fulfilled 52 games this season (42 in the League) and they scored 99 goals. W. G. Richardson (24), Wood (17), Glidden (16), Carter (11) and Cookson (11) all reached double figures.

Nine players appeared in 32 League games or more with Pearson, Shaw and Bill Richardson a trio of ever-presents.

The average League attendance at The Hawthorns rose by 7,700 to a healthy 21,722.

For all the effort put in by the players, not one earned full international recognition in 1930-31, although Joe Carter did represent the Football League against the Scottish League.

Magee, Cookson and Shaw, however, toured Canada with the FA party between May and July 1931 with Cookson collecting 26 of the 107 goals scored on that tour.

1931-32

Back in the top flight after a four-year absence, Albion began in style, beating the reigning champions Arsenal 1-0 at Highbury in the opening match, Stan Wood scoring in front of a 55,380 crowd.

Just over five weeks later on the same ground Arsenal got revenge with a Cliff Bastin goal in the 88th minute to win the FA Charity Shield.

Albion played very well during the first half of the season, and among some impressive victories were those of 4-0 v Blackpool,

Albion parade the FA Cup around Wembley after their 1931 victory over neighbours Birmingham.

in front of a 69,241 record crowd took Albion through to Wembley for the first time, but before the all Midland showdown with Birmingham, there were nine more League games to contest. From these Albion collected 11 vital points to keep bang on course for promotion. But it was now getting mighty close at the top.

A hard-fought but deserved 2-1

victory at Wembley over Blues at Wembley where W. G. Richardson's two goals proved decisive, earned Albion the first half of the double, but they still had it all to do.

They required maximum points from their remaining two League games to gain promotion with Everton – and they did it by beating Stoke City 1-0 at The Victoria Ground (W. G. Richardson on tar-

West Bromwich Albion, 1931 FA Cup winners and also promoted to Division One. Back row (left to right): Fred Everiss (secretary-manager), Mr J. Everiss (director), Mr L. Nurse (director), Harold Pearson, Mr W. I. Bassett (chairman), Mr E. Smith (assistant secretary). Mr J. Round (director), Mr H. Keys (director), Fred Reed (trainer). Middle row: Bill Richardson, Jimmy Edwards, Tommy Glidden, Tommy Magee, Joe Carter, Stan Wood. Front row: Jimmy Cookson, Bert Trentham, W. G. Richardson, Teddy Sandford, George Shaw, Bob Finch.

Chelsea and Derby County 4-1 v Blackburn Rovers, 5-2 at Manchester City, 5-1 at West Ham and 3-0 at home to Aston Villa.

In that impressive win at Upton Park on 7 November, W. G. Richardson created history by scoring four goals in a five minute spell right at the start of the game.

On the same day, the man he replaced, Jimmy Cookson, scored seven times for Albion's reserves in a 10-1 defeat of Liverpool at The Hawthorns.

As holders of the FA Cup Albion had again expected to do well in the competition but this time round they fell at the first fence, beaten 2-1 by neighbours Aston Villa at The Hawthorns.

Back in the League, points were picked up here and there and there was still an outside chance that Albion could win the title or take the runners-up spot, but during a cold, miserable four-week period in March three defeats (one of them at Goodison Park) were suffered and this meant a final placing of sixth for Albion, who ended ten points behind champions Everton (56-46). They actually finished the season with an 11 goal thriller at home to relegated Grimsby Town, losing 6-5 to the Mariners.

W. G. Richardson notched another 28 goals this term, while skipper Glidden claimed 20.

Seven players made 40 or more League appearances, Glidden being the only ever-present.

The average League attendance at The Hawthorns was up again – this time to 24,251.

Harold Pearson and George Shaw were both capped by England in the home international v Scotland at Wembley; and reserve full-back Hugh Foulkes played for Wales against Ireland and left-half Jimmy Edwards starred for the Football League versus the Scottish League.

Joe Carter had the misfortune to become the first Albion player to be sent-off at The Hawthorns when he took an early bath with visiting defender Rankine in the game v Blackburn Rovers in September 1931.

The following the month, the sudden death occurred of former Albion left-winger Jack Byers. He was 34. In May 1932, Albion's top-scorer in 1905-06, Adam Haywood, died aged 57.

1932-33

Two Welshmen, who both gained full caps for their country – wing-half Jimmy Murphy and the hard-shooting Walter Robbins – were just two of the many players seeking to establish themselves in the first XI at The Hawthorns when this 1932-33 campaign kicked off. Another was Arthur Gale, a schoolteacher, signed from Chester.

But secretary-manager Fred Everiss and his aides, including former player, now trainer Fred Reed, confidently stuck to the team which was now regarded as good as any in the top flight. And what a fine start Albion made, winning their first four matches and drawing the next two. They were in excellent form and scoring goals, and reports in the national press suggested that this could be Albion's season.

The Baggies continued to perform well (at home and away) and despite the occasional hiccup here and there, they were able to maintain a reasonably high level of consistency which enabled them to keep in touch with the leading group comprising Arsenal, Aston Villa and Sheffield Wednesday.

Albion looked superb around the turn of the year stringing together a run of seven League games without defeat (four wins) and although they were dumped out of the FA Cup by West Ham, the Baggies still looked capable of challenging for the title.

But sadly, and no-one really could explain it, Albion ended the season rather disappointingly by picking up only seven points from their last eight matches to finish in fourth place, just nine points behind champions Arsenal and only five fewer than runners-up Aston Villa.

W. G. Richardson was top-scorer with a season's tally of 31 goals. Carter netted 14 times and Glidden and Robbins each claimed 10. Albion's average home League attendance was down a fraction to 22,799.

Elsewhere, Albion's reserves won their fourth Central League title, amassing 58 points and scoring 106 goals in the process.

On the international scene, Teddy Sandford won his first and only England cap v Wales; Jimmy Murphy and Walter Robbins played for Wales in the internationals v England, Ireland and France, with Robbins also appearing against the Scottish, and he netted twice against the Irish. Stan Wood scored once from the left-wing for the Football League against the Irish League.

1933-34

Once more Albion had a reasonably good season in 1933-34, taking seventh position in the First Division with a total of 44 points, well behind the champions Arsenal on 59. Fielding a relatively settled side during the first half of the campaign, they were forced into changes during the second period and among those who showed a lot of promise (for the years to come) were wing-half Jack Sankey, little left-winger Walter Boyes and versatile forward Arthur Gale.

'W. G.' Richardson was enjoying a purple patch, scoring in nine consecutive League games between 4 February and 1 April.

HAWTHORNS DIARY

Albion, 1934-35. Back row (left to right): Fred Everiss (secretary), Fred Reed (trainer), Harry Raw, Harold Pearson, Joe Carter, George Shaw, Claude Jephcott (director). Middle: W. G. Richardson, Teddy Sandford, Bill Richardson, Billy Bassett (chairman), Tommy Glidden, Jimmy Edwards, Bert Trentham. Front: Stan Wood, Jack Sankey, Wally Boyes, Harry Jones, Jimmy Murphy.

Albion never got themselves into a position to challenge for honours. They had some good spells and some indifferent ones, with their best sequence of results coming between the end of September and the end of December when they won seven and drew six of their 16 matches.

Then they started 1934 off in terrific style, beating Manchester City 7-2 at Maine Road, with the great Frank Swift in the home goal. But after an FA Cup defeat against Chelsea, Albion's League form became a bit of a mishmash from thereon in, although they did end with a flurry, collecting five wins from their last eight matches as well as drawing 4-4 at Villa Park.

Albion scored 78 League goals, with W. G. Richardson claiming 26 of them and Glidden 13. Carter and Sandford also reached double figures with ten apiece.

Two players were ever-present – skipper Glidden and Teddy Sandford.

Goal-ace Jimmy Cookson said farewell to The Hawthorns at the start of this season, leaving for Plymouth Argyle, and Tommy Magee also left the club after 15 years and 434 appearances for the Baggies. He signed for Crystal Palace.

Albion's average home League crowd in 1933-34 was 20,078 – a fall of more than 2,700.

The reserves had another excellent season and retained the Central League title with a superb record of 28 wins and 101 goals for a total of 64 points. A record crowd of 22,372 saw the home game with Aston Villa in March.

At international level, wing-half Jimmy Murphy and winger Walter Robbins helped Wales win the Home international championship for the second season in a row. Murphy added two more caps to his Welsh collection when he lined up against Scotland and England, while Robbins scored against the Scots.

Full-backs Bert Trentham and George Shaw represented the Football League v the Irish league and the Scottish League respectively.

In August 1933, former Albion player and Director 'Jem' Bayliss died at the age of 70. And in December 1933, another former Hawthorns star, goalkeeper Jim Stringer, died at the age of 55.

In August 1933 another Everiss, Fred's son Alan, joined the Hawthorns' office staff, while in January 1934 former Baggies' winger Claude Jephcott was co-opted on to the Albion board of directors.

1934-35

For the second time in four seasons Albion marched out at Wembley Stadium – but on this occasion they ended up second best, losing 4-2 to Sheffield Wednesday in the 1935 FA Cup Final after conceding two late goals.

Equalising twice through Walter Boyes and Teddy Sandford, Albion looked the stronger team during the latter stages, despite carrying two 'injured' players – Tommy Glidden and Joe Carter – but some slack defending allowed the Owls in for two killer strikes. Albion's 'keeper Harold Pearson and full-back George Shaw were the ones at fault, but 'W. G.' Richardson had a rare off day, and should have scored to give Albion a 3-2 lead with a quarter-of-an-hour remaining.

En route to Wembley, Albion knocked out Port Vale, Sheffield United (7-1 at home), Stockport County (5-0 away), Preston North End and Bolton Wanderers (after a replay) in the semi-final. Arthur Gale, deputising for Glidden, scored in each round up to the semi-final, but he was dropped for the Final in favour of his captain along with Harry 'Popeye' Jones, who had deputised for Carter since early March.

It was a big mistake to rely on the fitness of Glidden and Carter and had Jones (or even Jack Sankey) accompanied Gale on the right-wing at Wembley then things might well have been totally different.

100 YEARS AT THE HAWTHORNS

In the First Division, Albion stuttered along to finish in ninth position with 44 points, 14 short of the champions Arsenal.

They had some bright and breezy periods, none more so than in November/December when they ran up four successive victories including a thumping 4-0 home win over Tottenham. In eight games leading up to Christmas Albion won seven times, their only defeat was a record 9-3 thrashing at Derby on 8 December. Considering that Albion were unchanged for the tenth successive match, this was an amazing result but injuries to centre-half

Richardson, Sankey and Glidden on a glue-pot of a pitch certainly contributed to Albion's downfall.

From 23 March to 4 May Albion lost only once in nine League outings and this was at a time when the Cup Final was firmly on their mind.

The team throughout the campaign was fairly settled but with injuries creeping in after Christmas, Gale, Sankey, and Jones (who had been signed from Preston North End in May 1933), along with winger Sid Rawlings and full-back Bob Finch all pulled their weight.

W. G. Richardson (33), Teddy

Sandford (24) and Wally Boyes (22) scored 79 goals between them this season, while Bert Trentham and 'W. G.' were the only ever-presents in the League. Pearson, Murphy and Boyes each missed one match,

The average League attendance at The Hawthorns in 1934-35 was up by more than 2,000 to 22,350.

Albion's reserves also pulled in some big crowds as they made it a hat-trick of Central League title victories, scoring a record 121 goals in the process of obtaining 62 points.

'W. G.' Richardson (after a long wait) and Wally Boyes were both capped by England against Holland

Albion's Tommy Glidden (left) and Sheffield Wednesday's Ronnie Starling with referee Mr A. E. Fogg before the 1935 FA Cup Final which the Owls won 4-2.

HAWTHORNS DIARY

Albion staff in 1935-36. Back row (left to right): Sammy Short (trainer), Teddy Sandford, Jim Singleton, Arthur Hickman, Harold Pearson, Harry Lowery, Sid Swinden, W. G. Richardson, Bert Trentham, Bill Richardson, Bill Tudor, Norman Male, Herbert Hunt, Jack Lewis, Arthur Brookes, Jimmy Murphy, Fred Powell (groundsman). Second row: Fred Reed (trainer), Tommy Glidden, Joe Guest (assistant trainer), Harry Jones, 'Bos' Trevis, Ted Crowe, Walter Robbins, Major H. Wilson Keys (director), Jimmy Adams, Lol Coen, Jack Sankey, Jack Screen, Stan Wood, Harry Kinsell, Joe Carter, Alan Everiss (office clerk). Third row: Mr A. C. Jephcott (director), Mr L. Nurse (director), Hugh Foulkes, Alf Ridyard, Harry Raw, Mr W. I. Bassett (chairman), Bob Finch, Geoff Spencer, Harry Ashley, Mr J. Round (director). Fred Everiss (secretary-manager). Front row: Jimmy Edwards, George Shaw, Tommy Green, Syd Rawlings, Jack Rix, Jim Driscoll, Arthur Gale, Wally Boyes, Cliff Grosvenor.

in Amsterdam, Boyes helping to set up the winning goal for Worrall.

Jimmy Murphy added to his collection of Welsh caps by playing against England, Scotland and Ireland and represented a Wales/Ireland XI against the Football League. Another international trial took place at The Hawthorns on 27 February 1935 before a 12,845 crowd, England (with Albion's Sandford in the line-up) drawing 2-2 with The Rest.

November 1934 saw the death of former Albion centre-forward Billy Lee.

1935-36

'W. G.' Richardson set a new scoring record for Albion this season by claiming a total of 40 goals – 39 in the First Division and one in the FA Cup. He was in terrific form from October onwards after a rather slow start (only two goals in the first eight games). He scored four times in a crushing 7-0 win at Villa Park,

did likewise in a 5-2 Boxing Day home triumph over Middlesbrough, netted hat-tricks in successive matches against Blackburn Rovers (won 8-1) and Liverpool (won 6-1) and also weighed in with five separate braces. And still he couldn't get into the England team.

Amazingly Richardson's goals failed to inspire Albion. They finished the season in 18th position – just three points away from relegation. They lost six home matches and 14 on their travels, and there is no doubt that it was their abysmal form on opponents' grounds which let them down.

Secretary-manager Fred Everiss relied on the experience of his senior professionals for most of the season but injuries and loss of form certainly damaged his plans and, in fact, a total of 27 players were called into action during the course of the campaign – the most used at first team level since 1921-22.

'W. G.' Richardson was the main-

stay of the side, missing only one League game (a 2-1 home defeat by Chelsea) while Jack Sankey, George Shaw, Bert Trentham, Bill Richardson and new-signing Jack Mahon (from Leeds United) all managed to get into the thirties. Mahon was the main goalscoring support to 'W. G.' with a total of 17 goals.

In the FA Cup Albion went out in the fourth round, beaten at the third attempt by Bradford Park Avenue, this after they had ousted Hull City 2-0 in their opening tie.

Albion's reserve team couldn't maintain their fine record by adding a fourth successive Central League championship to the hat-trick achieved since 1932-33 and this season they had to settle for fourth place.

The average League attendance at The Hawthorns rose to 23,064, the second best since 1921.

Jimmy Murphy collected three more Welsh caps when he played

Pre-season training at The Hawthorns in 1936.

against Scotland, England and Ireland, and Walter Robbins joined him for the Scottish game. Wally Boyes played for England v Scotland in the Jubilee international, and for the Football League against the Irish League (one goal).

Albion's splendid right-wing duo of Tommy Glidden and Joe Carter both ended their playing days at The Hawthorns. Joining Albion in 1922, Glidden scored 140 goals in 479 first-team games for the club, and skippered the side to that unique double in 1931. He chose to retire (through injury) and became coach at The Hawthorns, later becoming a Director. Carter joined Tranmere Rovers after scoring 155 goals in 451 games for the Baggies.

1936-37

This was not a good season for Albion...they finished 16th in the First Division (escaping relegation by a mere six points); conceded 98 goals – a club record in a League

campaign; suffered the heaviest defeat in their history by losing 10-3 at Stoke; were defeated by Preston North End in the FA Cup semi-final at Highbury and mourned the death of one of their greatest servants, chairman William Isaiah Bassett.

After winning only two of their opening eight League games, Albion never really threatened and they struggled for long periods, failing to get any sort of rhythm.

They were very poor away from home, losing 15 of their 21 matches and conceding 66 goals. Among those defeats were some hefty ones. Apart from that disaster at Stoke, Albion crashed 6-2 at Manchester City, 5-3 at Portsmouth, 4-1 at both Bolton and Middlesbrough and 5-2 at Wolves.

At home they played a lot better and a thrilling 10-goal encounter with FA Cup finalists Sunderland finished 6-4 in their favour.

In the Cup itself Albion looked powerful when beating Spenny-

moor United 7-1 in the third round; but made hard work of knocking out Darlington 3-2 (W. G. Richardson netting a hat-trick) and Coventry by the same score at Highfield Road.

A never-to-be-beaten record attendance of 64,815 packed into a snow-bound Hawthorns to see Albion beat mighty Arsenal 3-1 in the quarter-final, but in the Highbury semi-final against Preston, the death of chairman Billy Bassett seemed to get to the players and they never performed, losing rather disappointingly by 4-1.

Three goalkeepers were used during the campaign – Billy Light, signed from Southampton in March 1936 and the man who started between the sticks at The Victoria Ground when the Potters rattled in those ten goals on 4 February, the evergreen Harold Pearson and Jimmy Adams, who was to serve the club throughout the War.

Several players were coming

towards the end of their Albion careers, including full-back George Shaw, centre-half Billy Richardson, wing-half Jimmy Edwards and left-winger Stan Wood.

Another Shaw, Cecil (no relation to George) was signed from Wolverhampton Wanderers, and he had the misfortune to miss a penalty in the Cup-tie at Coventry, having previously had a 100 per-cent record from the spot.

W. G. Richardson with 22 League and Cup goals, was once more Albion's leading marksman. Harry Jones, who took over the inside-right berth, netted 18, Jack Mahon obtained 14 and Walter Robbins scored 10.

Wally Boyes and 'W. G.' Richardson made most League appearances (39) and apart from Cecil Shaw, there were other club debuts for centre-half Bill Brockhurst, inside-forward Sammy Heaselgrave and wingers Jimmy Prew and Lol Coen.

At the end of the season goalkeeper Harold Pearson moved to Millwall after appearing in 303 games for Albion. Jimmy Murphy collected two full Welsh caps v Scotland and Ireland, and helped his country win the International Championship for the third time in the 1930s.

The average League attendance at The Hawthorns this season dropped to 21,707.

At the club's AGM it was announced that Mr Lou Nurse was to take over as club chairman from the late Billy Bassett. Norman Bassett followed his father on to the board in August 1937.

1937-38

This turned out to be a disastrous season for Albion. They were relegated to the Second Division as wooden spoonists, conceding a 91 goals in the process, and crashed out of the FA Cup to Third Division (North) opponents York City.

After ten League games had been played Albion had chalked up six victories and were well placed in the Division. But a run of four successive defeats saw them slip below the halfway mark and they never recovered after that. From mid-December to early March they recorded just two wins from 12 games and following their Cup exit, results got even worse with only four more victories arriving from the last 15 matches. Amazingly, Albion could and should have stayed up despite their mediocre form. There were so many other teams battling against relegation as the season drew to a close, and it transpired that three more points would have saved the Baggies from the drop. Yet they ended the campaign by losing their final three fixtures and finished up with 36 points, the same as Manchester City, but two fewer than Stoke City, Birmingham, Portsmouth and Grimsby Town, who all escaped the drop.

Albion suffered some hefty defeats, losing 4-0 at Stoke, 6-1 at home to Sunderland, 5-3 at Derby and Everton, 4-2 v Bolton, 7-1 at bottom club Manchester City (an astonishing scoreline this) and 4-1 on the last Saturday at Middlesbrough.

Their best wins were almost all at home: 4-0 v Chelsea, 5-1 v Liverpool and Huddersfield and 4-3 v Brentford and Birmingham. They also won 4-1 at Grimsby.

In an attempt to stave off relegation Albion signed two well established players, Scottish international wing-half Sandy McNab from Sunderland and England left-winger Joe Johnson from Stoke City; blond half-back Harry Lowery, goalkeeper Harry Baldwin and defenders Idris Bassett and Cyril Davies were also introduced to the team.

W. G. Richardson again topped the scoring list with 17 goals. Jack

Mahon netted 13 and Harry Jones 11, while the up-and-coming Ike Clarke from Tipton scored six times.

Cecil Shaw and Teddy Sandford, who was now playing at centre-half, were both ever-presents, and winger Jack Mahon missed just two matches.

The average League attendance at The Hawthorns rose to 23,246.

In February 1938 Wally Boyes moved to Everton (after 165 games for Albion) and at the end of the season George Shaw went to Stalybridge Celtic, having made 425 appearances for the Baggies.

Stan Wood joined Halifax Town after 280 games and 66 goals for Albion.

On the international front, Jimmy Murphy concluded his Welsh international career (15 caps) by playing against Scotland and England. In later years (1956-63) he was the Welsh international team manager.

In December 1937 Chippy Simmons, scorer of Albion's first goal at The Hawthorns in 1900, died at the age of 59.

1938-39

Back in the Second Division for the first time since 1931, Albion were marked up as one of the favourites to win promotion in what turned out be the last full League season before the outbreak of World War Two. But they never really got in a challenge after Christmas – and when the curtain came down in April they found themselves in tenth position, ten points behind champions Blackburn Rovers and nine fewer than runners-up Sheffield United.

Albion had a pretty good first half to the campaign – they won three of their opening four matches, and then recorded nine victories from 13 games between mid-September and early December. But once into the New Year their overall performances deteriorated and after going out of the FA Cup (beaten 2-0 by Portsmouth after 5-1 in a replay at Old Trafford) League points were hard to come by, only 17 gained out of the last 38. And to cap it all, a meagre crowd of just 3,109 attended the final League game of the season at The Hawthorns against Norwich City when debutant George Banks scored twice.

Of Albion's 18 League wins, 15 came at home, including those of 5-2 v Newcastle United, 5-1 v Sheffield Wednesday and 6-0 v Bury, while the three achieved on opponents' grounds were all useful, 3-2 at Norwich, 3-0 at Burnley and 5-1 at Millwall.

Among Albion's 15 defeats was a 5-1 hammering at Newcastle, who gained sweet revenge for their heavy reverse at The Hawthorns.

Harry Jones took over the mantle as leading scorer this season, accumulated 20 goals. Ike Clarke and Joe Johnson each struck 15 and Sammy Heaselgrave weighed in with 11, including a hat-trick in a 4-3 home defeat by second-placed Sheffield United. W. G. Richardson, struggling with injury, netted just five. Albion's average home League attendance was 18,467 – the lowest since 1929-30.

Sandy McNab was capped by Scotland against England this season and was selected for the Scottish FA tour of Canada and U.S.A.

Players who left the club in the summer of 1939 included Teddy Sandford, who joined Sheffield United after scoring 75 in 317 games for the Baggies and Walter Robbins, who signed for Newport County. Jimmy Murphy was transferred to Swindon Town in March while Jack Mahon left early on for Huddersfield Town.

Bob Finch signed for Swansea Town just before the outbreak of the War. He made 234 appearances for Albion.

Among the players introduced to the first team during the season were flying winger Billy Elliott, who had been rejected by Wolves, full-back Harold White, centre-halves Billy Gripton and Billy Tudor and stocky inside-forward Meynell Burgin. As many as 14 players made their first team debuts for Albion in 1938-39.

In February 1939, the death was announced of former Albion winger Jack Crisp.

Wartime Football 1939-46

Along with scores of other clubs Albion were forced to abandon their Football League programme between September 1939 until August 1946, due, of course, to the wartime conditions in Europe.

Players' contracts were suspended and they were free to join the forces or go into social industry. Fred Everiss was left as the only full-time paid official at The hawthorns. Travelling problems were reduced for Fred by the assistance of a wonderful body of supporters who placed their cars at the disposal of the players despite petrol rationing. Other fans darned and repaired the matchday shirts and socks and when replacements became essential they would hand in clothing coupons out of their own meagre allocations.

During this enforced lay-off, Albion played 298 first-team games, including 266 in regionalised League and Cup competitions and the three 1939-40 Second Division matches subsequently declared null and void.

Albion played in the Midland Regional League in 1939-40, in the Football League (South) Midland Group in 1940-41, in the Football League (South) in 1941-42 and the Football League (North) in 1942-43, 1943-44 and 1944-45. In the transitional season of 1945-46, when teams were slowly getting back into some sort of order after the hostilities, Albion reverted back to the Football League (South).

Each season provided various cup competitions and in 1941-42 Albion reached the semi-final of the Football League War Cup but lost 7-0 on aggregate to arch rivals Wolves.

Albion were Cup winners once – lifting the Midland War Cup in 1943-44 when they beat Nottingham Forest 6-5 on aggregate in the two-legged final. Albion triumphed 4-3 in the second-leg after extra-time fielding this team: Norman Heath; Jim Southam, Jack Smith; Len Millard, Billy Gripton, 'Sandy' McNab; Sammy Heaselgrave, Jack Acquaroff, Ike Clarke, Charlie Evans and Frank Hodgetts. Acquaroff (2), Hodgetts and Clarke scored the goals.

This second leg clash at Nottingham is the longest match an Albion team has ever played in, lasting 119 minutes.

Almost 120 players appeared in those 298 games, 42 of them guests.

In season 1942-43 Albion made use of 54 players – a club record. As many as 43 were chosen for Regional League matches and 23 'guests' were selected during the campaign.

Top appearance maker for Albion during 1939-46 was Billy Gripton (207); Billy Elliott played in 169 matches, Len Millard in 157, 'Sandy' McNab 147, Jack Sankey 143, Cecil Shaw 141, Charlie Evans 135, Jimmy Adams 131, Sammy Heaselgrave 127, Ike Clarke 114, Frank Hodgetts 112, Idris Bassett 108, 'W. G.' Richardson 106 and Joe Johnson 102.

Hodgetts became the youngest player ever to appear in Albion's first team when he made his debut in the home game v Notts County in October 1940 at the age of 16 years, 26 days.

Leading scorer was Billy Elliott with 128 goals; 'W. G.' Richardson netted 123, Clarke 77, Jones 60, Heaselgrave 50, Robbie Newsome 34 and Charlie Evans 33. In all Albion scored 795 goals (673 in League and Cup).

Albion's 1939-46 wartime record (League and Cup):

Season	P	W	D	L	F	A
1939-40	37	23	5	9	107	67
1940-41	32	14	5	13	92	82
1941-42	31	18	4	9	115	69
1942-43	38	17	6	15	84	83
1943-44	39	14	11	14	90	93
1944-45	40	15	11	14	75	74
1945-46	46	23	9	14	110	74
Totals	263	124	51	88	673	542

- The two Albion-Chelsea League games in 1945-46 realised 20 goals – Albion won 8-1 at home and lost 7-4 in London.

- 45 hat-tricks were scored by Albion players during World War Two. 'W. G.' Richardson netted 12, Clarke 10 and Harry Jones 8.

- In March 1942, Albion full-back Harold White was awarded the Military Medal, only the second professional footballer to be decorated during World War Two.

A junior player, J. E. Britnell, was awarded the DFC in 1946.

- Albion's best wartime wins were 10-1 v Luton (1941), 8-2 v Swansea (1941), 8-1 v Notts County (1941), 8-1 v Chelsea (1945), 8-2 v Wolves (away, 1941), 7-0 v Northampton (1941), 7-1 v Walsall (1944) and 6-0 v Northampton (1945).

Their heaviest defeat was 10-3 at Walsall in 1941, and they also lost 9-0 at Leicester in 1943, crashed 8-0 at Coventry also in 1943 and 8-2 to

An Albion reserve line-up in the wartime season of 1941-42. Back row (left to right): George Banks, Harry Kinsell, George Willetts, Cyril Davies, Harry Lowery. Front row: Frank Hodgetts, Arthur Wilkes, Bobby Newsome, Alan Parker, Arthur Griffiths, Len Millard.

Aston Villa in 1942 and Stoke (home) in 1944.

- Albion reserves beat a Smethwick League XI 17-0 in a friendly in January 1945. Tommy Bowen scored seven of the goals and a young Ray Barlow six.

- On 20 October 1945 a Victory international was staged at The Hawthorns between England and Wales. Albion's full-back Harry Kinsell played for England, but ended up a loser as the Welsh won the game 1-0 in front of an all-ticket crowd of 54,611 which paid record receipts of £8,753.

- Albion's right-winger Billy Elliott played twice for England during the war, lining up against Wales in 1943-44 and in the Victory international v Scotland in 1945-46. Kinsell also played in the Victory international v Ireland in 1945-46. Welshman Doug Witcomb played in six wartime internationals against

England, two in 1939-40, two in 1940-41 and two in 1941-42. He also played in the Victory international v Scotland in 1945-46.

Elliott and Kinsell also played regularly for Army and Combined Services XIs during the War, both in the UK and in Europe.

In June 1946, a new signing from Ireland, centre-forward Dave Walsh represented the Republic of Ireland twice v Portugal and Spain.

- On a sad note, seven former Hawthorns players died during the wartime period: 1919-20 championship-winning star Alf Bentley (in April 1940), full-back Amos Adams (1941), wing-half Harry Hadley (in September 1942), left-winger George Dorsett (in April 1943), centre-half Abe Jones (in the summer of 1943), Lance Corporal George Handley, who was a England junior international and also played for Crystal Palace (in Sicily in July 1940); and wing-half Jack Manners (in May 1946). Also Walter Wheatley, an Albion trialist, lost his life in July 1940, while serving with the Royal Warwickshire Regiment in Sicily and William Albert Darby, an Albion reserve centre-forward who was scored 16 goals in a Colts game, was tragically killed whilst serving with the Coldstream Guards in Anzio, Italy in February 1944.

In December 1943 Sam Guest, trainer of six Central League championship winning sides, passed away, aged 62.

One of the club's greatest-ever goalscorers, 'W. G.' Richardson, moved on to Shrewsbury Town in 1945 after netting 328 goals in 444 first-team games for the Baggies over a period of 16 years. After retiring he returned to The Hawthorns, where he became trainer-coach, a position he held until his death in 1959.

Prior to the resumption of League football in August 1946, Albion toured Belgium and Luxembourg, playing three games in Verviers, Esch-sur-Alzette and Brussels.

1946-47

In the summer of 1946, Albion's secretary-manager Fred Everiss and two directors went over to Ireland to sign centre-forward Dave Walsh from Linfield. And what a great start the Irishman made to his career in England, scoring in each of his first six League games for Albion to set a club record.

Walsh was a superb marksman, who went on to score 100 goals for Albion and play in 29 full internationals for Ireland and the Republic of Ireland with Albion and Aston Villa. He claimed 29 goals in his first season with Albion, but his noble efforts – and those of his fellow countryman Jack Vernon, who was bought from Belfast Celtic in February 1947 – couldn't lift the team above seventh position in the Second Division table. And with 48

points Albion found themselves 14 adrift of the champions Manchester City and had ten fewer than runners-up and promoted Burnley.

Albion made a decent start to their League programme, winning seven of their opening 11 matches. But only one victory was registered out of the next eight and although they picked up again either side of Christmas with five more wins from eight games, they were never really in a strong enough position to challenge for honours, even though the season was extended to the end of May because of the arctic weather conditions which gripped the country from early January.

Their biggest win was at Newport where they whipped the Welshmen 7-2, Ike Clarke scoring four times, but they lost heavily at Bury (4-0) and Manchester City (5-0) They played some exciting football at home where they recorded excellent wins over Fulham 6-1, Nottingham Forest 5-1 and Leicester City 4-2 but they did crash 5-2 to both Barnsley and Plymouth Argyle in front of their own fans.

In the FA Cup Albion went out in the fourth round, beaten at home by the eventual finalists Charlton Athletic after earlier accounting for Leeds United.

Behind Walsh in the scoring charts was Ike Clarke with 19 goals while Billy Elliott netted 11.

Right-back Jim Pemberton (a wartime find) and winger Elliott appeared in most League games, 41 and 40 respectively. And among the other players who made their debuts during the war and did well this season were goalkeeper Jimmy Sanders (bought from Charlton Athletic), centre-half George Tranter, defender Len Millard, Irish inside-forward Jimmy Duggan, wing-halves Cliff Edwards and Glyn Hood, the versatile Ray Barlow, utility star Reg Ryan and inside-forward Billy Lunn.

Sanders, Millard, Barlow and Ryan all became Albion greats and helped the team win the FA Cup and finish runners-up in the First Division in 1954.

Albion's average home League attendance this season, like those of every other club, showed a dramatic rise from the last pre-war campaign of 1938-39, shooting up to 24,672 from 18,467.

Doug Witcomb won three full caps for Wales this season (two with Albion v Scotland and England and one with Sheffield Wednesday v Ireland). Walsh played twice for Ireland (against Scotland and Wales) and twice for the Republic of Ireland against the Rest of Europe at Hampden Park in front of 134,000 fans.

On 14 October 1946, the Albion secretary Fred Everiss was presented with a silver casket and a cheque for £1,330 at a ceremony in the Grand Hotel, Birmingham to mark the completion of 50 years service with Albion. many ex-players and football dignitaries were present. At the club's A.G.M. in the summer of 1947, Major H. Wilson Keys, a director since 1930, took over as chairman from Lou Nurse.

1947-48

Albion began this season supremely well, winning nine of their opening 13 League matches, giving away only 11 goals in the process. They had a reasonably settled side with Len Millard lining up alongside Jim Pemberton at full-back. Jack Vernon and Glyn Hood were looking good in defence while Billy Elliott, Ike Clarke, Dave Walsh, George Drury (ex-Arsenal) and Frank Hodgetts were doing the business in attack. Two goalkeepers had been used – Tommy Grimley and Jimmy Sanders

– while Reg Ryan, Gil Williams and Billy Lunn and a few others were ready in waiting.

Albion continued to play well and pick up points and between late October and mid-December they claimed another four wins to keep in touch with the top clubs. However, the period from late December through to the end of February was a disaster with only one League win coming from nine games. And Tottenham Hotspur knocked Albion out of the FA Cup in the fourth round.

At this juncture the changes were being coming thick and fast with a certain Arthur Rowley now in the attack alongside Walsh, and goalkeeper Norman Heath establishing himself between the posts.

Albion couldn't get back on the track and although they improved late on with a flurry of goals, they again finished a disappointing seventh with 45 points, 14 less than the champions Birmingham City and 11 behind runners-up Newcastle United.

Jack Haines (signed from Leicester City in a part-exchange deal which sent Peter McKennan to Filbert Street) scored a hat-trick in Albion's best win of the season – 6-0 at home to Bradford Park Avenue – while Arthur 'Biff' Taylor from Dudley netted five times in four games at the end of the campaign.

Walsh once more topped the scoring charts with 22 goals (all in the League). Rowley netted five times, four coming in the League, which marked the beginning of his record haul of 434 in this competition gathered almost exclusively during the next 17 years – after leaving Albion.

There were two ever-presents – Pemberton and Millard – while Elliott was an absentee on three occasions.

The average League attendance at The Hawthorns in 1947-48 was the best-ever at 30,856 – a rise of more than 6,200 on the previous season. Almost 52,000 saw the game against Birmingham in March – the biggest on the ground for a League match since December 1937.

Both Vernon and Walsh were each capped three times by Ireland in the games against England, Scotland and Wales. Walsh was a scorer v England in a dramatic 2-2 draw at Liverpool and also played for the Republic of Ireland versus Portugal and Spain (one goal).

In the League game against Doncaster Rovers at The Hawthorns on 3 April Welshman Alun Evans of Albion suffered a blow to the head which resulted in his retirement and in later life caused him to lose his sight in one eye.

1948-49

On 12 July 1948, Fred Everiss, after 46 years in office, resigned as secretary-manager at The Hawthorns and in September he became a director of the club. He was replaced as secretary by his brother-in-law Ephraim Smith (a servant of the club since 1906) while Welshman Jack Smith became Albion's first-ever full-time team manager, taking over on 22 June 1948.. He arrived from Molineux where he had been a coach, having earlier played for Wolves, Bristol Rovers, Swindon Town and Chelsea in the League, and Albion as a 'guest' during the war. Within nine months Smith had guided the Baggies back to the First Division after an 11-year absence and there is no doubt that his experience as a player had a lot to do with Albion's success.

After a rather indifferent start (three wins from nine games) Albion gradually began to hit top form and from late September to Christmas they played some exciting football, winning 11 matches out of 14 to surge towards the top of the table. Three defeats in four either side of the New Year disrupted the team slightly but, aided by two hard-earned FA Cup wins against Lincoln City and Gateshead, and a 3-0 triumph over First Division Chelsea, in which Walsh grabbed a hat-trick, they picked up the momentum again; as Easter approached they

Albion skipper Jack Vernon shakes hands with West Ham captain Sam Small in the 1947-48 season.

Newly-promoted Albion ready to start the 1949-50 season. Back row (left to right): Fred Reed (trainer), Eddie Wilcox, Joe Kennedy, Harry Kinsell, Ray Barlow, Bobby Barker, Glyn Hood, Jack Haines, Reg Ryan, W. G. Richardson (coach). Front: Len Millard, Billy Elliott, Cyril Williams, Dave Walsh, Jack Vernon, Jim Sanders, Jim Pemberton, Arthur Smith, Jack Boyd.

were well in touch with Fulham and Southampton at the top, although Saints were some way clear in terms of points gained. Knocked out of the Cup at Molineux, Albion didn't let that defeat disturb their routine and they played really well during April, collecting five important wins, four on the trot. Southampton's challenge faded and with Fulham looking strong, Albion moved into second place with promotion finally being clinched with a 3-0 away victory at Filbert Street in the penultimate game of the season. In fact, if Albion had won (and not lost) at Grimsby on the final Saturday they would have gone up as champions.

Dave Walsh top-scored with 28 goals (in League and Cup); Jack Haines netted 14 and Cyril Williams, who had been recruited from Bristol City, struck nine. Goalkeeper Jimmy Sanders was in superb form all season; an ever-present, he saved nine penalties. Len Millard and Walsh each missed one game, Billy Elliott was absent from two, while Jim Pemberton, Jack Vernon, Haines, Williams, Harry Kinsell and Glyn Hood all made 30

or more appearances. Ray Barlow and Joe Kennedy both made important contributions as well.

Albion's average home League attendance rose to a club record 33,379 – and there were 16 turnouts in excess of 30,000, with a best of 47,028 witnessing the Southampton game in November.

Arthur Rowley left the club during the season, joining Fulham who were also promoted. Ernie Shepherd was transferred to Albion from Craven Cottage and he figured in three promotion-winning teams this season, Albion, Fulham and Hull City who came up from Division 3 North.

Inside-forward Haines capped a fine season by winning an England cap v Switzerland, scoring twice in a 6-0 win at Highbury. Both Vernon and Walsh played for Ireland against England, Scotland and Wales, with Walsh scoring twice against both the English and Scots. He also lined up for the Republic of Ireland against Switzerland, Portugal, Sweden and Spain, hitting one goal v the Swedes.

In June 1949 the death took place of former Albion and Liverpool player Harry Chambers, at the age of 53.

1949-50

Albion began their first season back in the top flight with a 1-0 home win over Charlton Athletic, fielding this team: Sanders; Pemberton, Millard; Kennedy, Vernon, Barlow; Elliott, Williams, Walsh, Haines and George Lee, the latter having been signed from Nottingham Forest.

But the Baggies found it difficult to maintain any sort of consistency and, in fact, they recorded only three more wins in the next 12 matches. Scoring goals was becoming a problem — only 17 in their opening 13 fixtures – but successive home victories over Portsmouth (3-0) and Everton (4-0) boosted confidence before they were hammered twice in the North East, 5-1 at Newcastle and 3-0 at Middlesbrough. They bounced back from these defeats with a 4-1 victory over Fulham and then drew at Maine Road and won at Charlton, before losing at home to Manchester United which triggered off their worst spell of the season — two wins in 14 League outings — and they went out of the FA Cup at the hands of Cardiff City.

In March 1950, Albion's manager Smith went out and paid £20,000

Albion players training in 1951. Left to right: Les Horne, Reg Ryan, Glyn Hood (heading) and Jack Vernon.

for a 21-year-old winger from Port Vale by the name of Ronnie Allen. Allen was to become one of the greatest players ever to don a Baggies' shirt. He scored 234 goals in 458 games for the club and later had two spells as manager at The Hawthorns. Almost 61,000 fans turned up to see Allen make a scoring debut for Albion in the 1-1 home draw with Wolves and he netted another four goals before the season ended, helping Albion edge up to 14th position as they claimed four wins from their last six matches.

Walsh was once more leading scorer with 15 League goals to his name. Sanders was again an ever-present between the posts, while Pemberton, Millard, Kennedy, Vernon, Walsh and Reg Ryan, who was now established in the side at left-half, all appeared in 34 or more games.

Albion's average home League attendance of 38,819 was a new club record – and was 5,440 better than the previous season's figure.

Vernon added to his collection of international caps by captaining Ireland against Scotland and England, while Walsh also played against Wales as well as lining up for Eire versus Finland, Sweden and England, the latter at Goodison Park when the English lost for the first time on home soil to a 'foreign' country. Reg Ryan also played for Ireland against Wales and for Eire versus Sweden and Belgium.

In March 1950 former Albion goalkeeper Ike Webb died at the age of 75.

In the summer of 1950 veteran trainer Fred Reed was replaced at another ex-player, Arthur Fitton.

1950-51

Stan Rickaby, who had been signed from Middlesbrough towards the end of the previous season, established himself as Albion's right-back this term, in place of Jim Pemberton., while centre-forward Fred Richardson and inside-left Andy McCall also made their mark. Richardson was signed to replace Dave Walsh, who was surprisingly (from a supporters' point of view) transferred to Aston Villa while McCall arrived from Blackpool.

Other favourites on the move around this time included Haines (to Bradford), Bobby Barker (to Shrewsbury), Charlie Evans (to Stafford Rangers), Cyril Williams (to Bristol City).

Taking the season as a whole, it was a disappointing one for Albion, who finished 16th in the table with 37 points, only five clear of relegation. They won just 13 matches and had two long, inept spells – the first covering 15 games from 19 August to 28 October which brought them just three wins, and the second between late-December and late-March which again produced only two wins in 13 games. There were some useful performances however. The reigning League champions Portsmouth were walloped 5-0 at The Hawthorns, Everton were beaten 3-0 at Goodison Park and

Arsenal succumbed 2-0 in the Midlands. Albion also suffered some heavy defeats, among them a 5-0 thrashing at Tottenham and 3-0 hidings at Highbury, Manchester United and Sheffield Wednesday.

There was no joy in the FA Cup either as Albion went out in the third round to Derby County after a replay.

Allen, in his first full season, topscored with ten goals, Barlow netted nine and Richardson eight.

Barlow was the only ever-present in the ranks; Rickaby missed one game as did Vernon while Allen and the dependable Millard missed two matches.

Norman Heath, a wartime signing, was now making his name in the Albion goal and star of the future, right-winger Frank Griffin, signed from Shrewsbury Town in April 1951, made his debut in the last game of the season at Sunderland.

The average League attendance at The Hawthorns fell by 7,727 to 31,082, and only 39, 066 witnessed the local derby with Wolves, the lowest for this prestigious Black Country fixture since October 1936.

On the international front, Vernon added four caps to his Irish collection by playing against France, England, Scotland and Wales, while Walsh scored for Eire against Norway. Ryan played for the Republic of Ireland against Norway (twice) and Argentina.

During the course of the season Albion lost two more great stalwarts who had been in fragile health. In October 1950, Claude Jephcott, a former Albion player, director and current vice-chairman, died at the age of 59, and in March 1951, Fred Everiss, who had been at the helm for so long, passed away at the age of 68.

Earlier, in September 1950, Albion's 1912 FA Cup Final inside-right Harry Wright, died at the age of 60.

Jim Pemberton decided to retire (through injury and ill-health) in March 1951 after 172 peacetime games for Albion.

Billy Elliott also called it a day, quitting the League scene in July 1951 after scoring 157 goals in 330 first-team games for Albion from 1938. Wing-half Glyn Hood also retired.

1951-52

Albion did not make the greatest of games to this season, winning only one of the opening 11 League matches. They managed just five victories from the first 21 of the campaign and when the New Year arrived they found themselves in a spot of bother at the wrong end of the table. Thankfully they improved as the season wore on and after notching up six wins from their last eight matches they eased themselves up to 13th position with 41 points, 16 fewer than the champions Manchester United and 13 more than relegated Huddersfield Town in 21st place.

Albion won only a third of their 42 matches, the best being another emphatic 5-0 home victory over Portsmouth. They also beat both Newcastle United and Wolves 4-1 away with Ronnie Allen scoring a hat-trick at Molineux, and defeated Liverpool 5-2 at Anfield. Burnley inflicted upon Albion their heaviest League defeat, hammering them 6-1 at Turf Moor, while Arsenal raced to a 6-3 victory at Highbury and Manchester United won 5-1 at Old Trafford.

Albion's FA Cup exploits ended in round five when they lost to a late penalty at Blackburn having ousted Bolton and Gateshead in previous rounds.

Allen, who was now playing in the centre-forward position (on the say so of Jack Vernon) top-scored with 35 goals. George Lee netted 12 and Griffin 9, while a promising youngster named Johnny Nicholls weighed in with five, having made his debut in that Cup-tie at Ewood Park.

Heath and Sanders shared the goalkeeping duties; Rickaby and Millard were confident full-backs; Vernon – in his last season with the club – was his usual self at centre-half, being flanked at various intervals by Jimmy Dudley, Joe Kennedy, Ray Barlow and Reg Ryan. The latter two also figured in the forward-line where Griffin, Lee and of course, Allen all did well, as did Arthur Smith, McCall and Richardson to a lesser degree. Rickaby and Ryan were the only ever-presents in the first XI.

Albion's average League attendance this season dropped to 29,712 – the lowest since 1946-47.

Allen, after another fine season, won the first of his five England caps when he lined up against Switzerland in Zurich. Vernon played in two more internationals for Ireland v Scotland and England and captained the Rest of the United Kingdom against Wales at Cardiff. Reg Ryan was capped by the Republic of Ireland against West Germany (twice), Austria and Spain and both Barlow and Kennedy (as captain) represented England 'B' against France.

Vernon, after five great years with Albion, returned to his native Ireland to play for Crusaders. He had scored once in 200 games for the Baggies. Other players to leave the club included Richardson, who moved to Chester, McCall joined Leeds United and Arthur Smith went to Plymouth Argyle.

During the summer of 1952, two more former Hawthorns favourites, who both starred in the 1910-11 Second Division championship-winning side and in the 1912 FA Cup Final, passed away.

Fred Buck died in June, aged 71 and the following month George Baddeley, the oldest player ever to appear in a League game for Albion, died at the age of 78.

Jack Smith also quit as team manager (April 1952), handing over the duties to the former Newcastle United and Blackburn defender Jesse Carver, who came in basically as a coach. Carver had been successful in this capacity in Holland and Italy.

In the furore surrounding Jack Smith's departure, one of the directors, Norman Bassett, was asked to resign and was replaced by Sam Shepherd. Tommy Glidden, Albion's former captain, and Jim Gaunt, had joined the board some months earlier, in August 1951.

1952-53

Under Carver's shrewd coaching methods Albion got off to a flying start this season, winning seven of their opening nine matches. Three of those victories were away from home, at Tottenham (4-3 in sweltering heat), Cardiff City and

Arthur Fitton is about to be ducked by Ronnie Allen, watched by Len Millard, Frank Griffin and the rest of the Albion players, at the Droitwich Brine Baths in October 1952.

Manchester City, while Stoke City, Cardiff, Newcastle and Liverpool were beaten at The Hawthorns. Allen with seven goals was in fine form and the team as a unit was playing well.

Then came a poor run of results with only one win in seven games, but this was soon over and as the winter set in so Albion again picked up the momentum, running in five more victories by the end of the year, including a magnificent 5-4 triumph at Hillsborough.

A shock, however, at this juncture was the loss of coach Jesse Carver who returned to Italy in December.

Albion then started 1953 off with a cracking 5-3 win at Newcastle and also progressed in the FA Cup by knocking out West Ham 4-1 at Upton Park. Then, after a 5-0 defeat at Burnley and a 5-1 hammering at Stoke, Albion appointed Vic Buckingham, ex-Spurs left-back, as their new manager.

He moved down from Bradford Park Avenue (February 1953) and saw Albion quickly go out of the Cup (at the fourth attempt to Chelsea), but he realised that he had inherited a fine squad of players. He took his time regarding any alter-

ations and slowly but surely worked things out for the good, seeing Albion end the season confidently, by losing only one of their last six matches to take fourth place, their highest finish since 1932-33.

Albion rounded off the season by visiting the Irish Republic to play in two exhibition games against Select XIs of Waterford and Bohemians.

Allen netted 21 goals to head the scoring charts once more; Lee scored 11, Griffin and Ryan nine apiece and Nicholls seven. Rickaby

and Dudley were both ever-presents; Allen, Millard, Barlow and Lee missed one game each; Ryan was absent twice with Heath (36) and Griffin (35) also giving good service. A player who made his debut this season in place of the injured Joe Kennedy, was Liverpool-born centre-half Jimmy Dugdale, who was to become a real star in the middle-line.

Albion's average home League attendance went up by 1,800 to 31,527 and 54,480 fans witnessed the local derby with Wolves in October.

Reg Ryan was the only player to win senior international honours this season, lining up for the Republic of Ireland against France and Austria. Barlow won a second England 'B' cap against Scotland and he also twice represented the Football League v the League of Ireland and the Danish Combination. In the close season he toured South America and U.S.A. with the England party.

In July 1953, Buckingham made his first major signing, bringing centre-forward Derek Kevan down to The Hawthorns from his former club Bradford Park Avenue for a fee

New manager Vic Buckingham (second left) and the Albion players listen to a recording of the second-half commentary of their FA Cup game with Chelsea in 1953.

of just £3,000. And what a buy it was.

1953-54

Albion came so close this season to becoming the first team this century to achieve the League and FA Cup double.

They beat Preston North End 3-2 in the Cup Final, but sadly injuries and international call-ups ruined their chances of winning the League Division One trophy as they finished a cruel second to rivals Wolves after a titanic battle for the championship. In fact, Albion had already lost the League before going to Wembley.

From the word go it was a two-horse race for the championship between Albion and Wolves – and, in truth, it was Albion who looked the better equipped and more force-

ful and enterprising side for most of the time – that is until they collapsed late on, allowing their arch rivals to go on and lift the star prize by a margin of four points (57-53).

Albion lost just one of their first 15 League games (3-2 at home to Charlton).But then they managed just four victories in their next ten, yet after embarking on that terrific Cup run they still managed to keep in touch with Wolves with some important wins. Then injuries to key players, namely goalkeeper Norman Heath (at Sunderland) and right-back Stan Rickaby (in the Cup semifinal at Villa Park), plus England call-ups for strikers Allen and Nicholls took their toll, and from their last ten matches Albion conjured up a mere six points out a possible 20 and waved goodbye to the title in the process.

Their away form was superb early on, the highlight being a wonderful 7-3 win at Newcastle where Johnny Nicholls struck his first hat-trick in front of a 58,075 crowd.

Burnley were also defeated 4-1 at Turf Moor, and in fact, Albion won their first six away games, scoring 21 goals.

At The Hawthorns they were equally as impressive and among their triumphs where were those of 4-0 v Huddersfield, 5-2 v Chelsea and 6-1 against Cardiff City, with Allen scoring a hat-trick in each game.

Albion were unbeaten over Christmas when they ran up successive home wins over Liverpool (5-2) and Preston (3-2) and then they started off on that road to Wembley by taking out Chelsea 1-0 and Rotherham United 4-0.

Albion players enjoy a cruise on the River Thames on the eve of the 1954 FA Cup Final against Preston North End.

HAWTHORNS DIARY

Albion skipper Len Millard with the Cup after the Baggies win over Preston.

As they progressed in the Cup so their League form began to suffer but after defeating Newcastle United 3-2 in the fifth round courtesy of another Allen treble in front of a packed house of 61,088 spectators and Spurs 3-0 in the quarter-final, the double still looked on. But then it started to go wrong.

Port Vale were beaten 2-1 in the semi-final at the cost of Rickaby and soon afterwards Heath was so badly injured at Roker Park that he never played again.

Buckingham brought in his reserves – Joe Kennedy, Wilf Carter, Fred Cox (his old Spurs team-mate) and ex-Wrexham right-back Stuart Williams – but the results went against Albion and after losing their last two matches – 6-1 at Villa Park and 3-0 at Portsmouth – they watched as the League trophy annoyingly found its way to Molineux.

Albion however, celebrated at Wembley and won the Cup for the fourth time, as goals from Allen (2, one a penalty) and Frank Griffin (the winner in the 87th minute) saw off Preston in front of a near 100,000 crowd. So it was a 'double' in the end for the West Midlands – but not as Albion had hoped it would be.

Allen top-scored with 34 League and Cup goals, and his strike partner Nicholls netted 32. Not for nothing were they known as 'The Terrible Twins.'

Right-half Jimmy Dudley was an ever-present while Lee was absent once and Millard twice.

Albion's average home League attendance went up to 38,279 – the second best in the club's history. The top League attendance was that of 53,210 for the 2-1 win over the then FA Cup holders Blackpool.

Over 134,000 fans saw Allen and Nicholls both score in England's 4-2 international win over Scotland at Hampden Park and the same two players won further caps against Yugoslavia in Belgrade. Rickaby also played for England – against Ireland, while Stuart Williams represented Wales v Austria. Ryan was capped three more times by the Republic of Ireland, twice against France (he scored in one) and once v Luxembourg (when he also found the net).

Allen and Nicholls gained England 'B' caps – the former v Switzerland and Scotland, Nicholls as 'sub' v the Swiss. Nicholls also won an England under-23 cap against Italy in Bologna.

Jimmy Dugdale also played at 'B' team level for England against Switzerland, Yugoslavia and Scotland, who had Albion's Jimmy Dudley in their side, while Ray Barlow, Dugdale and Stan Rickaby played for the Football League v the League of Ireland.

In March 1954, Albion's popular goalkeeper from the 1890s, Joe Reader, died at the age of 88.

He had served the club as a trainer and steward after his playing days until the early 1950s.

1954-55

Albion started this season's League programme like they ended the previous one, losing two matches in a row – at Sunderland 4-2 and Newcastle 3-0. But they responded quickly and won seven of their next eight matches to fly to the top of the table.

At this juncture the team was playing exceptionally well – and scoring goals. They defeated Arsenal 3-1, gained revenge over Newcastle with a 4-2 home victory and beat Leicester City 6-4 in a thrill-in-minute encounter at The Hawthorns with Johnny Nicholls hitting his second hat-trick for the club. They even shared eight goals in the FA Charity Shield game with Wolves at Molineux where Allen slotted in another hat-trick in front of a 45,000 crowd.

But after an exciting 3-3 draw at Chelsea, where Len Millard scored a late equaliser in front of a 67,440 crowd, and a 5-3 defeat at the hands of the crack Hungarian side Honved in a prestige friendly in Brussels, performances began to falter and only three victories came from the next 20 matches as Albion plummeted down the Division, heading fast towards the relegation zone. It was an amazing turn around in form – and to add salt to the wounds, the Baggies went out of the FA Cup to Charlton, 4-2 in a fourth-round tie at The Hawthorns.

Manager Buckingham was pulling his hair out in an effort to halt Albion's decline; he was also recovering from a car crash, suffered on his way home from Albion's friendly at Hereford which produced an amazing scoreline of 10-5 in favour of the Bulls on 1 November.

As a desperate measure he moved Ray Barlow into the attack, brought in Billy Brookes at left-half, played Stuart Williams at right-back and Wilf Carter at inside-right. And these changes worked. Wolves were beaten 1-0 at home to stop the rot and as the season wound down the Baggies hauled themselves to safety with further victories over Charlton, Bolton, Portsmouth, Manchester City and Huddersfield. They eventually finished 17th – a drop of 15 places from the previous season, and avoided the drop by five points after conceding 96 goals.

Their heaviest defeats came at Portsmouth (6-2), Leicester (6-3) and Sheffield Wednesday (5-0).

Ronnie Allen bagged another 30 goals this term and he also headed the Division One scoring list. George Lee netted 13 times and Nicholls 12.

Allen, Jimmy Dudley and skipper Len Millard were all ever-present although six other players made 30 or more first-team appearances. Players making their debuts included Tipton-born Alec Jackson, winger Allan Crowshaw and goalkeeper Geoff Barnsley, while Stan Rickaby and Reg Ryan both moved on. The former joined Derby County for £3,000 after more than 270 appearances for the club and the latter became player-manager of Poole Town after starring in 205 senior games for Albion.

The average home attendance dropped, not surprisingly, by over 7,000 to 31,247 and the turnout of just 7,764 for the game with Chelsea on a freezing cold Wednesday afternoon in March was the lowest at The Hawthorns since May 1937.

But then it all went wrong again as Albion suffered seven defeats in Final of the FA Youth Cup, but lost 7-1 to Manchester United on aggregate over two legs.

On the international scene, Ronnie Allen won two more England caps v Wales and the World champions West Germany, both at Wembley, scoring against the latter nation; Ray Barlow won his long-awaited first cap v Northern Ireland and he also played for the Football League side v the League of Ireland; Stuart Williams played for Wales against England and Ireland and Reg Ryan represented the Republic of Ireland against Norway – and he scored.

Ryan left The Hawthorns for Derby County in the close season after scoring 31 goals in 272 games for Albion. Stan Rickaby and Norman Heath also left the club. Rickaby later emigrated to Australia.

In August 1954, Howard Gregory, left-winger when Albion won the League Championship in 1920, died at the age of 60.

1955-56

For the second season running Albion made an uneasy start to their League programme, losing two and drawing one of their opening four matches. But Derek Kevan was introduced to the action and he scored twice on his debut v Everton after replacing the injured Ronnie Allen. Another future England international, right-back Don Howe, also played his first game for the club against the Merseysiders. These two players were to become key men in the Baggies' first team over the next eight years.

Between early September and 5 November Albion's form improved and seven more victories were recorded. Allen returned and was again finding the net on a regular basis.

HAWTHORNS DIARY

their next eight outings to slide down towards the bottom end of the table.

Changes were made to the team as Buckingham brought in Crowshaw, wing-half Gerry Summers, Maurice Setters (signed from Exeter) and left-winger Graham Williams from Rhyl, soon to become a Welsh international and later a Cup Final left-back.

Shortly after Christmas the tide turned and over an eight-week period Albion regained their composure, started winning again and slowly moved up the Division. But after going out of the FA Cup to neighbours Birmingham City on a snowbound Hawthorns pitch, their League form took a turn for the worse with six defeats coming in the next nine outings. Inside-right Bobby Robson was signed from Fulham for £25,000 in March, but he didn't have the greatest of baptisms, Albion suffering successive 4-0 defeats in his first two outings. Thankfully the season was all but over by now and when the final curtain came down Albion found themselves in 13th place with 41 points, six clear of relegation.

In the latter half of the season youngsters Brian Whitehouse and Roy Horobin were blooded and a record £25,000 signing from Fulham, Bobby Robson, came into the side at inside-right.

Allen (18 goals) was top-scorer again; Lee netted 12 and Nicholls eight.

There were no ever-presents, but Jim Sanders (41), Jim Dudley (41), Len Millard (40), George Lee (40), Ray Barlow (38) and Ronnie Allen (34) all made worthy contributions – as always.

Albion's average home League attendance was 26,922, the lowest since 1946-47, and a drop of over 4,000 on the previous season.

At international level Stuart

Williams earned another three caps for Wales, lining up against England, Scotland and Austria. Joe Kennedy captained England 'B' v Yugoslavia and Scotland and Don Howe won his first England under-23 cap v Scotland.

In the summer of 1956 Bobby Robson went on the FA tour of South Africa and played in four 'test' matches.

Albion's reserves had their best season since the War as they finished sixth in the Central League.

In October 1955, Hubert Pearson, Albion's goalkeeper in the 1912 FA Cup Final and 1920 League championship winning side, died at the age of 69. He was followed in June and July 1956 by two playing colleagues, Bobby McNeal (aged 65) and Joe Smith (66) who also won League championship medals.

1956-57

For the third season running Albion failed to get off to a good start, winning only three of their opening 12 League games.

Manager Buckingham was concerned and made frequent changes, bringing in Kevan at centre-forward, switching Allen to the left-wing, re-introducing Nicholls at inside-left (in place of Brian Whitehouse), inserting Setters for Jim Dudley, and recalling the experienced Len Millard for Stuart Williams at left-back.

Things improved and four wins were registered off the reel with no goals conceded. Albion, though, stuttered their way through December and January, managing only one League win – 1-0 at home to Newcastle, this being the last Christmas Day game at The Hawthorns. They got through the opening rounds of the FA Cup, beating Doncaster Rovers in a replay and Sunderland, but their overall form left a lot to be desired. Roy Horobin was now in the side at outside-left and he did well, helping Albion through a sticky patch as they claimed four important victories to avoid being caught up in a relegation dogfight.

Progress was made to the semi-final stage of the Cup as Blackpool and then Arsenal fell by the wayside (both after replays) but Albion couldn't get to grips with the League situation. They won only two more matches (out of the last ten) and they also lost to Aston Villa in the

Jim Sanders punches clear from Aston Villa's Pace and Dixon as Brookes and Dudley cover at The Hawthorns in August 1956.

Cup semi-final, going down 1-0 in a replay at St Andrew's after allowing their arch rivals to snatch a late equaliser to make the score 2-2 in the initial encounter at Molineux.

Albion's final League position was 11th with 42 points, 13 more than relegated Cardiff City.

Derek Kevan took over the mantle of leading scorer this term with a total of 20 goals. Allen netted 15, Robson 13 and Whitehouse 10.

Don Howe made the most League appearances (41) and Albion's average home League attendance was 23,343 – more than 6,500 down on 1955-56, and the lowest average turnout at The Hawthorns since 1938-39. The audience of 6,397 for the mid-week game with Blackpool was Albion's smallest since April 1939.

International honours this season were gained by Derek Kevan who scored on his full England debut v Scotland at Wembley, and was also capped at under-23 level against Bulgaria, Romania and Czechoslovakia and Don Howe, who played for both the England 'B' side v Scotland and the under-23 team v France and Scotland and for the Football League v the Scottish League.

This season saw the departure of Johnny Nicholls, who joined Cardiff City in May after scoring 64 goals in 145 games for the Baggies. Fellow inside-forward Wilf Carter also left, signing for Plymouth Argyle in May 1957, while left-half Gerry Summers was transferred to Sheffield United.

Among the newcomers was trainer Dick Graham, a former Northampton Town, Leicester City and Crystal Palace goalkeeper who arrived in November 1956.

In the summer of 1957 Albion travelled behind the Iron Curtain and played three prestigious friendly games in Russia, winning two (3-0 v Dynamo Tbilisi and 4-2 v CDSA

1957-58

This season Albion scored 112 League and Cup goals and netted six in a floodlit friendly against the CDSA Army side from Moscow. Playing attacking football with five forwards, Albion certainly gave their fans value for money although at times the defence wasn't all that secure, conceding 70 in the League. Albion, in fact, had a tremendous first half to the season, losing only once in their first 21 matches – 2-1 at home to Arsenal in September.

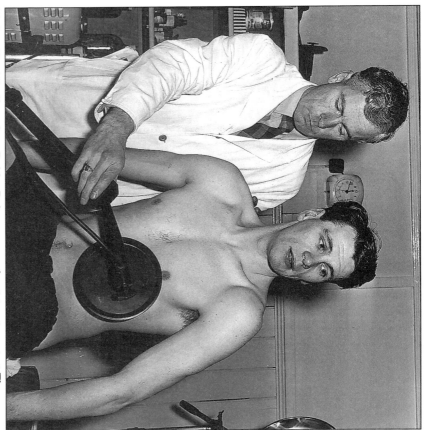

Trainer Fred Pedley gives Bobby Robson some heat treatment at The Hawthorns in 1958.

Red Army) and drawing the other (1-1 v Zenit), thus becoming the first British professional team to record a victory in the USSR.

In February 1957, former Albion centre-forward Harry 'Popeye' Jones died at the age of 45. He scored 104 goals in 169 first team outings for the club and received the Royal Humane Society Medal when he dived into a freezing canal to save the life of a young child.

They were well on course for the championship after recording some splendid victories including a 9-2 hammering of Manchester City, their best ever League win at The Hawthorns. Frank Griffin netted a hat-trick in this game as all five front men scored to destroy City's much vaunted 'M' plan.

Either side of the New Year Albion went nap in three successive games, winning 5-3 at Birmingham City, 5-1 at home to Burnley and 5-1 v Manchester City in the FA Cup. They then drew 3-3 with Nottingham Forest in the Cup before going to The City Ground and winning the fourth-round replay 5-1 with only ten men after Setters had been carried off injured.

At this stage of the season Albion were playing sensational football and there was every chance that they could go on and complete the League and Cup double which had eluded them four years earlier.

Sadly though, as Sheffield United

HAWTHORNS DIARY

were ousted in the fifth round of the Cup, Albion's influential right-winger Frank Griffin fractured his leg. It was a body blow but the team battled on and in the quarter-final faced Manchester United only a few weeks after the Munich Air disaster. The game at The Hawthorns ended 2-2, but in the cauldron of Old Trafford the Baggies were beaten in the very last minute in front of an emotional 60,523.

Amazingly, three days later, Albion returned to the same ground for a League game and whipped United 4-0 in front of 3,000 more spectators. That Cup defeat rocked morale however, and Albion's League form deteriorated. They fell away to finish fourth after gaining just two wins in their last nine outings. Wolves won the title with 64 points, 14 more than Albion.

Three players scored 78 of Albion's 112 League and Cup goals between them: Allen 28, Robson 27 and Kevan 23.

Robson (41) and Ray Barlow (40) appeared in most League games.

Albion's average home League attendance was up by 9,200 to 32,558, and 221,253 fans witnessed the four FA Cup-ties at The Hawthorns (average 55,313). A crowd of 56,904 attended the local derby with Wolves – the best League crowd on the ground since March 1950.

Don Howe won 11 of his 23 England caps this season, appearing against Wales, Ireland and Scotland in the Home International Championship, the friendlies against France, Portugal and Yugoslavia and in the World Cup v USSR (three times), Austria and Brazil.

Derek Kevan played in ten of those internationals, missing the game against France – and he scored twice at Hampden Park v the Scots and also v USSR and Austria (once each). Bobby Robson netted twice on his England debut v France and he, too, played against the Russians (twice) Brazil and Austria in the World Cup Finals in Sweden.

Stuart Williams was also on World Cup duty with Wales and he played in ten internationals this term v England, Scotland, Israel (twice), Ireland, Hungary (twice), Mexico, Sweden and Brazil.

Howe appeared in three England under-23 games v Bulgaria, Scotland and Wales. Kevan and Maurice Setters also played against the Bulgars, with Setters also lining up versus Romania, Scotland and Wales. Ronnie Allen, Howe, Kevan and Robson all played for the Scottish Football League XI v the Scottish League at Newcastle with Kevan scoring a hat-trick, and Barlow captained the 'League' side v the League of Ireland.

Robson (3) and Allen (2) scored all England's goals v a Sheffield XI (won 5-4).

At the end of this season three 1954 FA Cup winners left the club – goalkeeper Jimmy Sanders, with 391 appearances behind him, signed for Coventry City; skipper Len Millard joined Stafford Rangers after 21 years and 625 appearances for Albion and left-winger George Lee moved to Lockheed Leamington, having scored 65 goals in 295 games during his ten years at The Hawthorns.

1958-59

This turned out to be another good season for Albion who finished a creditable fifth in the First Division with 49 points (12 fewer than champions Wolves). They also reached the fifth round of the FA Cup and scored another 93 goals.

A 6-0 win at Birmingham in pouring rain was one of the many fine away displays put on by Albion; others were at Portsmouth (won 6-2), Villa Park (won 4-1) and Preston (won 4-2). The best home performances came against Chelsea (won 4-0), and Tottenham (won 4-3). On the down side Albion lost 5-2 at Wolves, 5-0 at Tottenham, 4-2 at home to Burnley and 4-3 at Highbury, despite Derek Kevan's hat-trick.

Albion lost only one of their first nine League games; they won eight out of 12 between mid-October and the end of December and over a four-week period from the end of March they lost one in ten, gaining six more victories.

Kevan with 29 goals was top marksman. Allen scored 17 and Burnside 12.

Kevan (41), Setters (41), Hogg (40), Howe (40), Stuart Williams (40), Allen (36) and Barlow (36) played in most League games.

The average League crowd at The Hawthorns was 31,547 – a thousand down on 1957-58.

Clive Jackman, who had been signed the previous season from Aldershot, started off in goal but was badly injured at Villa Park in October and never played for Albion again. His place went to Ray Potter, a bargain buy from Crystal Palace. Chuck Drury, a local lad, who made his debut at Bolton in February 1958, had some useful outings in the half-back line, while wingers Jimmy Campbell and Derek Hogg, the latter signed from Leicester City in the summer, did well.

During the season Albion did not introduce one newcomer into their first team – the only time this has happened.

During 1958-59, Howe collected nine more England caps, playing against Ireland, USSR, Wales, Scotland, Italy, Brazil, Peru, Mexico and the U.S.A. Kevan also played against Mexico and the U.S.A. (scoring in each game). Stuart Williams added three Welsh caps to his tally, playing in the games v Scotland,

England and Ireland. Setters earned five more call-ups for the England under-23s – against Poland, Czechoslovakia, France, Italy and West Germany and Howe also played for the Football League v the League of Ireland.

In the summer of 1959 Albion toured Canada and North America, playing nine games of which seven were won, including those of 6-1 v Ontario All Stars, 15-0 v Alberta All Stars (when Robson scored six goals), 7-1 v the Scottish club Dundee in Calgary, 10-1 v Manitoba All Stars and 9-0 v Ottawa All Stars.

However, on his return to England Albion's manager Vic Buckingham parted company with the club – and into his place (in July 1959) stepped the former Manchester City full-back and ex-Peterborough United manager Gordon Clark, who had been with Albion since 1955, acting as scout and then assistant-manager.

Frank Griffin also left in the summer, joining Northampton Town after failing to make a full recovery from his broken leg mishap. He scored 52 goals in 275 games for the Baggies.

In October 1958 a member of Albion's 1912 FA Cup Final team, Ben Shearman, died at the age of 74. In March 1959 one of Albion's finest-ever goalscorers, 'W. G.' Richardson collapsed and died while playing in a Charity Match in Birmingham. He was only 49 and netted 202 goals in 320 League games for Albion over a ten-year period: 1929-39. And the following month former Albion wing-half and director Dan Nurse died at the age of 85.

1959-60

For the third season running Albion finished in the top five of the First Division, this time taking fourth spot behind Burnley, the champi-ons, Wolves and Tottenham. Albion amassed only six points fewer than Burnley and if they hadn't gone through a sticky patch when they collected a mere seven points out of a possible 20 during September and October, then it could well have been a completely different story.

Early on they beat Manchester United 3-2 and Leicester City 5-0 at home, then followed up with a 3-0 victory over Leeds (despite missing two penalties), whipped Luton 4-0 and defeated Arsenal 4-2 at Highbury.

After Christmas further wins came against Preston 4-0 at home and Leeds 4-1 at Elland Road (when they were brilliant) and late on Everton were hammered 6-2 at The Hawthorns (when Derek Kevan netted five times) and Birmingham City were walloped 7-1 at St Andrew's (Allen and Kevan both claiming hat-tricks). Albion's heaviest defeat of the season came at West Ham where they lost 4-1 and they also went down 4-2 at home to Fulham.

Albion's FA Cup journey this season ended in the fifth round at Leicester where they lost 2-1 despite a rare Joe Kennedy goal.

Scottish goalkeeper Jock Wallace was signed in October from Airdrieonians to replace the out-of-form Ray Potter. Graham Williams established himself in the left-back position during the second half of the season, likewise outside-right Alec Jackson after recovering from a broken leg, while a certain Bobby Hope was given his debut as a 16 year-old on the last day of the season v Arsenal. In the January tough guy Maurice Setters, who had been unsettled for some time, joined Manchester United for £30,000, a club record.

Kevan top-scored again with 29 senior goals; Allen netted 15 and Burnside and Jackson 12 apiece.

1960-61

Albion slipped down to tenth in the First Division this season after a rather disappointing set of results. Their home form let them down badly (eight defeats) and with 11 losses away from home, they were Kevan was the only ever-present in the side, while Howe, Kennedy and Robson, who was now playing as a wing-half, were absent just once. The average League attendance at The Hawthorns this term was 27,504 – 4,000 less than in 1958-59.

Howe collected his remaining three England caps this season v Wales, Sweden and Ireland; Robson played against Spain and Hungary; Graham Williams won his first Welsh cap v Ireland, playing alongside his team-mate Stuart Williams, who was also capped against Scotland and England.

Setters took his tally of England under-23 caps to 11 with outings against Hungary and France and Graham Williams won his first Welsh under-23 cap v Scotland. Football League honours went to Howe, who played against the Irish League and Robson who confronted the Scottish League.

At the end of the season Ray Barlow left Albion after 16 years and 482 appearances. He signed for neighbouring Birmingham City.

Another departure was that of Jimmy Dudley who moved to Walsall in December 1959 after 319 League and Cup games. Brian Whitehouse also left – for Norwich City in March 1960.

In September 1959, the death occurred at the age of 67, of former Albion wing-half Sammy Richardson.

1960-61

At Albion's AGM, assistant-secretary Alan Everiss took over as club secretary from Ephraim Smith who retired after 54 years loyal service to the club.

never in with a chance of challenging for honours. They accumulated 41 points – only nine more than relegated Newcastle United, whom they crushed 6-0 at The Hawthorns with an Alec Jackson hat-trick. This was their best win of the campaign, coming immediately after five successive defeats at the start of the League programme. Manchester City were beaten 6-3 at The Hawthorns, Allen – in his last season with the club – netting a hat-trick, with Albion crashed to a 7-1 defeat at Chelsea (Jimmy Greaves doing the damage with five goals) and they also lost 4-2 at Wolves and 4-2 at home to Fulham.

Albion's best spell – 11 games which included nine wins, seven on the bounce – came right at the end of the season after Clive Clark, a flying left-winger signed from Q.P.R. for £20,000, and Jack Lovatt had joined Jackson, Burnside and Kevan in attack.

Albion's interest in the FA Cup ended at the first hurdle, beaten 3-1 at lowly Lincoln.

Kevan, with 18 goals, was chief marksman yet again; Burnside netted 13 and Jackson 12.

Howe was the only ever-present; Jackson missed one game and Robson two, and all told manager Clark used 25 players including two ex-Walsall stars, lanky wing-half Peter Billingham and centre-half Stan Jones.

Albion's average home League crowd in 1960-61 was 24, 707 – their lowest since 1957.

On the international stage Derek Kevan won his 14th and last cap for an unbeaten England in an 8-0 Wembley win over Mexico. Robson also played and scored against the Mexicans as well as lining up against Northern Ireland, Luxembourg, Spain, Wales, Scotland (netting the first goal in a 9-3 win), Portugal and Italy. Graham Williams represented Wales against the Republic of Ireland, Scotland and England and his namesake Stuart played against Eire, Spain (twice), Northern Ireland and Hungary.

Robson also represented the Football League v the Italian League and captained the League XI v the Scottish League. Howe also appeared in this latter game.

Clive Clark won an England under-23 cap v Wales – his only representative honour in a fine career. Graham Williams also featured in this game. And at the season's end Don Howe toured New Zealand with the FA party.

At the end of the season Albion gave free transfers to two great players – Ronnie Allen and Joe Kennedy, who had both starred in that 1954 FA Cup win. Allen joined Crystal Palace after scoring 234 goals in 415 games for the Baggies, while Kennedy teamed up with Chester, having amassed 397 appearances for the club.

Derek Hogg was also on the move earlier this season, moving to Cardiff City. Stan Steele, signed from Port Vale in March, played one game for Albion (at Blackburn) before returning to the Potteries' club in August and trainer Dick Graham also departed for Crystal Palace (November 1960). He was replaced by Wilf Dixon.

In September 1960, former Albion winger Walter Boyes died suddenly at the age of 47 and in February 1961 Sid Bowser, an Albion player between 1908 and 1924, passed away at the age of 69. Both players won England recognition.

1961-62

In October 1961 silver-haired Archie Macaulay, the former Arsenal and Scottish international wing-half, took over as manager at The Hawthorns – taking over from Gordon Clark who joined former boss Vic Buckingham at Sheffield Wednesday.

However, for Albion this turned out to be a disappointing season. They had a disastrous set of League results during the first half of the campaign, registering only five wins, two of them emphatic

4-0 successes over Arsenal and Blackburn Rovers, both at home. They held their own between December and March before a gallant late run, when only two defeats were suffered in their last 12 League games, saw the Baggies pull themselves clear of relegation trouble to finish in ninth position with 43 points, 13 behind the champions Ipswich Town.

There is no doubt that at one stage relegation was certainly a possibility but Albion's battling performances paid off and towards the end of the season they were playing some delightful football. Indeed, they ended on a high with six wins out of eight, starting off with a terrific 5-1 scoreline at Molineux against arch rivals Wolves. Albion then ran up five victories on the trot, including a 4-0 pounding of Chelsea and a last-day slaughter of Blackpool, who crashed 7-1 at The Hawthorns with Derek Kevan slamming in four goals.

Albion's heaviest defeats of the campaign were 4-1 at Chelsea and Manchester United, and they also lost 4-2 at home to Tottenham, who also dumped them out of the FA Cup in the fifth round by the same score in front of a near 55,000 crowd – this being the last time the 50,000 barrier has been broken at The Hawthorns. Albion had accounted for Blackpool (after a replay) and Wolves in the earlier rounds.

Kevan headed the scorers with 34 goals (in League and Cup) and was joint top-scorer in the First Division with Ipswich's Ray Crawford (later

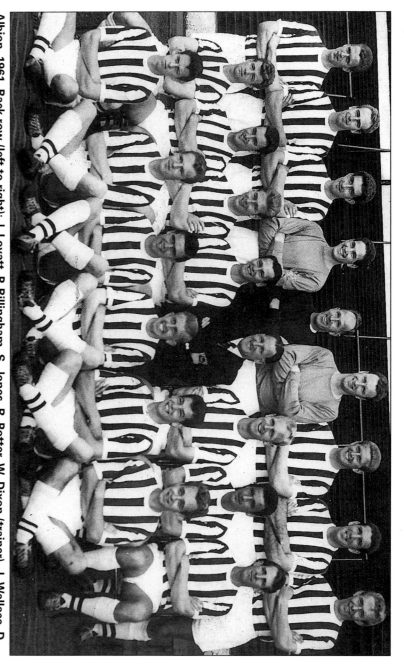

Albion, 1961. Back row (left to right): J. Lovatt, P. Billingham, S. Jones, R. Potter, W. Dixon (trainer), J. Wallace, D. Kevan, S. Williams, R. Cram. Middle: C. Clark, G. Williams, C. Drury, R. Robson, Gordon Clark (manager), D. Howe, A. Jackson, D. Burnside. Front: K. Smith, G. Carter, R. Hope, C. Brookes, J. Bannister, B. Macready.

to play for Albion), while Keith Smith netted 19 in his first full season of first team action.

Four players – Don Howe, Stan Jones, Alec Jackson and Derek Kevan – were all ever-present this season. And there was a League debut for goalkeeper Tony Millington (later to play for Wales).

Albion's average home League attendance dropped by almost 4,000 to just under-21,000, and for the first time since 1957 there wasn't a crowd at The Hawthorns of more than 40,000.

The World Cup Finals took place in Chile during the summer of 1962. Two Albion players – Don Howe and Bobby Robson – went to South America with the England squad but neither played. Robson thus ended his international career with a total of 20 full caps, having added the last five to his tally this season against Luxembourg, Wales, Portugal, Northern Ireland and Switzerland. He left Albion in August 1962, returning to his for-

mer club, Fulham after scoring 61 goals in 257 appearances since 1956.

Stuart Williams collected six more Welsh caps (four as captain) when playing against v England, Scotland, Northern Ireland, Brazil (twice) and Mexico; David Burnside starred in an under-21 international for England v Turkey and newcomer Tony Millington kept goal for Wales under-23 v Scotland and Northern Ireland. Don Howe represented the Football League v the Irish League, Robson played for the Football League XI against the League of Ireland and Alec Jackson starred against the Scottish League at Villa Park.

In July 1962, the death was announced at his home in Great Bridge of Fred Morris, Albion's ace goalscorer who played for the club either side of World War One. He was 68.

After starting off reasonably well when they suffered only three defeats in their opening ten matches (whipping Fulham 6-1 with Derek Kevan scoring four times and squeezing past Bolton 5-4 with another Kevan hat-trick in the process) their overall form dipped alarmingly from late September, and they recorded just four wins before the grim winter conditions took over. In fact, from Albion's point of view, things got worse out on the pitch before they got better, and with the freezing weather playing havoc with the fixture list (very few games were played between 15 December and 2 March) it was certainly looking glum around The Hawthorns.

Defeat in the FA Cup to Nottingham Forest in the fourth round (after Plymouth had been hammered 5-1 in Devon in the third), didn't help morale one iota and when Derek Kevan was sensationally transferred to Tommy Docherty's Chelsea for £50,000 in

1962-63

This turned out to be Albion's worst

March (this after he had said farewell to the Hawthorns fans with a blistering hat-trick in a 6-1 win over Ipswich Town), Albion's season was all but over.

Manager Macaulay departed, replaced in April 1963 by the former England international inside-forward Jimmy Hagan, and just as if to say 'welcome' things perked up a little towards the end of the campaign, Albion winning four and drawing two of their last eight matches. But it was, in truth, a very disappointing season for all concerned at the club.

Kevan with 16 goals again finished up as top scorer. Keith Smith and Alec Jackson offered support with 14 apiece.

Graham Williams and Stan Jones each made 40 League appearances with Don Howe (38) and Clive Clark and Bobby Cram weighing in with 36. Debutants this term included midget Scottish right-winger Kenny Foggo, centre-forward Max Murray, another Scot who arrived from Rangers, but returned to his homeland (with Third Lanark) in double-quick time, inside-forward Ronnie Fenton, a £15,000 buy from Burnley and full-back Ray Fairfax, whose first outing was at Anfield in front of 44,000 fans.

Stuart Williams, after making 246 appearances in 12 years with Albion and gaining a club record 33 caps for Wales, left to join Southampton along with Davey Burnside, who scored 42 goals in his 135 outings for the club. Centre-forward Keith Smith also moved on, signing for Peterborough United after netting 34 times in just 70 outings for the Baggies.

The average League attendance nose-dived to 18,637 – the lowest since 1938-39 and the turnout of 10,759 v Bolton was the worst for six years.

Even Albion's reserves didn't do much better, finishing 12th in the

Central League – their lowest position since 1959.

Tony Millington, who had the misfortune to concede 15 goals at Molineux this season when Albion lost 7-0 to Wolves in a re-arranged First Division game and 8-0 in a reserve fixture, won his first three Welsh caps v Scotland, Hungary and England. Fellow countryman Graham Williams also played against the Hungarians as well as Northern Ireland. Millington also earned under-23 recognition for Wales v Scotland and Northern Ireland.

In September 1962 'Sandy' McNab, the former Albion and Scotland wing-half, died at the age of 50 after a short illness.

Major H. Wilson Keys was replaced as Albion chairman by 'Jim' W. Gaunt at a board meeting on 9 April 1963 with Tommy Glidden stepping up to vice-chairman.

1963-64

Albion began this season with two new players in their line-up – left-half Terry Simpson (signed from Peterborough United) and centre-forward John Kaye (bought from Scunthorpe United). They settled in well and a month or so into the League programme, two more new faces were introduced – Scotsman Doug Fraser (secured from Aberdeen) and Oldham-born teenager Tony Brown, who on his debut at Ipswich, scored the first of 313 goals for the Baggies and made the first of 826 appearances – both club records.

Albion's pre-November performances were generally good. Playing confidently they ran up some impressive victories, including those of 4-0 over Arsenal, 3-0 v Fulham, 4-3 in the local derby with Aston Villa and 3-1 against Birmingham City – all at home.

In fact, they lost only three of

their opening 13 matches but then had a run of six without a win. A transfer rebellion early in December was quickly followed by the infamous tracksuit saga when manager Hagan refused to allow the players to wear tracksuit bottoms in freezing temperatures. This was thankfully resolved and Albion quickly put together a seven-match unbeaten League sequence either side of Christmas which included a thrilling 4-4 home draw with Tottenham. Exit from the FA Cup, beaten in a fourth-round replay at Arsenal after an eventful 3-3 draw at The Hawthorns, triggered off an indifferent stretch which lasted from February onwards, and only two more victories were recorded in the last eight League fixtures.

Albion finished the season in tenth position with 43 points, 14 behind the champions Liverpool, but well clear of next-to-bottom Bolton Wanderers (28 pts).

Winger Clive Clark had a fine season, top-scoring with 17 goals. John Kaye netted 12, Kenny Foggo 11 and Ronnie Fenton 10, while a young Micky Fudge weighed in with four, including a hat-trick in a 4-2 win over Everton.

Goalkeeper Ray Potter, centre-half Stan Jones, Terry Simpson and 'Chippy' Clark were all ever-present; the average League attendance at The Hawthorns rose slightly to 20,552; Albion's second XI finished runners-up in the Central League – their highest position since 1934-35 – and skipper Graham Williams played in three internationals for Wales v England, Scotland and Northern Ireland.

In April 1964, full-back Don Howe was transferred to Arsenal for £40,000 after 379 appearances for Albion. Chuck Drury (to Bristol City) and Alec Jackson (to Birmingham City) also moved on...and the first of a number of Throstle Clubs

Albion in 1963-64. Back row (left to right): Alan Scarrott, Brian Macready, Ray Fairfax, Ron Bradley, Dick Sheppard, Ray Potter, Tony Millington, Danny Campbell, Eddie Readfern, Mick Swinnerton, Ian Collard. Second row: Wilf Dixon (trainer), Trefor West, Gerry Howshall, Campbell Crawford, Geoff Carter, Jack Lovatt, Fred Pedley (physiotherapist), Jack Bannister, Dick Krzywicki, Bobby Cram, Bill Williams, Ray Treacy, John Jarman (coach), George Lee (coach). Third row: Ken Foggo, Bobby Hope, Ronnie Fenton, John Kaye, Stan Jones, Jimmy Hagan (manager), Terry Simpson, Don Howe, Graham Williams, Alec Jackson, Chuck Drury. On ground: Tony Brown, Chris Tudor, Micky Fudge, Dennis Clarke, Brian Lobban, Kenny Stephens.

(for Baggies' supporters) opened near the Woodman pub on the Handsworth side of the ground.

In July trainer Wilf Dixon moved to Blackpool. Four years later he was Everton's trainer in the FA Cup Final v Albion at Wembley. His successor was John Jarman, who was followed by the former Walsall centre-half Albert McPherson a year later.

1964-65

Albion opened this season by gaining a point from a 2-2 draw in front of 52,000 fans at Old Trafford – and four days later Tony Brown scored his first hat-trick for the club in a 4-1 home win over Sunderland, who fielded 15 year-old goalkeeper Derek Forster.

However, after one win was been gained from the next eight matches, manager Hagan laid out £25,000 for

the Notts County striker Jeff Astle – and what a terrific buy it turned out to be.

He made his Albion bow in a 4-2 defeat at Leicester, but then scored twice on his home debut as Wolves were demolished 5-1 in early October.

Astle and Kaye gelled together immediately and with Clive Clark (now temporarily at outside-right) and Bobby Hope both in good form Albion's forward-line looked strong and penetrative. But sadly the results didn't come and Albion failed to register a single win from ten games between 7 November and 16 January. And they also lost interest in the FA Cup, defeated 2-1 at home by Liverpool.

A 2-0 defeat of Tottenham at The Hawthorns ended that dismal run and from February until the end of

the season Albion played positive football, winning seven and drawing three of their final 15 matches. They ran up their best score of the season when thrashing Leicester 6-0; Everton were again battered 4-0 and West Ham were beaten 4-2 at The Hawthorns just three days after they had eclipsed Albion 6-1 at Upton Park when Brian Dear netted five times.

Albion took 14th position in the First Division table with 39 points, nine clear of Wolves who were relegated.

Astle and Clark were joint top-scorers with 11 goals apiece. Full-back Bobby Cram netted nine goals which included a hat-trick v Stoke City at The Hawthorns.

Once again goalkeeper Ray Potter played in every game while Stan Jones missed just one.

HAWTHORNS DIARY

There were also debuts for several other players including Graham Lovett, Ian Collard, Dick Krzywicki and Ray Crawford, the former England international centre-forward, signed from Wolves.

Departures included Tony Millington to Crystal Palace and Ronnie Fenton to Birmingham City.

The average League attendance at The Hawthorns fell by 1,100 to 19,405 and for the first time since 1935-36, Albion's best single turnout failed to top the 30,000 mark.

Graham Williams was the only player to receive international honours, playing times for Wales against Scotland, Denmark, England, Greece (twice), Northern Ireland (scoring his first goal for his country), Italy and the USSR.

During the summer of 1966 Albion went on a short Dutch tour, losing 2-1 to Alkmaar but defeating ADO The Hague 2-1 and Ajax 1-0. The latter team was managed by former Albion boss Vic Buckingham.

1965-66

Albion entered the Football League Cup for the first time this season – going on to win the trophy by beating West Ham United 5-3 in the last of the two legged Finals.

En route to the Final Albion ousted Walsall (3-1 at home), Leeds United (4-2 away), Coventry City (6-1 in a Hawthorns replay – Jeff Astle netting a hat-trick), Aston Villa (3-1 also at home) and manager Jimmy Hagan's former club, Peterborough United in the two-legged semi-final (2-1 at home and 4-2 at London Road when Tony Brown hit a treble). They then lost 2-1 at Upton Park in the first leg of the Final on 9 March but turned things round in the return leg at The Hawthorns a fortnight later to crush the Hammers 4-1 after a magnificent first-half performance in front

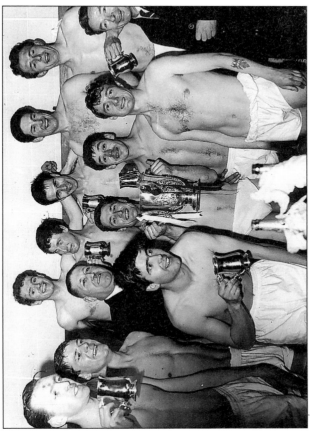

Albion, winners of the 1966 League Cup.

of a 32,000 plus crowd. This victory booked Albion a place in the Fairs Cup for 1966-67 – their first taste of competitive European club football.

In the League itself Albion did very well and claimed sixth position with 50 points – 11 behind the champions Liverpool. This was their highest finish for six years and was due to an excellent run of nine games without defeat from early April to when the last ball was kicked in May.

Prior to that Albion's form had been in and out. They began with six wins, two defeats and a draw from their opening nine matches. Then they fell away somewhat before losing one in seven during October and November. Only one victory was recorded over an eight-match period either side of Christmas and after crashing out of the FA Cup 3-0 at Bolton, Albion then claimed just two more victories in eight outings before ending the season with a flourish.

Their best wins were those of 6-2 v Stoke City (a hat-trick here for John Kaye and an own-goal by ex-Baggies' star Maurice Setters), 6-2 v Fulham, 5-1 at Sunderland on New Year's day, 5-3 at home to Nottingham Forest and 5-1 v Leicester.

Their heaviest defeats were suffered at Leeds and West Ham where they lost both games 4-0.

Early on in the season Jeff Astle cracked in two hat-tricks in seven days, v Sheffield Wednesday (won 4-2 at home) and Northampton Town (won 4-3 away).

Tony Brown top-scored with 27 goals (in League and Cup). Jeff Astle netted 24, John Kaye 23 and Clive Clark 12. In total Albion registered 119 goals at competitive level.

Substitutes were used for the first time this season and Graham Lovett was Albion's first No.12 to be called off the bench, replacing Kenny Foggo at Northampton in September.

Doug Fraser and John Kaye were ever-presents and the average League attendance at The Hawthorns was 19,781 – up by just 376.

Albion's second XI finished fifth in the Central League with Terry Simpson playing in all 42 games – an unusual occurrence in reserve football.

Skipper Graham Williams took his tally of Welsh caps up to 21 with appearances against Northern Ireland, Brazil (twice) and Chile while Albion's young Republic of Ireland striker Ray Treacy made his international debut against West Germany, also playing at half-back for his country's under-23 team v France. John Kaye represented the Football League against the League of Ireland (scoring two goals) and matches saw them rise eight places to safety.

They ended with a 6-1 home win over Newcastle (another hat-trick for 'Bomber' Brown) having earlier beaten Fulham 5-1 and Tottenham 3-0 (thanks to another Brown treble). A nine-goal thriller at Goodison Park finished 5-4 in Everton's favour while League champions Manchester United won 4-3 at The Hawthorns in mid-December.

Albion's first taste of European football ended in the second round when they lost 6-1 on aggregate to Bologna in the Fairs Cup. They began well with a 6-3 aggregate win over D.O.S. Utrecht (Brown registering another hat-trick in a 5-2 win at home) but a 3-0 first leg reverse in Italy gave Albion a mountain to climb.

Prior to the opening of the 1965-66 season Albion took part in the New York International Tournament, winning just one of six matches against Kilmarnock, Ferencvaros (Hungary) and Polonia Bytom (Poland). In the 1966 close season they toured South America, playing matches in Peru, Uruguay, Argentina and Brazil, losing just once. The tour ended in the magnificent Maracana Stadium in Rio de Janiero where Albion beat Flamengo 2-1.

1966-67

Albion's first Wembley appearance for 13 years was certainly 'unlucky' as they lost 3-2 to Third Division Queen's Park Rangers in the League Cup Final, this after having led 2-0 at half-time.

Albion looked certain to retain the trophy after former Rangers winger Clive Clark had netted twice in the first-half but inspired by Rodney Marsh, and in front of a near 98,000 crowd, the Londoners hit back to win with a disputed goal by Mark Lazarus.

On their way to Wembley, Albion ousted Aston Villa 6-1 (with a Bobby Hope hat-trick), Manchester City 4-2, Swindon Town 2-0, Northampton Town 3-1 and West Ham 6-2 on aggregate in the semi-final (winning 4-0 at home with an Astle hat-trick and drawing 2-2 away). But they blew it in the second half of the Final and for thousands of disappointed fans it was a long trek back to the Midlands.

In the bread and butter of League football Albion put in far too many indifferent performances and eventually finished in 13th position with 39 points, ten clear of the danger-zone. They were in relegation trouble as March arrived but eight wins and two draws from their last 11 matches saw them rise eight places to safety.

It was also no go in the FA Cup as Albion were shot out in the fourth round, beaten 5-0 at Leeds, their worst ever defeat in this competition.

On Boxing Day, 1966 (v Spurs) Albion handed club debuts to right-back Dennis Clarke and centre-half John Talbut, the latter a £30,000 transfer from Burnley. A month later goalkeeper John Osborne was signed from Chesterfield for £10,000 and in February 1967, defender Eddie Colquhoun arrived from Bury.

Clark – the only ever-present this season – was Albion's leading marksman with 29 goals; Jeff Astle netted 22 and Tony Brown 19. Clark, in fact, set a record by scoring in every game of the League Cup competition including both legs of the semi-final. The average League attendance at The Hawthorns increased by over 3,500 to 23,352 – Albion's best since 1960-61.

Graham Williams played in three more games for Wales v Scotland, England and Northern Ireland; Ray Treacy represented the Republic of Ireland against Spain and Czechoslovakia; Bobby Hope was capped by Scotland at under-23 level v Wales and Dick Krzywicki played for Wales at the same level v Scotland and England.

In May and June 1967 Hope, Doug Fraser and Eddie Colquhoun toured Israel, Hong Kong, Australia, New Zealand and Canada with the Scottish FA party.

Whilst they were away Jimmy Hagan quit as Albion's manager (May) and soon afterwards the club transferred Ray Potter to Portsmouth, Terry Simpson to Walsall and Campbell Crawford to Exeter City.

Bobby Cram was also on the move to Bromsgrove Rovers and then started a new life in Canada with Vancouver Royals. He came back to haunt Albion, however, in April 1971 when he skippered Colchester United to a surprise Watney Cup Final win at The Hawthorns, albeit in a penalty shoot-out.

Two ex-Albion players passed away during the season… in November 1966, right-winger Billy Elliott, 47, died while holidaying in the Canary Islands and in February 1967, former Albion left-winger Stan Wood died at the age of 61.

1967-68

Alan Ashman, a former Cumbrian chicken-farmer and Nottingham, Forest centre-forward left Carlisle United to take over as manager of Albion in May 1967 – and what a terrific first season he had at The Hawthorns. Albion. After a difficult first FA Cup game at Colchester Albion settled down, defended reso-

HAWTHORNS DIARY

lutely and scored telling goals to reach Wembley for the second successive season – and this time they won, beating Everton 1-0 after extra-time to lift the FA Cup for the fifth time. It was a great occasion, especially for Jeff Astle, who scored the winning goal in the 92nd minute.

Albion eventually overcame Colchester 4-0 (after a 1-1 draw), then took out Southampton (3-2 away with Graham Williams temporarily in goal, also after a replay), Portsmouth 2-1 at Fratton Park, Liverpool (at the third attempt, finally winning 2-1 at Maine Road) and Birmingham City 2-0 in the semi-final at Villa Park.

Everton were favourites to win but Albion battled on with grim determination and won with this line-up: John Osborne; Doug Fraser, Graham Williams; Tony Brown, John Talbut, John Kaye (who had been converted to a defender when Eddie Colquhoun broke a leg at Newcastle); Graham Lovett, Ian

Collard, Jeff Astle, Bobby Hope and Clive Clark. Dennis Clarke came on for Kaye at the start of extra-time to become the first 'sub' used in an FA Cup Final.

The team also did themselves justice in the First Division after a disappointing start when they had two wins, two draws and five defeats in the first nine games. But from their other 33 matches Albion registered 15 victories and ten draws to finish a creditable eighth in the table with 46 points, 12 behind the champions Manchester City, whom they defeated twice (3-2 at home and 2-0 at Maine Road) over Christmas.

Wolves 4-1, Sheffield United 4-1, Burnley 8-1 (Albion's best home League win since September 1957), Stoke City 3-0, European Cup winners-to-be Manchester United 6-3 and West Ham United 3-1 were all defeated at The Hawthorns as Albion turned on the style. But there were one or two upsets with Everton winning 6-2 on Albion soil just two months before the Cup Final (Alan

Ball scored four goals) while both Southampton (4-0 at the Dell), Coventry City (4-2) and Liverpool (4-1 at Anfield) also gave Albion a hiding.

Albion didn't do well at all in the League Cup, losing to Reading in the opening round. But it was the other Cup they which drew their interest – and what a great day out it turned out to be – especially after that Wembley disappointment a year earlier.

Jeff Astle was easily top-scorer with 35 goals, including three hat-tricks, two in three days v Manchester United and West Ham late in the season. Clive Clark and Tony Brown with 15 apiece, followed the 'King' in the scoring charts. Indeed, Astle became the only Albion player to score in every round of the FA Cup in a winning season.

John Talbut, as reliable as ever at centre-half, appeared in all 53 League and Cup games; Doug Fraser and Jeff Astle followed him home with 51 outings apiece.

This time Albion show off the FA Cup, won in 1968. Back row (left to right): Doug Fraser, John Kaye, Graham Lovett, John Osborne, Ian Collard, Jeff Astle, John Talbut. Front row: Tony Brown, Asa Hartford, Alan Ashman (manager), Bobby Hope, Graham Williams.

The Cup-winning team tour the streets of West Bromwich in 1968.

Welsh international winger Ronnie Rees (signed from Coventry City), Ray Fairfax (to Northampton Town) and Stan Jones (back to Walsall).

The average League attendance at The Hawthorns went up by over 2,500 to 25,837 and the 45,992 audience for that epic nine-goal encounter with Manchester United was Albion's best for a League game since 1959.

Graham Williams won his 25th cap for Wales v Northern Ireland and fellow Welshman Ronnie Rees was capped against West Germany; Ray Treacy claimed his fourth cap for Eire v Czechoslovakia – and he scored his first international goal; Doug Fraser and Bobby Hope won their first caps for Scotland against the Netherlands and Eddie Colquhoun gained Scottish under-23 honours v England.

Treacy left for Charlton Athletic in February 19068 and other departures included Foggo (to Norwich City), Ray Fairfax (to Northampton Town) and Stan Jones (back to Walsall).

Albion's reserves finished third in the Central League – just to add sugar to the icing on the Cup.

Albion's current first team trainer was former player Stuart Williams, who was appointed in February 1968.

In December 1967, former Albion centre-half and club trainer Fred Reed died at the age of 73.

1968-69

After an eventual and sometimes controversial end-of-season tour to East Africa, where they played five undefeated friendlies, it was so near yet so far for Albion this season when they almost made it to Wembley for the third successive season. But alas they failed in the semi-final of the FA Cup, losing 1-0 to Leicester City at Hillsborough,

Allan Clarke scoring in the 86th minute. And on a freezing cold evening at The Hawthorns Dunfermline Athletic knocked Albion out of the European Cup-winners' Cup, beating them 1-0 on aggregate in the quarter-final. In the First Division Albion finished in tenth spot with 43 points (24 adrift of the champions Leeds United) and went out of the League Cup, beaten by lowly Peterborough United 2-1 at London Road in the third round. And they also lost 6-1 to Manchester City in the FA Charity Shield game at Maine Road prior to the start of the League programme.

All in all it was an eventful season as the average League crowd at The Hawthorns dropped to 25,091.

For most of the time manager Alan Ashman stuck by the players who did West Bromwich Albion Football Club so proud in 1967-68.

Ronnie Rees, Asa Hartford and Clive Clark shared the left-wing

HAWTHORNS DIARY

with Rees also appearing on the right with Dick Krzywicki. Ray Wilson established himself in the side at left-back and Len Cantello made his debut in midfield, while Dennis Martin (signed from Carlisle United) and youngsters Lyndon Hughes and Alan Merrick all played their first games for the Baggies.

Albion won just three of their opening 11 games before registering four victories on the trot, including a 6-1 home thrashing of Coventry City. However, only three wins came from the next 15 fixtures – the best being 4-0 at Q.P.R. Then, surprisingly, after their FA Cup exit at Sheffield, Albion played exceedingly well, winning five of their last seven fixtures which included a 4-3 triumph over Tottenham and a 5-1 home success over Newcastle.

Albion's two heaviest defeats in their League programme came at Maine Road and The Hawthorns. They crashed again to Manchester City, this time by 5-1 and were hammered 5-2 by Nottingham Forest in front of their own supporters.

In the FA Cup, Norwich City 3-0, Fulham 2-1, Arsenal 1-0 and Chelsea 2-1 were all knocked out before Leicester ended the Baggies' Wembley hopes in front of 53,207 fans in the semi-final.

Jeff Astle (26) and Tony Brown (23) were the leading marksmen, and both Brown and John Talbut were League ever-presents.

The reserves again finished in third place in the Central League.

In May 1969 Albion played three matches in the Palo Alto Tournament in California. Three other matches were also played in Canada, including a 12-0 defeat of Edmonton All Stars.

Albion's Youth team – under coach Jimmy Dunn, ex-Wolves and derby County – reached the Final of the FA Youth Cup but lost 6-3 on aggregate to Sunderland. Dunn later

took over as first team trainer from Stuart Williams in February 1970.

Jeff Astle won the first of his five England caps, lining up against Wales; Doug Fraser and Bobby Hope played for Scotland against Cyprus and Denmark respectively; Ronnie Rees represented Wales against Italy and Graham Williams played in his last and 26th international match for Wales against Italy.

Eddie Colquhoun was transferred to Sheffield United in October 1968; Dennis Clarke joined Huddersfield Town in January 1969; Ronnie Rees left for Nottingham Forest the following month; 'keeper Dick Sheppard moved to Bristol Rovers in June 1969 and soon afterwards Clive Clark, after nine years at The Hawthorns, was sold to Queen's Park Rangers (in part-exchange for Allan Glover) having scored 98 goals in 353 appearances for the Baggies.

1969-70

Albion recruited their first-ever £100,000 player in June 1969, bringing Colin Suggett to The Hawthorns from Sunderland. Goalkeeper Jim Cumbes was another new face – bought from Tranmere Rovers for £30,000 – so too was inside-forward Danny Hegan, recruited from Ipswich Town in a deal which took Ian Collard to Portman Road.

Suggett made a great start to his Baggies' career, scoring twice in an opening day 2-0 League victory at Southampton.

But it was not to last – for 'Suggo' or Albion – and only two more wins were recorded in the next 15 First Division matches as the team slipped deep into relegation trouble.

John Osborne, a young Gordon Nisbet, later to become an England under-23 international right-back, and Cumbes all played in goal during the first month but it was 'Ossie' who held on to his position despite some poor League results.

In the League Cup though Albion made good progress at the expense of Aston Villa, Ipswich Town, Bradford City and Leicester City and as they tangled over two semi-final legs with Carlisle United so their First Division form improved considerably with five wins coming in the space of six weeks.

Carlisle were duly despatched from the League Cup 4-2 on aggregate as Albion reached their fourth major Cup Final in five years and although they went out of the FA Cup, beaten 2-1 by Sheffield Wednesday despite a thumping goal from Tony Brown, Albion were undefeated in four First Division games in January.

February wasn't so good and as the League Cup Final showdown with Manchester City arrived, Albion's form was somewhat mixed.

At Wembley, in front of almost 98,000 fans, Albion took an early lead thanks to Jeff Astle's looping header but on a soggy pitch, ruined by a recent horse show, City, inspired by Francis Lee, slowly got on top and went on to steal the prize with a 2-1 scoreline. If Suggett had scored when facing an open goal in the second half then Albion would probably have celebrated another famous victory. But he missed his chance and Glyn Pardoe snatched the winner to leave Albion with nothing to show for their efforts.

After this disappointment the season fizzled out. Nottingham Forest were beaten 4-0 in the last home game and Albion eventually finished 16th with 37 points – their lowest position in the top flight since 1954-55, and their lowest points total since 1950-51.

Astle, with 30 goals, finished up as top marksman and was also the First Division's leading scorer; Suggett scored 15 and Tony Brown 13. Suggett was also the only ever-present and had a fine season.

The average League crowd at The Hawthorns rose by almost 2,800 to 27,871 with 45,120 witnessing the 2-1 victory over Manchester United in October when Alistair Robertson made an impressive debut in club. He made 360 appearances, as a player after 16 years with the revenge in the penultimate month of the season with a 7-0 drubbing of Albion at Old Trafford.

Albion's reserves took the runners-up spot in the Central League – their best placing since 1963-64.

Jeff Astle had four more outings for England, lining up in the 'home' games with Portugal and Wales and in two World Cup matches in Mexico versus Brazil and Czechoslovakia. He also played and scored in 'B' internationals v Colombia (one goal) and an Ecuador XI (three goals) and netted twice for the Football League v the Scottish League.

Dick Krzywicki won two full caps for Wales v East Germany and Italy; Danny Hegan was capped by Northern Ireland against USSR while at under-23 level, both Asa Hartford (Scotland) and Ray Wilson (England) were capped against Wales.

Albion troop off the Wembley stage in disappointment after losing the 1970 League Cup Final to Manchester City after extra-time.

At the end of this season – after Albion had contested four unbeaten matches in the Anglo-Italian tournament – Graham Williams retired as a player after 16 years with the club. He made 360 appearances, scored 11 goals, and skippered the Baggies to victory in the 1966 League Cup and 1968 FA Cup Finals. Joining Albion's coaching staff, he remained at The Hawthorns for a further two seasons before taking over as player-manager of Weymouth.

*In 1969-70 there were no fewer than 11 Scottish-born players registered with Albion: Mark Cowan, Doug Findlater, Doug Fraser, Asa Hartford, David Hogg, Jim Holton, Bobby Hope, Hugh MacLean, Hugh Reed, Ally Robertson and Ray Wilson.

1970-71

Despite producing some useful performances, especially at home, Albion had another poor season in the First Division and finished 17th in the table, one position lower than in 1969-70. They amassed only 35 points – eight clear of relegation – and at one stage were among the clubs fighting to avoid the drop.

It was their lowest points tally since 1926-27 and the least number of victories since 1903-04.

Up to Christmas they held their own, winning six and drawing eight of their 22 matches. Stoke City were beaten 5-2, the League champions Everton were humbled 3-0 and a Tony Brown hat-trick saw off Tottenham 3-1 – all at home. But among their eight defeats were

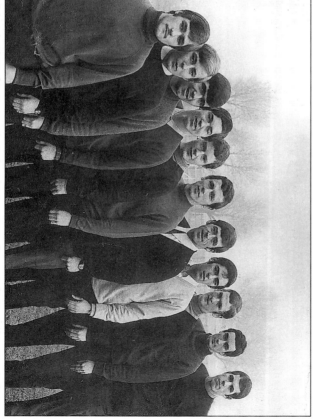

Albion had 11 Scots on their books in 1969. From left to right: Hugh Reed, Asa Hartford, Bobby Hope, David Hogg, Doug Findlater, Ray Wilson, Doug Fraser, Mark Cowan, Ally Robertson, Hugh MacLean and Jim Holton.

HAWTHORNS DIARY

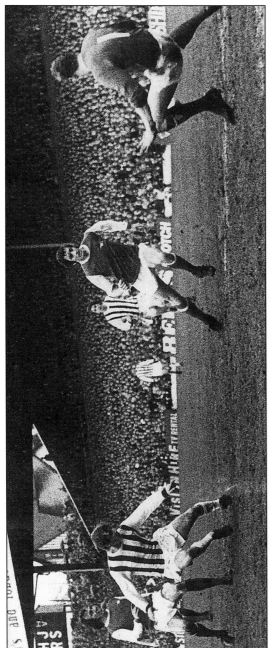

Asa Hartford scores an equaliser in the 2-2 draw with double winners Arsenal at The Hawthorns in April 1971.

those of 6-2 at double-chasing Arsenal, 4-1 at Manchester City and a 3-0 reverse at Crystal Palace.

And in the League Cup Albion suffered their heaviest defeat in the competition, losing 5-0 to Spurs at White Hart Lane.

John Wile, who was to go on and appear in 500 League games for Albion, arrived at the club in December from Peterborough United – to replace John Talbut – while right-winger George McVitie had come down from Carlisle United. Hartford was now on the left-wing and Cumbes was back in goal.

The on-field results, however, were still disappointing and only four more victories were registered before the season ended – and there was no joy in the FA Cup either, Albion going out to Ipswich Town in the fourth round.

Tony Brown with 30 goals, was Albion's leading scorer and his form this season (for he was also the only ever-present) earned him his only England cap v Wales at Wembley. Astle netted 15 times and Suggett seven.

The average League crowd at The Hawthorns was down by almost 2,200 to 25,691 and the highest attendance was that of 41,134 for the visit of Manchester United in March when a Tony Brown treble gave Albion a deserved 4-3 victory.

Elsewhere at international level Asa Hartford collected his second Scottish under-23 cap v Wales and both Jeff Astle (2 goals) and Tony Brown (1) scored in the Football League XI's victory over the Irish League; the 'Bomber' also played against the Scottish League.

George McVitie toured the Republic of Ireland and Australia with the FA party.

Albion again played in the ill-fated Anglo-Italian Cup but failed to make progress yet again after losing three and drawing one of their four matches.

Unfortunately, this was Alan Ashman's last season as manager of Albion. He was replaced by former player Don Howe in July 1971.

And defender John Talbut also left the club – signing for the Belgium side KV Mechelen after 192 games for the Baggies.

Doug Fraser also left The Hawthorns, joining Nottingham Forest in January after 325 appearances for Albion.

In September 1970 the death took place of the legendary Jesse Pennington, who died in Kidderminster at the age of 87. He joined Albion in 1903, played 495 competitive games for the club and won 25 England caps before retiring in 1922. Also laid to rest at the age of 66,

was star centre-forward Jimmy Cookson, who, between 1927 and 1933, scored 110 goals in 131 appearances for Albion.

1971-72

With former Baggies and England international Don Howe back at The Hawthorns as team manager, and supported by Brian Whitehouse and physiotherapist George Wright from Arsenal, Albion had hoped for far better things this season but instead of challenging for honours at the top they had to fight for their lives to avoid relegation.

After entering the Watney Cup and losing in the Final on penalties to Colchester United, Albion triumphed in their opening two League games (at West Ham and v Everton) but then went nine without a victory and soon afterwards had another disastrous spell when a further ten matches passed by without a single win.

By this time 17 matches had been played and only ten goals had been scored.

At this juncture they were in deep, deep trouble. Attendances had dropped to below the 20,000 mark and the goals had completely dried up. At the back Albion looked reasonably sound with Wile and Robertson starting their long association together at the heart of the defence, following John Kaye's move to Hull City after 361 games for the club. Hartford, Hope and Cantello were in midfield and Graham Smith (ex-Colchester) was now challenging Osborne for the goalkeeping berth with Jim Cumbes transferring to Villa Park.

Bobby Gould had moved from Molineux to join Astle, Suggett and Brown in attack but he was never the answer as Howe struggled to get his players motivated.

There were early exits from both knockout competitions, Albion suffering their first-ever home defeat in the League Cup, going out to Spurs 1-0 while Coventry City dismissed them from the FA Cup, winning 2-1 at The Hawthorns.

Back in the League important points were won with victories over Liverpool, Ipswich Town, Manchester United, Leicester City and Southampton but there were some crucial defeats as well against Everton and Manchester City.

Thankfully Nottingham Forest and Huddersfield got out off at the bottom (they both went down) as Albion edged to safety to finish in 16th position with 35 points, ten more than Forest.

It was a close call and the fans weren't too impressed, although the average home attendance of 25,784 was fractionally up on the previous season.

Tony Brown top-scored with 18 goals and Bobby Gould netted 12 – the only two players in double figures.

John Wile was the only ever-present in the side, and in March Ally Brown was bought from Crystal Palace to start a long association with the club.

Despite this being such a poor season, three Albion players received international recognition. Hartford gained six full caps for Scotland, lin-

ing up against Peru, Wales, England, Yugoslavia, Czechoslovakia and Brazil. Len Cantello and Gordon Nisbet both played for England under-23's v East Germany and Hartford also earned an under-23 call-up against England.

In May 1972, completely out of the blue, Bobby Hope was sold to Birmingham City after 13 years at The Hawthorns, during which time he scored 42 goals in 403 senior appearances.

Graham Lovett, another 1968 FA Cup winner, also left The Hawthorns, moving to non-League Worcester City, and John Osborne announced his retirement, claiming that he was not enjoying football anymore under Don Howe.

In May Albion made a short tour of Yugoslavia, playing matches at Split, Mostar and Sarajevo.

In January 1972, Stan Davies, the former Albion and Welsh international forward, died at the age of 73.

1972-73

Everyone at The Hawthorns anticipated a far better season this time round than the last – but nobody really expected the team to be relegated. But down they went, into the Second Division for the first time in 24 years and in truth Albion didn't deserve to stay up.

Albion warmed up with a friendly in Rotterdam and a short three-match tour of Sweden, winning the Orenduscupen tournament.

They began their League programme miserably, losing four and drawing three of their opening seven matches while scoring just three goals. Three wins followed in quick succession but there followed another horrid spell of five defeats out of eight as the team slipped into the bottom group. And to add to their worries Albion went out of the League Cup to Liverpool.

A 2-1 triumph over Stoke City eased the pain slightly but from early December through to mid-February, despite the introduction of record signing left-winger Willie Johnston from Rangers for £138,000, Albion were dire, crashing to six more defeats. They now looked relegation certainties and after going out of the FA Cup to Leeds United, after a four-match marathon with Nottingham Forest and a 2-0 win over Swindon, it was going to require a Houdini escape act if relegation was to be averted.

Frequent changes were made to the side – David Shaw came down from Huddersfield Town, Jeff Astle was recalled after being out of the first team for ten months and Allan Glover and Roger Minton were also called into action.

Goalkeeper John Osborne was also coaxed back from retirement at the beginning of March.

It became a case of 'any two from four' as the season slowly unfolded, Albion and Crystal Palace being the favourites to go down but Norwich City and Coventry City were also in danger.

As it happened Albion played their worst football at a time when points were so vital. Their final 12 League games produced only seven points (out of a possible 24) and the nail was driven firmly into their relegation coffin when fellow strugglers Norwich won a 'four-pointer' 1-0 at The Hawthorns, leaving Albion to win their remaining two matches to have any chance of staying up.

They failed – losing them both: 2-1 at home to Manchester City (a result which saw them relegated) and 3-2 at Birmingham.

Everyone at The Hawthorns was distraught after that mid-week game. Albion finished rock bottom, going down with Palace; Norwich escaped, gaining four more points than Albion whose

HAWTHORNS DIARY

tally of 28 was their lowest since the 42 match programme was introduced in 1919-20. And the Baggies' total of 38 goals was the lowest since 1903-04.

Tony Brown netted 16 goals (including two in the Texaco Cup) to head the scoring list (no-one else reached double figures). Asa Hartford missed only one League game, John Wile was absent from two and Brown both missed three.

Among the departures this season were Bobby Gould (to Bristol City – he was later to return as Albion's manager), George McVitie (to Oldham Athletic) and Colin Suggett (to Norwich City).

Albion's average home League attendance dropped alarmingly by 4,350 to 21,438 – the lowest since 1966.

Not surprisingly not one single Albion player gained full international honours this season; Len Cantello added five England under-23 caps to his collection, playing

against Wales, the Netherlands (twice), Denmark and Czechoslovakia; Hartford represented Scotland against England and Wales also at this level.

In March 1973 the death occurred at the age of 73 of Albion's 1931 FA Cup winning full-back George Shaw. And in November 1973 former Albion goalkeeper George Ashmore died, aged 75.

1973-74
Playing in the Second Division for the first time since 1949, Albion got off to a sound start, winning their opening two matches – 3-2 at Blackpool and 1-0 at home to Crystal Palace. But then they failed to win any of their next ten League games, slipped out of the League Cup at the hands of lowly Exeter City, and saw attendances at The Hawthorns drop to under 12,000.

Peter Latchford was now in goal; former 'keeper Gordon Nisbet was playing at right-back with Alan

Merrick his partner (Ray Wilson was out injured). Wile and Robertson were the two centre-halves; Tony Brown, Cantello, Hartford and Allan Glover were manning midfield between them while Ally Brown, Shaw and Willie Johnston occupied the front positions.

A 2-0 home victory over Sheffield Wednesday in late October helped boost confidence and for a time results were favourable, with seven more victories coming before the end of the year including a 2-0 Boxing Day win over Aston Villa in front of 43,119 fans at The Hawthorns. This was the first time the clubs had ever met each other in the Second Division. Albion were now in with an outside chance of promotion, but once into 1974 Albion's form slumped again, although they did knock First Division Everton out of the FA Cup, winning 1-0 in a fourth-round replay after a goalless Sunday after-

Albion, 1974-75. Back row (left to right): Weir, Thompson, Cooper, Foulkes, Tranter, W. Hughes, Mayo, Clarke, Edwards, Bulloch, Buckham. Second row: Don Howe (manager), Geoff Wright (assistant manager), Glover, Nisbet, Robertson, Minton, Ward, Latchford, Osborne, Regan, Turner, Robson, Trewick, A. McPherson (coach). Brian Whitehouse (coach). Seated: Shaw, L. Hughes, Merrick, Johnston, Wile, A. Brown, T. Brown, Cantello, Hartford, Wilson, Davies. On ground: Donaghy, Lynex, Gregson, Rumjahn, Rushbury, Leetion, Close, Wassell.

noon draw at Goodison Park in front of 53,000 fans. Albion, though, went out to Newcastle United in the next round at The Hawthorns.

Back in the League they were hesitant and lacked confidence and managed to record just one late victory in all matches before closing on 44 points to take eighth position.

It was, in truth, a disappointing season and manager Don Howe admitted that the players weren't good enough to regain their place in the top flight.

Tony Brown headed the scorers yet again with 23 goals, including seven in successive January matches against the Nottingham clubs (a hat-trick v County in the FA Cup and a four-timer at The City Ground in a League match with Forest).

Latchford and Wile were both ever-present and, in fact, Latchford after some impressive displays, was capped twice by England at under-23 level, lining up v Poland and Wales. Len Cantello also won further under-23 honours v Poland and Denmark.

The average League attendance at The Hawthorns this season was only 16,001 – the lowest since 1929-30 when it was just over 14,000.

In July 1974 – after ten glorious years with Albion – Jeff Astle said farewell, joining the South African club, Hellenic. He scored 174 goals in 361 appearances for the club.

In May 1974 the death occurred of former Albion and England wing-half Tommy Magee, who spent 15 years at The Hawthorns (1919-34) appearing in 434 games and gaining both League championship and FA Cup winners' medals with the Baggies, the only player to achieve this feat. He was 75.

Two months later, in July 1974, former Albion skipper and club director Tommy Glidden, another key member of that 1930-31 dou-ble-winning side, passed away at the age of 72. He scored 140 goals in 479 appearances for the Baggies between 1922 and 1936.

Just over two months later club president and former chairman Major H. Wilson Keys died, aged 82. And ex-Albion and Wales inside-right Ivor Jones also passed on at the age of 75.

1974-75

In August 1974 Asa Hartford left Albion for Manchester City for a record fee of £225,000. He scored 26 goals in 275 games for the club. Three years earlier a proposed £177,000 move to Leeds United had fallen through because of Hartford's heart abnormality (which initially hit the headlines for all the wrong reasons).

Hartford's absence from Albion's midfield was sorely missed as they again stuttered along early on, winning only two of their first eight League matches. A run of three successive victories halted that sequence but another six-match winless spell followed before manager Howe started to ring the changes.

Dave Rushbury replaced Ally Robertson in defence and John Osborne was brought back between the posts.

The results improved with five wins coming in quick succession including four on the bounce with no goals conceded.

Albion were now edging towards the top six but their inconsistency remained and again they slipped into mediocrity before a late flourish saw them register six victories and a draw from their final 11 fixtures to push up to sixth place with 45 points – eight short of promotion.

It was all too disappointing for the hardy supporters who occasionally let their feelings be known with one home attendance dropping to as low as 7,812 for the visit of Notts County on 2 April – the lowest for a League match at The Hawthorns since 1957.

And Albion's also made early exits from the League Cup (beaten in a replay by Norwich City in round 3) and from the FA Cup (ousted by Carlisle United in round 4).

Albion's best League win of the season was a 4-0 home success over Sheffield Wednesday when Ian Edwards scored on his debut.

The team's heaviest defeats came against Southampton (at home) and Sunderland (away) each by 3-0.

Tony Brown – yet again – finished up as leading scorer with 13 goals... Gordon Nisbet (41), John Wile (38) and Willie Johnston (38) made most League appearances. and towards the end of the season a certain Bryan Robson was introduced to first team action, making his debut in a 3-1 win at York, four days before manager Don Howe lost his job.

He was to be replaced in the summer by Albion's first-ever player-manager.

The average League gathering at The Hawthorns in 1974-75 was a meagre 12,679 – the lowest for 60 years. The best turnout was that of 29,614 for the visit of Aston Villa in December.

Albion's reserves finished third in the Central League – an improvement of five places from the previous season.

There were no full international honours handed out to Albion players this season.

A short Belgian tour to Mechelen and Diest was undertaken prior to the start of 1974-75 and departures during the season included goalkeeper Peter Latchford (to Celtic) and Lyndon Hughes (to Peterborough United).

At the club's AGM in September

HAWTHORNS DIARY

1974, Jim Gaunt stepped down as chairman. he subsequently became president of the club while FA 'Bert' Millichip took over as chairman with Tom Silk his vice-chairman.

In April 1975 the death was announced of former Albion inside-forward of the 1930s Sammy Heaselgrave. He was 58.

1975-76

In June 1975 Republic of Ireland international midfielder Johnny Giles, formerly of Manchester United, moved to The Hawthorns from Leeds United for a fee of £45,000 to become Albion's first-ever player-manager. And what an impact the Dublin-born star had, both on the players and the supporters.

After a quick tour of Ireland and matches v Shamrock Rovers and Finn Harps, it was down to business.

After a wobbly start Albion improved dramatically with Giles dominating in centre-field where he was partnered by fellow Irishman Mick Martin (signed from Old Trafford) and Len Cantello. After being next to bottom in October they slowly but surely climbed the ladder.

Giles' international team-mate Paddy Mulligan arrived from Crystal Palace to take over at right-back. Former Walsall striker Joe Mayo replaced England's 1966 World Cup hero Geoff Hurst, who was bought as a stop-gap from Stoke City and with Ally Brown, Tony Brown, Willie Johnston, Bryan Robson, centre-backs John Wile and Ally Robertson, and veteran goal-keeper John Osborne all pulling their weight and playing out of their skins, Albion went on to win promotion after a terrific second-half to the season.

During that shaky opening period Albion won just once in ten games and went out of the League

Tony Brown's famous winner at Oldham in April 1976 which took the Baggies back to Division One.

Cup to Fulham. They suffered only one defeat in their next ten outings but either side of Christmas, again went through a sticky patch, record-ing a solitary victory at Nottingham Forest. But into 1976 things really took off. And besides making progress in the FA Cup Albion grad-ually got themselves into a strong enough position from where they could mount a serious late challenge at winning promotion. They had a few hiccups here and there, which included elimination from the FA Cup (at Southampton) and the loss of a crucial home game to fellow promotion-chasers Bristol City, but with the fans behind them Giles and his players knew what was required when they travelled to Boundary Park, Oldham for their final game of the season. They HAD to win to regain their First Division status – and backed by more than 15,000 fans, Albion did the business with a goal by Tony Brown early in the sec-ond half. That 1-0 victory took the Baggies back into the top flight, along with Sunderland (the champi-ons) and Bristol City – and the sup-porters celebrated long and loud.

Albion finished a point ahead of Bolton (53-52).

The Browns scored 23 goals between them, Tony 12 and Ally 11, while Joe Mayo netted eight.

John Osborne and Ally Robert-son were both ever-present with Ossie keeping a club record 22 clean-sheets in the League and he conceded only 33 goals (12 at home).

Albion were promoted scoring just 50 goals, the lowest total of any promoted side since Notts County netted 46 in 1922-23.

The average League crowd at The Hawthorns rose by over 4,500 to 17,233, with four games towards the end of the season attracting audi-ences of more than 20,000.

Johnny Giles won his first cap with Albion, captaining Eire v Turkey. Mick Martin and Paddy Mulligan also played in that interna-tional, as well as against Poland, while Martin was also captain versus Norway.

Martin was actually sent-off in the Turkey match to become the first Albion player to be dismissed in a full international.

100 YEARS AT THE HAWTHORNS

Albion played three games in the Anglo-Scottish Cup this season, winning one, losing one and drawing one. The reserve team finished runners-up in the Central League and the club's youngsters won the FA Youth Cup this season, beating rivals Wolves 5-0 on aggregate (2-0 away, 3-0 at home) with a team which included Mark Grew, Derek Statham, Wayne Hughes, Derek Monaghan, Steve Lynex and Kevin Summerfield.

David Shaw (to Oldham Athletic) and Alan Merrick (to Minnesota Kicks) were the main departures this season. Seven years later Merrick won a full U.S.A. cap, having taken on U.S. citizenship.

In January 1976, the death took place of Albion's 1912 FA Cup Final centre-forward Bob Pailor. He was 88. And three months later former Albion 1930s winger Arthur Gale died at the age of 73.

1976-77

During the scorching hot summer of 1976 Johnny Giles dropped a bombshell and quit as Albion's manager – but after some serious talking was persuaded to stay on...for at least another season.

After again playing three games in the Anglo-Scottish Cup (one win, two defeats this time) Albion's first match back in the top flight took them to Elland Road to face Giles' former club Leeds United – and in front of a sun-drenched 40,248 crowd the Baggies earned a point from a 2-2 draw, United equalising in the last minute.

An early set-back was a home defeat in the League Cup at the hands of Brighton after Liverpool had been overcome in an earlier round in a Hawthorns replay. Willie Johnston was sent-off v Brighton for aiming a kick at the referee and was subsequently banned for five matches.

Albion recovered, however, to produce some splendid football, especially in October when, inspired by Johnston, they came back from 2-0 down to beat Tottenham Hotspur 4-2, thrashed Manchester United 4-0 a fortnight later (in the club's 3,000th League match) and then defeated West Ham United 3-0, all at home.

Shrugging off a nightmare performance at Portman Road where they lost 7-0 to Ipswich Town, Albion bounced right back and continued to play some delightful football to comfortably hold their own amongst the big boys.

Giles brought fellow Irishman Ray Treacy back to The Hawthorns to replace Ally Brown in attack and he also signed David Cross from Coventry City to take over from Joe Mayo at centre-forward. With a new team-plan, coupled with new faces, the results improved even more and from mid-February to early April only one defeat was suffered in 11 League outings – this despite going out of the FA Cup in a Hawthorns replay to Manchester City.

Goalkeeper Tony Godden was brought in after Osborne had been injured at Highbury, and a dynamic new forward arrived on the scene – Laurie Cunningham – signed from Leyton Orient for £110,000.

He and Godden made impressive debuts in a 2-0 win at Tottenham but Albion's season ended disappointingly with a 4-0 defeat at Villa Park – Giles' last game in charge.

Albion finished in a very respectable seventh position with 45 points, 12 behind the champions Liverpool.

Besides those superb wins in October Albion also gained sweet revenge over Ipswich, winning 4-0 with a Bryan Robson hat-trick; they also hammered Leicester City 5-0 at Filbert Street, playing some exquisite ground soccer, and clipped Everton 3-0 at The Hawthorns. They also took another hiding, losing 6-1 at Sunderland in February.

David Cross top-scored with 12 goals and Tony Brown and Bryan Robson each claimed eight and Mick Martin seven.

Albion, 1977-78. Back row (left to right): D. Statham, R. Ward, T. Godden, J. Osborne, T. Thompson. Middle: G. Wright (physiotherapist), L. Cunningham, M. Martin, A. Brown, J. Trewick, B. Whitehouse (coach). Front: P. Mulligan, L. Cantello, J. Wile, Ronnie Allen (manager), B. Robson, W. Johnston, D. Close. Tony Brown was still playing in the NASL when the photograph was taken.

HAWTHORNS DIARY

Rock solid centre-backs Ally Robertson and John Wile were both ever-present, while Paddy Mulligan missed two League games and a young Derek Statham made his name at left-back.

Albion's average home League attendance was 24,523 – a rise of almost 7,300 – and 41,867 fans saw the 1-1 draw with Aston Villa, the first game between the clubs in the top flight since November 1966.

Players who moved on included Mayo and Glover (both to Orient), Dave Rushbury (to Sheffield Wednesday), Ian Edwards (to Chester) and Gordon Nisbet (to Hull City). In March 1977 Ray Wilson announced his retirement because of injury at the age of 29.

Willie Johnston played seven times on the wing for Scotland, lining up against Sweden, Wales, Northern Ireland, England, Chile, Argentina and Brazil. Giles, Martin and Mulligan all played for Eire against England, Turkey, France (twice), Poland and Bulgaria, while Treacy was capped against the Poles and the French. Martin (v Bulgaria) and Johnston (v Argentina) were both sent-off.

Laurie Cunningham became the first black footballer to represent England in a major international when he starred in the under-21 game v Scotland at Sheffield, scoring a goal to mark the occasion. He also played against Finland and Norway (as sub) while Wayne Hughes represented Wales under-21's v both England and Scotland.

In December 1976, George James, Albion's centre-forward of the 1920s, died at the age of 77, He scored 57 goals in 116 outings for the club. And in January 1977, another two former Albion players – Joe Carter and Cecil Shaw – died in Handsworth, Birmingham. Carter, a member of Albion's unique double-winning side of

1930-31, passed away at the age of 75. He scored 155 goals in 451 games for the club between 1921 and 1936. Full-back Shaw was 65 and played for Albion between 1936 and 1947, appearing in 251 first team matches.

1977-78

On 22 June 1977 former Baggies' favourite Ronnie Allen returned to The Hawthorns as Albion's manager and shortly after the season had commenced he introduced Cyrille Regis from non-League Hayes.

And it wasn't long before the 19 year-old strapping centre-forward from French Guyana was hitting the headlines – scoring twice on his first team debut in a 4-0 League Cup win over Rotherham United and then following up with a cracking goal on his League debut against Middlesbrough.

Albion began the season well, beating Chelsea 3-0 and drawing at Leeds. And from the day Regis arrived on the scene the results got even better, Albion losing only twice in 15 League games up to December, although they did lose 1-0 to Bury at a foggy Gigg Lane in the League Cup.

There were some impressive wins – 3-0 at Newcastle, 3-1 v Birmingham, 4-0 over Manchester United (again) and 2-0 against Leicester City.

At West Ham (a 3-3 draw in November) Tony Brown became the first Albion player to make 500 League appearances.

With Regis, Cunningham, Tony Brown, Bryan Robson, Len Cantello and Willie Johnston all attack-minded Albion were a potent force but as 1977 ended so Ronnie Allen resigned as manager, choosing to reap the rewards offered to him in sunny Saudi Arabia.

Into his place stepped the charismatic former Oxford United player

Ron Atkinson from Cambridge United – and immediately Albion were on TV, in the spotlight, receiving world-wide coverage and a team going places.

Regis, like he had done earlier, scored on his FA Cup debut as Blackpool were swept aside 4-1 in the third round. Although Albion's League form went off the boil, the team made excellent progress in the Cup, seeing off Manchester United 3-2 in a splendid Hawthorns replay, winning by the same score at Derby and then ending Nottingham Forest's long unbeaten run with a competent 2-0 quarter-final victory at home.

The crowds were now flocking to The Hawthorns – almost 37,800 fans saw that Manchester United Cup replay and 36,500 witnessed the Forest tie. Right-back Brendon Batson had arrived from the manager's old club, Cambridge United, to team up with Statham and Ally Brown had been brought back in place of Cross (transferred to West Ham).

Wembley's twin towers were beckoning – but alas, it was not to be, as Albion, failing to rise to the occasion, were beaten 3-1 by Ipswich Town in the semi-final at Highbury. Besides losing the match they also lost skipper John Wile with a nasty head wound, suffered when Brian Talbot put Town in front, and had Mick Martin sent off.

It was disappointment all round, but Albion battled on in the League and finished well, winning six of their remaining nine matches to take sixth position in the table and so qualify for the UEFA Cup. Amassing 50 points, they were only seven behind runners-up Liverpool. It had been a terrific season – especially after Atkinson had arrived – and the future was certainly looking rosy.

Tony Brown with 23 goals was

once more Albion's top scorer, ahead of Cyrille Regis with 18 in his first season of League soccer.

Tony Godden and Ally Robertson were both ever-present, while Tony Brown (41) and Derek Statham (40) were close behind.

Albion's average home League attendance fell slightly to 24,133, but the five Cup-ties at The Hawthorns realised an average of 26,533.

At the start of this season Albion had entered the Tennent-Caledonian Cup, and after beating St Mirren in the semi-final they defeated the host club, Rangers 2-0 at Ibrox Stadium (Cunningham netting both goals) to lift the trophy in front of a 35,066 crowd. Ex-Ranger Willie Johnston was 'Man of the Match'. Albion also took part in the Trofeo Costa Blanca in Spain immediately afterwards.

Then at the end of the season, in May 1978, Albion made an historic trip to China and Hong Kong, playing five matches, all of which five ended in victories. Each game attracted a capacity crowd and 89,400 – and a huge television audience – saw Albion beat the Chinese national team 2-0 in Peking.

Argentina staged the World Cup Finals in 1978 and Albion's Willie Johnston was in the Scottish party, but was sent home in disgrace, after failing a drugs test. He had taken stimulants before the opening Group match v Peru and was never to play for his country again. The winger did, however, win six caps this term, playing against East Germany, Czechoslovakia, Wales (twice), England and of course Peru. Paddy Mulligan played in three international for Eire against Bulgaria, Norway and Denmark, and Laurie Cunningham starred for England under-21's v Norway, Finland (one goal scored) and Italy. Derek Statham won his first under-21 cap against Finland and Albion's reserve defender John Anderson was capped at under-21 level by the Republic of Ireland against Northern Ireland.

At the end of the campaign goalkeeper John Osborne left Albion after 11 years with the club. He appeared in 312 games and gained an FA Cup winners' medal in 1968.

1978-79

Manager Ron Atkinson, his new assistant Colin Addison, the players, the chairman (Bert Millichip) and scores of supporters believed this was going to be Albion's season. There were some cracking performances especially in the League, FA Cup and UEFA Cup, but at the end of the day there was sadly no silverware to display in the trophy room.

Fielding, whenever possible, an unchanged line-up from August through to mid-January, Albion were as good as any team in the Division and they secured some terrific wins, including those against Bolton 4-0, Chelsea 3-1 (at Stamford Bridge), Leeds 3-1 (at Elland Road, where Tony Brown broke Ronnie Allen's club scoring record), 7-1 at home to chocolate-coloured Coventry City, 3-0 at rivals Wolves, a quite magnificent 5-3 triumph in front of 45,000 fans at Old Trafford when both Cantello and Regis scored stunning goals, and a 3-1 New Year's Day win over Bristol City on a snow-covered Hawthorns pitch.

The bad weather then set in and Albion's rhythm was disrupted. At the time they were right in touch with the leaders Liverpool and Nottingham Forest, and the championship was there for the taking. But only one more game was played in January – a 1-1 draw at Norwich which took them to the top of the table – and when play restarted again, two crucial encounters were lost in succession, at Liverpool where David Mills a record £516,000 buy from Middlesbrough made his debut, and at home to Leeds. Albion never got in another serious challenge after that but still registered some fine wins including those of 3-1 at Coventry, 4-0 v Manchester City and 2-0 at Everton. But it was Liverpool who went on to take the star prize ahead of Forest, who edged Albion into third place by winning 1-0 at The Hawthorns on the last day of the season. This was Albion's best League placing since 1954.

In the League Cup, Albion went out early on to Leeds United and in the FA Cup they reached the fifth round before losing in a replay to Southampton after extra-time.

Meanwhile, in their first taste of UEFA Cup soccer Albion did superbly well, reaching the last eight before losing to Crvena Zvezda (Red Star) of Belgrade.

Galatasaray (Turkey) and Sporting Braga (Portugal) were both dismissed over two legs before Albion stylishly ousted Valencia, winning 2-0 at The Hawthorns after a splendid 1-1 draw in Spain. Then, after losing 1-0 in Yugoslavia – and after Regis had levelled things up in the second leg – Albion surrendered a last-minute goal to lose the tie 2-1 on aggregate, leaving them with nothing to show for their efforts.

Nevertheless it was a splendid season under Atkinson whose motivating skills were there for all to see and admire. Among the number of records set was the least number of Division One defeats in a season (seven) and the most away points ever gained (28).

Ally Brown took over as Albion's leading scorer this term with 24 goals in League and Cup; Regis netted 17, Laurie Cunningham 16 and Tony Brown 14.

Tony Godden and skipper John Wile were both ever-present and

Brendon Batson, Ally Brown and Bryan Robson each had 41 League outings.

England schoolboy international full-back Martyn Bennett made his Albion debut v Everton and England youth international inside-forward Kevin Summerfield was introduced as a substitute v Derby County. Of the other newcomers, Scottish international goalkeeper David Stewart from Leeds United was unable to get into Albion's first team and left for Swansea City in 1980 without making a League appearance.

The average League attendance at The Hawthorns went up by over 2,500 to 26,702 – Albion's best since 1969-70.

Before the season kicked off properly Albion enjoyed an 8-1 testimonial match success at Motherwell, then visited Syria for two prestige games. At the season's end Albion returned to Denmark for the first time in 70 years to play three friendly matches. The last of these – a 7-0 win over IHF on 31 May was Albion's 76th match – the most they have ever played in one campaign.

On the international scene, Laurie Cunningham won three England caps v Wales, Sweden and Austria. He also played for the 'B' side v Czechoslovakia with Cyrille Regis who came on as a substitute. Bryan Robson played against the Austrian 'B' team, scoring the only goal of the game.

Gary Owen joined Albion from Manchester City in May 1979 for £465,000 and immediately played in two England under-21 internationals v Bulgaria (captain) and Sweden (sub). Bryan Robson also represented his country at this level against Wales, Bulgaria (as sub) and Sweden (one goal) as did Derek Statham, while Regis collected under-21 caps against Denmark, Bulgaria and Sweden, scoring goals in the latter two matches. John Anderson

enjoyed his four more Eire under-21 appearances, playing against USSR, Argentina, Hungary and Yugoslavia.

Paddy Mulligan won more Republic of Ireland honours v England (as captain), Denmark, Bulgaria (sub) and West Germany.

Both Laurie Cunningham and Willie Johnson left Albion – joining the Spanish giants Real Madrid and the Canadian club Vancouver Whitecaps respectively, with Cunningham's fee being set at a record £995,000. In his two years at The Hawthorns he had become a real superstar, scoring 30 goals in 114 outings. Johnston – a great favourite with the fans – spent seven years with Albion and netted 28 goals in 261 games. Earlier, in December 1978, Mick Martin was transferred to Newcastle United for £100,000.

In May 1979 Len Cantello was transferred to Bolton Wanderers for £400,000 – leaving immediately after his testimonial match. He scored 21 goals in 369 games for Albion, occupying a variety of positions. A month later Paddy Mulligan rejoined his old buddy Johnny Giles at Shamrock Rovers.

In February 1979, former Welsh international Walter Robbins, an Albion player during the 1930s, died at the age of 68.

1979-80

In July 1979, to replace Johnston, Albion boss Ron Atkinson signed Peter Barnes from Manchester City, paying a club record £748,000 for the England winger. He also added another striker to his squad, bringing in John Deehan from arch rivals Aston Villa for a fee of £424,000. Deehan was the first player to move from Villa Park to The Hawthorns for 70 years – George Harris being the last in 1909. And experienced defender Garry Pendrey arrived from St Andrew's – shortly after

playing for his former club Blues against Albion in his Testimonial match.

This was Albion's Centenary Season and it was celebrated with a 1-0 win over the Dutch side Ajax at The Hawthorns on 11 August.

After a very poor start to the League campaign (only one win from their opening nine matches) Albion recovered reasonably well to finish in a mid-table position of tenth with 41 points. They lost only 12 of their 42 League games but drew a club record 19, including 11 away from home. Ten of the last 15 matches were drawn – six of them 0-0 – and if some of those results had been converted into victories the Baggies would have finished much higher in the table.

Albion claimed two 4-0 home victories over Manchester City in mid-September and Southampton the following month. They also beat Coventry City 4-1 at The Hawthorns and defeated both Bristol City and Crystal Palace 3-0.

Nottingham Forest inflicted the worst defeat on the Baggies, winning 5-1 at The Hawthorns early on in the campaign. Albion also lost 4-0 to one of their bogey sides, Ipswich.

There was an eight-goal thriller on a sodden Hawthorns' pitch in March when Albion were held 4-4 by struggling Bolton Wanderers. Peter Barnes scored a hat-trick for Albion, including two penalties.

Albion failed to make progress in any of the Cup competitions this season. They went out of the League Cup to Norwich City in the fourth round (after a replay) then lost 2-1 at West Ham in the third round of the FA Cup, again in a replay when Tony Brown scored his last ever goal for the club. Albion also crashed out of the UEFA Cup at the first hurdle to the East German side Carl Zeiss Jena, losing both legs, 2-0 away and

Albion playing staff in 1979-80, the club's centenary season. Back row (left to right): D. Statham, C. Regis, T. Godden, D. Stewart, A. Brown, J. Trewick, B. Robson. Front: T. Brown, A. Robertson, B. Batson, Geoff Wright (physiotherapist), J. Wile, Ron Atkinson (manager), D. Mills, G. Owen, P. Barnes.

2-1 at home; Ally Brown received his marching orders at half-time in the second leg at The Hawthorns

Barnes was Albion's top marksman this season with 15 goals; Bryan Robson netted ten and Cyrille Regis nine.

Both goalkeeper Tony Godden and skipper John Wile were ever-present, while defender Barry Cowdrill and midfielder Remi Moses made their senior debuts.

The average League attendance at The Hawthorns dropped by 4,000 to 22,735 with under 11,800 attending that mid-week match with Bolton.

A brief overseas tour was made to the Gulf region in January to play prestige matches in Abu Dhabi and Bahrain.

On the international front, Peter Barnes played for England against Denmark and Wales. Bryan Robson was capped at senior level against the Republic of Ireland and Australia, for the 'B' team v Spain and

for the under-21s against Denmark, Bulgaria (as captain) and Scotland twice, scoring once against the Scots. Gary Owen skippered the England under-21s versus Denmark, East Germany and Scotland twice, and he too scored against the Scots. And Cyrille Regis and Derek Statham also played in under-21 matches, the former against Scotland and East Germany, the latter v Denmark.

After 20 years as club secretary long-serving employee Alan Everiss J.P. was replaced by Tony Rance but remained associated with Albion as a shareholder and in 1981 was appointed to the Board of Directors. Mick Brown joined Albion at the start of the season as assistant-manager and in March 1980 physiotherapist George Wright left for Vancouver Whitecaps. He was replaced by Richard Roberts.

In June 1979 the death was announced of Albion's 1931 FA Cup-winning full-back Bert

Trentham. He was 71. And on 21 January 1980 Cyril Williams, who played as an inside-forward for Albion shortly after World War Two, was killed in a car accident in Bristol. He was 59.

1980-81

This turned out to be a far better season for Albion who finished fourth in the First Division with 52 points, gained from 20 wins and 12 draws.

An uneasy start was followed by two excellent runs, one covering ten matches (just one defeat) and another of eight in which Albion were unbeaten. Only one defeat was suffered in ten outings between Boxing Day and early March and Albion ended the campaign with four wins from their last seven fixtures.

Albion's best League victory came late on – 4-2 at home to Tottenham when Peter Barnes was outstanding.

HAWTHORNS DIARY

There were also solid 3-0 home wins over Middlesbrough and Norwich and just after Christmas Manchester United were defeated 3-1 in front of more than 30,000 fans at The Hawthorns.

Liverpool gave Albion their worst hiding of the season, winning 4-0 at Anfield while Coventry beat the Baggies 3-0 at Highfield Road.

Albion didn't do too well in Cup competitions, falling to Manchester City in the League Cup after a marathon with Preston North End and losing 1-0 at Middlesbrough in the fourth Road of the FA Cup.

Cyrille Regis top-scored with 17 goals; both Ally Brown and Bryan Robson netted 11 apiece and Peter Barnes weighed in with 10.

Like the previous season goalkeeper Godden and centre-half Wile were both ever-present and up-and-coming midfielder Remi Moses missed just one League game.

The reserves were Central League runners-up, nine points adrift of Liverpool. Goalkeeper Mark Grew played in all 42 games.

The average attendance at The Hawthorns was down considerably to 20,382 – the lowest since 1975-76.

During the season overseas trips were made to Yugoslavia for the Trofeo Marjan tournament, Italy (to Napoli), Kuwait, Sweden and Canada (a short tour of three matches). Albion also travelled to Belfast where they beat Linfield 2-0 in a friendly.

Barnes added four more England caps to his tally, playing against Brazil, Wales, Spain and Switzerland (the latter two as sub). Robson also represented his country against the same four nations as well as performing against Norway, Romania (twice), Scotland, Switzerland again and Hungary.

Four Albion players – Barnes, Brendon Batson, Cyrille Regis and Derek Statham (one goal scored) – played for England 'B' versus the U.S.A. Batson also starred against Australia and Spain and fellow fullback Statham also appeared against Spain and scored.

Moses, after a superb season, was capped by England at under-21 level against Norway (as sub), Switzerland (twice), the Republic of Ireland, Romania and Hungary, while Gary Owen captained the England under-21 side against the Swiss (one goal) and Romania.

On 9 June 1981 Ron Atkinson stunned the club and its supporters by quitting as Albion manager to fill the hot seat at Old Trafford, taking Mick Brown and Brian Whitehouse with him. Into his position – for a second spell as Baggies' boss – stepped Ronnie Allen. On the playing side, Peter Barnes moved to Leeds United for £930,000, a record fee for the Elland Road club, and John Trewick went north to Newcastle United for £234,000.

A sad loss in September 1980 was the death of vice-chairman Tom Silk who was killed with his wife Ruth while piloting his aircraft in the South of France. He was returning from a short break to watch Albion's League Cup-tie at Everton.

In June 1980, FA 'Bert' Millichip was elected chairman of the FA Council.

In July 1981, Billy Gripton, Albion's centre-half from the mid-1940s, died at the age of 61, and shortly afterwards Gripton's successor, Jack Vernon, one of Albion's finest-ever defenders, and an Irish international, who also played for Great Britain and the United Kingdom, died in Belfast. He was also 61 and appeared in 200 games for Albion between 1947 and 1952.

inasmuch as they lost two Cup semi-finals, both in London and by the same scoreline of 1-0 and had to fight for their lives to stave off relegation; they also went out of the UEFA Cup in the first round and one of the club's finest post-war players – Bryan Robson – was transferred to Manchester United in October for a record £1.5 million, Remi Moses (valued at £500,000) going with him to join their former boss, Ron Atkinson, at Old Trafford.

Tony Brown also left the club – joining Torquay United after 20 years at The Hawthorns during which time he broke records galore.

As Allen sought to get a balanced team he made numerous signings and team changes (some not to the fans' liking) and introduced a new coach, the former Albion wing-half Gerry Summers.

Steve Mackenzie was acquired from Manchester City for £650,000; Andy King arrived from Everton for £445,000 and soon after Robson's departure, the Dutch international Maarten Jol was snapped up from Twente Enschede for £200,000. He was joined later in the season by fellow Dutch international, Romeo Zondervan, who also came from the Enschede club at a similar price. Clive Whitehead (from Bristol City for £100,000) was another recruit while former youth team players Mark Grew, Derek Monaghan, Mickey Lewis, Gary Childs, Alan Webb and Kevin Summerfield, along with Martyn Bennett all got first team outings.

In the First Division Albion's form was very mediocre and they finished 17th in the table, a drop of 13 places from the previous season. At one stage they were staring relegation straight in the face but did just enough towards the end of the campaign to survive the dreaded drop, amassing 44 points, just two clear of the relegation trap-door.

1981-82

Season 1981-82, from Albion's point of view, was bitterly disappointing

Under the old points system (two for a win instead of three) Albion would have totalled 33 points, three less than when they were relegated in 1937-38.

The team got off to a bad start, winning only two of their opening 12 games and after that they struggled for long periods.

Their form improved slightly either side of Christmas — but once Albion had set off on that FA Cup run, and were battling on in the League Cup, results in the First Division began to suffer even more with only two victories being recorded (from 16 games) between early February and the end of April. A nervous but welcome 2-1 win at Wolves eased relegation worries but Albion then lost three consecutive home games and only two victories late on made Albion safe — their 2-0 home success over Leeds United condemning the Elland Road club to the Second Division. This game on 18 May was marred by crowd disturbances when unruly Leeds fans smashed down the retaining wall behind the Smethwick end goal and threatened to disrupt the game — even cause it to be abandoned.

Albion's best League win of the season was a 4-1 triumph over Swansea City when Cyrille Regis scored a splendid hat-trick. Their heaviest defeat was a demoralising 4-2 home reverse at the hands of lowly Notts County on a miserable March evening in front of just 12,759 hardy supporters.

In the League Cup semi-final, Albion were ousted over two legs by Tottenham Hotspur. En route to the semis Albion knocked out Shrewsbury Town, West Ham United (at the third attempt), Crystal Palace and Aston Villa (1-0 away) before falling to Spurs at White Hart Lane after a 0-0 draw at The Hawthorns.

In the FA Cup Albion put out Blackburn Rovers, Gillingham, Norwich City and Coventry City before losing 1-0 to Second Division side Queen's Park Rangers at one of their bogey Cup grounds, Highbury. Clive Allen's fortunate goal undid Albion late in the second half.

Regis scored cracking goals in the two home ties against Norwich and Coventry.

The Swiss side Grasshoppers of Zurich eliminated Albion from the UEFA Cup in September winning 1-0 on home soil and 3-1 at The Hawthorns for a 4-1 aggregate victory.

In August 1981 Albion won the Sevilla Tournament in Spain, defeating Real Betis 4-1 and Sevilla 2-0.

Regis top-scored this season with 25 goals while skipper John Wile was the only ever-present. Owen (39) and Batson (39) each missed three games. Striker Nicky Cross made an impression in his first season with the seniors by appearing in 22 matches.

The average League attendance at The Hawthorns was down again, this time by 3,500 to 16,851 — and the turnout of 11,733 for the game with Manchester City on 21 April was Albion's lowest home League attendance for seven years.

Bryan Robson played for England against Norway and scored — this being his only goal for his country as an Albion player.

Cyrille Regis was also capped for England v Northern Ireland, Wales and Iceland.

Steve Mackenzie appeared in three England under-21 games v Norway and Scotland (twice) and Remi Moses came on as a substitute against Norway, as did Gary Owen, who also lined up against Hungary as captain.

In July 1982 manager Ronnie Allen was persuaded to stand down, moving 'upstairs'. He handed over his duties to Ron Wylie, the former Aston Villa and Birmingham City player.

Players who were shipped out this season included Andy King (who rejoined his old club Everton with Peter Eastoe moving to The Hawthorns), Tony Brown (after 20 years with Albion) and Kevin Summerfield (to Birmingham City). Earlier striker John Deehan had moved to Norwich City.

1982-83

Albion's new striker from Goodison Park, Peter Eastoe, a former Wolves player, made a disappointing debut — a 2-0 opening day League defeat at Liverpool, but in his first home game he got off the mark as Albion whipped Brighton 5-0. He then followed up with further goals in a splendid 3-1 victory over Manchester United and a 3-0 away win at Stoke.

At this juncture things were looking rosy for new manager Wylie. However, two League reverses temporarily disrupted the run but four more wins out of five either side of a heavy aggregate defeat (4-7) at the hands of Nottingham Forest in the Milk Cup took Albion into the top three. Then, to everyone's dismay, things started to go wrong all of a sudden.

Brendon Batson was injured during a 6-1 thumping at Ipswich, and only two more victories were recorded from the next 12 matches. Batson's injury brought his first team career to a virtual end and he was very much missed. He was replaced at right-back by the versatile Clive Whitehead and later by Alan Webb.

Goalkeeper Paul Barton was recruited from Crystal Palace and soon afterwards striker Garry Thompson arrived from Coventry City. But Albion struggled to get back on the rails. They had already gone out of the FA Cup at Tottenham when an amazing run of four consecutive goalless draws during February and March, quickly followed by six successive defeats, saw them slip down to mid-table. However, they ended the campaign well – with a sequence of three wins and a draw – but a final position of 11th could and should have been a lot better.

Occasionally the team produced some exciting football – revenge was gained over Ipswich in excellent style with a 4-1 win in March and Birmingham City were eased out 2-0 in the local derby.

But it was on the whole another disappointing season, emphasised to a certain extent by the average League attendance at The Hawthorns of 15,260 – Albion's lowest in the First Division since 1914-15.

On the overseas front, Albion travelled to the Netherlands to play Twente Enschede and also to Cyprus for a game against a Limasol Select XI.

Regis top-scored with 11 goals followed by Eastoe with 9 and Thompson with seven. Romeo Zondervan made most League appearances (40) and Gary Robson

was introduced to first team football, having two outings as a substitute.

Robson helped Albion's reserves to win the Central League Division One title. Barry Cowdrill skippered the team which lost just five out of 30 games.

Derek Statham played in three internationals for England – against Wales and Australia (twice), while Regis won his fourth cap against West Germany.

Under-21 honours went to Regis (as captain) v Denmark and Owen with two appearances v West Germany (two goals scored).

In March 1983, striker Ally Brown was transferred to Crystal Palace after spending 11 years at The Hawthorns during which time he netted 85 goals in 359 appearances.

David Mills (to Sheffield Wednesday) and Mark Grew (to Leicester City) also moved to pastures new.

In the summer of 1983 centre-half John Wile – after almost 13 years with Albion – moved back to his former club Peterborough United as player-manager. He appeared in 715 first-team games for the Baggies (500 in the Football League) and skippered the team in three Cup semi-finals as well as acting as a terrific ambassador when Albion toured China in 1978. Wile was later to return to the club as chief executive.

In March 1983, the death occurred of former Albion goalkeeper Jimmy Adams, a wartime stalwart, at the age of 75.

At the club's AGM in August 1983, Bert Millichip handed over the position of Albion chairman to Sid Lucas, Millichip himself assuming the role of president. Brian Boundy was elected as vice-chairman.

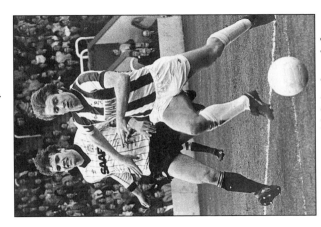

Peter Eastoe (right) signed from Everton in 1982 and in his first season, with eight goals was second-highest scorer behind Cyrille Regis.

down the road to sign Ken McNaught from his old club Aston Villa to fill the centre-half berth vacated by John Wile and the Scotsman made his debut, ironically, at Villa Park on the opening day of the season when Albion lost a seven-goal thriller by 4-3.

Another defeat quickly followed at Stoke, but a six-match unbeaten run pushed Albion up the table, only for them to fall back as they registered just three victories in their next 13 outings and went out of the Milk Cup to Aston Villa after ousting Millwall (5-4 on aggregate) and Chelsea at Stamford Bridge in the opening two rounds. This sudden reverse in fortunes led to Wylie and coach Mike Kelly leaving The Hawthorns (13 December 1983) with Johnny Giles returning to Albion as a replacement, along with coaches 'Nobby' Stiles and Norman Hunter.

But the little Irishman found it tough as Albion continued to lose matches.

Two welcome wins were obtained after Christmas (one of them a 3-1 home triumph over Aston Villa) but things didn't improve all that much on the field and after losing at home to Third Division Plymouth Argyle in the FA Cup and suffering a humiliating 5-0 defeat against Nottingham Forest at The Hawthorns soon afterwards, Giles went out and signed two midfielders – Steve Hunt from Coventry City and Tony Grealish from Brighton.

Both made their debuts in a 1-0 win at Tottenham and with ex-Aston Villa and England winger Tony Morley in good form, Albion slowly eased their way out of trouble with two wins and a couple of draws to finish 17th.

It had been a difficult season all round with chronic injury problems and as a result the average League attendance at The Hawthorns

1983-84

Manager Ron Wylie went four miles

slumped to 14,620 – the lowest since 1975.

One overseas trip was made in August 1983 – to the Netherlands where Albion won two and drew one of their three matches.

Garry Thompson was leading scorer with 17 goals, four more than Cyrille Regis, Paul Barron and Ken McNaught were both ever-present and there were also first team debuts for defenders Wayne Ebanks and Michael Forsyth and midfielders Gary Childs and Kevin Kent.

Unlike Giles' previous reign as manager, there was surprisingly only one Irishman at the club this season – Tony Grealish.

In fact, Grealish gained two full caps for Eire, playing against Poland and China, while Steve Hunt won two England caps, coming on as a substitute against Scotland and the USSR He also toured Brazil, Uruguay and Chile with the England party without playing.

In August 1983, Albion's outside-left from the 1937-46 era, Joe Johnson, died at the age of 72, and in November, former Albion goalkeeper Norman Heath passed away at the age of 59.

In the summer of 1984 former commercial manager Gordon Dimbleby moved in to replace Tony Rance as Albion's secretary.

Players who were transferred out included Romeo Zondervan (to Ipswich Town), Maarten Jol (to Coventry City) and Alan Webb and Derek Monaghan (to Port Vale).

1984-85

This turned out to be another mediocre season for Albion. They finished twelfth in the First Division with just 55 points, went out of then Milk Cup in the fourth round, beaten 4-1 at Watford, and were eliminated by Third Division Orient, also away, in the third round of the FA Cup. And the club also lost the services of Cyrille Regis, who was sensationally bought by Coventry City's manager Bobby Gould for £300,000 in October 1984 after scoring 141 goals in 371 first-team appearances since 1977. Regis later returned to The Hawthorns as a coach (working under managers Ray Harford and Denis Smith).

Albion, fielding a settled side of Godden; Whitehead, Statham; Hunt, Bennett, Robertson; Grealish, Thompson, Regis/N. Cross, Mackenzie and Morley, won only three of their opening 12 League games, one of them a brilliant 4-1 home success over Nottingham Forest when Thompson scored a hat-trick.

Giles then turned to Canada for reinforcements: Manchester-born left-winger Carl Valentine was signed from Vancouver Whitecaps in October and was quickly followed by his playing colleague David Cross, back for a second spell at The Hawthorns, and then the former Manchester United, Sunderland, Rangers and Northern Ireland full-back Jimmy Nicholl arrived from Toronto Blizzard. In February 1985 former Wolves goalkeeper Paul Bradshaw was also secured from Vancouver Whitecaps.

With three of these four new faces in the side the results improved for a time with seven wins coming before the turn of the year, including an excellent 5-2 home triumph over Coventry City and a smart 2-0 success at West Ham. But in between times Albion suffered a 4-0 hammering at Arsenal.

The second half to the season was a real disaster, Albion earning just six victories (four at home, two away) from 21 outings. They were turned over 5-0 at home by Liverpool, went down 3-1 at Villa Park, lost 4-3 at Southampton and crashed 4-1 at Everton.

The only bright spot, in truth, was a 5-1 demolition of West Ham in early May.

The supporters certainly vented their annoyance as the average League attendance at The Hawthorns dropped again – this time to 13,958 – Albion's lowest in the top flight for 70 years. Only 7,423 fans witnessed the 1-0 home win over Sunderland and under 8,900 attended that romp over the Hammers.

The only ever-present this season, Garry Thompson, also finished as top marksman with 21 goals; Steve Hunt netted 11.

Ken McNaught (Sheffield United), Mickey Lewis (Derby County), Wayne Ebanks (Port Vale), Tony Morley (Seiko, Hong Kong), David Cross (Bolton Wanderers) and Paul Barron (Queen's Park Rangers) all found new clubs in the course of the season.

Albion made several overseas jaunts in 1984-85, travelling to Sweden, Hong Kong and Tunisia.

Tony Grealish added six more Republic of Ireland caps to his tally by playing against Mexico, USSR (as captain), Norway, Denmark, Spain (as sub), and Switzerland, and Jimmy Nicholl lined up for Northern Ireland against Finland, England, Turkey and Spain.

Four ex-Albion players passed away during the course of the season – left-winger and former club trainer Arthur Fitton died in September 1984, aged 72; Jack Sankey, a wing-half during the late 1930s/early '40s, died in January 1985, also aged 72; Charlie Wilson from the 1920s (the youngest player ever to appear in a League game for Albion) died in March 1985, aged 79, and centre-half Bill Richardson, a member of the 1931 and 1935 FA Cup Final teams, died in June 1985 at the age of 77.

1985-86

Without a shadow of doubt this was

HAWTHORNS DIARY

Albion's worst-ever season – especially at The Hawthorns. Some supporters never even saw them win a match while thousands more were so disappointed and disgruntled after the first two months of the campaign that they either threw away their season tickets or decided to stay at home instead of travelling to The Hawthorns. This resulted in the average League attendance falling yet again to a moderate 12,194.

Only 6,021 spectators turned up for the match with Sheffield Wednesday on 22 April – the lowest since April 1939.

Relegation seemed a formality as early as January.

Tony Brown was appointed first team coach in place of Norman Hunter at the start of the season.

Johnny Giles resigned as manager in September by England World Cup winner and former Manchester United star 'Nobby' Stiles, who in turn, handed over the reins to ex-Aston Villa and Blues' boss Ron Saunders in February 1986.

Cup in the third round and the Milk Cup (to Aston Villa) in round four, although they did reach the semi-final of the Full Members Cup (beaten by Chelsea).

Throughout the season players shuffled to and from The Hawthorns.

At the start Garth Crooks (ex-Stoke City and Tottenham Hotspur) and Imre Varadi (formerly of Sheffield Wednesday, Newcastle United and Everton) were paired up front to replace Garry Thompson, who went to Hillsborough. Then the lanky George Reilly arrived from Newcastle. He did better towards the end of the season when joined by Craig Madden from Bury. And a certain Steve Bull was also called up, along with Gerry Armstrong, formerly of Tottenham Hotspur, Watford and Real Mallorca, who had starred for Northern Ireland in the 1982 World Cup and fellow countryman Robbie Dennison from Glenavon.

In midfield Welsh international Mickey Thomas (bought from

Chelsea) and Martin Dickinson (ex-Leeds United) along with Andy Thompson and Darren Bradley (signed from Aston Villa) joined the two Steves, Hunt and Mackenzie, while Paul Dyson (another former Stoke player) partnered long-serving Ally Robertson at the heart of the defence and Colin Anderson, ex-Torquay United, had a few games at left-back. Stuart Naylor, transferred for £100,000 from Lincoln City, replaced Tony Godden and Paul Bradshaw in goal and three more youth players, David Burrows, Carlton Palmer and Mark Robinson also made their debuts.

Gary Owen, Paul Bradshaw, Mickey Thomas, Jimmy Nicholl, Carl Valentine, Micky Forsyth, Steve Hunt, Garry Armstrong and Tony Godden all left The Hawthorns in the most traumatic of seasons.

Albion started off badly, deteriorated terminally and subsequently suffered relegation for the sixth time at The Hawthorns.

Several unwanted club records were created as Albion plummeted into the Second Division…

- Fewest wins (four).
- Record number of defeats (26).
- Least number of away wins (one).
- Fewest home wins (3).
- Most home defeats (10 from 21 games played), equalling the record set in 1950-51.
- Least number of home points gained (17).
- Fewest number of home goals scored (21).
- Lowest number of points gained (24 – from 42 games).
- Nine consecutive League games lost (between 20 August and 28 September 1985)
- Most players used in a season (34).

Albion, 1985-86. Back row (left to right): Micky Forsyth, Jimmy Nicholl, Martyn Bennett, Tony Godden, Paul Bradshaw, Barry Cowdrill, Carlton Palmer. Middle row: George Wright (physiotherapist), Tony Brown (coach), Gary Robson, Colin Anderson, Nicky Cross, Clive Whitehead, Derek Statham, Steve Hunt, Nobby Stiles (assistant manager). Front row: Carl Valentine, Steve MacKenzie, Johnny Giles (manager), Garth Crooks, Imre Varadi, Tony Grealish.

1986-87

Playing in the Second Division for the first time in 11 years, and with two new strikers in the side – Stewart Evans (bought from Wimbledon) and Scotsman Bobby Williamson (signed from Rangers) – Albion got off to a poor start, losing 2-0 at Hull, but they soon picked up and lost only twice in the next ten outings although they did crash out of the League Cup, beaten 5-1 on aggregate by Derby County.

To boost his ranks manager Ron Saunders recruited winger Robert Hopkins from Manchester City (Imre Varadi going in the opposite direction). Hopkins had been with the boss at both Villa Park and St Andrew's.

As Christmas approached Albion were in mid-table, not too far off the leading group, but a disastrous run either side of the New Year knocked them back.

A 3-2 FA Cup defeat at lowly Swansea City didn't help matters and, in fact, between 19 December and 4 April, Albion recorded just one victory in 15 League games – a best-of-the-season 4-1 triumph at home to Stoke City – while suffering eight defeats.

At this juncture the Baggies were in trouble but the double-signing of former Albion youngster Steve Lynex (from Leicester City) and striker Don Goodman (from Bradford City) boosted the team and the threat of relegation was lifted with three wins and two draws from six matches in April.

Albion finally finished in 15th position with 51 points, just three clear of the drop-zone.

Garth Crooks with 11 goals, was Albion's top-scorer; Bobby Williamson (in his first season of English football) netted eight.

Only Stuart Naylor and Paul Dyson played in every game and for the first time since 1905-06, the average League attendance at The Hawthorns was under 10,000 at 9,280, the worst single turnout being that of 6,198 for the visit of Sunderland in early April.

Not one Albion player received senior international honours and during the course of the season the following all left The Hawthorns: Bull, Dennison and Thompson (to

Gordon Dimbleby resigned as club secretary in October and was replaced by John Westmancoat (from Walsall). Assistant-secretary and former player Ray Fairfax also left (for Port Vale) but at the same time a new commercial manager, Tom Cardall, was signed up after working for the club's lottery.

Tony Grealish appeared in two internationals for Eire v the USSR and Denmark, Jimmy Nicholl played for Northern Ireland against Turkey, Romania, England, France, Algeria, Spain and Brazil and Gerry Armstrong starred against Turkey, Romania, England and France (the latter three as sub.). Carl Valentine was capped for Canada v Honduras, and Mickey Thomas represented Wales v Hungary (his 50th cap) and Saudi Arabia (as sub).

For the record, Imre Varadi top-scored with 13 goals and Derek Statham played in most League games (37).

- Most home goals conceded in First Division (36).
- Most away goals conceded in First Division (53), equalled by Oxford United.
- Lowest home League crowd since World War Two (6,021).
- Five goalkeepers used in season.
- Nine teenage players given their club debuts.
- Albion remained bottom of the League from the third match until the end of season.
- Albion had three managers during the season.
- And to cap it all Albion's second XI suffered relegation as well.

Albion, 1986-87. Back row (left to right): David Burrows, Craig Madden, Stuart Naylor, Barry Cowdrill, Andy Thompson. Middle row: Graham Doig (physiotherapist), Martin Dickinson, George Reilly, Steve Bull, Steve MacKenzie, Robbie Dennison, Carlton Palmer, Keith Leonard (coach). Front row: Stewart Evans, Clive Whitehead, Martyn Bennett, Ron Saunders (manager), Paul Dyson, Darren Bradley, Bobby Williamson.

Wolves), Madden (to Blackpool), Robinson (to Barnsley), Whitehead (to Portsmouth), Grealish (to Manchester City), Crooks and Mackenzie (to Charlton Athletic) and Evans (to Plymouth).

Old favourite Ally Robertson also joined Wolves after 729 appearances for Albion's first team. In 569 games of all types he had played alongside John Wile, the most durable defensive partnership in Albion's history.

In September 1986, Joe Kennedy who helped Albion win promotion in 1949 and the FA Cup in 1954, died at the age of 60.

John Westmancoat left Albion in October 1986 for Birmingham City. her was replaced in office by Gordon Bennett, managing director of Bristol Rovers. Norman Bodell replaced Roy Horobin as chief scout and ex-Burnley goalkeeper Alan Stevenson took over from Tom Cardall – temporarily absconded to Aston Villa – as Commercial manager.

1987-88

Another disastrous season for Albion who finished in their lowest-ever League position – 20th in Division Two – only one point clear of relegation.

Ron Saunders remained in charge for the first month of the campaign before being replaced by Ron Atkinson who became the third manager to return to a second spell at The Hawthorns, following Ronnie Allen and Johnny Giles.

He was faced with a tall order – to refloat a sinking ship.

With coach Colin Addison he set about a difficult task with confidence but the players simply weren't good enough and the results, both at home and away, were sometimes shocking.

There was another swift turn round in players – strikers Andy Gray (ex-Dundee United, Aston Villa, Wolves, Everton and Scotland) and Stewart Phillips (from Hereford United), winger Tony Morley (for a second time from Den Haag), midfielders Tony Kelly and Brian Talbot (both from Stoke City), defenders Simeon Hodson (from Newport County), Graeme Hogg and Kenny Swain (on loan from Manchester United and Portsmouth respectively), Stacey North (from Luton Town) and goalkeeper Peter Hucker (a loan signing from Oxford United) – all arrived at The Hawthorns, but – with Martyn Bennett and Paul Dyson out with long term injuries plus the inevitable suspensions – Atkinson was never really able to field a settled side, Yet The Hawthorns' loyalists stood by their team – and the manager – and, indeed, the average attendance at home games was 10,079, around 800 up on the previous season's figure.

Among some horrible home defeats were those against Leeds United and Millwall (both by 1-4); Swindon Town (1-2, when Tony Kelly was sent off), Blackburn Rovers (0-1) and Reading (0-1), the latter being Albion's worst display of a sorry season.

Quite surprisingly, on their travels Albion should have won at Aston Villa, Middlesbrough and Ipswich – three of the better sides in the Division – and they were unlucky at Plymouth, where they fought back from 1-3 down to draw 3-3, and at Leicester, where they were beaten 3-0. But in truth the side was one of the poorest Albion supporters had seen for years.

Thirty players were used (it was 34 and 28 respectively in 1985-86 and 1986-87)… and there lay the trouble.

Atkinson knew he wanted to strengthen his squad, but money was scarce and one or two senior professionals performed well below par.

Brian Talbot's arrival (in January) certainly made a difference to the midfield, but it was far too late in the day to expect miracles.

In comparison with their League form Albion fared no better in the three Cup competitions they entered, losing in the first round of the Littlewoods Challenge Cup to neighbours Walsall, in the third round of the FA Cup to the eventual winners Wimbledon and in the Simod Cup to Ipswich Town.

One consolation was that Albion's second string gained promotion from the Central League Division Two and won the Birmingham Senior Cup for the first time since 1895.

Andy Gray top-scored this season with ten goals; Tony Morley netted eight. Carlton Palmer made most full League appearances (36) but Goodman played in 40 matches (six as a sub).

A check behind the scenes saw Bert Millichip still holding the position of president. Sid Lucas Brian Boundy, who resigned in June 1988, as vice-chairman.

In August 1988 Lucas himself stood down to be replaced by John Silk.. Other Board members in 1987-88 were Trevor Summers, Joe Brandrick and Mike McGinnity. Gordon Bennett was now Albion's secretary, having replaced John Westmancoat in December 1986.

There were no major international honours for Albion players this season.

On the move in the summer were Martin Dickinson (to Sheffield United), Bobby Williamson (to Rotherham United), Barry Cowdrill (to Bolton Wanderers), Steve Lynex (to Cardiff City) and George Reilly (to Cambridge United).

1988-89

Three newcomers – left-back Arthur Albiston (from Manchester United), centre-half Chris Whyte (ex-Crystal Palace and Arsenal) and the South African striker John Paskin – all figured in Albion's first team during the early stages of this season which celebrated 100 years of the Football League. And after an excellent first half to their 46-match programme, Albion hit top position on 2 January following a splendid 4-0 home win over Shrewsbury Town.

Albion were now under new management, Ron Atkinson having left for Spain in October (with Colin Addison) to be replaced by Brian Talbot as player-manager a month later.

When Talbot took over Albion were in 13th position, but they got their act together and moved steadily up the table.

Indeed, when they reached pole position, they certainly looked promotion candidates, but then it all went wrong (we've heard that before).

After going out of the FA Cup to Everton (in a replay) Albion's form changed dramatically and the second-half of the season realised just 28 points out of a possible 68, having collected 44 from their first 24 matches. They eventually slithered down the table to finish a disappointing ninth, three places short of the Play-off zone.

Perhaps the crucial talking points, inside the club and among the fans, surrounded the injuries to two key players – leading scorer Don Goodman and Colin Anderson – who at the time (January), were both in tip-top form. During their absence Albion's form nose-dived... and, in fact, Goodman never regained full fitness, Colin West (ex-Sheffield Wednesday and Sunderland) coming in to replace him, and enabling Carlton Palmer to go to Hillsborough.

Tony Ford, another former Stoke City player, also moved into The

Hawthorns to play wide on the right, Kevin Bartlett was recruited from Cardiff City to boost the attack and Ian Banks and Paul Raven were also added to the squad, while David Burrows was sold to Liverpool for £500,000.

In hindsight Albion drew far too many matches (a club record 18) and failed to score sufficient goals, only 55 in the League and none against relegated Walsall. Their best win was an emphatic 6-0 hammering of Stoke City a week before Christmas, while their heaviest defeat was only 2-0.

A noteworthy success was a fine 4-1 away win at St Andrew's in October and just over a month later Albion beat Crystal Palace 5-3 in a dramatic confrontation at The Hawthorns.

Albion were ousted early on from the Littlewoods Cup by Peterborough United and went out of the sponsored Simod Cup, losing 5-2 at West Ham.

Goodman (16 goals) finished up as leading scorer with Robson (9) and West (8) also in the frame.

Defender Stacey North was the only ever-present in the side,

becoming the first Albion player to appear in 46 League matches in a season, while 'keeper Stuart Naylor was absent from two matches.

The average League attendance at The Hawthorns was 12,766 – up by 2,687 on the 1987-88 figure.

At international level David Burrows was called up by England under-21 v Sweden prior to his move to Liverpool and Stuart Naylor and Tony Ford gained England 'B' honours against Switzerland and Norway. Naylor also played against Iceland 'B'; Gary Robson represented the Football League v The Skol Northern League, playing alongside his elder brother, Bryan.

Just before the season ended Dr John Evans, a lifelong Albion supporter, was appointed club secretary in succession to Gordon Bennett who had decamped to Norwich City. Dr Evans had been associated with Nuneaton Borough and Northampton Town and was a fully qualified referee with a senior FA coaching certificate.

Among the season's departures were Arthur Albiston (to Dundee), Ian Banks (to Barnsley), John Paskin (to Wolverhampton Wanderers),

Don Goodman scores against Swindon Town at The Hawthorns in 1988-89.

Ronnie Robinson (to Rotherham United), Andy Gray (to Rangers), Stewart Phillips (top Swansea City), Tony Morley (to Tampa Bay Rowdies), Robert Hopkins (to Birmingham City), Tony Kelly (to Shrewsbury Town) and Paul Dyson (to Darlington).

In August 1988, the death took place in Buxton of former Albion centre-forward Bobby Blood, who scored 26 goals in 153 games between 1921 and 1924. He was 94.

Cliff Edwards, a former Albion half-back and club director, died in March 1989, aged 68.

And in July 1989, the tragic death occurred of Laurie Cunningham, who was killed in a car crash on the outskirts of Madrid. He was just 32 years of age and had scored 30 goals in 114 games for Albion (1977-79).

1989-90

This turned out to be yet another poor season for Albion who finished 20th in the Second Division, equalling their lowest ever League position and for the second time in three years they had to squeeze out of relegation trouble.

A disastrous home record was perhaps responsible for their inept campaign, Albion winning only six and losing nine of their 23 League matches at The Hawthorns, conceding 37 goals in the process, the most by any club at home in the Division.

They also lost to Bradford City 3-1 at home in the Littlewoods Cup before pulling off a miraculous 5-3 victory at Valley Parade in the second leg to go through on the away goal rule. Albion then beat Newcastle 1-0 at St James' Park before going out of the competition to Derby County, who also won 5-0 at The Hawthorns in the Zenith Data Systems Cup-tie between the clubs.

Over 30 players were used in League and Cup competitions with four different goalkeepers employed before the end of September. Manager Brian Talbot utilised five different right backs and five central defenders (No.5) and made eight changes on the left-wing.

Injuries caused a lot problems for the boss who hardly ever fielded an unchanged team. More than 20 players visited the treatment room at various times, three with broken legs. But in all honesty it was inconsistency which was the key to Albion's failure to gain results out on the park.

The team managed no more than two League wins on the trot and Third Division football looked a cast iron certainty after just one victory was recorded in eight games immediately after New Year. During this period Albion surprised their critics by knocking two First Division sides – Charlton Athletic and Wimbledon – out of the FA Cup before losing at home to neighbours Aston Villa.

Twelve vital points were gained with wins over Bradford City and Watford at home and from trips to Hull City and Brighton which lifted the Baggies to safety – but it was mighty close.

The best win of the season was a 7-0 hammering of Barnsley, a game which marked the end of Martyn Bennett's career with Albion. He retired from League action with a back injury after more than 200 outings for the club. And manager Brian Talbot quit as a player at the season's end after more than 21 years in the game.

Newcomers in the Baggies' camp included John Thomas (from Bolton Wanderers), Gary Hackett and Steve Parkin (both from Stoke City), Irish international Bernard McNally (Shrewsbury Town), former England international Mark Barham, ex-Walsall star Craig Shakespeare (from Sheffield Wednesday), Graham Harbey (Ipswich Town) and Gary Bannister (Coventry City). Among the few youngsters to emerge were defender Daryl Burgess and striker Adrian Foster.

Don Goodman was leading scorer with 21 goals; Chris Whyte (44), Tony Ford (42), and Bernard McNally (41) appeared in most League games and the average attendance at The Hawthorns was 11,313 – around 1,400 down on the previous season's figure.

In the summer The Hawthorns pitch was completely returfed.

Players on the move included Chris Whyte (to Leeds United for £550,000), Kevin Bartlett (Notts County), Martyn Bennett (Worcester City), Paul Bradshaw (Peterborough United), Gavin Ward (Cardiff City), Mark Barham (Brighton) and John Thomas (Preston North End).

In November 1989, the former Albion wing of the 1930s, Jimmy 'Spud' Murphy, a wing-half who played for Wales and managed Manchester United, died at the age of 81. He had been the Welsh international team manager for eight years: 1955-63.

1990-91

At 4.44pm on Saturday 11 May 1991, Albion were relegated to the Third Division for the first time in the club's history after what was their worst ever season of League football, even surpassing that dreadful 1985-86 campaign.

A dejected chairman John Silk admitted that it was a 'black day' for all Albion supporters, but vowed 'we'll be back.'

That was no consolation for the loyal followers, however, who had backed the team all down the line during a traumatic season in which the average home attendance rose by 688 to 12,001.

It was amazing that Albion ended

their League programme with a nine-match unbeaten run (seven draws) and still went down – but they managed only four League victories from 23 games between 1 January and 11 May and that proved crucial. During this spell they also crashed out of the FA Cup, losing 4-2 at The Hawthorns to non-League Woking – a humiliation which led to the immediate departure of manager Brian Talbot. Second XI coach Stuart Pearson took charge for six games before ex-player Bobby Gould moved into the hot seat.

Earlier in the campaign Bristol City and Barnsley had knocked the Baggies out of the League Cup and Zenith Data Systems Cup respectively. Barnsley's 5-3 win at The Hawthorns included a hat-trick by former Albion midfielder Ian Banks in a 12 minute spell during the second half.

Almost immediately Gould – not a popular choice with the fans – came under pressure as Albion suffered six straight defeats which plunged them deep into relegation trouble.

On transfer deadline, in an effort to avoid the drop, Gould splashed out £250,000 on striker Paul Williams from Stockport County (a former Hartlepool reject who was soon to be capped by Northern Ireland.), £35,000 on veteran midfielder Winston White from Burnley and took Kwame Ampadu on loan from Arsenal.

It didn't work. Williams failed to score in any of his ten appearances and Albion bagged just 13 points out of the last 27, drawing six of their final seven games by 1-1 to make it 18 shared encounters for the season (equalling a club record). They even missed two penalties in the home draw with Port Vale and failed to beat fellow strugglers Watford and Hull City.

Albion travelled to Twerton Park, Bath for the last game of the season knowing that must beat Bristol Rovers to stay up. They could draw 1-1 after Rovers had been reduced to ten men as early as the third minute – and thus, after 3,634 First and second Division matches down the years, Albion descended ignominiously into the Third Division for the first time ever.

Albion's home form let them down badly. They collected only 32 points out of 69 and won just seven of their 23 matches.

Conceding late goals also proved costly and at the end of the day Albion got what they deserved.

In May 1991 the club's reserve squad won the Pontins League Second Division championship, having captured the Birmingham Cup a few weeks earlier.

Gary Bannister with 14 League and Cup goals was leading scorer ahead of Colin West and Tony Ford – was the only ever-present in the team.

Players who were transferred to Albion during the 1990-91 season included England international Graham Roberts (a £200,000 buy from Chelsea), goalkeeper Mel Rees (from Watford), and central defender Gary Strodder (who cost £190,000 from West Ham). On the move were Stacey North (to Fulham), Colin Anderson (to Walsall) and Wayne Dobbins (to Torquay United).

In July 1991 Sid Lucas resigned from the Board to be replaced by local businessman Clive Stapleton. In the previous month the club president Bert Millichip was knighted for services to football.

At international level, striker Paul Williams was capped (as sub) by Northern Ireland against the Faroe Islands.

And in April 1991 Albion's 1954 FA Cup Final left-winger George Lee died in Norwich at the age of 70. He scored 65 goals in almost 300 games for Albion between 1949 and 1958.

1991-92

Playing in the Third Division for the first time, Albion's 1991-92 season was one of the most turbulent in the club's history and it ended in sheer frustration and total disappointment as Albion missed out on the Play-offs by finishing seventh in the table, their lowest-ever League position.

Manager Gould attempted to win promotion by using virtually the same band of players who had been relegated the year before. He domineered his staff and introduced maverick ideas which worked initially, but after selling star striker Don Goodman to Sunderland manager Denis Smith for £1 million (replaced eventually by Bob Taylor, a £350,000 buy from Bristol City in February) and after going back to the top of the table in February after an emphatic 3-0 win at Birmingham, there followed a shattering demise which left the fans calling for the heads of both the manager and the entire board.

The team simply disintegrated under pressure, results were disastrous and when Gould sacked his coach Stuart Pearson there was uproar among the fans. Things went from bad to worse after that and shortly after the season ended Gould was dismissed, chairman John Silk resigned (replaced by Trevor Summers) and the former Argentinian World Cup star Ossie Ardiles arrived at The Hawthorns to take over as manager.

When the 1991-92 campaign opened Albion were marked up as one of the favourites to win promotion and they started well, recording a best-ever opening day result in a League campaign by beating Exeter City 6-3 at home in the first-ever

HAWTHORNS DIARY

game in the Division. An early exit game in the Division. An early exit from the Rumbelows sponsored League Cup to Swindon meant very little as the League results continued to favour the Baggies, but then came the collapse which dismayed the fans. And not only did Albion's form suffer in the League, they had earlier gone out of the FA Cup at lowly Leyton Orient and were beaten at home by Exeter City in the Autoglass Trophy.

A staggering number of 34 players were used by Gould with only one ever-present (left-back Graham Harbey). The defence at times looked solid enough; the midfield struggled to a certain extent, certainly over the last three months, and scoring goals proved mighty difficult, more so after Goodman's departure.

Of the 46 League matches

played, 14 were drawn (only Bolton and Bradford City drew more) and eight matches were lost by the odd goal.

The average League crowd at the Hawthorns was 12,707, a rise of over 700 on the previous season's figure and even Albion's reserve side had a bad time, suffering relegation from the Pontins League Division One (being replaced by Wolves.).

Among the newcomers were Wayne Taylor (mentioned earlier), Wayne Fereday (from Bournemouth), loan signings Alan Miller (Arsenal), Frank Sinclair (Chelsea) and Andy Dibble (Manchester City) and youngsters Carl Heggs and Roy Hunter.

Mel Rees (Sheffield United), Colin West (Swansea City), Tony Ford (Grimsby Town), Graham Harbey (Stoke City), Gary Bannister

(Nottingham Forest), Adrian Foster (Torquay United), Graham Roberts (Enfield) and Steve Parkin (Mansfield Town) were among the many departures.

There were no major international honours gained by Albion players this season but Kwame Ampadu represented the Republic of Ireland under-21 XI v Switzerland.

In September 1991, Peter McKennan, an Albion inside-forward from the 1940s, died in Scotland aged 83.

In April 1992, former Walsall and Albion goalscorer Gilbert Alsop died at the age of 81.

1992-93

This turned out to be a memorable season for West Bromwich Albion Football Club as the team won a Cup Final at Wembley on their first visit to the Empire Stadium for 23 years.

Albion, 1992-93. Back row (left to right): Ian Hamilton, Carl Heggs, Paul Raven, Stuart Naylor, Gary Strodder, Daryl Burgess, Bob Taylor. Middle row: Danny Thomas (physiotherapist), Simeon Hodson, Roy Hunter, Wayne Fereday, Darren Bradley, Steve Lilwall, Dennis Mortimer (coach). Front row: Bernard McNally, Gary Robson, Kwame Ampadu, Keith Burkinshaw (assistant manager), Ossie Ardiles (manager), Craig Shakespeare, Stacy Coldicott, Gary Hackett.

It was indeed a success story for manager Ossie Ardiles and his assistant Keith Burkinshaw, as the players responded magnificently out on the field.

There was certainly an air of anticipation and optimism as the season kicked off with a 3-1 home win over Blackpool in front of 16,500 sun-drenched supporters. Despite an early exit from the Coca-Cola Cup, beaten by Plymouth Argyle, Albion prospered in the League and hit top spot after beating Huddersfield in the second match. They held poll position until mid-October but then a couple of indifferent results saw them slip down to third before they regained top slot again at the end of that month.

At this stage in the proceedings Bob Taylor was scoring at will and was ably assisted up front by Kevin Donovan (bought from Huddersfield Town) and Simon Garner, ex-Blackburn Rovers.

Goalkeeper Stuart Naylor, left-back Steve Lilwall (who a few months earlier had been playing for Kidderminster Harriers), centre-halves Paul Raven and Gary Strodder and midfielders Darren Bradley, Bernard McNally and Ian Hamilton were all doing the business in a workmanlike side as Albion powered on.

Luckless Aylesbury, hammered 8-0, and Wycombe Wanderers 1-0 (in a replay) were ousted from the FA Cup as 1992 gave way to 1993. Albion were still in there with a great chance of winning automatic promotion, but then came a poor spell. Defeat in the FA Cup at home to West Ham and against bogey side Stoke City in the Autoglass Trophy disrupted the Ardiles plans and Albion slithered down to fourth place in the Division.

Enter striker Andy Hunt (signed initially on loan from Newcastle United) to partner Taylor in attack.

Albion celebrate after the 1993 Division Two Play-off Final at Wembley.

He netted a hat-trick on his home debut against Brighton and claimed nine crucial goals in the last ten League games as the Baggies finished fourth in the table, missing automatic promotion by just five points.

They were paired with Swansea City in the two-legged Play-off semi-final and after losing 2-1 at the Vetch Field, goals by Hunt and Hamilton in a tension-packed second leg took Albion through to Wembley where they beat Port Vale 3-0 to the delight of more than 42,000 travelling supporters. Admittedly Vale had Peter Swan sent off when the game was goalless but Albion always looked the more likely winners and so it proved. Andy Hunt, 'Man of the Match' Nicky Reid (with his only goal for Albion) and Kevin Donovan were the crucial goalscorers.

It was celebrations all round for Ardiles and Co.

Bob Taylor ended the season with 37 goals, only four short of breaking W. G. Richardson's club record 40 in 1935-36. He and Ian Hamilton (10 goals) were both ever-present and the average League attendance at the Hawthorns was 15,161 – a rise of 2,454. A crowd of 26,045 saw the pulsating return Play-off game with Swansea.

Andy Hunt (initially on loan from Newcastle United), Nicky Reid and Simon Garner (Blackburn Rovers), Tony Lange (Wolverhampton Wanderers), Kevin Donovan (Huddersfield Town), Ian Hamilton (Scunthorpe United) and Micky Mellon (Bristol City) were all new signings who helped Albion to win promotion.

Gary Robson (to Bradford City), Paul Williams (Stockport County), Simeon Hodson (Doncaster Rovers) and Craig Shakespeare (Grimsby Town) all departed.

In November 1992 former Albion chairman Sid Lucas, who had given unstinting service to the club as a director, died at the age of 70 and in this same month a former Albion right-winger of the 1960s Hughie Reed, died suddenly at the age of 42.

In May 1993 ex-goalkeeper Mel Rees died of cancer at the age of 26 and the following month former Albion manager Archie Macaulay died, aged 76.

Kevin Donovan's great diving header in the 3-2 home win over Wolves in September 1993.

1993-94

Albion began the 1993-94 season without Ossie Ardiles. The friendly and likeable Argentinian quit The Hawthorns, to the obvious disappointment of the board, players and, indeed, the supporters, to take charge of his former club Tottenham Hotspur. Chairman Trevor Summers quickly promoted Keith Burkinshaw to the manager's chair, stating that it was of prime importance that continuity should be maintained.

It proved to be a difficult and at times very tense season as Albion, attempting to consolidate themselves in the First Division. scrambled to safety on the very last day of the campaign by virtue of a nail-biting 1-0 victory at Fratton Park against Portsmouth; Lee Ashcroft's header did the trick, much to the relief of the 10,000 travelling Baggies' supporters. Anything else than a win would have sent the Baggies straight back down from where they had just escaped.

Surprisingly, Albion played well during the opening two months or so, actually rising to fourth in the table. But by mid-October they were right down amongst the strugglers and although they picked up around Christmas time, moving up to 16th,. thereafter it was a real battle for survival. Injuries and suspensions were frequent and only occasionally was the manager able to field an unchanged side.

Nevertheless certain players performed well below par for far too long and although Bob Taylor and Andy Hunt claimed 30 League goals between them, Albion's overall scoring record let them down badly, especially away from home where they netted less than one goal a game.

In the FA Cup Albion made an inglorious exit from the competition, losing 2-1 at non-League Halifax Town, a truly dreadful result. Albion also took part in the Coca-Cola Cup (losing to Chelsea) and played six matches in the revamped Anglo-Italian Cup.

Thirty players were called into action including newcomers Neil Parsley and Kieran O'Regan (both secured from Huddersfield Town), Ashcroft (bought from Preston North End for £225,000), defender Paul Mardon and midfielder David Smith (both from Birmingham City) and left-back Paul Edwards, signed from Wolves.

Two loan players – striker Graham Fenton (Aston Villa) and left-back Paul Williams (Coventry City) – added some impetus to the side, but despite pleas from the fans Albion failed to secure the transfer of the latter on a permanent basis.

Taylor with 21 goals was again Albion's leading scorer. Defender Daryl Burgess made the most League appearances (43) and the average League attendance at The Hawthorns was a creditable 16,868 – a rise of 1,707 on the 1992-93 figure.

And to the delight of the fans Albion beat arch rivals Wolves twice this season.

Another bonus was the reserve team's winning promotion from the Pontins League Division Two under the guidance of former player and now coach John Trewick.

Players leaving The Hawthorns included Wayne Fereday (to Cardiff City), Gary Hackett (Peterborough United), Simon Garner and Nicky Reid (Wycombe Wanderers) and Kwame Ampadu (Swansea City).

In the summer of 1994, Trevor Summers relinquished his position of chairman, handing over the seat to Tony Hale. Clive Stapleton became vice-chairman in November.

During the close season The Hawthorns pitch was re-laid with enhanced drainage.

1994-95

Like it had been in 1993-94, Albion were again involved in a battle to stave off relegation – and once more they just managed to hold on to their First Division status, avoiding the drop with two games remaining following a 0-0 home draw with Derby County.

Following massive redevelopment work at The Hawthorns Albion were required to play their first five League matches away from home, drawing two and losing three, quickly finding themselves on the bottom of the table.

They picked up slightly once they started to play in front of their own fans (a 1-1 draw with Grimsby, followed by a 1-0 win over Burnley) but for long spells during a mediocre campaign Albion were lingering far too near the trap-door for comfort. Inconsistency was their main problem and if it hadn't been for their reasonable home form – they won 13 times including a 2-0 triumph over Wolves, a 5-1 drubbing of promotion-chasing Tranmere Rovers (when Lee Ashcroft netted a hat-trick), a 2-0 defeat of Reading and a 1-0 victory over Bolton – then they would have gone down.

In late October manager Keith Burkinshaw was replaced by the ex-Nottingham Forest and Birmingham City striker and former Walsall player-boss Alan Buckley, who moved back to the Midlands from Grimsby, where he had been an outstanding success. He was accompanied by his assistant Arthur Mann who had played for Manchester City against Albion in the 1970 League Cup Final at Wembley.

From a position of 23rd Buckley quickly turned things round and within three months Albion had risen to 16th. But after going out of the FA Cup at the hands of Coventry City in a Hawthorns replay when Darren Bradley was sent-off, Albion's League form began to wane and they slipped back to 19th position in early March before edging clear with a late flurry, beaten only four times in their last 12 outings which included six victories. Early on Albion had suffered the humiliation of losing to Third Division Hereford United in the Coca-Cola Cup, the Bulls being the first club to play, and win, at the newly-designed Hawthorns, which was officially opened on Boxing Day when 21,071 fans saw Bristol City beaten 1-0 with a flukey own-goal by Stuart Munro.

There's no doubt that injuries and suspensions played their part in a difficult season; although Albion were well covered in defence and attack... it was in midfield where they were found wanting.

Goalkeeper Stuart Naylor, defenders Paul Raven, Gary Strodder and Paul Mardon (the club's 'Player of the Year') and wide men Kevin Donovan and Lee Ashcroft all had good campaigns. Midfielder Ian Hamilton and strikers Andy Hunt and Bob Taylor were not at their best, although the latter pair did suffer with injuries and illness, likewise Daryl Burgess and Darren Bradley.

Midfielder Mike Phelan, a much-heralded close season recruit from Manchester United, rarely lived up to his large signing-on fee.

The left-back position was a problem until Buckley signed Paul Agnew from his old club, Grimsby, and he also brought in Tony Rees as an extra attacker.

Hunt with 13 goals, was Albion's top-scorer, followed by Ashcroft and Taylor each with 11.

There were no ever-presents, Naylor and Taylor both missed four League games and Hunt five. Albion's average home League attendance was 15,219, down by 1,621 on the previous season.

Several players of first team pedigree were moved on during and at the end of the season: Tony Lange (went to Fulham), Roy Hunter (to Northampton Town), Bernard McNally (to Hednesford Town), Darren Bradley (to Walsall), Neil Parsley (to Exeter City), Steve Lilwall (to non-League Rushden & Diamonds), Scott Darton and Micky Mellon (both joined Blackpool), Carl Heggs (to Swansea City) and Gary Strodder (to Notts County).

Four former Albion players and a manager died during the season.

In November goalkeeper Harold Pearson passed away in West Bromwich, aged 86. He appeared in 303 games (1925-37) and starred in the 1931 and 1935 FA Cup Finals.

In May Teddy Sandford, who played with Harold in those Cup Finals, died in Birmingham at the age of 85. He scored 75 goals in 317 games (1930-39). A month earlier, Johnny Nicholls, an FA Cup winner in 1954, died of a heart attack on his way home from Albion's League game with Middlesbrough. He was 64 and scored 64 goals in 145 matches between 1952 and 1957.

Right-back Jim Pemberton died in Wolverhampton in February, aged 78. He played 172 games for Albion (1946-50) and finally Vic Buckingham, Albion's manager from 1953-59, died in January, aged 79.

Pearson, Sandford and Nicholls were all England internationals while Buckingham played for England during the War.

1995-96

This turned out to be quite an extraordinary season for Albion. Not many clubs can say they have been second and 23rd in the same Division during the same campaign and one step from a Wembley Final... but that's precisely what happened to Albion.

In October they could well have gone top, yet in January – after a club record 11 straight defeats – they were one off the bottom and struggling.

They had started off very well with new signing Dave Gilbert (from Grimsby), strikers Bob Taylor

HAWTHORNS DIARY

and Andy Hunt and defenders Paul Mardon and Paul Raven in fine form.

By the end of October with 13 games played but no longer in the Coca-Cola Cup (beaten by Reading in round 2), Albion travelled to Millwall knowing that victory would take them to the top. But they were beaten 2-1 and this reverse set the Baggies on an astonishing run of successive League defeats, with only one win coming in the next 15 games.

Manager Alan Buckley refused to panic and despite a 4-3 FA Cup defeat at Crewe, Albion slowly but surely got themselves back on track, although they did miss out on a trip to Wembley by losing to Port Vale in the area final of the Anglo-Italian Cup.

Into the camp came veteran goalkeeper Nigel Spink (from Villa Park), full-backs Paul Holmes (from Everton) and Shane Nicholson (from Derby), on-loan midfielder Peter Butler (from Notts County) and Dutchman Richard Sneekes (a £400,000 buy from Bolton). And with Sneekes in excellent goalscoring form (he netted ten times in the last 13 matches) Albion eased themselves up to a creditable 11th spot in the table after collecting 24 points out of 39 during the last third of the campaign – a campaign which was split into three, each completely different in terms of performances.

Taylor skippered the side during the second half of the season and was top marksman with 23 goals. He netted his first hat-trick for the Baggies (in a 4-4 draw with Watford) and claimed his 100th for the club in the final League game v promoted Derby County.

Daryl Burgess and Andy Hunt appeared in most League games (45 each) and the average League attendance at The Hawthorns was 15,166 – up by around 850 on the previous season.

Among the players leaving Albion were veteran goalkeeper of more than 400 senior appearances Stuart Naylor, who moved to Bristol City, Tony Rees went to Merthyr Tydfil, Paul Edwards joined Hednesford Town and Mike Phelan went to Norwich City.

At international level this season the only honour went to central defender Paul Mardon who earned a Welsh cap when he came on as a substitute against Germany.

In February 1996, former Albion goalkeeper Bill Harris died, aged 77 and another 'keeper, Jock Wallace, died in July 1996, aged 61.

1996-97

Yet another very ordinary season for Albion who struggled to finish a moderate 16th in the First Division. And they also went out of both Cup competitions in the opening rounds, losing to Third Division minnows Colchester United in the Coca-Cola Cup and to Premiership outfit Chelsea in the FA Cup. A pre-season success, however, was forthcoming when Albion won the Isle of Man Festival Trophy by winning their three games without conceding a goal.

Expectations were thus high when the League programme kicked off, especially after that splendid late surge of goals from the Dutchman Richard Sneekes at the end of the previous campaign.

But alas, Albion started off disappointingly and never recovered – pointingly and never recovered – and the fans soon started to show their disgust, more so after arch rivals Wolves came to The Hawthorns and won 4-2.

Canadian goal-ace Paul Peschisolido's outings were restricted because of international call-ups; fellow striker Bob Taylor couldn't get fully fit; defender Paul Mardon was also sidelined through injury; ex-Grimsby Town goalkeeper Paul

Crichton never endeared himself to the supporters and midfielder Peter Butler missed the first four months owing to an injury suffered in a behind doors pre-season friendly against Coventry City.

Manager Alan Buckley switched his line-up around as best he could in an effort to find a winning formula, yet with the odd exception here and there Albion failed to impress as a unit and indeed, failed to maintain any sort of consistency, except for a brief unbeaten period approaching Christmas.

After losing to Chelsea in the Cup – when Australian defender Shaun Murphy made an impressive debut – and going down again to Wolves, Buckley's job was put on the line. That line snapped soon afterwards and he was sacked; this allowed former Blackburn Rovers boss Ray Harford to take over, bringing with him ex-Baggies' favourite Cyrille Regis as coach, accompanied by John Trewick.

At this juncture (February) Albion were in relegation trouble, but the form of the teams below them didn't improve and so they survived, ending up 13 points clear of the trap door.

Among the new faces who came into The Hawthorns camp this season were Australian-born right-back Andy McDermott (secured from Q.P.R. for £400,000), midfielders Paul Groves (bought from Grimsby for £600,000) and Graham Potter (enrolled from Southampton), Peschisolido (another £600,000 buy from Birmingham City), goalkeeper Alan Miller (signed for £400,000 from Middlesbrough, who, in fact, had been on loan at Albion in 1991) and Shaun Murphy (from Notts County).

Albion's best wins were those of 5-1 at home and 4-2 away over Norwich City, Peschisolido netting a hat-trick at Carrow Road and 4-0 v

100 YEARS AT THE HAWTHORNS

Albion, 1996-97. Back row (left to right): Arthur Mann (assistant manager), Lee Knight, Simon Buckley, Michael Rodosthenous, Paul Raven, Shane Nicholson, Chris Hargreaves, Andy Hunt, Daryl Burgess, Paul Mardon, Ian Hamilton, Dean Bennett, Richard O'Kelly (youth coach). Middle row: John Trewick (coach), Paul Mitchell (physiotherapist), Bob Taylor, Stacy Coldicott, Lee Ashcroft, Paul Agnew, Gary Germaine, Nigel Spink, Shaun Cunnington, Paul Groves, Peter Butler, James Willis, Ronnie Allen (coach), Mark Ashton (community officer). Front row: Kevin Donovan, Paul Peschisolido, Richard Sneekes, Dave Gilbert, Alan Buckley (manager), Gareth Hanmer, Paul Holmes, Julian Darby.

Southend United and 4-1 over QPR both at The Hawthorns. Apart from those Wolves defeats, Albion also crashed 5-0 at Ipswich and 4-0 at Portsmouth.

Andy Hunt and Richard Sneekes (each with 45) and Supporters' 'Player of the Year' Ian Hamilton (39) made most League appearances. Hunt also top-scored with 16 goals, one ahead of Peschisolido. And Albion's average League attendance was 15,131 – only 35 down on the previous season.

There were international call ups for Peschisolido, who represented Canada in World Cup-ties v Panama (twice), Cuba (twice), Mexico, USA and El Salvador. In two of these matches he was sent-off.

In contrast Albion were the only club in the British Isles not to have a player red-carded during the full playing season.

During the season Lee Ashcroft left for Preston and in the summer Albion bid farewell to Paul Agnew,

Sean Cunnington, Kevin Donovan, Julian Darby Paul Groves and Roger Joseph. Donovan and Groves teamed up with Alan Buckley at Grimsby.

Two of Albion's 1954 FA Cup winners passed away during the season. In February, Reg Ryan died in Birmingham, aged 71, and the following month, Len Millard left us at the age of 78.

A sad loss was the death in November 1996 of director Terry Guy at the early age of 56.

Shortly before Christmas plans to float Albion shares on the Alternative Investment Market were passed by an overwhelming vote of shareholders and when the shares were launched the following month Albion were valued at £7.5 million.

In March 1997 former club captain John Wile was appointed Albion's first ever chief executive and he subsequently joined the Board of directors two months later

in May.

Also in May 1997 Albion announced a new sponsorship deal with the West Bromwich Building Society worth over £800,000 over a three-year period. This came into effect during the 1997-98 season.

1997-98

For Albion the 1997-98 season was one of two completely different halves. From August to December, under manager Ray Harford, the Baggies were up with the leaders. But following Harford's sudden 'transfer' to Queen's Park Rangers and the arrival of new boss Denis Smith from Oxford United, their fortunes dipped and they slipped slowly and agonisingly down the table and out of the promotion race. They eventually finished a moderate tenth, ending the campaign well with good wins over Sheffield United and promoted Middlesbrough and deserved draws against high-flying Sunderland and the champions Nottingham Forest, the

HAWTHORNS DIARY

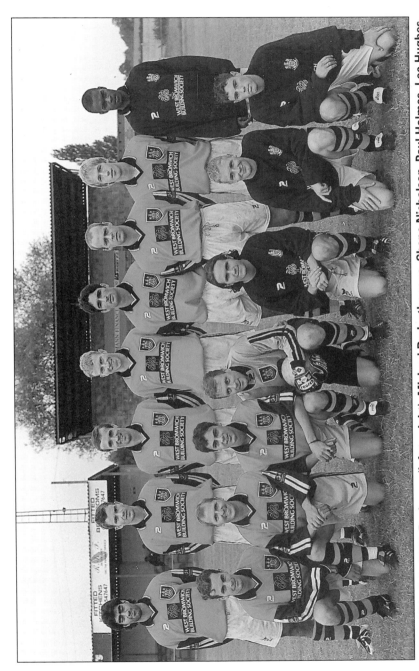

Albion XI in July 1997. Back row (left to right): Michael Rodosthenous, Shane Nicholson, Paul Holmes, Lee Hughes, Shaun Murphy, Tony Dobson, Graham Potter, Darren Cunningham. Front Row: Darren Bowman, Dave Gilbert, Dean Bennett, Paul Crichton, Dean Craven, Carl Tranter, Adam Buckley.

latter game attracting a 23,013 attendance at The Hawthorns.

Albion, in fact, topped the table in early September and were hardly out of the top four until Christmas; they had reached the third round of the Coca-Cola Cup before losing to mighty Liverpool. But once into the New Year their form went pear-shaped. Confidence seemed to drain away and although they just about kept in touch with the promotion contenders until mid-February, there was no way the team was going to make the Play-offs. And so it proved.

It must be said that Albion scrambled a series of home wins to keep them in the top bracket but their away form at times was very poor. They even crashed to arch rivals Aston Villa 4-0 in the FA Cup and were slammed 5-0 at The Valley by Premiership-bound Charlton Athletic. One consolation was that they won at Molineux and so completed the double over Wolves, both scorelines finishing 1-0.

But on the other foot, all three rele-

gated clubs took points off Albion – Manchester City did the double, Stoke managed two draws and Reading won at Elm Park.

One consolation was that Albion mastered the Potters 3-1 in an FA Cup-tie at The Hawthorns in January (Denis Smith's first win as the Baggies' manager and against his former team) and so ended a long chapter of failure against one of their bogey clubs.

Injuries to key players didn't help matters and during the course of the season 34 players were called into action by the two managers.

On the bright side a £250,000 signing from Kidderminster Harriers, Lee Hughes, did exceedingly well in his first season of League football, finishing joint top-scorer with Andy Hunt on 14 goals.

Matt Carbon and Sean Flynn, both of whom were signed from Derby County, battled hard and long in defence and midfield respectfully; Northern Ireland international James Quinn, a £500,000 capture from

Blackpool, did well as an attacking midfielder once he had settled down and record buy Kevin Kilbane, a left-winger who cost £1.25 million from Preston North End, played in 50 of Albion's 53 first team matches this term. Another Irishman, Mickey Evans, arrived from Southampton for £750,000 and loanees James Thomas (Blackburn Rovers), Paul Beesley (Manchester City) and ex-Liverpool star Steve Nicol (from Sheffield Wednesday) plus winger Franz Carr all had outings as did Australian international full-back Jason Van Blerk, also from Manchester City

Unfortunately this was to be the last time strikers Andy Hunt and Bob Taylor were to wear Baggies' shirts. They both left The Hawthorns on 'free transfers' at the end of the season – Hunt to newly-promoted Charlton Athletic and Taylor to relegated Bolton Wanderers where he had been on loan since January. Between them Hunt and Taylor scored 198 goals for Albion in a combined total of 521 appearances (Taylor netting 113 times).

Of the cluster of other players who left the club, Ian Hamilton joined Sheffield United, Paul Peschisolido went to Fulham for £1 million, goalkeeper Nigel Spink signed for Millwall and both Stacy Coldicott and David Smith joined the clan of ex-Baggies stars at Grimsby; Dave Gilbert, Shane Nicholson and Peter Butler also moved on, Nicholson later teaming up with Chesterfield.

Albion's average home attendance of 16,639 was more than 1,500 up on the previous season.

In February 1998 the 'B' international between England and Chile was staged at The Hawthorns.

Kevin Kilbane played for the Republic of Ireland v Iceland, the Czech Republic (as sub) and Argentina; James Quinn turned out for Northern Ireland against Slovakia and Switzerland; Paul Peschisolido before his transfer, was capped by Canada v Jamaica and El Salvador and Andy McDermott won two Australian under-23 honours, both v New Zealand.

Behind the scenes, Tom Cardall was appointed Public Relations Manager in recognition of his hard work on the club's commercial front.

1998-99

One has to say that Albion began this season – their 100th in the Football League – with high hopes of challenging for promotion – the bookies thought so as well, marking them down as 16-1 to finish in the top six.

Manager Denis Smith had augmented his squad with the signing of winger Mark Angel from his old club Sunderland and the recruitment of the Italian midfield duo of Mario Bortolazzi (from Genoa) and teenager Enzo Maresca (from Cagliari), and he also upgraded talented youngster Adam Oliver to the professional ranks. The season began well enough with a 2-2 away draw at demoted Barnsley, a 2-1 Worthington Cup first leg win over Brentford and a 4-1 home victory in the League over Sheffield United.

A disappointing 3-0 reverse in the return leg at Brentford meant an early departure from the Worthington Cup but Albion quickly made amends and jumped up to third place in the table with a competent 3-0 win at Port Vale (a hat-trick here for Lee Hughes – his first for the club). A 2-0 home triumph over Norwich City followed, Dutchman Fabian DeFreitas, signed from Osasuna, scoring both goals on his Baggies' home debut, having entered the action as a substitute at Vale Park, the previous week.

At this juncture Hughes was in tip-top form and had already scored six goals.

Then, perhaps surprisingly, Albion suffered four defeats in their next six outings and slipped quickly down to 11th.. The first set-back was at Grimsby where they crashed 5-1 and this was followed by other reverses at home to Bolton Wanderers and Bradford City and away at Oxford. In the Bolton game both Sean Flynn and Kevin Kilbane netted splendid goals but striker Micky Evans was injured and missed the next six matches.

October started brightly enough for Albion with a 4-1 defeat of Watford at The Hawthorns but in their next home game they threw away a two-goal lead and lost to Sunderland.

Results were evenly matched during late October and early November and a crowd of 22,682 saw Albion beat arch rivals Wolves 2-0 in their home local derby at the end of November.

This game against Wolves was to be Alan Miller's last appearance of the season between the posts – he was replaced by £250,000 signing from Oxford United, Phil Whitehead.

From that moment on Albion became something of a hit and miss side – win one, lose one, draw one – and they even suffered another embarrassing defeat in the FA Cup, losing 1-0 at Second Division Bournemouth.

Come mid-January Albion were down in ninth place. But with Hughes still scoring well and heading towards the 30 goal mark a place in the Play-offs was still in their sights.

Sadly though Albion's form dipped during February and March when only two League wins were recorded from eight games, and promotion-chasing Birmingham City won the local derby 4-0 at St Andrew's.

After a 3-0 reverse at Sunderland on 3 April Albion hit rock bottom two days later when they crashed 5-1 at home to bottom of the table Crewe Alexandra. This was their fourth League defeat on the trot and it sparked off some ugly scenes after the final whistle as several very irate and extremely disgruntled supporters demonstrated outside the ground, demanding vociferously that the Board should resign.

Manager Smith persevered in difficult circumstances – as did chairman Tony Hale and his fellow directors – to see the season through.

Albion, in fact, ended the campaign in 12th position after winning just one of their last ten matches (1-0 at home to relegated Bury). They suffered seven defeats in their final eight away games, the exception being a praiseworthy 1-1 draw with arch rivals Wolves at Molineux – a result which severely dented the Molineux club's Play-off hopes.

Incidentally this encounter at Wolves was Albion's 4,000 League game. They played their 2,000th home match the previous week when they drew 2-2 with Portsmouth.

Hot-shot Hughes – who shocked the club by handing in a transfer request on 1 May – finished up as leading scorer with a total of 32 goals; DeFreitas was the second highest with seven. Kevin Kilbane made most League appearances – 44 out of a possible 46 – and the average League attendance at The Hawthorns was 14,582 – a drop of more than 2,000 on the 1997-98 figure…which was a big concern to the Board.

Albion debutants this season were the two Italians – Bortolazzi and Maresca – DeFreitas and Phil Whitehead, teenagers Gabbiadon, Oliver and Justin Richards and winger Mark Angel.

And Jason Van Blerk set a new club record by collecting 13 yellow cards.

On the international scene Kevin Kilbane (Republic of Ireland) and James Quinn (Northern Ireland) both represented their country at senior level; Daniel Gabbiadon played for the Welsh under-21s, likewise Kilbane for the Republic of Ireland under-21 side while at youth team level Adam and James Chambers, besides being the first set of twins ever to play in an Albion team, also became the first twins to appear in the same England side when they came on as substitutes in the Nigeria under 20 international tournament in April 1999.

Teenagers Enzo Maresca (Italy juniors and under 18) and Adam Oliver (England under 18 and under 20) were also honoured this season.

During 1998-99 five Albion players – Chris Adamson (to IK Brage in Sweden and Mansfield Town), defenders Tony Dobson (Gillingham), Paul Mardon (Oldham Athletic) and Paul Raven (Rotherham United) and striker Brian Quailey (Exeter City) – all went out on loan. Dobson later moved to Northampton Town while goalkeeper Paul Crichton was transferred to Burnley and Stacy Coldicott went to Grimsby Town for £100,000.

At Board level Paul Thompson quit in February 1999 to be replaced six weeks later by the former chairman of West Midlands Travel Don Colston.

Albion also swapped goalkeeping coaches – former Irish international Gerry Peyton (appointed October 1998 in place of Eric Steele) being replaced in February by Tony Parks,

the ex-Spurs and Falkirk custodian who was still registered as a player with Scarborough, managed by former Albion No.2 Colin Addison.

Nick Worth (from Burnley) came into the club as the new physiotherapist in place of Paul Mitchell who returned to Grimsby and Albion also employed fitness coach/dietitian Frank Nuttall, who had been a player with Celtic.

Bobby Hope, the former Albion midfield star, became the club's youth development liaison officer under youth development manager John Trewick and this meant that five 1970s playing stalwarts: John Wile, Cyrille Regis, Trewick, Hope and Ally Brown (steward of the nearby Throstles' supporters' club) were all back with Albion in one guise or another.

In the latter months of 1998 two former Albion goalkeepers died – Dick Sheppard (of a heart attack in November) and John Osborne (from cancer in December). In February 1999 Arthur Mann, former Albion assistant-manager, was tragically killed in an accident at his Birmingham place of work involving a fork lift truck. He was 51 and played for Manchester City against Albion in the 1970 League Cup Final at Wembley.

1999-2000

Soon after the 1998-99 League season had ended two established West Bromwich Albion directors – Barry Hurst (on 17 May) and Clive Stapleton (23 May) – both resigned from the board and in the aftermath of their departure leading shareholders, guided by former Albion director and millionaire businessman Paul Thompson, called an Emergency General Meeting scheduled for 8 July, whereby it was anticipated that chairman Tony Hale's position might come under threat.

Thus, at the time of going to print the immediate composition of the Albion board remained unsure.

Also behind the scenes at The

Hawthorns, manager Denis Smith's assistant, Malcolm Crosby, left Albion to take up a coaching position with Premiership club Derby County and into his place Smith was considering upgrading former player and coach Cyrille Regis.

Striker Lee Hughes, who dropped a bombshell shortly before the end of the previous campaign, was offered a substantial pay rise to stay at The Hawthorns.

Ex-Albion player and manager Bobby Gould quit his position as manager of Wales and another former Albion boss, Ossie Ardiles, became manager-coach of Croatia Zagreb.

Meanwhile Albion's playing preparations for the 1999-2000 season began with a tour of Denmark in July and the last campaign of the 20th century commenced in earnest on Saturday, 7 August when Albion entertained Norwich City at The Hawthorns prior to an intriguing Worthington League Cup encounter at Halifax.

Manager Denis Smith and his coaching staff, along with the players, were quietly confident that 1999-2000 would be a good season for Albion. However, in July, Smith left Albion and in August, Brian Little was appointed. But as far as the supporters were concerned, deep down they firmly believed that once again a lot of pressure would be placed on the shoulders of hot-shot Lee Hughes (if he stayed at The Hawthorns).

If he could come up with another 25-30 goals and his fellow strikers could weigh in with a similar number, then who knows what might transpire.

A top six finish is certainly within Albion's capabilities. Anything less would be a major disappointment - again!

So let's hope that Albion can celebrate the year 2000 in style and likewise celebrate their 100th year at The Hawthorns by playing in the Premiership for the first time ever.

Time will tell.

Some Memorable Victories

Football League

6 October 1900 v Manchester City won 3-2 (Division 1)

This was Albion's first League win at The Hawthorns. They took a fourth-minute lead via an Abe Jones header but Albion's 'keeper Joe Reader conceded an own goal five minutes later. Half-way through the first half Billy Richards restored Albion's lead, and on 60 minutes Ben Garfield put away Jack Chadburn's centre before the Billy Holmes got a second for the visitors. City also had two second half goals disallowed, much to Albion's relief.

22 February 902 v Blackpool won 7-2 (Division 2)

On a heavy pitch, Albion extended their unbeaten home run to 12 matches with this excellent victory over the Seasiders. After going a goal down to George Anderson within ten minutes they hit back immediately when Jack Kifford equalised with a splendid free-kick. Tom Worton quickly made it 2-1 and on the half-hour mark Jim Stevenson scored a third goal. In the 34th minute Worton netted Albion's fourth and eight minutes later Chippy Simmons fired in number five, the same player adding a sixth goal just before half-time. Anderson reduced the arrears early in the second period, but Albion wrapped things up with a seventh goal in the 63rd minute through Simmons who clinched his hat-trick. The half-time score of 6-1 is still the highest interval lead held by Albion in any League fixture.

27 September 1902 v Newcastle United won 6-1 (Division 1)

After three straight wins Newcastle were hammered by newly-promoted Albion before 22,160 fans. Billy Lee scored first on three minutes; Fred Buck made it 2-0 15 minutes later and ten minutes after that Chippy Simmons bundled in a third goal. Newcastle pulled one back through Scotsman Bob McColl just on half-time, before Buck hit Albion's fourth goal in the 49th minute. In the 70th minute Jim Stevenson's pile-driver made it 5-1 and after Albion's Jack Kifford had missed a penalty Jimmy McLean ended the scoring with a sixth goal six minutes from time. This result caused something of a sensation in football circles.

22 November 1902 v Blackburn Rovers won 5-3 (Division 1)

With five successive League wins behind them in-form Albion took the lead on three minutes through Billy Lee. A minute later Rovers drew level through Harry Morgan

Billy Lee, who was on target early against both Newcastle and Blackburn.

after 'keeper Ike Webb had been baulked by his own defenders. In the 21st minute Simmons headed in Worton's centre for Albion's lead, only for Rovers to equalise again through George Robertson, assisted by Billy Bow. And it was the visitors who scored next, Arnold Whittaker finding the net via the crossbar. Rovers played with ten men in the second half and Albion capitalised on this, drawing level in the 51st minute when Kifford followed up his penalty kick to toe-end the ball past 'keeper Billy Joyce. Stevenson made it 4-3 with 20 minutes remaining and Worton added a fifth goal towards the end.

24 September 1904 v Doncaster Rovers won 6-1 (Division 2)

Only 5,261 spectators turned up for this game, and they had to endure a tedious first half when Albion scored once – on 20 minutes when George Dorsett's shot-cum-centre flew into the net after deflecting off Harry Aston's shoulder. After the break however, Albion were unstoppable and they gave Rovers a real walloping. In the 50th minute Bill Davies' corner was converted by Dorsett; on the hour mark another delightful Davies flag-kick led to Albert Lewis finding the net and in the 67th minute Walter Jack headed in Aston's cross for 4-0. A fine dribble and shot by in-form Dorsett made it 5-0 in the 75th minute and with ten minutes left Jack scored again from Davies' cross. Len Hyde pulled a goal back for Rovers with time running out.

11 November 1905 v Bradford City won 6-1 (Division 2)

Albion, with four straight wins under their belts, scored twice in the first ten minutes through Fred Shinton, and Adam Haywood. In the 33rd minute Andy McGeachan replied for Bradford from a corner, but two minutes later Shinton made it 3-1. It was all Albion in the second half. Simmons lashed in a rebound to make it 4-1 and after City's Jack Halliday had gone off and Jimmy Conlin was sent-off, Albion made good use of the space to score twice more through Shinton and Simmons. The attendance was 9,000.

26 December 1905 v Barnsley won 5-3 (Division 2)

An eventful encounter saw Albion, unbeaten in 11 games, twice come from behind despite playing the last 40 minutes with only ten men. Barnsley scored first in the tenth minute after a defensive mix-up but

Fred Shinton was in terrific form for Albion in the 1900s and in the games against Bradford City, Barnsley and Grimsby he especially shone.

Simmons quickly equalised. In the 22nd minute Billy Law crossed for Shinton to put Albion in front. But back came Barnsley who drew level right on half-time. After Albion had been reduced to ten men when George Young went off injured, Jack Manners sliced the ball into his own net to put visitors ahead at 3-2. But urged on by 23,021 fans, they were level through Shinton on 72 minutes and four minutes later Simmons put Albion in front at 4-3. Simmons then completed his hat-trick to give Albion a fine win.

25 December 1906 v Grimsby Town won 6-1 (Division 2)

Over 19,000 fans saw Albion make it six home wins on the trot. Tom Dilly scored the Baggies' opening goal on 15 minutes. Two minutes later Adam Haywood added a second from Dilly's pass and four minutes after that Shinton fired in number three. Grimsby's Fred Robinson reduced the deficit with a header on 50 minutes before hot-shot Shinton scored three fine goals in 12 minutes

21 December 1907 v Lincoln City won 5-2 (Division 2)

In front of 7,000 fans, Albion fell behind to a Billy Langham goal on 25 minutes. But soon afterwards Buck was tripped in the area, and the same player got up to score from the spot. Albion ran the show after and in the 77th minute David Walker gave them the lead. Two minutes later Jordan made it 3-1. Lincoln hit back and after Jesse Pennington had miskicked Langham scored his second goal. Albion were then awarded a second penalty but this time Jim Saunders saved Buck's shot. Amazingly two minutes later Albion got a third spot kick and this time Walker scored with ease. Harry Wilcox rounded things off with a fifth goal on 88 minutes. Thus in a 12 minute spell five goals (one a penalty) were netted and another penalty missed.

2 January 1909 v Grimsby Town won 7-0 (Division 2)

Albion extended their unbeaten League run to 13 matches with this crushing win over the Mariners. Kicking with the wind towards the Birmingham Road goal, Albion got off to a flying start on a heavy pitch when debutant Sid Bowser latched on to a Buck pass to score in the second minute. On 15 minutes Bill Garraty set up Bowser for goal number two and after Buck had shot wide from the penalty spot on 27 minutes Garraty swept in Albion's third goal ten minutes from half-time.

Another smart goal from Buck followed in the 48th minute and 24 minutes later Albion were 5-0 up thanks to a terrific long range shot by Jack Manners. Sixty seconds later, with Grimsby's defence in tatters, Thompson's centre was put away by

to sew up the points, the impressive Haywood assisting in all of them.

Garraty and two minutes from time Bill Davies' inch-perfect pass was forced in by Thompson.

5 November 1910 v Leicester Fosse won 5-1 (Division 2)

A crowd of 15,200 saw Albion, undefeated in eight matches, make a flying start, Bowser scoring in the seventh minute from Pennington's free-kick. Amos Lloyd made it 2-0 in the 20th minute and the same player scored again five minutes from half-time. Straight after half-time Leicester reduced the arrears through Fred Osborn, but in the 68th minute Albion went 4-1 up through Billy Wollaston. Three minutes later Lloyd was brought down inside the area and Buck smashed in the penalty to end the scoring. This impressive victory signalled to the rest of the Second Division that Albion's youngsters meant business in then promotion stakes and so it proved to be.

29 April 1911 v Huddersfield Town won 1-0 (Division 2)

This win clinched promotion for Albion after seven years in the Second Division and the best crowd of the season, 30,135, saw them do it.

Albion had to go out and beat Huddersfield; a draw would have been enough but the players weren't to know that at the time.

At the time of kick-off Albion led the Division with 51 points from 37 games; Chelsea and Bolton Wanderers were second and third respectively, each with 49 points from 36 matches.

Albion defended the Smethwick End in the first half and after winning half-a-dozen free-kicks and going close on a couple of occasions, they took the lead in the 26th minute when Huddersfield defender Fred Bullock fouled Billy Thompson inside the penalty area.

Skipper Fred Buck took the spot-kick, firing the ball straight through the legs of Welsh international goalkeeper Dr Leigh Richmond Roose.

Albion defended for long periods in the second half but with Joe Smith, Jesse Pennington, Jack Manners and Bobby McNedal outstanding they were able to hold on to record a famous victory, which was made all that much sweeter as Chelsea lost to Gainsborough Trinity and Bolton succumbed at Birmingham. Aston Villa were also defeated at Anfield, allowing Manchester United to win the First Division title.

Fred Buck, depicted here by an artist whose work appeared in Albion News, scored the match-winning penalty against Huddersfield in April 1911.

24 March 1913 v Tottenham Hotspur 4-1 (Division 1)

On a glorious sunny day Albion and Spurs put on a grand show with the Baggies running out deserving winners in front of a near 14,000 crowd.

For Albion it was their first win of the year and they opened the scoring on 11 minutes when Bowser netted after Ben Shearman's effort had been partially cleared. After some exciting moments Spurs equalised through Herbert Bliss just after the half-hour mark following a collision between Albion 'keeper Len Moorwood and Arthur Grimsdell. Six minutes later the Baggies regained the lead when Shearman

SOME MEMORABLE VICTORIES

107

scored with a low drive to the keeper's right. Bob Pailor made it 3-1 on 52 minutes with a splendid shot from distance and the same player scored again 12 minutes later with another powerful drive. Boswer then hit the post as Albion kept up the pressure.

26 September 1914 v Liverpool won 4-0 (Division 1)

Over 18,000 fans, some of them Belgian refugees, saw Liverpool, runners-up in the FA Cup Final only five months earlier, blitzed by a keen Albion side for whom England amateur international Harold Bache played superbly well. Alf Bentley opened the scoring on 13 minutes after some fine work by Bache and Fred Morris.

Morris then nipped in with a second goal on 40 minutes following some clever play by Shearman and Bache. Nine minutes after the restart Morris netted his second and Albion's third goal from Louis Bookman's centre and with ten minutes remaining Bentley added a fourth with a 12-yard shot.

Sadly, just over 16 months later, Harold Bache, who made such a sensational impact in this match as an unorthodox centre-forward, lay dead on a Flanders battlefield.

25 October 1919 v Notts County won 8-0 (Division 1)

Albion, minus four key players but with eight wins to their credit from their first ten matches, outplayed County before a 36,086 crowd with Morris scoring five goals. His first came in the ninth minute when he blasted Howard Gregory's pass beyond Albert Iremonger in the County goal. His second – after enormous Albion pressure – arrived in the 40th minute when he netted confidently after a fine 35-yard solo run. In the 51st minute he completed his hat-trick with another well-

Fred Morris scored five goals against Notts County in October 1919.

taken shot following Gregory's adroit square ball, and then County's defender Jack Foster turned Jack Crisp's centre into his own net to make it 4-0 after 61 minutes. Morris duly added two more goals in quick succession – his fourth in 70th minute was set up by the marauding Crisp (making it 11 goals in 11 games for the striker) and two minutes later he put Albion 6-0 in front after Crisp had again manufactured an opening. Gregory sneaked in unnoticed to claim Albion's seventh goal in the 79th minute after Morris had struck the bar and with five minutes remaining Tommy Magee notched number eight, darting through a huge gap in the County defence to score with ease.

26 December 1919 v Sunderland won 4-0 (Division 1)

A crowd of 43,579 saw this Boxing Day encounter at a rain-swept Hawthorns and it was Albion who pulled all the crackers on their way to a first ever Division One champi-

onship, to record their fifth successive League victory.

Their first goal came on 14 minutes when Magee scored a disputed goal after he cashed in on a weak back pass by Bob Young. It was tit-for-tat up to the break but then it was all Albion. In the 52nd minute Morris put away a back-header from Bentley following Crisp's cross. In the 75th minute Gregory sent Morris through for his second goal and two minutes from time Bentley scored from six yards. Bobby McNeal's shot almost split the crossbar in the closing minutes and Crisp had a 'goal' ruled out for offside right at the death.

1 May 1920 v Chelsea won 4-0 (Division 1)

Before kick-off the First Division championship trophy was presented to Albion's skipper Pennington, who proudly held it aloft to the delight of the home supporters in the 35,668 crowd.

Albion had already scored 100 League goals prior to this game, needing one more to beat Sunderland's record for most in the top Division …and they did just that on 17 minutes when McNeal, bursting into the penalty area, hammered the ball home from 12 yards after excellent work by Andy Smith, Gregory and Morris.

Albion's second goal arrived in the 46th minute. A long cross, pumped high into the air by Crisp, was headed on by Gregory. Chelsea's 'keeper Jim Molyneux palmed the ball away, but the referee and linesman agreed that it had crossed the line.

Four minutes, Smith, moving on to Morris's short pass, cracked in a beauty from 15 yards and in the 58th minute Bentley scored from close range after Gregory and Crisp and teased the Chelsea defence.

100 YEARS AT THE HAWTHORNS

30 October 1920 v Huddersfield Town won 3-0 (Division 1)

After crashing to a 5-1 defeat at Huddersfield seven days earlier, Albion turned things round in the return fixture and whipped the Terriers 3-0 in front of 44,049 fans. After a tentative start, Albion went in front on 15 minutes when Bowser cracked home a penalty past keeper Alex Mutch after Andy Smith had been brought down. Smith himself tucked in number two with sweet aplomb in the 63rd minute and a minute later Morris, moving on to Claude Jephcott's pass, made it 3-0.

14 October 1922 v Arsenal won 7-0 (Division 1)

Albion lost 3-1 at Highbury seven days before this fixture and were determined to gain sweet revenge – and they did just that in fine style with a very professional perfor-

Jack Crisp scored twice in the seven-goal mauling of Arsenal in October 1922.

mance. Arsenal set the early pace but against the run of play Morris scored twice in the space of three minutes either side of the half-hour mark to put Albion in control. Arsenal came back and dictated play

on 37 minutes after some fine work by Morris and Gregory, and the same player added a second three minutes after the interval when he blasted the ball home after a defensive mistake. Gregory made it 3-0 in the 53rd minute from Magee's long pass and Blood completed his hat-trick with 11 minutes remaining, cracking the ball home right-footed after Jimmy Spencer had created space. Morris's excellent 82nd minute strike – from Blood's pass – gave Albion a nap hand.

for long periods, but it was Albion who ended with a flourish, netting five more goals between the 71st and 84th minutes at the Smethwick end through Morris, who claimed two more, Crisp (2) and the impressive Gregory.

24 November 1923 v Everton won 5-0 (Division 1)

On a bitterly cold day Everton's goalkeeper Tommy Fern made three fine saves early on, but then the visitors lost right-back John McDonald with a broken nose and Albion took over. Bob Blood opened the scoring

Bob Blood hit a hat-trick against Everton in November 1923.

for Albion in front George James put Albion in front after just five seconds – the fastest goal ever scored at The Hawthorns. It was 2-0 after four minutes when Joe Carter scored from Jack Byers' centre. Forest, with the wind behind them, hit back through Irish international Pat Nelis in the 33rd minute from a disputed corner. Three minutes into the second half Albion went 3-1 up when James netted from 'Tug' Wilson's pass. Gibson then hit a post for Forest before James fired home Tommy Glidden's centre in the 65th minute to complete his hat-trick. The same player

13 December 1924 v Nottingham Forest won 5-1 (Division 1)

The Albion forward line which hammered Forest in December 1924. From left to right are Tommy Glidden, Joe Carter, George Jones, Tug Wilson and Jack Byers.

SOME MEMORABLE VICTORIES

made it 5-1 seven minutes from time with a drive from 20 yards. An attendance of 16,227 saw Albion go to the top of the table after this result.

24 October 1925 v West Ham United won 7-1 (Division 1)

After winning only three of their opening ten League games of the season Albion had the better of the first half and led 3-0 at the interval. In the 22nd minute Hammers' left-half Albert Cadwell handled, allowing Stan Davies to net the spot-kick. Six minutes later Glidden scored with a fine cross-shot from Carter's pass and two minutes before the break Davies fired home from Glidden's centre. Seven minutes into the second half 'Tug' Wilson hit Albion's fourth goal and in the 64th minute – after Glidden had struck

the bar – Carter made it 4-0. Jimmy Ruffell reduced Albion's lead in the 73rd minute with a penalty after a foul by Fred Reed on Watson. But Albion scored twice more through Davies (his hat-trick) in the 79th minute and Carter in the 81st to win in a canter. The attendance was 20,851.

12 March 1927 v Aston Villa won 6-2 (Division 1)

On a chilly but bright afternoon in front of 50,392 fans Albion won the toss and attacked the Smethwick End. After dominating the first half, they had only one goal to show for their efforts, a 21st-minute shot from Glidden. Carter put Albion 2-0 up in the 50th minute and nine minutes later Davies netted from close range. Just past the hour mark Davies slammed in Albion's fourth

goal and two minutes later Glidden made it 5-0. Villa reduced the deficit through Dicky York in the 73rd minute, but Sammy Short restored Albion's five-goal lead on 83 minutes, only for York to round off the scoring with a late strike for outplayed Villa. Remarkably, at this stage in the season, Villa were in fifth place and Albion last and doomed to relegation.

17 September 1927 v Blackpool won 6-3 (Division 2)

This game was a triumph for Albion's centre-forward Jimmy Cookson who scored a double hat-trick. A crowd of 20,203 saw him claim his first goal in the sixth minute before Blackpool drew level through Sid Tuffnell on 33. In the second half it was action all the way. In the 47th minute Peter Thorpe handled and Cookson smashed in the penalty. Ten minutes later Cookson completed his first 'hat-trick' by gliding in a Glidden pass. Tuffnell reduced the arrears, but then Cookson blasted in his second hat-trick in the space of seven min-

Jimmy Cookson, scorer of all six goals when Blackpool came under the hammer in September 1927.

utes to give Albion a commanding 6-1 lead. In the 63rd minute he netted from close range; then he reacted quickly to net a rebound and in the 70th minute fired in Wilson's pass. Blackpool came again and Horace Williams made it 6-3 with a 35 yarder ten minutes from time. Just before the end Cookson had a seventh 'goal' disallowed for offside, a somewhat questionable decision.

23 February 1929 v Barnsley 6-2 (Division 2)

After a series of mediocre performances Albion at last put on a superb show of attacking football in front of 13,810 spectators to overwhelm the Tykes. Defending the Birmingham Road goal Albion took the lead on ten minutes when George Shaw netted a penalty after Bill Batty had handled Glidden's shot. In the 20th minute, Cookson's effort rebounded to Gale. He passed to Glidden who netted from 25 yards. Barnsley's Frank Eaton reduced the arrears three minutes

Tommy Glidden scored twice against Barnsley in February 1929. He ended the season with 21 goals in 40 League games.

later after Jimmy Proudfoot's shot had been saved by 'keeper George Ashmore, but the limping Carter made it 3-1 with a perfect header from Stan Wood's cross on 58 minutes and 90 seconds later Glidden raced away to add number four. A penalty by Batty (after a push by centre-half Bill Richardson) saw Barnsley get back to 4-2 in the 72nd minute only for Cookson to score a gem to make it 5-2 11 minutes later. In the last minute Harry Chambers struck a post and Cookson was there to net the rebound.

28 December 1929 v Wolverhampton Wanderers 7-3 (Division 2)

A moderate crowd of 20,211 saw this local derby. Albion, having beat Millwall 6-1 just 48 hours earlier were in top form and went in front after three minutes when defender Joe Evans, up for a corner, headed Glidden's second centre wide of 'keeper Billy Walker. Seven minutes later Frank Cresswell made it 2-0 when his 20-yard shot flew into the net off Harry Shaw. Billy Barraclough crossed for Walter Featherby to make it 2-1 in the 18th minute but two minutes later a move involving Wood and W. G. Richardson was finished off by Glidden (3-1). Soon after this Wolves' debutant 'keeper Walker raced out to meet Glidden. Both players kicked at the ball but Walker came off worst, shattering his right ankle. Centre-half Harry Marshall went in goal but was quickly replaced by Albert Kay, and two minutes later a long clearance by him led to Bob White making it 3-2. Albion went 4-2 up a minute into the second when Wood's low centre was missed by Richardson but not by Carter, and five minutes later a shot from Richardson was deflected into his own net by Shaw. On the hour Cresswell scored

from Wood's telling pass (6-2) and the same player then supplied the cross for Carter to head in number seven. Wolves rallied and Mark Crook laid on a 77th minute consolation goal for Jimmy Deacon.

19 April 1930 v Hull City 7-1 (Division 2)

The Hawthorns pitch resembled a quagmire but Albion were a revelation as they played 'perfect football' to win in style. A shade over 10,000 fans saw three goals in the first quarter of the game: Glidden (4 minutes), Cookson (16) and Glidden again (22) all netting with quality drives. Straight after half-time Cookson made it 4-0 with another clinical finish from Harry Boston's centre and the same player completed his hat-trick with another fine strike on 67 minutes after neat work by Glidden. A breakaway goal by Bertie Mills reduced the deficit three minutes later but hot-shot Cookson (74 minutes) from Wood's clever pass and Boston with a cracking half-volley (76) rounded off the scoring. Prior to this game Albion had won three League in succession; they won another seven after this encounter, making it 11 all told – a club record.

26 December 1930 v Barnsley 5-0 (Division 2)

Having drawn 0-0 with Barnsley at Oakwell 24 hours earlier, this return fixture turned out to be a canter – yet the scoreline did not represent Albion's supremacy. Admittedly Barnsley went down to ten men after 60 minutes when centre-half George Henderson was injured but by that time they were a well beaten side.

W. G. Richardson opened the scoring on 20 minutes with a simple goal after a defensive mix-up. A minute into the second half Wood cut in and made it 2-0 before

SOME MEMORABLE VICTORIES

W. G. Richardson heads home Glidden's right-wing cross against Charlton at The Hawthorns in May 1931 – and Albion have achieved the unique double of FA Cup and promotion.

Glidden drilled in number three after Richardson had done the spade-work. A George Shaw penalty – awarded for a foul on Glidden – put Albion 4-0 ahead on 77 minutes and Glidden completed the rout with a fifth goal a minute from time.

2 May 1931 v Charlton Athletic won 3-2 (Division 2)

Having beaten Birmingham 2-1 at Wembley the previous Saturday and

stuck to their task and a minute before half-time Glidden equalised. The second half was nerve-wracking, and it was Albion who grabbed the all-important goal in the 68th minute when W. G. Richardson headed Glidden's right-wing cross beyond 'keeper Robertson to clinch victory – and the double.

3 October 1931 v Derby County 4-0 (Division 1)

In front of the biggest crowd at The Hawthorns so far this season – 33,192 – Albion, with only two defeats against them in their previous 13 League games, put on an excellent display to beat a dogged County side who gave as good as they got in the first half. All four goals were splendidly taken, even Shaw's penalty opener on two minutes. Skipper Glidden fired in number two five minutes after half-time; Sandford rattled in Albion's third from 25 yards two minutes later and right on time W. G. Richardson ran forward to slot in number four after good work by Stan Wood.

26 December 1932 v Sunderland 5-1 (Division 1)

A crowd of 26,113 attended this Boxing Day treat and those present

followed up with a crucial 1-0 League win at Stoke on Thursday afternoon, Albion had to win this final game of the season to clinch that unique FA Cup and promotion double, and 52,415 fans saw them do just that. Dai Astley put the visitors ahead after eight minutes. Albion equalised in the 37th minute through Teddy Sandford only for Astley to edge Charlton back in front 45 seconds later. But Albion

Joe Carter helped Albion to a fine Boxing Day win over Sunderland in 1932.

Albion's Cup winning players are introduced to the crowd before beating Charlton to take the 1931 double.

saw Albion, with four defeats in the previous six matches, play some delightful football with wing-halves Jimmy Murphy and Jimmy Edwards in splendid form. Albion's first goal after 30 minutes was a real gem from W. G. Richardson. Two minutes later, after some smart interplay involving three players, Richardson made it 2-0 before a cleverly directed header by Joe Carter seven minutes from half-time put Albion in control at 3-0. Scottish international Ben Yorston then scored for the visitors with a cunning right-foot shot, only for Walter Robbins to hammer in a fourth goal for Albion which was followed late on by Richardson's hat-trick.

6 October 1934 v Leeds United won 6-3 (Division 1)

This game was full of creative, attacking football, played on slippery turf in front of 15,843 cold spectators. Albion, who had netted 13 goals in the previous five games, played well and always had the edge over their dogged opponents. The Leeds 'keeper was to blame early on when he allowed W. G. Richardson to score twice for Albion in the 14th and 16th minutes, each time from close range. On 32 minutes Albion's wing-half Murphy fouled Tommy Cochrane, allowing Jack Milburn to net the penalty (2-1). But three minutes later Albion regained their two-goal advantage when Sandford set up Richardson for his hat-trick. After both teams had hit the woodwork Boyes swooped on a defensive blunder to make it 4-1 on 74 minutes and almost immediately Joe Carter took Murphy's pass in his stride to put Albion 5-1 in front. Jack Mahon (later to join Albion) pulled a goal back for Leeds two minutes later, only for Richardson to pounce again from Sandford's pass to make it 6-2. With time running out Irish international Harry Duggan grabbed a third for a dejected Leeds side.

24 March 1934 v Sunderland 6-5 (Division 1)

Despite Albion having lost four successive League games this was a classic encounter, a great game of football, played on a soft pitch yet witnessed by only 11,889 fans.

Seven goals were scored in the first half. Carter set up W. G. Richardson on 55 seconds for Albion's first and after Bob Gurney had equalised with a scrappy effort in the seventh minute, Wally Boyes edged Albion back in front after Richardson had sold a dummy to allow Carter's centre to run through to the winger. Raich Carter's 20-yard rocket brought the scores level at 2-2 halfway through the first-half and two minutes later the unmarked Gurney put the visitors ahead. Back came Albion and in on 33 minutes Glidden cut in from the right to slam the ball past 'keeper Matthew Middleton and three minutes from the interval Glidden's curling corner was headed in by the alert Carter.

A period of calm then prevailed before the goals rained down again. On 75 minutes Raich Carter was fouled on the edge of the area by Bob Finch and Harry Shaw bent in the equaliser. Five minutes later Sandford rifled in a penalty after Boyes had been floored by Bill Murray and on 85 minutes it was 6-4 when Glidden's looping cross was missed by Richardson only for the ball to creep inside Middleton's far post. Three minutes later Gurney made it 6-5 and right on time the Sunderland man should have equalised but missed the target from three yards.

5 January 1935 v Middlesbrough won 6-3 (Division 1)

After three successive defeats a crowd of 18,582 saw Albion get back to winning ways with a fine display against a useful Middlesbrough outfit who were in the hunt right up until the last quarter of an intriguing match.

Arthur Gale's smart pass laid on Albion's opening goal for W. G. Richardson inside the first minute and after Middlesbrough had drawn level in the fifth minute with George Camsell's penalty (awarded after he

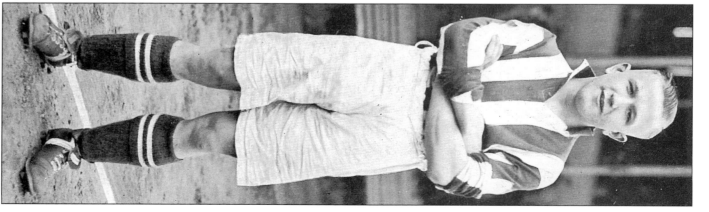

Wally Boyes, one of the stars of the victory over Leeds United in October 1934.

Arthur Gale laid on a goal for W. G. Richardson and then scored himself with a diving header against Middlesbrough in January 1935.

was fouled by Bert Trentham) Boyes fired Albion back in front from Richardson's neat through ball. Boyes' cross was converted by Gale's diving header on 27 minutes (3-1) and five minutes after the interval Camsell burst through to make it 3-2. The 'Boro centre-forward then had a goal disallowed before Sandford beat two defenders to slam in Albion's fourth goal, only for Ernie Coleman to reduce the score to 4-3 on 67 minutes. But Albion had the final say with two more goals – a 25-yard special fired into the top right-hand corner of the net by Sandford and an excellent over-head hook shot from Carter.

7 December 1935 v Everton won 6-1 (Division 1)

Before taking on Everton Albion had lost three games on the bounce, scoring only one goal, but in front of 17,151 fans they hit top form and ran up a convincing 6-1 scoreline which could easily have been doubled – all this after the Merseysiders had taken a shock third-minute lead when Jimmy Cunliffe tucked away Dixie Dean's headed pass.

Albion responded quickly and within 40 seconds W. G. Richardson had equalised from Wood's inviting centre. Two minutes later Carter's through ball was hammered home by winger Mahon and on the quarter-of-an-hour mark Richardson notched his second goal and Albion's fourth when he drove home Cookson's pass. At this juncture Albion were flying. Visiting 'keeper Ted Sagar then made three fine saves before Sandford, after beating three defenders, saw his 20-yard drive saved but followed up to net the rebound on 36 minutes.

Everton were stunned again four minutes before half-time when Carter scored following a deep free-kick by Shaw and another Sandford shot. Albion continued to press in the second half but managed only one more goal – Mahon blasting home Richardson's right-wing corner in the 53rd minute.

18 January 1936 v Blackburn Rovers won 8-1 (Division 1)

After scoring ten goals in the previous two home games, Albion were unstoppable against Rovers and netted another five in the first 20 minutes.

On seven minutes two Rovers' defenders – Jimmy Gorman and Arnold Whiteside – kicked at the ball together. It flew to W. G. Richardson who netted from close range. Fifty seconds later Mahon, free on the left, fired home number two via an upright.

In the tenth minute Richardson made a goal for Walter Robbins and five minutes later Mahon, cutting inside his full-back, scored also off a post as 'keeper Cliff Binns slipped.

In the 20th minute, a stinging drive by Sandford was spilled by Binns and Jack Sankey was on hand to fire home a half-volley.

In a rare attack Rovers pulled a goal back on 30 minutes when Jack Thompson smashed in a penalty after Trentham had handled, Thompson having put the ball in the net initially.

After the break Albion came again and in the 59th minute, Stan Wood's splendid cross was crashed home left-footed by Richardson. The same player then completed his hat-trick in the 78th minute, finding the net with a stinging 20-yard drive.

Albion's eighth and final goal was claimed by Mahon in the 89th minute, the winger scoring easily from Sandford's pass to claim his hat-trick.

1 February 1936 v Liverpool won 6-1 (Division 1)

A fortnight after that superb victory over Blackburn, Albion were back on the goal-trail with another great home win, this time over Liverpool in front of 23,080 spectators.

Albion scored first on four minutes when Wood's low centre from the left was fired in by W. G. Richardson. But Liverpool hit back and equalised on 11 minutes when Jack Balmer converted Freddie Howe's precise cross.

Four minutes later Albion regained the lead through Mahon, who found space to net Wood's low pass. Albion continued to dominate; Richardson and Carter hit the woodwork and Liverpool's giant South African goalkeeper Arthur Riley made three stunning saves in quick succession.

Seven minutes into the second half Richardson whipped in Sandford's pass to make it 3-1 and seven minutes later Albion's centre-forward drilled in Wood's centre for his hat-trick.

Liverpool were dead and buried at this stage and in the last six minutes Wood capped a superb afternoon's work by scoring two brilliant individual goals, twice racing away from the halfway line with defenders chasing after him.

Victory brought Albion's goal tally to 31 in six home matches, and in their next game they beat Leeds United 3-2.

27 February 1937 v Sunderland won 6-4 (Division 1)

Three years earlier Albion and Sunderland were involved in an 11-goal bonanza; this time 25,267 fans saw an equally exciting contest with the Baggies narrow winners once again.

On a heavy pitch the opening exchanges were even but then the goals started to arrive. On 30 minutes the ever-alert W. G. Richardson pounced to put Albion in front. League champions Sunderland, who went on to win the FA Cup this season, responded quickly and within five minutes Eddie Burbanks had levelled the scores following a weak back-pass by Bob Finch.

Two minutes later Raich Carter put the visitors in front with a crisp finish and straightaway Harry Jones was felled inside the box, but Sandford's weak penalty was saved by Johnny Mapson. After Boyes had equalised for Albion a minute into the second half, winger Lol Coen, playing only his third League game, put the Baggies back into the lead from Jones' flick on. But direct from the kick-off Carter, unmarked in the area, cracked home Sunderland's equaliser.

On 58 minutes Coen was fouled inside the penalty area and this time Cecil Shaw rapped home the spot-kick to give Albion a 4-3 lead. This was extended to 5-3 on 72 minutes when Jones scored from 12 yards and eight minutes later the same player made the score 6-3. Len Duns, a wartime guest with Albion, scored a fourth goal for a weary Sunderland side after Albion's keeper Jimmy Adams had brilliantly saved Carter's penalty following handball against Finch.

19 February 1938 v Liverpool won 5-1 (Division 1)

A crowd of 17,565 saw this well deserved Albion victory. With only one win in their previous nine League games Albion made a hesitant start before going into overdrive. In the 20th minute Jack Mahon's cross caught the Liverpool 'keeper Riley in two minds and W. G. Richardson darted forward to head home

(1-0). In the 36th minute, Cecil Shaw brought the ball 40 yards upfield before releasing Joe Johnson down the left. His cross was neatly lobbed home by Ike Clarke. In the 49th minute it was 3-0 when Johnson

The prolific W. G. Richardson scored a hat-trick against Liverpool in February 1936.

went on to win the FA Cup this season, responded quickly and within five minutes Eddie Burbanks had levelled the scores following a weak back-pass by Bob Finch.

tapped in after Richardson has missed Mahon's low cross from the right. Jack Balmer reduced the arrears in the 58th minute, converting Berry Nieuwenhuys' dipping centre, but seven minutes later Richardson fired in Johnson's left-winger cross to restore Albion's three-goal advantage.

Four minutes from time Richardson completed his hat-trick with a sharp finish after Johnson's left-wing centre had been knocked back into the middle by Mahon.

11 March 1939 v Bury won 6-0 (Division 2)

This was Albion's last six-goal romp before World War Two.

Bury, deep in relegation trouble in Division Two, were outplayed for long periods and, indeed, could have lost by a bigger margin had it not been for goalkeeper George Bradshaw who pulled off half-a-dozen splendid saves. Clarke netted Albion's first goal on 13 minutes

Ike Clarke, scored with a neat lob against Liverpool in February 1938.

with an 18-yard drive. Sammy Heaselgrave made it

2-0 with a downward header in the 36th minute from Johnson's high corner and three minutes later Johnson himself cut in from the left to grab Albion's third.

Albion's 'keeper Jimmy Adams then saved Reg Halton's 50th minute penalty, awarded for a foul by Sankey on Les Hart, before Johnson whipped in an unstoppable cross shot in the 61st minute to give his side a 4-0 lead.

Johnson was on fire at this stage and on 76 minutes he completed his first Albion hat-trick following a goalmouth melee, and eight minutes from time the England left-winger notched his fourth goal and Albion's sixth, by tapping home from close range after Harry Jones had bent the crossbar with a superb right-footed shot.

Ten minutes after half-time Albion made it 4-1 when Walsh set up Clarke. He laid the ball off to Ray Barlow who scored to the 'keeper's right.

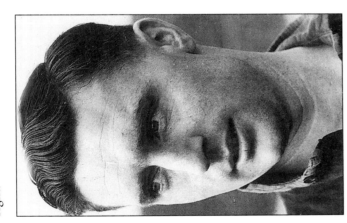

Dave Walsh held off two defenders to score in the 6-1 win over Fulham in November 1946.

23 November 1946 v Fulham won 6-1 (Division 2)

A crowd of 20,243 saw Albion's forward-line in sparkling form against the Cottagers, whose defenders were fully extended as they tried to stop the flood of attacks.

Albion took the lead on seven minutes when Clarke headed in full-back Shaw's deep free-kick from the left. Four minutes later it was 2-0 when Irish international Dave Walsh, taking Clarke's pass in his stride, held off two challenges to fire low past 'keeper Ted Hinton.

On 16 minutes Billy Elliott crossed from the right, Walsh's header was parried by Hinton, but Clarke was on hand to find the net.

Fulham clawed a goal back in the 35th minute when Albion's debutant 'keeper Tom Grimley let Ronnie Rooke's shot slip from his grasp and Bob Thomas netted from eight yards.

Taylor for Albion's third goal six minutes after half-time, before Arthur Rowley hit a post with a 55th minute penalty after Bradford's goalkeeper Tom Farr had brought down Taylor.

Five minutes later though, Haines scored a brilliant fourth goal for Albion from Taylor's astute pass and in the 69th minute Taylor netted himself from Rowley's through ball. With time running out Haines completed his hat-trick by converting Finch's centre with aplomb.

16 April 1949 v Bradford won 7-1 (Division 2)

Twelve months on and luckless Bradford were on the receiving end of another brilliant Albion display. With the Baggies going for promotion, over 39,000 fans saw them rattle in five goals in a marvellous 17-minute spell during the first-half.

In the 15th minute Walsh tucked home Barlow's delightful pass; five minutes later Roy White handled Elliott's centre and Walsh banged home the penalty; in the 23rd minute Walsh fed Haines who netted superbly on the run; on 28 minutes Walsh scored a brilliant individual goal, beating Les Horsman before tricking 'keeper Tom Farr and finishing deftly, and in the 32nd minute Haines fired home from 15 yards after Walsh had done the hard work. Hugh Morrow made it 6-0 in the 47th minute (from Haines' pass) before George Ainsley pulled a goal back for Bradford while Albion's centre-half Jack Vernon was receiving treatment on the touchline. Six minutes from time Walsh grabbed his fourth goal of the game after outwitting three defenders following Elliott's quick throw-in.

9 September 1950 v Portsmouth won 5-0 (Division 1)

A crowd of 34,460 saw Albion completely annihilate the League cham-

In the 64th minute Elliott and Clarke combined down the right, allowing Frank Hodgetts to steal in from the left to net from close range (5-1) and in the 85th minute Doug Witcomb centred for Barlow to score his second of the match and give Albion a 6-1 win.

17 April 1948 v Bradford won 6-0 (Division 2)

Having registered just two wins in their previous 12 League games and three in their last 18, this was a long overdue success for Albion, whose performance in front of 13,349 fans was one of their best for some considerable time. Yet surprisingly it took the Baggies over 20 minutes to score their first goal.

Following a series of attacks down the right, Arthur Taylor's persistence enabled Jack Haines to fire Albion in front in the 23rd minute. Just 90 seconds later Haines' pass was converted by Roy Finch (2-0). Finch then set up the hard-working

Ronnie Allen's second goal against Chelsea in October 1953.

pions Portsmouth, making them look like second-raters.

This was the first time Albion had scored five goals since returning to the First Division – and it may well have been more.

Albion took time to settle but once in control they played some excellent football before taking the lead in the 42nd minute, Walsh netting with an overhead kick from Elliott's centre.

Forty-five seconds later it was 2-0 as Walsh fed a short pass to Cyril Williams who then set up Elliott to finish powerfully.

Three minutes after the interval a perfect Ronnie Allen centre was headed home by Williams and although Pompey refused to knuckle under their spasmodic attacks were easily dealt with by Albion's defence. 'Man of the Match' Arthur Smith – with two classical finishes – made it 4-0 and then 5-0 in the 66th and 87th minutes, both goals set up by some fine interplay involving Walsh, Williams and Elliott. Just over 12 months later Albion repeated this dose again, hammering Portsmouth by the same score-line on the same pitch.

24 October 1953 v Chelsea won 5-2 (Division 1)

This was a cracking match seen by 35,443 spectators. For Albion it brought them their fifth straight win and their 12th of the season in only 15 games.

Vic Buckingham's men began well and from Frank Griffin's right-wing corner in the tenth minute Allen scored with a great swivelling volley. Two minutes later George Lee put in a cross from the left, the Chelsea defenders failed to clear and Allen drove the ball home (2-0). In the 17th minute Roy Bentley pulled a goal back for Chelsea from Eric Parsons' right-wing cross and the same combination brought the Londoners a shock equaliser six minutes from half-time.

In the second half though it was all Albion. In the 52nd minute another Griffin corner was rifled home by Allen; on the hour mark Johnny Nicholls chased a long clearance deep into the Chelsea half before scoring sweetly after a mis-kick by John Saunders, and with seven minutes left 'Ada' Lee raced away unchallenged to score Albion's fifth with a low drive from the edge of the area.

21 November 1953 v Cardiff City won 6-1 (Division 1)

A month after that excellent treble against Chelsea, Allen went one better with a four-timer against Cardiff City. In front of 39,618 fans, Albion found themselves a goal down inside six minutes when Ken Chisholm headed in at the far post.

SOME MEMORABLE VICTORIES

hat-trick goal (his third of the season) and six minutes into the second half hot-shot Allen made it 4-1 with a sweetly-struck daisy-cutter.

Allen himself laid on the pass for Nicholls to make it 5-1 in the 79th minute and seven minutes from time Nicholls confidently put away a Griffin corner.

25 September 1954 v Leicester City won 6-4 (Division 1)

Five goals were scored in each half of this ten-goal thriller – and there should and could have been many more. Over 48,000 fans saw Albion dominate the first half-hour against newly-promoted City. They took the lead in the 12th minute when Allen's 25 yarder found the net after taking a wicked deflection off Stan Milburn. Seven minutes later Griffin's high, looping right-wing cross deceived 'keeper Adam Dickson and dropped into the net behind him and in the 30th minute Griffin's low cross was smacked home by Nicholls.

In the 34th minute Leicester hit back through Derek Hines (from Jack Froggatt's cross) but five minutes from the break, Nicholls made it 4-1 with a flashing drive from just inside the area. After Allen and Lee

But the Baggies responded quickly and in the 14th minute a shot from Lee cannoned off a defender, leaving Allen unmarked in front of an empty net.

In the 28th minute Griffin raced away down the right. He fed Ryan whose pass was gleefully slammed into the net by Allen.

Seven minutes later some smart work by Ryan set up Allen for his

Another Allen goal, this time against Cardiff in November 1953.

had both hit the crossbar early in the second half, former Albion star Arthur Rowley pulled a goal back for City on the hour mark, and three minutes later Mal Griffiths made it 4-3. Albion though, moved up a gear...Lee scored with a cracking left-footer on 75 minutes and Nicholls completed his second Albion hat-trick six minutes later before Johnny Morris rounded off the scoring with a fourth goal for City on 85 minutes.

Johnny Nicholls – hat-trick hero against Leicester City in September 1954.

21 September 1957 v Manchester City won 9-2 (Division 1)

After some mixed early season performances — three wins, four draws and a home defeat in their opening eight matches — Albion went goal-crazy in this game and completely destroyed City's much vaunted 'M' plan in front of 26,222 fans. Right-winger Griffin was Albion's star performer, scoring his first hat-trick for the club and leading scorer Ronnie Allen (out injured) was never missed.

Howe fired the Baggies ahead on 21 minutes, his 35-yard drive deflecting off Keith Marsden before trickling agonisingly beyond City's giant goalkeeper John Savage.

Fifteen minutes later Griffin's pass found Barlow whose low shot deflected off Brian Whitehouse and left Savage stranded (2-0).

City pulled a goal back in the 39th minute when Roy Clarke fired home, but two minutes later Griffin, racing on to Barlow's astute pass, cracked home a beauty from 12 yards to make it 3-1.

Ten minutes into the second half Fionan Fagan made it 3-2, sliding the ball home after Marsden's shot had been blocked, but 50 seconds later Griffin, cutting in from the right, saw his shot parried by Savage only for Bobby Robson to net the rebound (4-2).

A minute later Ken Barnes (father of Peter, a future Albion winger) shot wide from the penalty spot after Barlow had fouled Fagan. Albion went straight to the other end of the field and Griffin, after dribbling past four defenders, scored a terrific fifth goal.

Roy Horobin was next on target with a fine left-foot shot (6-2) and in the 80th minute the Albion winger was brought down by City's centre-half Dave Ewing, enabling Howe to make it 7-2 from the spot.

A minute later Griffin completed his hat-trick from Horobin's pass and in the 84th minute Ewing conceded a second penalty when he floored Kevan. The England striker blasted in the spot-kick to complete the massacre and so give Albion their biggest League win at The Hawthorns. City's 'keeper Savage kicked the ball over the stand when this last Albion goal went in — to sum up his day.

Frank Griffin netted his only hat-trick for Albion in the 9-2 victory over Manchester City in September 1957.

26 October 1957 v Manchester United won 4-3 (Division 1)

This was a terrific match — full of high quality football and some superb goals. In front of 52,839 fans — the biggest crowd at The Hawthorns for a League match for three-and-a-half years — United took an early lead via a Tommy Taylor header on seven minutes. Robson equalised against the run of play nine minutes later before Taylor, with another powerful head-er, restored United's lead midway through the first half. Robson then nodded Albion level at 2-2 in the 27th minute before Kevan fired home superbly to give Albion the lead at 3-2 two minutes before the break.

On the hour mark Albion's 'keeper Jim Sanders dived to his left to keep out Johnny Berry's penalty and eight minutes later Allen swooped to put Albion 4-2 ahead only for Billy Whelan to reduce the deficit with 13 minutes remaining to set up an exciting finish during which time Barlow should have netted a fifth for Albion. A great game.

16 March 1958 v Everton won 4-0 (Division 1)

Bludgeon against rapier. Tanks (Derek Kevan and Co.) against old-fashioned field guns. That's what it was as Albion over-powered Everton in what turned out to be a very one-sided contest. A crowd of 28,915 saw Bobby Robson fire home Albion's first goal in the 15th minute after linking up with Ronnie Allen. Kevan

Jim Sanders made a vital penalty save against Manchester United in October 1957.

SOME MEMORABLE VICTORIES

Derek Kevan waits for an Everton slip at The Hawthorns in March 1958. The goalkeeper is Jimmy O'Neill.

later Kevan converted another fine Whitehouse pass, driving a first time shot home from ten yards. Former Albion star Arthur Rowley pulled a goal back for City in the 25th minute from an excellent Derek Hines pass – his 300th first-class goal of his career – and a minute later the visitors drew level when future Albion winger Derek Hogg pushed the ball through to Willie Gardiner whose first shot was saved by Albion 'keeper Clive Jackman only for the one-eyed Scottish centre-forward to smack in the rebound. Six minutes from the interval Robson centred for Whitehouse to ram in Albion's third goal, City's offside appeals falling on deaf ears.

Twenty minutes into the second half Graham Williams lobbed the ball down the middle for Robson to collect and shoot home from 12 yards; six minutes later Kevan crossed for Whitehouse to net number five and in the 80th minute Allen flicked the ball over his head, allowing Robson to net his second hat-trick and 27th goal of the season... and 25,389 fans saw it.

29 November 1958 v Tottenham Hotspur won 4-3 (Division 1)

Having scored in every League game of the season, Albion continued to

Brian Whitehouse scores against Leicester City in April 1958.

made it 2-0 seconds before half-time when he burst through from the halfway line past a static Everton defence to crack his shot wide of 'keeper Albert Dunlop. Allen made it 3-0 from the penalty spot in the 80th minute after Alan Sanders had floored the rampaging Kevan and it was the 'Tank' himself who snapped up number four, smashing home Roy Horobin's pin-point pass in the 86th minute.

12 April 1958 v Leicester City won 6-2 (Division 1)

After a barren spell of just one goal in five games Albion bounced back to form with a powerful display against Leicester.

In the 11th minute Brian Whitehouse crossed for Robson to score from close range and seven minutes

Tony Forrester marked an excellent debut with a goal against Spurs in November 1958.

find the net in this rip-roaring encounter with Tottenham Hotspur in front of 21,861 fans – and victory kept them just a point behind the League leaders, Arsenal.

Right-winger Tony Forrester made his senior debut and scored a fine goal to mark the occasion.

Albion opened the scoring in fourth minute when Howe netted with a well-placed free-kick. Eighteen minutes later Forrester slipped a neat pass through to Derek Kevan who scored easily from 12 yards and seven minutes before half-time 18 year-old Forrester slammed in Albion's third goal from just inside the area after a smart pass by Robson.

On a sticky surface, the Londoners stormed back after the interval and Bobby Smith scored two goals in the space five minutes. With a quarter-of-an-hour to go he cracked in Danny Blanchflower's pass and then netted from close range after a slip by Chuck Drury. A minute later he had a goal disallowed for offside. But Albion came again and with six minutes left, Allen blasted home a penalty after Blanchflower had hauled down Hogg. Dave Dunmore grabbed a third for resilient Spurs in the 87th minute.

5 September 1959 v Leicester City won 5-0 (Division 1)

Having lost at home to Spurs only three days earlier, Albion went to town against Leicester City and in front of 27,259 fans completely overwhelmed the Filbert Street side.

The visitors had goalkeeper Dave MacLaren stretchered off after 30 minutes; former Albion junior Gordon Wills taking over between the posts.

Bobby Dixon opened the scoring after only two minutes against Leicester in September 1959.

Outside-left Bobby Dixon gave Albion the lead on two minutes, converting Alec Jackson's clever pass, and then the same player had a goal disallowed for offside before Kevan whipped in number two on 25 minutes, the ball flying into the City net off 'keeper MacLaren's boot.

Facing a replacement goalkeeper Albion went to town and added three further goals (it should have been ten). Their third was claimed by Jackson, who hooked the ball in from eight yards on 43 minutes. The fourth came from Robson, in the 63rd minute when he drove in Dixon's precise pass and it was Robson again in the 75th minute when he slammed the ball home after three players had seen their shots blocked by desperate defending.

19 March 1960 v Everton won 6-2 (Division 1)

Albion found themselves 2-0 down after just 13 minutes of this amazing game. Everton's first goal on eight minutes was a simple tap-in for Scotsman Bobby Collins from Micky Lill's low cross and five minutes later Roy Vernon latched on to a long ball before beating Jock Wallace from 12 yards.

Albion pulled one goal back in the 30th minute when Bobby Robson set up Kevan for a block-busting finish, but then Collins hit a post as Albion back-pedalled.

Then, after some near misses at both ends, Albion scored five times in 16 minutes to demoralise the Merseysiders.

In the 71st minute Kevan equalised; two minutes later he made it 3-2 with his hat-trick goal (a brilliant header) and then Davey Burnside swooped in the 80th minute to score Albion's fourth. A left-foot rocket from Kevan made it 5-2 with eight minutes remaining and shortly afterwards Burnside rolled the ball in front of 'The Tank' who rammed in his fifth goal to bring up Albion's half-dozen.

It was the first time an Albion player had scored five goals in a game since Jimmy Cookson netted six against Blackpool in 1927.

5 September 1960 v Newcastle United won 6-0 (Division 1)

Having lost their opening five League games, conceding 12 goals in

SOME MEMORABLE VICTORIES

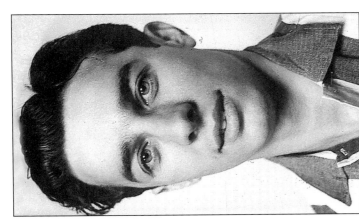

Alec Jackson, a thorn in the Newcastle defence when Albion romped to a 6-0 win in September 1960.

Ronnie Allen scored his final hat-trick for Albion in a 6-3 win over Manchester City in September 1960.

the process, Albion suddenly found their form and shooting boots to outclass their opponents in front of 22,548 spectators. Newcastle, minus their 'rebel' George Eastham, had no answer to Albion's forceful attacking play and fell behind on nine minutes when Jackson scored from close range after a shrewd pass by Burnside.

Burnside then made it 2-0 in the 34th minute after some neat right-wing play by Hogg and six minutes later Jackson netted number three with a crisp finish from Hogg's measured cross.

Ten minutes into the second half Jackson completed his hat-trick with another excellent strike from 12 yards after Hogg had again out-paced the Newcastle defence. Robson scored Albion's fifth from a free-kick, given for obstruction and Kevan rounded off the scoring by heading number six in the 67th minute after Hope had chipped the ball forward.

24 September 1960 v Manchester City won 6-3 (Division 1)

A crowd of 25,163 attended this highly entertaining encounter in which Allen scored his last hat-trick for Albion.

Burnside put the Baggies in front on ten minutes, netting easily after Jackson had bamboozled four City defenders.

Allen ran in unnoticed to steer home Jackson's pass to make it 2-0 in the 17th minute, only for City's Denis Law to sell Drury the perfect dummy, allowing George Hannah to reduce the deficit two minutes later.

Kevan raced on to cunning Robson's pass to smash in Albion's third goal in the 20th minute, only for Joe Hayes to head home Dave Wagstaffe's corner to make it 3-2 after goalkeeper Ray Potter had saved brilliantly from Law. In the 40th minute Kevan again bulged the net with a cracking drive after Jackson had set him up and seconds before half-time Law beat Joe Kennedy to tee up Colin Barlow, who duly made it 4-3. What a half.

In the 57th minute Allen capitalised on some defensive slackness to make it 5-3 (City appealed in vain for offside) and after Kevan had been deprived of his hat-trick through another dodgy offside decision, Allen completed his seven minutes from time with a thumping drive past Bert Trautmann after a wonderful back-heeler by the influential Burnside.

28 April 1962 v Blackpool won 7-1 (Division 1)

What a way to end a season – with a block-busting performance and plenty of goals. It was a pity that only 17,462 fans turned out to see Albion completely outplay the Seasiders in all departments to record their fifth League win on the trot and their best ever over Blackpool.

One of Derek Kevan's four goals in the 7-1 win over Blackpool in April 1962.

Albion's first goal came after just 30 seconds. Clive Clark crossed from the left and Jackson headed the ball back into the middle for Kevan to drive home. In the seventh minute it was 2-0. Blackpool's 'keeper Bryan Harvey saved Clark's low shot but Kevan, following up, netted from six yards.

Albion's third goal was scored in the 25th minute when Jack Lovatt sent Kevan racing through the centre. 'The Tank' deceived the advancing Harvey before banging the ball home to complete his hat-trick.

In the 42nd minute Ray Charnley rose high above Stan Jones to head home Des Horne's centre for Blackpool's only goal and a minute later Ray Parry bent the Albion crossbar with a 30-yard crackerjack.

Seven minutes after the interval Kevan's shot came back off a post and the alert Lovatt fired home. It was 5-1 in the 74th minute after Roy Greatrix had handled on the edge of the area allowing Robson to crack in the free-kick. Five minutes from time another handball decision, this time against Barrie Martin inside the box, Don Howe stroked in the penalty (6-1). And Kevan whipped in his 33rd of the season and Albion's seventh of the game three minutes from time after Lovatt's right-wing cross.

It was also Albion's 50th goal in the League at The Hawthorns in 1961-62.

8 September 1962 v Fulham won 6-1 (Division 1)

A goal down in 19 minutes, Albion rallied in such whirlwind style that only seven minutes later they were 3-1 up and flying.

Fulham's goal came when Tony Millington fisted away 'keeper Metchick's flighted cross, the ball falling nicely for Jackie Henderson to volley home from ten yards. Straight from the restart

Albion won a corner on the left. Clark's flag-kick was headed against the bar by Alec Jackson but Kevan followed up to nod the ball in. In the 22nd minute Don Howe's astute pass put in Keith Smith whose shot was saved by Tony Macedo. The ball was not cleared and after a scramble, Smith hammered the ball into the net. In the 26th minute Clark's corner was hooked on by Kevan and Smith swept the ball high into the net from eight yards.

Three minutes into the second half Kevan made it 4-1 when he head home Cram's cross. Nine minutes later Kevan scored number five to complete his hat-trick – all headers – from Smith's cross and the England striker rounded things off with a sixth Albion goal on 68 minutes when he lashed the ball home after Smith's effort had bounced back off a defender. In the 87th minute Clark beat Macedo but not the bar as Albion pressed forward.

Fulham goalkeeper Tony Macedo collects a high cross as Albion's Clive Clark looks on in September 1962. Albion won 6-1.

22 September 1962 v Bolton Wanderers won 5-4 (Division 1)

Two players – Albion's Derek Kevan and Francis Lee of Bolton – both scored hat-tricks in this nine-goal thriller in front of 18,670 fans. Kevan netted the opening goal after just 90 seconds. Bobby Cram pushed the ball through the middle and the burly Albion striker brushed aside Warwick Rimmer's challenge before firing past Eddie Hopkinson. In the 38th minute Bolton equalised when Lee, reacting quickly, netted after Doug Holden had crashed a terrific shot against the bar. A minute later another through pass by Cram found Ken Foggo unmarked inside the area and he scored with a well-placed shot. Two minutes after half-time Brian Birch was held back by Albion's 'keeper Millington and Lee whipped in the spot-kick (2-2) and in the 55th minute Holden crossed for Wyn Davies to put the visitors in front with a powerful header. Back came Albion and on 70 minutes Kevan raced on to Drury's long pass, but somehow miskicked, yet the ball had sufficient pace on it to deceive Hopkinson and cross the line (3-3). Just 85 seconds later Kevan, assisted by Smith, drive Albion into a 4-3 lead only for Lee to complete his hat-trick and bring Bolton level at 4-4 with his second penalty of the match awarded after Freddie Hill had been tripped by Drury.

With the game evenly balanced referee Mr M. Fussey of Retford awarded his third penalty of the game in the 80th minute after Rimmer had brought down Kevan. Howe duly obliged from the spot to bring Albion a merited victory.

9 March 1963 v Ipswich Town won 6-1 (Division 1)

This was Derek Kevan's last League appearance for Albion, and the big fella bowed out in style with a great

SOME MEMORABLE VICTORIES

hat-trick in front of a meagre crowd of 10,759... the lowest at The Hawthorns for eight years.

Kevan's strength and decisive finishing was too much for a frail looking Ipswich side, who ended the game with only nine men – goalkeeper Wilf Hall and forward Doug Moran leaving the action in the 14th and 65th minutes respectively, Hall with a fractured collarbone after colliding with Ronnie Fenton and Moran with a twisted knee. Kevan gave Albion the lead on 20 minutes, netting with a fine header past stand-in 'keeper Ted Phillips from Don Howe's free-kick. Ipswich fought back and equalised in the 35th minute through Ray Crawford – later to join Albion – who slammed in Jimmy Leadbetter's cross. But on the stroke of half-time Kevan met Clark's low centre to put Albion back in front.

In the 51st minute Phillips fumbled a Clark shot, leaving Alec Jackson a simple tap in, and on 68 minutes Clark cut in to send a thunderbolt shot into the net via the underside of the bar.

Cram laid on Albion's fifth goal for Smith in the 77th minute and Kevan completed his hat-trick with a close range header from Cram's lob with nine minutes remaining.

12 October 1963 v Aston Villa won 4-3 (Division 1)

Albion were missing their two international full-backs for this game – Howe and Graham Williams – and their two main strikers – Ronnie Fenton and John Kaye – and halfway through the first half it looked as though the Villa would run away with the match. They were 2-0 up with the match. They were 2-0 up and strolling after Albion's Scottish-born right-back Campbell Crawford had conceded an own-goal in the 21st minute and 45 seconds later Mike Tindall had headed home his side's second from Tony Hateley's cross. But Albion stormed back and three minutes before the break Cram, playing as an emergency centre-forward, sidefooted home Jackson's centre. In the 65th minute Nigel Sims saved Jackson's penalty after the the Albion player had been tripped by Alan Deakin, but the

'Tipton Slasher' quickly made amends for his error by equalising two minutes later with a fine right-foot shot after Deakin had failed to head clear.

Terry Simpson's excellent right-wing centre was slammed home by Tony Brown in the 69th minute for Albion's third goal and Foggo chased after Jackson's through ball, beat Charlie Aitken for speed and made it 4-2 with three minutes remaining. Tony Hateley headed a third goal for Villa in the very last minute, heading in Jimmy MacEwan's corner.

12 September 1964 v Stoke City won 5-3 (Division 1)

An exciting first-half was marred by an injury to Stoke's Calvin Palmer. The visitors, playing with pace and aggression in front of 24,505 fans, took the lead on eight minutes through John Ritchie, but Albion fought back and drew level in the 21st minute through right-winger Foggo. Two minutes later Albion went in front when full-back Cram moved forward to unleash a power-

Full-back Bobby Cram is on the way to his hat-trick against Stoke City in September 1964.

ful right-foot shot, the ball taking a deflection before looping over 'keeper Lawrie Leslie. In the 29th minute it was 2-2 when Dennis Viollet reacted smartly after Ritchie's shot had been blocked. Then the limping Palmer crossed for Ritchie to give Stoke the lead four minutes after half-time. Back came Albion and in the 57th minute, after Alan Bloor had floored Clark, Cram smashed in the penalty kick to bring the scores level at 3-3. Nine minutes later the unlucky Bloor then handled inside the area, allowing Cram to crack in his hat-trick goal after following up his penalty effort which was saved by Leslie. Cram therefore became the first Midlands full-back ever to score a hat-trick in a League game.

A Brown header in the 80th minute (from Bobby Hope's long high cross) ended the scoring.

● The *Sports Argus* celebrated Cram's feat that evening with the unforgettable banner headline: 'Bobby Crams in three.'

10 October 1964 v Wolverhampton Wanderers won 5-1 (Division 1)

Jeff Astle, a £25,000 buy from Notts County, celebrated his first game at The Hawthorns with two goals as Albion easily accounted for their arch rivals Wolves before a 23,006 crowd.

Albion opened the scoring in the 25th minute. Wolves 'keeper Fred Davies pushed Hope's swinging cross into the path of Kaye who, in turn, set up Astle who couldn't miss.. Eleven minutes after the break it was 2-0 when Clark pulled the ball back from Graham Williams' free-kick for Astle to net from close range.

On the hour Kaye moved on to Williams' low cross to fire home number three and five minutes later the impressive Clark raced down the left, crossed hard and low for Kaye to net number four.

Peter Knowles pulled a goal back for Wolves on 73 minutes, but with time running out George Showell brought down Clark and Cram hammered in the spot-kick.

13 March 1965 v Leicester City won 6-0 (Division 1)

With only three wins from their previous 15 League outings Albion played very well in the first half against a poor Leicester side to lead 4-0 at the break. England 'keeper Gordon Banks had a poor match by his standards, being responsible for two of Albion's goals. On three minutes he failed to get a fist on a high ball and Astle swooped to fire in the first goal. Five minutes later Hope's cross fell to Gerry Howshall whose 15-yard shot spun over Banks and into the net off defender Richie Norman.

On the half-hour mark Clark latched on to Astle's cushioned header (from Hope's cross) to make it 3-0 and a minute before the break, after City's Jimmy Goodfellow had gone off injured, Foggo fired one

John Kaye scored twice as Wolves were beaten 5-1 in October 1964.

past Banks from Stan Jones' long forward pass.

In the 64th minute Williams whipped in a 35 cracker which Banks might have saved and 15 minutes from time Astle made it the round half-dozen with a superb diving header from Foggo's pin-point cross. The attendance was 15,162.

4 September 1965 v Sheffield Wednesday won 4-2 (Division 1)

Astle scored his first Albion hat-trick in this see-saw game against the Owls which attracted a crowd of 15,229.

Albion, who had been beaten at home by Newcastle three days earlier, got off to a great start, scoring through Astle in the fourth minute, his header soaring into the net from Foggo's corner.

In the 23rd minute Peter Eustace equalised for Wednesday with a ten-yard drive after exchanging passes with John Quinn.

John Fantham then pulled Albion's defence apart to set up John Hickton for Wednesday's second goal in the 39th minute but Astle brilliantly headed in Foggo's cross to level the scores three minutes later.

Within a minute of the restart Astle had completed his hat-trick, Clark laying on the perfect pass for the striker to blast in from ten yards. Kaye made it 4-2 in the 66th minute after Doug Fraser had created the opening with a surging run.

18 September 1965 v Stoke City won 6-2 (Division 1)

Maurice Setters made an unhappy return to The Hawthorns; he conceded an own-goal and gave away a penalty as Albion went to the top of the First Division with this convincing win, which prompted a snappy *Birmingham Post* headline: 'Albion pace-setters outpace Setters.'

Watched by 24,374 spectators, Setters conceded his own-goal in the

Doug Fraser (arm raised) celebrates John Kaye's goal in Albion's 4-2 win over Sheffield Wednesday in September 1965.

18th minute, diverting Brown's low cross past his own 'keeper. On 27 minutes Kaye's header from Astle's pass made it 2-0 and then Setters made a rash challenge on Clark inside the area, allowing Cram to slam in Albion's third goal from the penalty spot on 34.

Roy Vernon reduced the arrears for Stoke five minutes before half-time after a mix-up in the Albion defence but a Brown cross-shot, from Astle's pass, and a Kaye header from Clark's centre in the space of three minutes soon after the restart put Albion firmly in control. Setters made amends for his errors by setting up Peter Dobing for Stoke's second goal on the hour, only for Kaye to complete his first Albion hat-trick in the 71st minute with another fine goal after good work by Astle and Brown down the right. Brown then hit the post two minutes from time.

6 November 1965 v Fulham won 6-2 (Division 1)

A crowd of around 20,000 saw Albion claim their second 6-2 score-

line of the season with a powerful display against Fulham – and star of the show was Graham Lovett who scored two splendid goals.

It took Albion 30 minutes to achieve the breakthrough, Ray Wilson heading home Kaye's measured cross.

Two minutes after half-time Brown latched on to Bobby Hope's long through ball to fire past Tony Macedo for Albion's second and five minutes later Lovett, after a brilliant 40-yard dribble, made it three.

Graham Leggatt pulled a goal back for the visitors on 58 minutes after 'keeper Dick Sheppard had mishandled a Terry Dyson shot but Kaye and Wilson worked an opening for Brown to make it 4-1 ten minutes later. With 16 minutes to go Lovett scored a majestic fifth goal after another exciting 40-yard run; Clark made it 5-1 in the 83rd minute after some smart build-up play involving Hope and Brown, and a minute from time former Albion star Bobby Robson ended the scoring with a 25 yarder for Fulham.

Graham Lovett, star of the show in another six-goal hammering of Fulham in November 1965.

10 September 1966 v Fulham won 5-1 (Division 1)

Fulham were well and truly thrashed and Cottagers' boss Vic Buckingham, who guided Albion to FA Cup glory in 1954, admitted afterwards: "it should have been double figures" as Astle (twice), Kaye (twice), Hope, Clark and Fraser all missed easy chances.

Left-winger Clark had a terrific game, giving England World Cup star George Cohen a torrid time. He not only scored twice but laid on a goal for Astle as well.

Albion scored first on 26 minutes when Cram's long ball was headed down by Brown for Clark to score from eight yards.

In the 54th minute Astle fired in number two from Clark's pass and in the 73rd minute Hope, receiving a pass from Kaye, slammed in Albion's third via a deflection. Two minutes later Clark made it 4-0 after a breathtaking dribble which saw him bewilder three defenders and in the 78th minute Hope, taking Fraser's pass in his stride, belted home number five past the luckless Macedo.

Steve Earle notched a a consolation goal for the visitors eight minutes from time.

13 May 1967 v Newcastle United won 6-1 (Division 1)

This was managerless Albion's best League win since March 1965.

Newcastle were never in with a shout, their goalkeeper Gordon Marshall had a nightmare match and if this had been a boxing contest the towel would have been thrown in after 60 minutes.

Albion dominated throughout and led 4-0 at half-time, much to the delight of their supporters in the 20,035 crowd.

Amazingly it wasn't until the 31st minute before they broke through. Kaye sent Foggo dribbling into the penalty area, and in a flash the impish Scot arrowed the ball left-footed inside 'keeper Marshall's near post.

Seven minutes later Brown rifled in Astle's splendid lobbed pass for 2-0 and in the 44th minute Brown netted again, netting on the turn after some clever footwork by Foggo.

Forty seconds before the break left-back Williams, out near the corner-flag, swung over a shot-cum-centre which baffled everyone before flying into the top of the United net.

Brown completed his hat-trick with a soft header (through Marshall's hands) on 69 minutes and in the 82nd minute Clark (with his 29th goal of the season) made it 6-0 after some excellent work by Kaye and the unselfish Astle. Newcastle poached a late consolation goal a minute from time when Peter Noble headed past John Osborne.

11 November 1967 v Burnley won 8-1 (Division 1)

Albion, ruthlessly seeking revenge for ten years of Burnley supremacy, soared to dizzy heights of goalscoring form to shame the thousands of supporters who missed a treat by choosing to stay at home. A delighted audience of 18,457 saw Alan Ashman's men put on a super show to destroy Burnley. All the goals were splendidly executed and there could have been several more – so well did Albion perform.

Clive Clark, scored his 29th goal of the season in the 6-1 win over Newcastle in May 1967.

Albion's opener was a long range floated drive from 'Man of the Match' Hope on 16 minutes. This was followed by a diving header from Clark four minutes later and in the 24th minute it was 3-0 when Brown's tame shot slipped through the hands and legs of Burnley 'keeper Harry Thomson.

In the 35th minute John Kaye, finding space, jabbed in number four after Clark had chased a lost cause and right on half-time Eddie Colquhoun scored a cracker from 20 yards.

Hope's second goal and Albion's sixth arrived in the 59th minute when the Scot cleverly lofted the ball over the advancing Thomson and goal number seven was a brave header from the industrious Clark, who arrived late to get on the end of Hope's inch-perfect cross. Astle finally got on the scoresheet in the 75th minute when he swerved the ball into the net from Kaye's pass.

Burnley salvaged some pride with an 86th-minute goal from Arthur Bellamy. Albion had three penalty appeals turned down, one of them blatant handball by Colin Waldron.

29 April 1968 v Manchester United won 6-3 (Division 1)

When United came to The Hawthorns they were chasing the League and European Cup double, while Albion had already booked their place in the FA. Cup Final. Almost 46,000 paid to get into the ground; another 5,000 entered illegally and there were 5,000 more locked outside. Those present saw a great game in which Albion stormed into a 4-0 lead inside an hour.

A mistake by Tony Dunne let in Jeff Astle for the first on nine minutes. Ronnie Rees netted the second in the 39th minute when Francis Burns completely missed Hope's low centre. Brown smacked in a twice-taken penalty on 57 minutes after

SOME MEMORABLE VICTORIES

127

Nobby Stiles had tripped Rees and Astle headed in number four in the 59th minute from Hope's free-kick awarded for a foul on Rees. Denis Law pulled a goal back for United from the penalty spot after Fraser had impeded Brian Kidd, but Albion went into overdrive and scored twice more through teenager Asa Hartford, who converted Astle's headed pass and Astle himself, who duly completed his hat-trick with a header from Lovett's centre. Two goals in the last 12 minutes by Kidd made the score more respectable. Albion went on to win the FA. Cup while United lifted the European Cup.

9 October 1968 v Coventry City won 6-1 (Division 1)

After being beaten three times in a row by Coventry during the previous year Albion completely outplayed the Sky Blues under The Hawthorns' floodlights to register a marvellous victory.

It took former City star Ronnie Rees only eight minutes to open Albion's account. The Welsh international slipped inside full-back Mick Coop to touch home Ian Collard's clever pass.

Only some brave saves by 'keeper Bill Glazier kept Coventry alive but two minutes into the second half Brown made it 2-0 when he thumped in a penalty after Brian Hill had floored Jeff Astle. Hill went off injured following this incident (replaced by John Tudor).

Five minutes later George Curtis failed to clear Rees' cross and Astle fired home the loose ball. After Hill had been replaced by John Tudor, Coventry clawed a goal back through an Ernie Hunt header but Albion responded quickly and Hartford made it 4-1 with a shot on the turn from 20 yards. Astle pounced to make 5-1 in the 75th minute after some poor defending

Asa Hartford, on target against Manchester United and Coventry in 1968 and Newcastle in 1969.

by Tudor and four minutes later a fizzing cross by Brown went into the Coventry net off Tudor's chest.

19 April 1969 v Newcastle United won 5-1 (Division 1)

A crowd of 22,481 saw Albion turn on a tremendous second half performance to humble Newcastle who at one stage looked destined to end the Baggies' six-match unbeaten run.

Newcastle dominated the first quarter of the game but then Albion got to grips in midfield and after Kaye had brilliantly headed them into a 25th-minute lead from Brown's well driven free-kick, it was no stopping Alan Ashman's marauders.

Brown also had a hand in Albion's goal in the 35th minute. United 'keeper Ian McFaul saved his cracking drive but Hartford, with his back to goal, netted with a fine overhead kick.

United got one back five minutes later when Bryan Robson, put clear by Alan Fogton, deceived John Osborne with a cleverly placed shot.

Albion's final goal burst started half-an-hour from the end.

A push by Ollie Burton on Clark

earned Albion a 60th minute penalty which was converted by Brown. Seven minutes later Lovett sent Clark streaking through for number four and ten minutes later, following some smart play by Hartford, Astle netted number five after Brown's shot had been blocked.

6 March 1971 v Manchester United won 4-3 (Division 1)

Albion's super striker 'Bomber' Brown sent out a 'cap me' message to England boss Sir Alf Ramsey with a glorious hat-trick in this showpiece which was eventually settled in injury-time.

When Albion and United meet on the same pitch they rarely fail to let the goals fly. This was no exception as four were rattled in during a scintillating 16-minute spell early in the second half to the delight of 41,134 excited fans.

George Best put United in front in the 18th minute, scoring low past 'keeper Jim Cumbes after outwitting John Wile.

Cumbes then saved brilliantly from Kidd before Brown equalised in the 32nd minute. Alex Stepney, under pressure, dropped Kaye's right wing cross and the Bomber pounced to net from close range.

This proved only an appetiser for the main feast and with just 35 seconds gone in the second half Brown netted again. Hartford sent George McVitie away down the right and was there to meet the winger's cross. His shot was blocked by a defender but Brown nipped in smartly to fire Albion ahead.

In the 55th minute United drew level when John Aston dived in bravely to head home Willie Morgan's cross.

Albion hit back strongly and within four minutes had taken the lead again. Brown, charging in from the right, held off Tony Dunne's challenge and let rip a terrific drive

Tony Brown hits one of his hat-trick goals against Manchester United in March 1971.

from 12 yards which flew high past the advancing Stepney.

On 61 minutes it was all square once more when Kidd, eluding his marker, jabbed home Aston's centre after some fine work by Bobby Charlton.

Both goals came under fire as the game wore on but it was Albion who took the points with Wile's injury-time header from McVitie's cross to the far post.

27 April 1972 v Chelsea
4-0 (Division 1)

Albion made a mockery of their low League position when they produced their biggest win of the season in this their last home game. It was an impressive display which made it difficult to realise that only two months earlier they were in relegation trouble while Chelsea were preparing to play in the League Cup Final.

The visitors, who were playing their third match in six days, went behind in the 27th minute. Brown, racing on to Bobby Gould's lob, hustled Paddy Mulligan to one side before firing low past Peter Bonetti.

Bobby Gould prodded in Albion's second goal in the 49th minute after John Dempsey had failed to deal with Wile's header following Hope's free-kick. Ally Brown stole between Ron Harris and Dempsey to flick home Hope's cross for number three

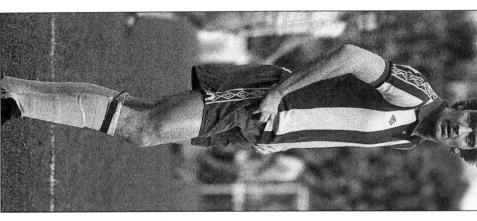

Ally Brown, scorer against Chelsea in April 1972.

on 72 minutes and nine minutes from time Hope and Gould combined to set up a simple chance for Len Cantello. It was all too easy.

11 April 1973 v Everton won
4-1 (Division 1)

Albion needed every point going as

David Shaw, on target against Everton in April 1973.

they entertained Everton in this crucial First Division game at The Hawthorns. Prior to kick-off Albion had not scored more than two goals in a League game all season. In fact, they had only managed seven in the last 14 outings. But against the Merseysiders (who lost their regular goalkeeper Ian Lawson just after an hour's play) they went to town and ran up a splendid 4-1 victory in front of 21,375 fans.

Astle opened the scoring in the 26th minute, Lawson failing to hold his well struck shot.

Harford, who was outstanding,

SOME MEMORABLE VICTORIES

made it 2-0 in the 60th minute, drilling in Cantello's short free-kick from 18 yards.

Then after Mick Lyons had taken over between the posts Dave Shaw made it 3-0 in the 63rd minute when he raced on to Alan Merrick's long pass to fire home from 12 yards.

A goal by Mick Bernard on 73 minutes pegged Albion back but three minutes later Shaw made it 4-1 when he netted with a spectacular overhead kick after Wile had nodded down Willie Johnston's left-wing corner.

● The *Daily Telegraph* headed its report: 'Albion head for safety.' How wrong that was. Albion lost their closing four matches and went down to the Second Division.

8 March 1975 v Sheffield Wednesday won 4-0 (Division 2)

Albion had won just two of their previous eight League games before

Ian Edwards, a debut goal against Sheffield Wednesday in March 1975.

taking on the Owls in front of 10,330 fans at The Hawthorns. Manager Howe handed senior debuts to goalkeeper Bob Ward and striker Ian Edwards and both per-

formed well as Albion strolled to victory after a dull first half.

Albion's first goal arrived on 47 minutes. Johnston outpaced Peter Rodriguez and from his cross Wednesday's Alan Thompson fouled Edwards. Tony Brown thumped in the penalty.

It was 2-0 in the 74th minute when Johnston fed a short corner to Allan Glover whose cross was volleyed home in a spectacular style by skipper Wile from ten yards. In the 83rd minute Edwards crowned his debut with a terrific goal. Picking the ball up five yards over the halfway line he raced clear of his markers before netting with a delightful ground shot.

Three minutes from time – after Rodrigues had gone off injured – Edwards set up Brown for goal number four.

20 March 1976 v Bolton Wanderers won 2-0 (Division 2)

This was a game Albion had to win as they endeavoured to gain promo-

A goal for Joe Mayo (No.9) in the vital promotion win over Bolton in March 1976.

tion from the Second Division – and win it they did with a competent display against their fellow promotion candidates.

After some nervous moments – in both penalty areas – Albion edged in front three minutes before half-time when Joe Mayo found himself with the easiest of headers six yards from goal after a perfect cross from Willie Johnston.

Then five minutes after the restart Wile was left unmarked as he went for a Johnny Giles free-kick to score Albion's second and decisive goal. Bolton rallied late on but Albion's defence held firm to register a priceless victory which took them to within a point of third-place Bolton. The attendance was 25,650 – the second biggest of the season at The Hawthorns.

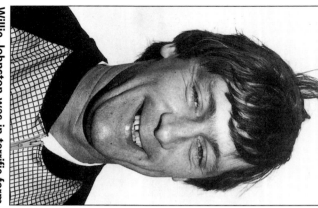

Willie Johnston was in terrific form on Albion's left wing in the 4-2 win over Spurs in October 1976.

2 October 76 v Tottenham Hotspur won 4-2 (Division 1)

Albion found themselves two goals adrift at half-time but a magnificent fightback after the interval, instigated by Johnston, saw them emerge as worthy winners.

A crowd of 23,461 saw Spurs take a lucky lead on 35 minutes. Peter

Taylor's deep cross was header back by Ian Moores only for Wile's clearance to fly into the net off striker Chris Jones.

Three minutes later it was 2-0 when Taylor was left unmarked to convert Alfie Conn's low centre which had been missed by Cantello.

Johnston started to weave his magic early in the second half. On 52 minutes he roasted Naylor before crossing only to see the Spurs defender Micky Stead inexplicably grab hold of the ball. Brown buried the spot-kick.

Ten minutes later Johnston laid the ball back to the supporting Cantello whose splendid cross was headed in by Martin.

Four minutes later Albion were in front when Johnston sped past Naylor for the umpteenth time. His cross was met by Mayo whose shot was charged down by Pat Jennings who then did well to smother another effort from Brown only for the lurking Ray Treacy to steer the ball home.

With two minutes left Johnston, Mayo, Treacy and Brown set up a fourth goal for Martin.

22 October 1977 v Manchester United won 4-0 (Division 1)

Unbeaten at home in six League and Cup games, Albion outfought, and outplayed the FA Cup holders to register a splendid victory.

Willie Johnston (right) and David Cross both played an important role in the 4-0 win over Manchester United in October 1977.

After an even opening period Albion took the lead in the 27th minute when Stepney saved David Cross's initial effort only for the striker to blast home Bryan Robson's return pass from the edge of the area.

In the 36th minute Johnston's left-wing corner curled away from goal towards Wile who leapt to steer a fine header into the United net via an upright.

Three minutes later Derek Statham surged forward and after his shot cannoned off Martin Buchan Cross was on hand to steer the ball past Stepney.

It was game over in the 56th minute when Laurie Cunningham stole in at the far post side-foot home Mulligan's fine cross after the Irishman had been set free by Johnston.

Cyrille Regis missed this game through tonsillitis.

21 October 1978 v Coventry City won 7-1 (Division 1)

Coventry – wearing a chocolate-coloured strip – were well and truly licked by a highly confident and very efficient Albion side in front of 27,409 spectators.

Cantello scored the opening goal in the 14th minute, finishing off Tony Brown's pin-point pass in style, the ball flying high into the net off diving 'keeper Les Sealey's outstretched arms.

Cunningham made it 2-0 in the 28th minute, tucking home a fine cross from the overlapping Brendon Batson. Seven minutes later Regis added number three with a powerful header after some excellent work by Cantello and Brown.

The impressive Cunningham grabbed his second goal and Albion's fourth in the 62nd minute, heading home Wile's flick-on from Brown's left-wing corner. And after Mick Ferguson had pulled one back

Len Cantello scored Albion's opening goal when Coventry were hammered 7-1 in October 1978.

for Coventry on 70 minutes when he headed in Tony Green's left-wing centre, Brown rammed in Albion's fifth goal on 76 minutes from Robson's pass. Regis claimed number six in the 82nd minute, storming through the middle of the Coventry defence before hammering his shot beyond Sealey, and Statham rounded things off with a seventh goal a minute from time, picking up the pieces after Terry Yorath had lost possession just outside the penalty area.

1 January 1979 v Bristol City won 3-1 (Division 1)

A dozen or so groundsmen, 50 stewards, 100 supporters and even a handful of Albion players helped shovel snow off the Hawthorns pitch to enable this vital League Division One game to go ahead. And after recording an excellent 3-1 victory over Bristol City in front of

31,738 frozen spectators, Albion leap-frogged over Everton to join Liverpool at the top of the First Division table – the last time they had enjoyed such a high placing since 1954.

On a skating rink of a pitch Albion played carpet football and got off to a perfect start, Ally Brown scoring in the 11th minute after City's 'keeper John Shaw had pushed out Robson's low drive.

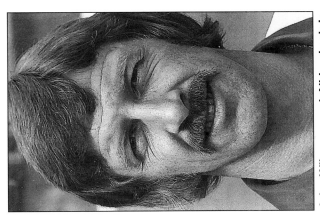

John Wile powered Albion back in front against Bristol City in January 1979.

City then survived four close shaves before grabbing an equaliser on 21 minutes. Batson conceded a penalty when he handled Tom Ritchie's header on the line. Ritchie's spot-kick hit a post but Barnsley referee Keith Styles ordered it to be retaken after Ally Brown had thrown a snowball at the ball. This time Peter Cormack netted comfortably.

Albion went back in front when Wile powered in Cantello's corner-kick in the 44th minute but after dominating the whole of the second half they had to wait until nine minutes from time to clinch victory, Ally Brown making amends for his 'penalty' misdemeanour by netting a beauty following the best move of the match.

100 YEARS AT THE HAWTHORNS

2 May 1981 v Tottenham Hotspur won 4-2 (Division 1)

Albion stretched their unbeaten home run to ten League games with this excellent victory over Spurs in front of 20,429 fans and the TV cameras.

Albion went in front on eight minutes when Robson's free-kick found Statham whose cross was put away by Ally Brown. Albion's second goal came courtesy of some vintage dribbling by Peter Barnes, who drifted in from the right and bemused three defenders before firing handsomely past 'keeper Milija Aleksic.

Mark Falco reduced the arrears on 58 minutes, turning sharply to fire hard and low past Tony Godden, but Robson made it 3-1 on 69 minutes after Remi Moses had set him up by jinking his way into the penalty area.

Spurs full-back Gordon Smith fired in a free-kick to make it 3-2 with seven minutes remaining but substitute Nicky Cross tied up the points for Albion with a fourth goal in the 85th minute, after a sloppy pass from Ricky Villa had fallen short of Steve Perryman.

Peter Barnes displayed some vintage dribbling skills against Tottenham in May 1981.

12 March 1983 v Ipswich Town won 4-1 (Division 1)

After scoring just twice in their previous eight League games Albion suddenly came to life and rapped in four against a luckless Ipswich side.

A crowd of 12,892 saw Albion take a ninth-minute lead through Garry Thompson who scored low to keeper Paul Cooper's right after some clever play by Nicky Cross. This was Thompson's first goal for Albion and the 50th of his career.

In the 32nd minute Albion

Garry Thompson hit two goals in the 4-1 win over Ipswich Town in March 1983.

SOME MEMORABLE VICTORIES

increased their lead with a superb goal from Statham. Romeo Zondervan started the move and after playing a neat one-two with Thompson Statham side-stepped Russell Osman to net from eight yards.

John Wark made it 2-1 ten minutes after the interval, heading Kevin O'Callaghan's cross past a flat-footed Paul Barron. But Albion upped the pace and when Regis pulled the ball back across goal in the 72nd minute Ipswich's Irvin Gernon glided the ball into his own goal. Three minutes later Thompson ended the scoring by lashing in Statham's long pass.

14 January 1984 v Aston Villa won 3-1 (Division 1)

Just 20,399 hardy supporters braved the chilling weather to watch this local derby which burst into life inside the last ten minutes.

After a dour first half Gary Shaw fired the visitors ahead in the 46th minute when he pounced on a loose ball inside the area.

Albion battled to get back on terms but found Nigel Spink in excellent form. Then a blizzard arrived and with fast time running out the game suddenly turned. On 84 minutes a mistake by Villa defender Allan Evans allowed Thompson to race in and equalise. Three minutes later Thompson rose, unmarked, to power home a great header from Clive Whitehead's high cross and with the snow swirling under the floodlights, Regis scored Albion's third goal after racing clear from the halfway line before netting past Spink with a fierce right-foot shot.

13 October 1984 v Nottingham Forest won 4-1 (Division 1)

Without a League win in six outings, Albion – and Garry Thompson in particular – suddenly found their shooting boots to out-gun a resilient Forest side in front of 12,991 fans.

Albion scored first in the 22nd minute when Steve Mackenzie's 25-yard special zipped past Steve Sutton.

Ten minutes later Nicky Cross got free down the left and his centre was headed home by Thompson.

After Ian Bowyer's shot had been deflected past Tony Godden following Bryn Gunn's free-kick in the 52nd minute, Albion went 3-1 ahead when Thompson was on hand to slam the ball home after Sutton could only touch on Clive Whitehead's centre. And with six minutes remaining Thompson claimed his hat-trick goal when he flicked the ball home following Gary Robson's cross from the left.

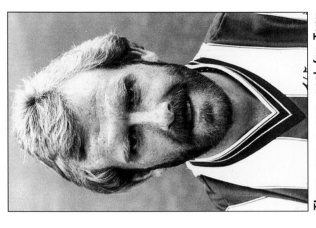

There was a rare goal for Tony Grealish in Albion's 5-1 win over West Ham in May 1985.

4 May 1985 v West Ham United won 5-1 (Division 1)

Albion rounded off their home League programme this season with a crushing victory over the Hammers – but only 8,878 spectators bothered to turn up to see it.

The deadlock was broken in the 25th minute when Steve Hunt rose at the far post to head Mackenzie's free-kick past Phil Parkes.

Ten minutes into the second half Ray Stewart equalised with a penalty after a dubious trip by Gary Owen on Clive Allen. Two minutes later Mackenzie scored a brilliant solo goal, netting from 20 yards and 12 minutes later the same player made it 3-1 after beating the offside trap to knock home Thompson's pass.

Albion's Republic of Ireland international midfielder Tony Grealish then scored a rare goal in the 76th minute, getting on the end of Hunt's long cross from the left, and the Canadian Carl Valentine created Albion's final goal eight minutes from time when gave Nicky Cross the opportunity he couldn't miss to complete the rout of the Hammers.

14 February 1987 v Stoke City won 4-1 (Division 2)

Two players, one long (George Reilly) and one short (Garth Crooks), helped Albion trounce promotion-chasing Stoke City out of sight.

Albion's emphatic victory was down to the lethal partnership up front of Reilly and former Potters' star Crooks, who led the visitors' defence a merry dance.

Garth Crooks scored twice against his former club when Albion beat Stoke City in February 1987.

Stoke, unbeaten in 15 games, fell behind in the 12th minute when Mackenzie's corner-kick was hooked in by Crooks.

A minute later Reilly controlled Crooks' deep centre and netted at the second attempt after on-loan 'keeper Hans Segers had saved his first effort.

In the 20th minute a lunging challenge by George Berry on Crooks from Carlton Palmer's tempting centre resulted in a penalty which Reilly buried with ease.

Four minutes before half-time Stoke's Phil Heath was sent-off for a second bookable offence after a reckless tackle on Robert Hopkins.

Albion's long-awaited fourth goal arrived in the 73rd minute when Crooks hammered in Hopkins' pass from the edge of the area. Five minutes later Stoke reduced the arrears when Keith Bertschin nudged in Lee Dixon's cross from five yards. Late on Crooks was denied his hat-trick by the crossbar.

4 November 1987 v Sheffield United won 4-0 (Division 1)

It was a pity that just 8,068 hardy supporters turned up to see this excellent Albion performance.

Playing with verve and commitment Albion went in front through Andy Gray on 15 minutes and were 2-0 up at the break following Don Goodman's 33rd minute effort. Bobby Williamson made it 3-0 early in the second half but an injury to United's on-loan goalkeeper Roger Hansbury ended the visitors' challenge. The luckless Martin Kuhl conceded an own goal to round off the scoring in the 68th minute.

Don Goodman starred in the win over Sheffield United in November 1988 and a year later against Crystal Palace.

18 December 1988 v Stoke City won 6-0 (Division 2)

Albion rose to third in the Second Division table after this resounding home win over Staffordshire rivals Stoke City in front of 17,634 fans. It was a most satisfying triumph for player-manager Brian Talbot who, 12 months earlier, had been considered good enough for Stoke's first team.

Ahead after just two minutes through Robson, Albion dominated for long periods and led 2-0 at the break following Goodman's 32nd minute effort. After the interval Albion moved up a gear and com-

26 November 1988 v Crystal Palace won 5-3 (Division 1)

Don Goodman was the star of this exciting encounter which attracted just over 11,000 fans to The Hawthorns. The £50,000 striker scored his first hat-trick for Albion to steer them to victory over a very useful Palace side. It was 1-0 to Albion at half-time, Goodman cashing in on Glenn Pennyfather's poor back-pass in the 42nd minute. Straight after the restart Bruce Dyer nipped in unnoticed to equalise for the Eagles, but Albion stormed back and surged into a 4-1 lead with three goals in 17 minutes. Goodman netted his second on 59 minutes when he sprung the offside-trap and then claimed his hat-trick goal in the 71st by heading home Colin Anderson's cross. Goodman laid on the fourth Albion goal for Robert Hopkins on 76 minutes. Gary Nebbeling reduced the deficit to 4-2 ten minutes from time and it was 4-3 soon afterwards when Geoff Thomas fired home. But Albion scored a fifth goal through John Paskin (89 minutes) and then 'keeper Stuart Naylor saved a last minute penalty from Palace's Ian Wright.

South African-born John Paskin scores against Stoke City in December 1988.

pletly over-run the Potters, scoring further goals through South African striker Paskin (70 and 76 minutes), Goodman again on 85 and Robson with his second of the match 90 seconds from time. Brian Talbot, Anderson and Wayne Dobbins were outstanding in midfield and between them contributed to all six goals. Tony Ford. Stoke's talented winger who was soon to move to The Hawthorns was so unnerved by Albion's onslaught that he was sent-off for the only time in his long career for a bad tackle on Colin Anderson in the 67th minute.

11 November 1989 v Barnsley won 7-0 (Division 2)

This one-sided encounter was marred by the sending-off of Tykes' substitute Sean Dunphy with a quarter-of-an-hour left following two fouls on the menacing Goodman. He was on the pitch for just 19 minutes. And it was Goodman who opened the scoring on three minutes, heading home Ford's splendid cross.

Ford himself nodded home McNally's centre for Albion's number two four minutes later. Brittle Barnsley stemmed the tide for the next 35 minutes but then hot-shot Goodman netted twice in the 43rd and 46th minutes to complete his only Albion hat-trick. First he slotted in McNally's pass and then brilliantly lobbed 'keeper Ian Wardle for his third goal.

Kevin Bartlett followed up with Albion's fifth goal in the 49th minute, prodding home the loose ball after Wardle had mishandled Ford's cross and then the same player side-footed home Goodman's pass for number six two minutes later.

McNally rounded things off with goal number seven in the 53rd minute, netting with a penalty after Carl Tiler had handled Ford's teasing cross.

Martyn Bennett made his last appearance for Albion in the 7-0 thrashing of Barnsley in November 1989.

This was Martyn Bennett's 217th and last game for Albion – and a crowd of 9,317 saw his farewell performance.

17 August 1991 v Exeter City won 6-3 (Division Three)

This was Albion's first game in the Third Division and 12,892 saw them record their first opening day victory for 18 years. Craig Shakespeare gave Albion a 30th-minute lead with a penalty. Mark Cooper equalised a minute before half-time, defeating

on loan 'keeper Alan Miller but straight from the kick-off Goodman was pulled down and Shakespeare netted his second spot kick. On 62 minutes Goodman made it 3-1 and two minutes later the same player headed Gary Bannister's cross against the crossbar before slotting in the rebound. Foster got on the scoresheet in the 76th minute and Paul Williams added a sixth goal 45 seconds later. Exeter rallied and Steve Moran and Gary Marshall scored consolation goals in the 82nd and 85th minutes as Albion eased up.

Don Goodman and Craig Shakespeare, two goals apiece against Exeter City in August 1991.

19 May 1993 v Swansea City won 2-0 (Division 2 Play-off semi-final second leg)

A full-house of 26,045 celebrated as Albion overturned a 2-1 first leg deficit to win through to the Second Division Play-off Final at Wembley. Both goals came in the opening period – the first from Andy Hunt in the tenth minute (from some neat build up play down the left) and the second from Ian Hamilton nine minutes later, again following some smart passing down Swansea;s right flank. Skipper Darren Bradley should have sewed it up at 3-0 in the

Ian Hamilton, whose Play-off semi-final goal against Swansea City in March 1993 sent Albion on the way to Wembley.

30 April 1995 v Tranmere Rovers won 5-1 (Division 1)

For 40 minutes this televised game was evenly matched, then Kevin

later.

arrears in the 58th minute before two excellent late strikes from Hunt (in the 83rd and 88th minutes) sealed Albion's victory in front of a crowd of 13,867.

27 November 1993 v Portsmouth won 4-1 (Division 1)

Albion played extremely well at times in this game and won well after the visitors had made a fight of it in the second half. First half goals by Bob Taylor (17 minutes) and Kieran O'Regan (41 – his first for the club) gave Albion the advantage. But Alan McLoughlin reduced the

second half but missed a sitter which meant a nerve-wracking last ten minutes. Two players were sent-off – Albion's Micky Mellon (53 minutes) and Swans's former Baggies striker Colin West (72 minutes). Mellon subsequently missed the Final victory over Port Vale.

Bob Taylor scored his 100th goal for Albion in the 3-2 win over promoted Derby County in May 1996.

5 May 1996 v Derby County won 3-2

Bob Taylor scored his 100th goal for Albion and Hunt ended his 17-game goal drought as Premiership-bound Derby County were beaten by a better side on the day. Albion took the lead via Andy Hunt with a delightful shot in the 12th minute but then Dean Sturridge seemed well offside when he equalised three minutes

wards the winger completed his hat-trick with a spot-kick after a foul on him by John McGreal, and Taylor hit home Albion's fifth goal on 84 minutes to round off the scoring. The attendance was 17,486.

18 December 1996 v Norwich City won 5-1 (Division 1)

This was a fine Albion performance and their goal-tally could well have been seven or eight at the end of the night. In front of 12,620 spectators, Hamilton opened the scoring in the 24th minute after Hunt had flicked on Sneekes' throw-in, and on the strike of half-time Andy Hunt netted number two heading home Paul Holmes' right-wing cross from eight yards.

Five minutes into the second half Hamilton was again on target as he waltzed round 'keeper Bryan Gunn after receiving Canadian international Paul Peschisolido's smart pass. 'Pesch' himself got on the scoresheet in the 62nd minute, turn-

Paul Peschisolido made one and scored one against Norwich City in December 1996.

make it 2-0 in the 62nd minute and although John Aldridge immediately clawed a goal back for Rovers from the penalty spot, Ashcroft drove in Albion's third goal midway through the second half. Soon after-

Donovan put Albion ahead with a close range effort. Just before half-time Tranmere's Dave Higgins was sent-off and after that it was all Albion. Lee Ashcroft raced clear to make it 2-0 in the 62nd minute and although John Aldridge immediately clawed a goal back for Rovers from the penalty spot, Ashcroft drove in Albion's third goal midway through the second half. Soon after-

Peter Butler then crossed for Richard Sneekes to put Albion ahead eight minutes before half-time. The 23,858 fans had to wait until the dying minutes to see the last two goals; Ashley Ward levelled for the visitors only for Taylor to stab the ball over the line for Albion's winner after Hunt's shot had been saved with 50 seconds left.

SOME MEMORABLE VICTORIES

ing in Hunt's low cross in a break-away. Two minutes later Hunt capitalised on some poor marking in the visitors' defence to push Albion 5-0 in front when he stroked the ball home following Paul Agnew's left-wing run and centre. In the 81st minute Norwich defender Danny Mills was sent-off for a foul but Hamilton squandered his hat-trick by blasting the resulting penalty high over the bar.

Norwich salvaged some pride with a late consolation from Keith O'Neill in the 88th minute.

15 August 1998 v Sheffield United won 4-1 (Division 1)

Albion were always in control of this game and recorded their first win of the season in emphatic style. Matt Carbon headed in at the far post following a corner for Albion's first goal on 24 minutes, and five minutes later Kevin Kilbane volleyed in James Quinn's cross from 16 yards to make it 2-0. Welsh international Dean Saunders reduced the arrears on 38 minutes, but two close range strikes from Lee Hughes in the 49th and 50th minutes put Albion back in control. Goalkeeper Alan Miller kept Albion in charge with a couple of excellent saves towards the end. The attendance was 16,901.

FA Cup

9 February 1901 v Manchester City won 1-0

Around 10,000 spectators saw Albion have two early 'goals' ruled out for offside in this first ever Hawthorns FA Cup-tie which was re-arranged due to the death of Queen Victoria. The only goal of the game came in the 30th minute when Simmons and Dick Roberts combined to set up Ben Garfield who scored from close range. In the second half Albion's goalkeeper Joe Reader made two fine saves from Welsh wizard Billy Meredith.

9 March 1912 v Fulham won 3-0

Heavy morning rain made the pitch very heavy. An excellent crowd of 41,440 saw Albion adapt to the wet and windy conditions far better than Fulham to run out convincing winners of this fourth-round tie. Amazingly there was a London referee in charge – Mr C. W. Gillett – but that didn't effect Albion's polished display and two first half goals by Bowser in the 30th and 32nd minutes, both at the Smethwick End, and both well-taken after neat approach work involving four players on each occasion, set the Baggies on their way. Wright added a third goal in the 78th minute to settle the outcome. Winger Claude Jephcott's electrifying runs as well as Bowser's marksmanship were the key factors in a rousing tie.

Sid Bowser, scorer of two FA Cup goals against Fulham in March 1912.

3 February 1923 v Sunderland won 2-1

This was a great second-round FA Cup-tie, witnessed by 56,474 spectators. Both sets of players wore black armbands following the death of Lord Kinnaird, president of the Football Association.

Albion had a chance to take the lead on 15 minutes but Morris blasted his penalty kick against the crossbar. Twelve minutes later, however, Morris made amends by putting his side ahead. Jimmy Spencer fired across the face of the goal; Gregory returned the ball for Morris to head home from eight yards.

Howard Gregory who laid on a goal against Sunderland in a famous FA Cup victory in February 1923.

Sunderland stormed back and after twice going close to the equaliser, they drew level in the 37th minute when Charlie Buchan, lurking near the touchline, turned to send a stunning 35-yard drive high into the Albion net past a bewildered Hubert Pearson in the Albion goal.

It was nip and tuck until the 63rd minute when Davies created space to set up fellow countryman Ivor Jones for the winning goal.

2 February 1924 v Corinthians won 5-0

Over 49,000 fans saw Albion easily beat the amateurs in this second round Cup clash. Morris headed home the first goal on 11 minutes (his last for Albion) and after Jack Phillips had struck the crossbar for the amateurs and Davies likewise for Albion, the latter netted with a penalty in the 35th minute. Right on half-time skipper Fred Reed added a third goal from a corner and eight minutes into the second half Carter dashed in to score number four. A quarter-of-an-hour from time Davies hit his second goal from 12 yards.

Tommy Glidden, on target against Bradford in February 1929.

16 February 1929 v Bradford won 6-0

This was a one-sided fifth round Cup-tie played in front of more than 30,000 fans. Albion were far too strong for Bradford who managed just two efforts on goal in the whole of the 90 minutes.

Albion took the lead in the eighth minute when Glidden, in space, scored from 20 yards at the Smethwick End. Seven minutes later it was 2-0 when Cookson converted Stan Wood's clever pass.

It was not until the 50th minute that Albion increased their advantage, Cookson finding the net again after some neat passing between Carter and Chambers.

A minute later Glidden fed Cookson who scored with a high shot just under the bar and in the 61st minute Cookson laid on a simple goal for Carter.

In the very last minute Cookson netted his fourth goal of the game from close range.

26 January 1935 v Sheffield United won 7-1

After going behind to a fifth-minute goal from Jack Pickering who was left unmarked to slot in Bill Boyd's knockdown, Albion stormed back to win this fourth round encounter in style.

Playing with a gale force wind at their backs, Albion replied to that early set-back with three goals in four minutes midway through the first-half. In the 23rd minute Trentham nodded a long ball down the middle and after a melee W. G. Richardson fired wide of 'keeper Roy John. A minute later Sandford whipped in a 30-yard pile-driver and 90 seconds after that Richardson followed up Gale's header to make it 3-1.

Eleven minutes into the second half Boyes sent Richardson through for goal number four and in the 71st minute Carter netted with a low right foot shot from the edge of the area to make it 5-1.

A thumping free-kick from Sandford in the 85th minute was followed three minutes later by Albion's seventh goal, scored by Gale after some excellent work involving Trentham, Boyes and Richardson.

The attendance was 34,908.

16 January 1937 v Spennymoor United won 7-1

The underdogs of Spennymoor were stunned by a three-goal blitz from Albion in the first ten minutes of this fourth-round tie.

6 March 1937 v Arsenal won 3-1

A record never-to-be-bettered Hawthorns crowd of 64,815 saw this sixth-round FA Cup-tie on a snow-bound pitch. At the time Albion were in the bottom five of the First Division, whereas the Gunners were in second place. But League form went out of the window as the Baggies rose to the occasion and pulled off a memorable victory. Albion took the lead on ten minutes when W. G. Richardson pounced on a mistake by 'keeper Frank Boulton. A minute before half-time, Mahon made it 2-0, firing home from 20 yards. Arsenal lost winger Jimmy Milne (injured) at the start of the second half but reduced the deficit through Cliff Bastin on 76 minutes when he fired home following an Alex James free-kick. Jimmy Adams then made three important saves in the Albion goal before Jack Mahon won the tie by heading Albion's third goal from Richardson's right-wing cross in the 88th minute. Albion's defensive strength, mar-

Sandford, unchallenged, opened the scoring with a deflected 20-yard drive in the seventh minute. Two minutes later Boyes crossed, Richardson headed down and 50 seconds after that Sandford teed-up Wood to drive in number three.

United battled back and Jack Hill reduced the arrears with a 'capital' shot on 30 minutes.

Three minutes after the interval Sandford scored again from distance; W. G. Richardson headed in Mahon's cunning cross to make it 5-1 in the 76th minute; Jones shot hard and low through goalkeeper Albert Heywood's legs to make it 6-1 with ten minutes remaining and soon afterwards Mahon cut the ball back for Richardson to make it seven. The attendance was 23,746.

Dave Walsh, a hat-trick hero against Chelsea in February 1949.

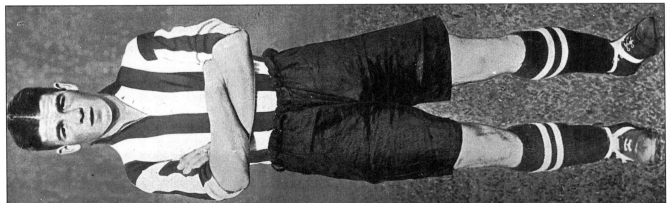

Teddy Sandford scored in Albion's big FA Cup wins over Sheffield United and Spennymoor and then skippered the side from centre-half in the famous Cup win Arsenal in 1937.

tialled by Sandford now playing at centre-half, was an important factor in a pulsating Cup-tie.

12 February 1949 v Chelsea won 3-0

Dave Walsh was a hat-trick hero of this fifth round victory by Second Division Albion over their First Division opponents. In front of a bumper 57,843 crowd – the best at The Hawthorns for 12 years – Albion held their own in the first half but then took the initiative to outwit and at times outplay the Londoners.

On 49 minutes Irish international Walsh hooked in a cross from Cyril Williams. He then had another 'goal' disallowed before John Harris misjudged the bounce of the ball to allow the Baggies' centre-forward to plunder number two halfway through the half.

Walsh completed his hat-trick with a terrific header from Elliott's angled cross ten minutes from time.

100 YEARS AT THE HAWTHORNS

The Albion team which beat Newcastle in the 1953-54 FA Cup fifth round.Back row (left to right): Ray Barlow, Jimmy Dugdale, Norman Heath, Len Millard, Stan Rickaby, Jimmy Dudley. Front row: Frank Griffin, Reg Ryan, Ronnie Allen, Johnny Nicholls, George Lee. Macot: Johnny Tromans.

20 February 1954 v Newcastle United won 3-2

A bumper crowd of 61,088 – with some 18,000 from Newcastle – packed into The Hawthorns for this fifth-round tie – and what a thrilling game it turned out to be. Albion, going for the League and Cup double, scored twice in the first quarter of the match through Allen. His first effort on five minutes was a right-foot shot from the edge of the penalty area after Ryan's effort had come back off a defender and his second on 23 minutes was a tap-in after Nicholls had struck the bar. Bobby Mitchell pulled a goal back following a deft free-kick on 64 minutes before Allen completed his hat-trick eight minutes later by cracking in George Lee's left-wing corner for one of the finest goals ever seen on the ground. Jackie

Milburn made it 3-2 late on from Billy Foulkes' right-wing cross, but Albion held firm with Wembley now only two games away.

Albion's half-back line of Dudley, Dugdale and Barlow was majestic – as it had been throughout the season.

26 January 1957 v Sunderland won 4-2

This fourth-round tie was a real humdinger of a contest which could have gone either way. A crowd of 42,406 turned out and they certainly got value for money with six goals, several near misses and action all the way.

Sunderland were the better side early on but it was Albion who scored first in the 14th minute when Frank Griffin's corner was headed out to Kevan whose right-footed

drive squirted past 'keeper Willie Fraser and into the net just inside the post.

In the 30th minute it was 2-0 when Roy Horobin's precise cross was superbly volleyed home by Allen.

Sunderland, showing a lot more purpose, pulled a goal back ten minutes into the second half when Charlie 'Cannonball' Fleming cracked Ernie Hannigan's pass high into the net. Allen then grazed a post before the visitors scored a shock equaliser, Billy Bingham outpacing the defence to shoot wide of 'keeper Jim Sanders in the 68th minute. Albion continued to press and seven minutes later regained the lead, Kevan scoring with a powerful cross shot in off a post from Allen's neat pass. Five minute from time Horobin, sent clear by Wilf Carter,

SOME MEMORABLE VICTORIES

and-a-half months earlier, Albion once again went goal-crazy, scoring another five and missing at least four more.

Despite a lot of early pressure and possession it took Albion 34 minutes to break through, Allen stabbing the ball home after Robson had miskicked at Horobin's low centre.

Roy Horobin (above) and Wilf Carter were both on song against Sunderland in January 1957.

settled the match with a deft finish to take Albion into the next round and an away tie at Blackpool

4 January 1958 v Manchester City won 5-1

Despite the fog, almost 50,000 fans attended this third round Cup-tie and having smashed City 9-2 in a First Division match only three-

the 89th minute. But right from the kick-off City's burly defender Dave Ewing sent his back pass wide of his own 'keeper to give Albion an impressive 5-1 scoreline.

19 February 1958 v Sheffield United won 4-1

United defended doggedly in the first half of this fourth-round replay, restricting Albion to just three attempts on goal. Indeed, it was 0-0 at the break, but then Albion slipped into overdrive and finished off the Blades with three goals in three minutes just past the hour mark. Robson opened the scoring from Kevan's pass; Kevan himself then thumped home Griffin's centre for number two and after Horobin had been sandwiched inside the area, Allen added a third from the penalty spot.

Soon after Albion's third goal in-form Griffin, who was on the fringe of the England team at the time, was crash-tackled by United's centre-half Joe Shaw and received a fractured right leg.

Albion, obviously shaken by this, conceded a goal with nine minutes left, Jimmy Dudley putting the ball past his own 'keeper but a late Kevan goal secured victory to send the majority of the 57,503 crowd home happy.

Ray Barlow, playing as a 'sixth forward', scored a superb goal against Manchester City in January 1958.

In a dim and misty second half, and with Barlow playing as a sixth forward, Albion attacked in force and in the 55th minute Barlow netted a superb second goal in off the foot of a post from Setters' free-kick. Three minutes later Horobin freed Griffin down the middle and the winger scored sweetly from ten yards. Four minutes later Kevan was fouled, but the referee played the advantage rule allowing Allen to curl in a fourth goal past the stranded Trautmann. City responded and after Fionan Fagan had struck an upright and Howe had cleared off the line, Joe Hayes found the net in

31 January 1968 v Colchester United won 4-0

After surviving the first game at Layer Road by the skin of their teeth Albion easily accounted for plucky Colchester United in this third-round replay, scoring three times in the opening half-hour.

Kaye put the Baggies on the road to victory in the tenth minute with a smashing goal. Running from the centre circle, he went past two United defenders before beating goalkeeper Ernie Adams with a 20-yard special.

On 17 minutes an inch-perfect pass from Hope was viciously put away by Astle who then added a third in the 30th minute after another superb pass from Hope.

Albion eased up after the break and the 38,448 crowd saw John Clark wrapped things up by obtaining a fourth goal ten minutes from time.

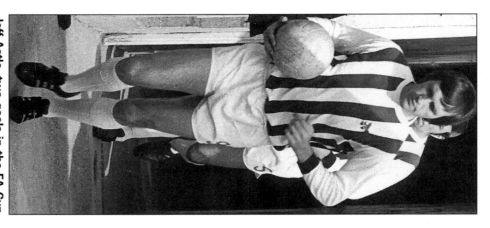

Jeff Astle, two goals in the FA Cup replay against Colchester United in January 1968.

5 January 1974 v Notts County won 4-0

Albion were in control of this third round Cup-tie from the tenth minute onwards. That's how long it took for Brown to open his account, netting from close range after Wile had headed Allan Glover's corner back across goal.

In the 24th minute Hartford flicked a short free-kick over the County wall. The alert Johnston darted round the back and scored with a great shot.

It was not until late on that Albion scored their other two goals. Brown raced on to Johnston's angled pass to make it 3-0 in the 87th minute and right on time Brown teased the retreating Magpies' defence to complete his hat-trick.

1 February 1978 v Manchester United won 3-2 (aet)

After holding Cup holders United to a 1-1 draw at Old Trafford on a glue-pot of a pitch four days earlier in front of 57,056 fans, Albion were confident of reaching the fifth round when the teams met again under The Hawthorns floodlights. And a crowd of 37,792 were present to witness what turned out to be a tremendous replay.

Johnston was left surprisingly unmarked by Jimmy Nicholl for most of the first half and he set up Albion's opening goal in the 14th minute, crossing for Ally Brown to head down to his namesake Tony who scored from close range.

Six minutes later United drew level through Stuart Pearson after some fine work down the right by Steve Coppell, Joe Jordan and Sammy McIlroy who supplied the final pass.

Four minutes into the second half Johnston sped past Jimmy Nicholl, cut in and crashed his shot against the United bar, only for Regis stormed in to net the rebound.

In the 51st minute Wile left the action after a clash with Jordan and as Albion clung on to their slender lead, Gordon Hill snatched a dramatic equaliser for United with barely a minute of normal time left, firing in off the post and Godden's body.

So it was extra-time and Albion snatched the lead again within two minutes of the restart. Ally Brown struck the bar this time and Regis bravely dived in to force the ball home. It was nail-biting stuff after that but that Albion stood firm to win a great match.

14 November 1992 v Aylesbury United won 8-0

Albion easily accounted for plucky non-League Aylesbury United in this one-sided first-round tie which attracted a crowd of 12,337. In winning Albion recorded their biggest home win ever in the FA Cup and, indeed, registered their biggest victory at The Hawthorns — in terms of goal-difference. And it was the first time the team had scored eight goals in a game since 1967.

Six players figured on the score-sheet: Kevin Donovan (3), McNally, Taylor, Robson, Paul Raven and Hamilton.

Albion were 4-0 up at half-time.

On 23 minutes Taylor and Hamilton linked up to enable Donovan to sweep home his ten-yard shot past 'keeper Tim Garner.

In the 34th minute a Simon Garner shot struck defender Collins and McNally was on hand to net from an acute angle.

Four minutes later Garner, looking for the 200th goal of his career, was again in the thick of the action providing a pin-point pass to Donovan, who found the net with a 25-yard drive.

Ninety seconds from the interval Taylor's looping header from Steve Lilwall's left wing cross drifted in over the hapless Garner.

Albion had to wait until the 73rd minute for their fifth goal – Robson driving home firmly from 15 yards after Taylor had allowed Lilwall's cross to run into the path of the substitute.

Two minutes later Robson flicked on Donovan's cross for Raven to net with a simple header and a simple four-yard tap-in by Hamilton, after

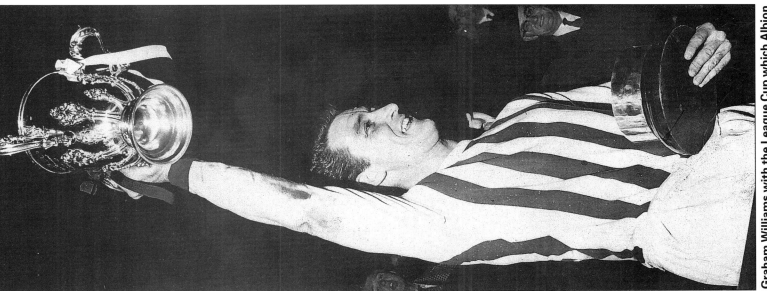

Graham Williams with the League Cup which Albion won in 1966.

some sloppy defensive play gave Albion their seventh goal in the 82nd minute. Four minutes from time Donovan completed his hat-trick with a right foot lob from just outside the area.

Football League Cup

22 September 1965 v Walsall won 3-1

Albion's first-ever League Cup-tie attracted a record crowd of 41,188 to The Hawthorns. In fact, it was the first time the teams had met each other at competitive level since 1900 and all credit to the Saddlers for making a fight of it. Brown put Albion in front just before half-time against the ruin of play, but after Colin Taylor had fired in a brilliant equaliser in the 65th minute Albion's defence came under considerable pressure. Then just after Nick Atthey's effort had been disallowed for offside, Walsall's centre-half Stan Bennett, who had played magnificently against the twin threat of Astle and Kaye, lobbed his own goalkeeper Terry Carling to concede an 80th minute own-goal and so hand the initiative back to Albion. Brown duly clinched matters three minutes later with the sort of goal he specialised in.

10 November 1965 v Coventry City won 6-1

Albion got off to a flier in this fourth-round replay, Astle firing Ray Fairfax's cross past City goalkeeper Bob Wesson after just 40 seconds play. But Coventry fought back and were level in the 28th minute when Alfie Hale and George Hudson set up Ernie Machin who finished with a well-directed ground shot.

Albion regained the lead on 40 minutes when Brown fired in a terrific shot through a crowd of players.

Albion then took the game by the scruff of the neck and stunned City with three decisive goals soon after half-time.

In the 58th minute Astle glanced in a header from Clark's centre; four minutes later Fraser burst down the middle to hammer in number four and 55 seconds after that the same player netted Albion's fifth goal with a tremendous right foot shot.

Astle duly completed his hat-trick by heading in number six from Kaye's cross with 15 minutes remaining.

23 February 1966 v West Ham United won 4-1

The second-leg of the 1966 League Cup Final saw Albion overturn a one-goal deficit against a Hammers' side which included Bobby Moore, Geoff Hurst and Martin Peters. In front of 32,013 fans, Albion started off like a house on fire, Kaye smashing home Cram's cross after only ten minutes. Nine minutes later Brown made it 2-0 and in the 28th minute Albion went 3-1 up (4-3 on aggregate) when Clark headed the ball practically out of 'keeper Jim Standen's hands. Left-half Williams made it 4-0 in the 35th minute with a crisp drive from 30 yards. West Ham rallied in the second half and Peters reduced the arrears in the 75th minute. But it was Albion's night and skipper Williams lifted the club's first trophy in 12 years and with it came a place in the Fairs Cup for 1966-67.

100 YEARS AT THE HAWTHORNS

14 September 1966 v Aston Villa won 6-1

Albion, with an inspired display, carved Villa to shreds in this second-round tie in front of 25,039 fans.

Villa conceded eight corners in the first ten minutes before falling behind in the 12th minute. Clark's effort hit the bar and was then cleared off the line by Keith Bradley but as the ball ran free, up stepped Fraser to thunder it past Colin Withers from 15 yards.

18 January 1967 v West Ham United won 4-0

A crowd of 30,193 saw Albion book their place in the Wembley League Cup Final with a rip-roaring first-half performance against a lack-lustre Hammers side.

Astle was Albion's hero with a cracking hat-trick and he may well have scored five or six goals, so well did the striker play against the likes of Ken Brown and Moore.

Astle's first goal came after just 50 seconds when he outjumped Brown to head in Collard's high cross.

After Peter Brabrook had flashed a drive over the bar for the visitors, Clark put Albion 2-0 up on 16 minutes when he glided in Kaye's low centre from the right.

Eight minutes later the Hammers' defence collapsed again as Kaye darted through the middle. His shot bounced off Eddie Bovington for Astle to fire home from close range.

Albion were in overdrive now and after another Astle header was ruled offside by referee Cattlin, the 'King' completed his hat-trick a minute from half-time, driving the ball in from ten yards after beating two men on the edge of the area.

Geoff Hurst and John Sissons went close for West Ham after the break while Clark, Astle (three times) and Kaye (twice) could well have added to Albion's goal-tally.

Substitute Dennis Martin got in the act with a fourth goal in the 70th minute before Frank Barton netted a late consolation for the Cumbrians with three minutes remaining.

penalty spot after Bobby Park had been fouled by Fraser but Albion responded with two more goals.

In the 69th minute Hope's deceptive right-wing cross wriggled past the clawing fingers of Withers and seven minutes from time the Scotsman completed his hat-trick with a splendid shot from an astute pass by Astle.

Bobby Hope, scored a hat-trick against Villa in the 1966 League Cup.

Six minutes later Fraser lobbed in Albion's second after a neat flick from Astle and in the 28th minute Hope scored number three following a penetrating run and cross by the nippy Foggo.

Hope hit the bar and Withers saved superbly from Astle as Albion continued to press.

In the 58th minute it was 4-0 when Clark delighted the crowd with a brilliant solo effort, twisting and turning past four defenders before firing past Withers.

Three minutes later Tony Hateley pulled a goal back for Villa from the

3 December 1969 v Carlisle United won 4-1

Albion had to come back from a 1-0 first leg deficit to win this League

Dennis Martin scored goal No.4 against his former club Carlisle United in the 1970 League Cup semi-final.

Carlisle chose to put up a nine-man defensive barrier in an effort to stop Albion's front men. It paid off in the first half but after the break Albion took control and won easing up. Despite losing injured centre-half John Talbut in the 20th minute, Albion always looked in control yet United could have taken a shock lead when Bob Hatton hit a post.

Albion finally broke through on 52 minutes when Hope scored with a superb cross-shot from a seemingly impossible angle.

Ten minutes later Colin Suggett, with perfect timing, side-footed home Hope's swift cross and four minutes after that Hope tapped a free-kick sidewards for Brown to ram in number three past the diving Alan Ross.

Cup semi-final against a battling Carlisle side and so reach their third Wembley Cup Final in four years.

25 October 1983 v Millwall won 5-1

Albion, trailing 3-0 from the first leg of this second round Milk Cup-tie against George Graham's Millwall, played exceedingly well in the return fixture and completely out-fought and outwitted the Lions to go through 5-4 on aggregate.

Albion managed only one goal in a tight first half, scored by Garry Thompson after 42 minutes, who clipped home Gary Owen's delicate chip over the Millwall defence.

Crowd trouble caused a ten minute delay to the start of the second half, but once they were back on the field Albion went for broke. In the 48th minute Regis headed in Albion's second goal from Barry Cowdrill's. Six minutes later, after David Cusack had dragged down Thompson, Owen fired in a penalty to bring the aggregate scores level and on 70 minutes Thompson scored his second of the night with a brave diving header from Owen's pass. Regis made it 5-0 with 15 minutes left after Zondervan had opened up the Lions' defence, and right on time substitute David Martin pulled one back for the Lions, who by this time had completely lost their roar and the match. The attendance was 13,331 – around 3,300 supporting Millwall.

European Competitions

9 November 1966 v DOS Utrecht won 5-2 (Fairs Cup)

A crowd of 19,692 witnessed Albion's first-ever European home game and the Baggies made hard work of it at times before overcoming the Dutch side in this Fairs Cup encounter. Albion had drawn the first leg in Holland 1-1 and were firm favourites to win the return

game at The Hawthorns – but they had fit-again hat-trick hero Tony Brown to thank for their 6-3 aggregate victory.

Bomber's and Albion's first goal came from a 13th minute penalty after defender Eddy Achterberg had foolishly handled Hope's cross and four minutes into the second half Astle headed on for Clark to nod in number two. Utrecht pulled a goal back on 58 minutes when Leo de Vroet scored from a corner but 11 minutes later Brown got on the end of Hope's measured cross to head Albion into a 3-1 lead. That was increased to 4-1 in the 75th minute when Kaye cracked in Astle's downward header and almost immediately Arie de Kuyper's shot was deflected in by Fraser for 4-2. Brown duly completed his hat-trick with a smart finish with two minutes remaining.

27 November 1968 v Dinamo Bucharest won 4-0 (European Cup-winners' Cup)

Slowly almost gently Albion ushered aside Dinamo Bucharest to enter the quarter-finals of the European Cup-winners' Cup. After a battling 1-1 draw in Romania Albion easily won this second round, second leg encounter in front of 33,059 spectators.

Surprisingly it took the Baggies 35 minutes to breach the visitors' defence. Clark, back in the side for the suspended Ronnie Rees (sent-off in the first leg), had an effort saved but Graham Lovett was on hand to drill in the loose ball.

Eight minutes later Fraser centred into the packed goalmouth; Lovett missed the ball but Brown, lurking behind him, crashed it high into the net off the underside of the bar (2-0).

Six minutes after the interval Albion scored again. Rugged defender Mircea Stoenescu floored Clark inside the area and Brown smashed in the penalty past the

'keeper's right arm. And to round off the victory the unmarked Astle stroked in goal number four in the 72nd minute after the ball broke kindly for him following Cornel Popa's strong tackle on the impressive Clark.

6 December 1978 v Valencia won 2-0 (UEFA Cup)

After holding the Spanish club with their World Cup stars to a 1-1 draw in Valencia, Albion were quietly confident of making progress into the quarter-finals of the UEFA Cup when the teams met in the second leg at The Hawthorns. In front of an excited 35,118 crowd Albion took the game to the Spaniards from the first whistle and always look the more likely side to score – and so it proved. Brown rapped in the opening goal in the fifth minute from the penalty spot after Luis Cordero had handled and then the same player sewed things up late in the second half with a stunning right foot volley on 79 minutes. In between times Cunningham headed against a post, Regis fired inches wide and Brown had a 20-yard effort saved by Fernandez Manzanedo. Valencia's World Cup stars Mario Kempes and Rainer Bonhof were both kept at bay by the efficient marking and tackling of Wile, Ally Robertson and Robson. Brown and Statham both had goals disallowed by fussy referee Robert Wurtz.

8 May 1970 v AS Roma won 4-0 (Anglo-Italian Tournament)

Albion scored four times in the last half-hour of this highly-charged but entertaining Anglo-Italian match. Victory took the Baggies to the top of their group with seven points.

Hope finally opened the floodgates in the 61st minute with a soft goal as goalkeeper De Min allowed the ball to slip under his body.

Brown added a second in the

John Talbot scored his only goal for Albion in the Anglo Italian Tournament win over AS Roma in May 1970.

79th minute with a smart header and the same player made it 3-0 seven minutes later with another exquisite finish. Centre-half Talbut ventured upfield to head home Albion's fourth in the last minute – his only goal for the club. Suggett missed several clear-cut openings for Albion, three in the second half. The attendance was a respectable 11,833.

Wartime

27 October 1945 v Chelsea 8-1

Albion gave 19 year-old defender Glyn Hood his senior debut in this return Football League South fixture with Chelsea, the Baggies having lost 7-4 at Stamford Bridge a week earlier.

But this time it was all Albion who raced to a convincing victory with seven second half goals.

Clarke gave Albion a 20th-minute lead which was cancelled out in the 33rd minute by Reg Williams after some slack marking in the Baggies' defence. Clarke then fired Albion ahead at 2-1 in the 48th minute and Doug Witcomb netted a delighted free-kick for the third just two minutes later. Arthur Rowley plundered number four in the 68th minute after 'keeper Robertson had fumbled Clarke's low shot. Two minutes later Clarke completed his hat-trick with a fine right-footed shot to make it 5-1 and Rowley added number six in the 78th minute from Frank Hodgetts' cross. It was ginger-headed Hodgetts who stole in to net goal number seven with ten minutes remaining and Clarke weighed in with his fourth goal of the afternoon from a corner in the 83rd minute.

This was a terrific result for Albion's left-half Len Millard (married that morning) and his best man Frank Hodgetts.

Doug Witcomb was one of the scorers when Chelsea were beaten 8-1 in October 1945.

Friendly

29 October 1957 v CDSA (Moscow) won 6-5

It was amazing that on such a wet and miserable night more than 52,800 fans should attend The Hawthorns to see the first-ever visit to West Bromwich of a Russian soccer team. And what a night it was – 11 goals, several near misses and a ball juggling act of the highest quality by Albion youngster Davey Burnside during the half-time interval... and all this in front of the live TV cameras at The Hawthorns for the first time. The occasion was the official inauguration of Albion's first set of floodlights.

After the pre-match preliminaries had taken a quarter-of-an-hour to complete, the Army side took the lead on 17 minutes through Vasily Busunov only for

Albion programme for the 11-goal game against CDSA in October 1957.

Howe to level things up on 28 minutes with a sizzling 20-yard drive. Encouraged by this Albion swarmed forward and seven minutes before half-time another vicious 20-yard strike, this time from Robson, put them 2-1 in front.

Albion's delight however, was short-lived as the Army side equalised two minutes later when Vladimir Emishev crossed low for Valentin Babukin to fire past Jim Sanders.

On 44 minutes winger Griffin made it 3-2. Shooting low towards goal, he saw the ball squeeze in at the far post after taking a slight deflection off Kevan – but 'Frank' claimed it.

Immediately after the restart a sharp movement split the Russian defence wide open. Kevan raced into the area, was felled by a clumsy challenge and Allen scored from the spot.

Soon afterwards Kevan was brought down again but this time Allen, changing from right foot to his left, sent his spot-kick a fraction wide of goalkeeper Yuriy Beljoev's right-hand post (a rare miss).

Busunov scored a third goal for the Army side in the 62nd minute and it looked as though Allen's 12-yard miss might prove crucial, but Kevan put the centre-forward's mind at rest with two fine goals in the 64th and 82nd minutes to push Albion 6-3 ahead. But the resolute Russians had other ideas and they netted twice more through Busunov on 83 minutes (his hat-trick goal) and Emishev (88) to make it 6-5 on the night. Great stuff.

FA Youth Cup Final

3 May 1976 v Wolverhampton Wanderers won 3-0

Having won 2-0 at Molineux in the first leg of this FA Youth Cup Final, it came as no surprise when Albion again outclassed their arch rivals to win the return clash at The Hawthorns by a bigger margin and so lift the trophy 5-0 on aggregate.

In front of a 15,558 crowd Albion scored their first goal in the 20th minute when George Berry, pressurised by Mark Trenter and Derek Monaghan, lost his bearings and steered the ball past his own keeper, Tony Walker.

Six minutes later John Loveridge centred from the right but Walker lost the ball completely and it fell behind him for Albion's second goal.

After Wayne Hughes had rattled the Wolves crossbar Monaghan raced in to net goal number three in the 68th minute following Trenter's deft header.

Albion's victorious youngsters with the FA Youth Cup in May 1976.

...and some Heavy Defeats

Football League

20	Oct	1900	v Nottingham Forest lost 6-1
27	Apr	1912	v Sheffield Wednesday lost 5-1
26	Dec	1923	v Bolton Wanderers lost 5-0
5	Sep	1925	v Sunderland lost 5-2
30	Apr	1932	v Grimsby Town lost 6-5
23	Oct	1937	v Sunderland lost 6-1
21	Sep	1946	v Barnsley lost 5-2
19	Apr	1947	v Plymouth Argyle lost 5-2
10	Mar	1956	v Manchester City lost 4-0
15	Dec	1956	v Sheffield Wednesday lost 4-1
10	Nov	1962	v Blackburn Rovers lost 5-2
24	Nov	1962	v Nottingham Forest lost 4-1
7	May	1963	v Everton lost 4-0
18	Jan	1964	v Manchester United lost 4-1
16	Mar	1968	v Everton lost 6-2
7	Sep	1968	v Nottingham Forest lost 5-2
10	Feb	1973	v Crystal Palace lost 4-0
16	Mar	1974	v Middlesbrough lost 4-0
1	Sep	1979	v Nottingham Forest lost 5-1
8	Feb	1984	v Nottingham Forest lost 5-0
23	Mar	1985	v Liverpool lost 5-0
21	Sep	1985	v Manchester United lost 5-1
26	Dec	1987	v Millwall lost 4-1
30	Jan	1988	v Leeds United lost 4-1
1	Nov	1989	v Newcastle United lost 5-1
12	Apr	1993	v Plymouth Argyle lost 5-2
18	Sep	1993	v Crystal Palace lost 4-1
19	Mar	1995	v Swindon Town lost 5-2
21	Nov	1995	v Norwich City lost 4-1
5	Apr	1999	v Crewe Alexandra lost 5-1

FA Cup

| 14 | Jan | 1905 | v Leicester Fosse lost 5-2 |
| 5 | Jan | 1991 | v Woking lost 4-2 |

Zenith Data Systems Cup

| 29 | Nov | 1989 | v Derby County lost 5-0 |
| 21 | Nov | 1990 | v Barnsley lost 5-3 |

Birmingham Senior Cup

| 4 | Sep | 1905 | v Aston Villa lost 5-1 |

Lord Mayor of Birmingham Charity Cup

21	Sep	1903	v Small Heath lost 5-4
2	Oct	1912	v Aston Villa lost 5-1 (Final)
13	May	1932	v Aston Villa lost 4-0 (Final)

Wartime (League & Cup)

26	Apr	1941	v Aston Villa lost 6-1
9	May	1942	v Wolves lost 4-0
10	Apr	1943	v Birmingham lost 4-0
19	Feb	1944	v Stoke City lost 8-2
28	Oct	1944	v Aston Villa lost 5-1
15	Apr	1946	v Charlton Athletic lost 5-2

Friendlies, Testimonials & Other Matches

20	Oct	1902	v Aston Villa lost 5-1
25	Apr	1914	v Corinthians lost 4-0
8	May	1935	v Football League XI lost 9-6
23	Sep	1939	v Wolverhampton Wanderers lost 5-3
26	Apr	1941	v Aston Villa lost 6-1
28	Apr	1965	v WBA Past XI lost 6-4

...plus some high-scoring draws

Football League

7	Oct	1925	v Notts County 4-4
17	Sep	1933	v Blackburn Rovers 4-4
26	Dec	1963	v Tottenham Hotspur 4-4
11	Apr	1966	v Arsenal 4-4
18	Mar	1980	v Bolton Wanderers 4-4
12	Mar	1996	v Watford 4-4

Watney Cup Final

| 7 | Aug | 1971 | v Colchester United 4-4* |

*Colchester won 4-3 on penalties.

Wartime

| 23 | Aug | 1918 | v Wolverhampton Wanderers 4-4 |
| 11 | Sep | 1943 | v Northampton Town 4-4 |

Testimonial Match

| 25 | Apr | 1956 | v International XI (N. Heath) 5-5 |

Hawthorns Hat-tricks

Scored by Albion Players

George Dorsett, hat-tricks against Doncaster Rovers and Burton United in 1904.

Howard Gregory scored three times against Spurs in 1915.

Football League

1	R. Roberts	(3)	v Bolton Wanderers	8 Dec 1900
2	C. Simmons	(3)	v Blackpool	22 Feb 1902
3	T. Worton	(3)	v Newton Heath	8 Mar 1902
4	G. Dorsett	(3)	v Doncaster Rovers	24 Sep 1904
5	G. Dorsett	(3)	v Burton United	8 Oct 1904
6	F. Shinton	(3)	v Bradford City	11 Nov 1905
7	C. Simmons	(3)	v Barnsley	26 Dec 1905
8	F. Shinton	(4)	v Clapton Orient	6 Oct 1906
9	F. Shinton	(4)	v Glossop North End	3 Nov 1906
10	F. Buck	(3)	v Bradford City	17 Nov 1906
11	T. Dilly	(3)	v Chesterfield	24 Nov 1906
12	F. Shinton	(4)	v Grimsby Town	25 Dec 1906
13	W. Jordan	(3)	v Gainsborough Trinity	16 Feb 1907
14	R. Pailor	(3)	v Newcastle United	10 Feb 1912
15	A. Bentley	(4)	v Burnley	6 Sep 1913
16	H. Gregory	(3)	v Tottenham Hotspur	6 Apr 1915
17	S. Bowser	(3)	v Bradford City	27 Sep 1919
18	F. Morris	(5)	v Notts County	25 Oct 1919
19	F. Morris	(4)	v Arsenal	14 Oct 1922
20	S. Davies	(3)	v Sheffield United	31 Mar 1923
21	R. Blood	(3)	v Everton	24 Nov 1923
22	J. Carter	(4)	v Tottenham Hotspur	8 Dec 1923
23	R. Blood	(3)	v Sheffield United	3 May 1924
24	C. Wilson	(3)	v West Ham United	15 Nov 1924
25	G. James	(4)	v Nottingham Forest	13 Dec 1924
26	G. James	(3)	v Aston Villa	28 Feb 1925
27	S. Davies	(3)	v West Ham United	24 Oct 1925
28	C. Wilson	(3)	v Birmingham	6 Feb 1926
29	J. Cookson	(6)	v Blackpool	17 Sep 1927
30	J. Cookson	(4)	v Reading	21 Jan 1928
31	J. Cookson	(3)	v Bradford	7 Sep 1929
32	T. Glidden	(4)	v Swansea Town	26 Oct 1929
33	J. Cookson	(4)	v Hull City	19 Apr 1930
34	J. Cookson	(4)	v Southampton	3 May 1930
35	W. G. Richardson	(3)	v Leicester City	24 Dec 1932
36	W. G. Richardson	(3)	v Sunderland	26 Dec 1932
37	J. Carter	(3)	v Manchester City	17 Apr 1933
38	W. G. Richardson	(4)	v Derby County	30 Sep 1933
39	W. G. Richardson	(4)	v Leeds United	6 Oct 1934

100 YEARS AT THE HAWTHORNS

40	W. G. Richardson	(4)	v	Middlesbrough	26 Dec 1935
41	J. Mahon	(3)	v	Blackburn Rovers	18 Jan 1936
42	W. G. Richardson	(3)	v	Blackburn Rovers	18 Jan 1936
43	W. G. Richardson	(3)	v	Liverpool	1 Feb 1936
44	W. G. Richardson	(3)	v	Grimsby Town	10 Oct 1936
45	W. G. Richardson	(3)	v	Liverpool	19 Feb 1938
46	S. Heaselgrave	(3)	v	Sheffield United	10 Sep 1938
47	H. Jones	(3)	v	Tottenham Hotspur	24 Sep 1938
48	J. Johnson	(4)	v	Bury	11 Mar 1939
49	I. Clarke	(3)	v	Bury	5 Apr 1947
50	J. Haines	(3)	v	Bradford	17 Apr 1948
51	D. Walsh	(3)	v	Bradford	8 Sep 1948
52	C. Williams	(3)	v	Lincoln City	11 Dec 1948
53	D. Walsh	(4)	v	Bradford	16 Apr 1949
54	R. Allen	(3)	v	Bolton Wanderers	26 Dec 1951
55	R. Allen	(3)	v	Huddersfield Town	10 Oct 1953
56	R. Allen	(3)	v	Chelsea	24 Oct 1953
57	R. Allen	(4)	v	Cardiff City	21 Nov 1953
58	J. Nicholls	(3)	v	Leicester City	25 Sep 1954
59	F. Griffin	(3)	v	Manchester City	21 Sep 1957
60	R. Robson	(4)	v	Burnley	28 Dec 1957
61	R. Robson	(3)	v	Leicester City	12 Apr 1958
62	D. Kevan	(5)	v	Everton	19 Mar 1960
63	A. Jackson	(3)	v	Newcastle United	5 Sep 1960
64	R. Allen	(3)	v	Manchester City	24 Sep 1960
65	D. Kevan	(3)	v	Sheffield United	18 Nov 1961
66	D. Kevan	(4)	v	Blackpool	28 Apr 1962
67	D. Kevan	(4)	v	Fulham	8 Sep 1962
68	D. Kevan	(3)	v	Bolton Wanderers	22 Sep 1962
69	D. Kevan	(3)	v	Ipswich Town	9 Mar 1963
70	M. Fudge	(3)	v	Everton	31 Mar 1964
71	T. Brown	(3)	v	Sunderland	26 Aug 1964
72	R. Cram	(3)	v	Stoke City	12 Sep 1964
73	J. Astle	(3)	v	Sheffield Wednesday	4 Sep 1965
74	J. Kaye	(3)	v	Stoke City	18 Sep 1965
75	T. Brown	(3)	v	Tottenham Hotspur	26 Dec 1966
76	T. Brown	(3)	v	Newcastle United	13 May 1967
77	J. Astle	(3)	v	Sheffield United	30 Sep 1967
78	J. Astle	(3)	v	Manchester United	29 Apr 1968
79	J. Astle	(3)	v	West Ham United	1 May 1968
80	J. Astle	(3)	v	Crystal Palace	10 Jan 1970
81	T. Brown	(3)	v	Tottenham Hotspur	12 Dec 1970
82	T. Brown	(3)	v	Manchester United	6 Mar 1971
83	B. Robson	(3)	v	Ipswich Town	16 Mar 1977
84	P. Barnes	(3)	v	Bolton Wanderers	18 Mar 1980
85	C. Regis	(3)	v	Swansea City	5 Sep 1981
86	G. Thompson	(3)	v	Nottingham Forest	13 Oct 1984
87	A. Morley	(3)	v	Huddersfield Town	24 Oct 1987
88	D. Goodman	(3)	v	Crystal Palace	26 Nov 1988
89	D. Goodman	(3)	v	Barnsley	11 Nov 1989
90	A. Hunt	(3)	v	Brighton & Hove Albion	3 Apr 1993
91	L. Ashcroft	(3)	v	Tranmere Rovers	30 Apr 1995

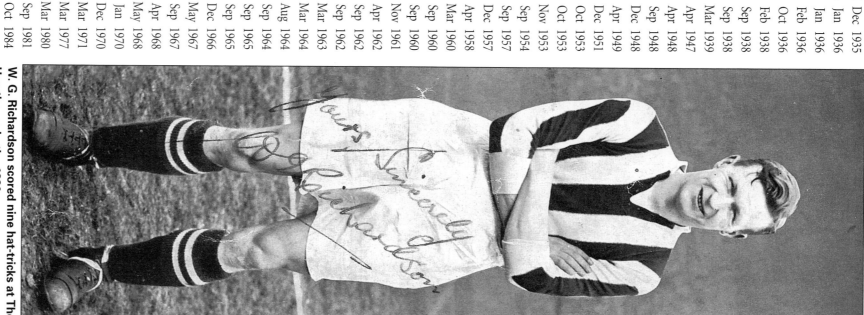

W. G. Richardson scored nine hat-tricks at The Hawthorns in the 1930s.

HAWTHORNS HAT-TRICKS

Ronnie Allen scored five League hat-tricks at The Hawthorns.

Derek Kevan scored six League hat-tricks at The Hawthorns, including a five-timer against Everton in March 1960.

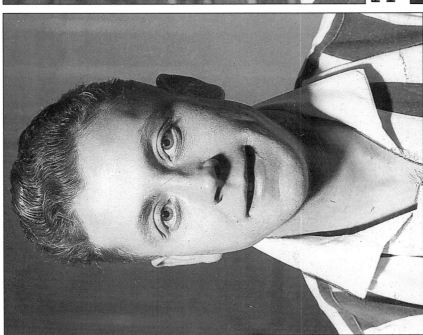

Joe Johnson netted four goals in a 6-0 win over Bury in March 1939.

Bobby Robson – four goals in the 5-1 win over Burnley in December 1957.

100 YEARS AT THE HAWTHORNS

Jeff Astle scores one of his hat-trick goals against Sheffield Wednesday in September 1965.

Cyrille Regis – three goals for Albion against Swansea City in September 1981.

Andy Hunt marked his home debut with a hat-trick against Brighton in April 1993.

Lee Hughes scored two League hat-tricks at The Hawthorns in 1998.

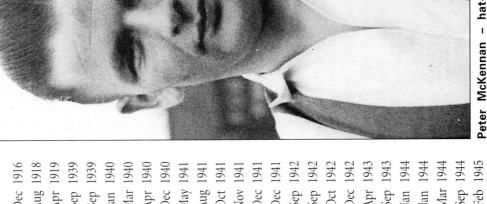

Peter McKennan – hat-trick hero against Northampton Town in 1941.

92	R. Taylor	(3)	v	Watford	12 Mar 1996
93	A. Hunt	(3)	v	Reading	10 Sep 1996
94	L. Hughes	(3)	v	Crystal Palace	5 Sep 1998
95	L. Hughes	(3)	v	Huddersfield Town	14 Nov 1998

FA Cup

1	G. James	(3)	v	Luton Town	10 Jan 1925
2	J. Cookson	(4)	v	Bradford	16 Feb 1929
3	W. G. Richardson	(3)	v	Sheffield United	26 Jan 1935
4	W. G. Richardson	(3)	v	Darlington	30 Jan 1937
5	D. Walsh	(3)	v	Chelsea	12 Feb 1949
6	R. Allen	(3)	v	Newcastle United	20 Feb 1954
7	D. Kevan	(3)	v	Plymouth Argyle	9 Jan 1960
8	T. Brown	(3)	v	Notts County	5 Jan 1974
9	K. Donovan	(3)	v	Aylesbury	14 Nov 1993

League Cup

1	J. Astle	(3)	v	Coventry City	10 Nov 1965
2	R. Hope	(3)	v	Aston Villa	14 Sep 1966
3	J. Astle	(3)	v	West Ham United	18 Jan 1967

Fairs Cup

| 1 | T. Brown | (3) | v | DOS Utrecht | 9 Nov 1966 |

Wartime

1	J. Mann	(3)	v	Aston Villa	26 Dec 1916
2	J. Roberts	(3)	v	Wolverhampton W	23 Aug 1918
3	T. Magee	(3)	v	RAF	22 Apr 1919
4	E. Jones	(3)	v	Tottenham Hotspur	2 Sep 1939
5	H. Jones	(3)	v	Stoke City	30 Sep 1939
6	H. Jones	(3)	v	Walsall	20 Jan 1940
7	H. Jones	(3)	v	Birmingham	25 Mar 1940
8	H. Jones	(3)	v	Luton Town	13 Apr 1940
9	W. G. Richardson	(3)	v	Leicester City	21 Dec 1940
10	W. G. Richardson	(6)	v	RAF	24 May 1941
11	H. Jones	(4)	v	Cardiff City	30 Aug 1941
12	W. G. Richardson	(5)	v	Swansea Town	18 Oct 1941
13	W. G. Richardson	(6)	v	Luton Town	22 Nov 1941
14	P. McKennan	(3)	v	Northampton Town	6 Dec 1941
15	W. G. Richardson	(3)	v	Birmingham	20 Dec 1941
16	W. Elliott	(3)	v	Northampton Town	5 Sep 1942
17	L. Millard	(3)	v	Leicester City	12 Sep 1942
18	L. Millard	(3)	v	Wolverhampton W	3 Oct 1942
19	W. Elliott	(3)	v	Leicester City	26 Dec 1942
20	W. G. Richardson	(3)	v	Northampton Town	26 Apr 1943
21	W. Elliott	(4)	v	Derby County	11 Sep 1943
22	H. Ball	(3)	v	Walsall	15 Jan 1944
23	W. Elliott	(3)	v	Walsall	15 Jan 1944
24	W. Elliott	(3)	v	Wolverhampton W	18 Mar 1944
25	I. Clarke	(3)	v	Coventry City	30 Sep 1944
26	I. Clarke	(3)	v	Birmingham City	17 Feb 1945
27	I. Clarke	(3)	v	Northampton Town	17 Mar 1945

Scored by Opposing Players

Football League

Player			Opponent	Date
G. Morris	(3)	v	Nottingham Forest	20 Oct 1900
D. McLean	(3)	v	Sheffield Wednesday	27 Apr 1912
W. Roberts	(3)	v	Preston North End	25 Mar 1921
L. Davies	(3)	v	Cardiff City	10 Nov 1923
D. Jack	(4)	v	Bolton Wanderers	26 Dec 1923
D. Halliday	(3)	v	Sunderland	5 Sep 1925
J. Sullivan	(3)	v	Notts County	7 Nov 1925
C. Wilson	(3)	v	Stoke City	31 Aug 1927
H. Andrews	(3)	v	Notts County	3 Sep 1928
M. Holmes	(3)	v	Grimsby Town	30 Apr 1932
J. Dyson	(3)	v	Grimsby Town	30 Apr 1932
R. Gurney	(3)	v	Sunderland	24 Mar 1934
R. Carter	(3)	v	Sunderland	23 Oct 1937
J. Calder	(3)	v	Bolton Wanderers	6 Nov 1937
R. Thomas	(3)	v	Plymouth Argyle	19 Apr 1947
J. Rowley	(3)	v	Manchester United	18 Aug 1951
D. Viollet	(3)	v	Manchester United	20 Dec 1955
F. Lee	(3)	v	Bolton Wanderers	22 Sep 1962
F. Pickering	(3)	v	Blackburn Rovers	10 Nov 1962
A. McEvoy	(3)	v	Blackburn Rovers	23 Nov 1963
D. Herd	(3)	v	Manchester United	17 Dec 1966
A. Ball	(4)	v	Everton	16 Mar 1968
G. Birtles	(3)	v	Nottingham Forest	1 Sep 1979
I. McCulloch	(3)	v	Notts County	24 Mar 1982
I. Wark	(3)	v	Liverpool	23 Mar 1985
J. Deehan	(3)	v	Ipswich Town	13 Sep 1986
E. Sheringham	(3)	v	Millwall	26 Dec 1987
S. McCarthy	(3)	v	Plymouth Argyle	16 Apr 1990
S. Farrell	(3)	v	Fulham	1 Jan 1992
S. Thornmber	(3)	v	Swansea City	25 Jan 1992
S. Castle	(3)	v	Plymouth Argyle	12 Apr 1993
P. Thorne	(3)	v	Swindon Town	19 Mar 1995
D. Gordon	(3)	v	Crystal Palace	23 Dec 1995
I. Roberts	(3)	v	Wolverhampton W	15 Sep 1996

FA Cup

Player			Opponent	Date
A. Mountenay	(3)	v	Leicester Fosse	14 Jan 1905
R. Ayre	(3)	v	Charlton Athletic	29 Jan 1955
T. Buzaglo	(3)	v	Woking	5 Jan 1991

Friendly Matches

	Player			Opponent	Date
1	F. Buck	(3)	v	Past Albion XI	24 Dec 1900
2	C. Clark	(3)	v	All Stars XI	15 May 1967
3	D. Goodman	(3)	v	Tottenham Hotspur	19 Feb 1988

	Player			Opponent	Date
28	R. Barlow	(3)	v	Tottenham Hotspur	22 Sep 1945
29	I. Clarke	(4)	v	Chelsea	27 Oct 1945
30	W. Elliott	(3)	v	Southampton	24 Nov 1945
31	I. Clarke	(3)	v	Newport County	13 Apr 1946

Billy Elliott netted six hat-tricks at The Hawthorns during wartime football.

Former Walsall centre-forward Gilbert Alsop scored four goals against a Football League XI in 1935.

Zenith Data Systems Cup

D. Saunders	(3)	Derby County	29 Nov	1989
I. Banks	(3)	Barnsley	21 Nov	1990

Birmingham Cup

C. Millington	(3)	Aston Villa	4 Sep	1905

Birmingham Charity Cup

S. Doncaster	(3)	Aston Villa	2 Oct	1912

Staffordshire Cup

C. Millington	(3)	Aston Villa	2 Oct	1905

King George V Jubilee Trust

R. Dix	(3)	Football League XI	8 May	1935
G Alsop	(4)	Football League XI	8 May	1935

Wartime

J. Morrison	(3)	Tottenham Hotspur	2 Sep	1939
J. Mullen	(3)	Leicester City	21 Dec	1940
F. Broome	(3)	Aston Villa	25 May	1942
G. Hinsley	(3)	Walsall	27 Nov	1943
F. Steele	(4)	Stoke City	19 Feb	1944
T. Sale	(3)	Stoke City	19 Feb	1944
G. Edwards	(3)	Aston Villa	2 Apr	1945
D. Massart	(3)	Birmingham City	12 May	1945
M. Tadman	(3)	Charlton Athletic	15 Apr	1946

Friendlies

F. Creek	(3)	Corinthians	28 Mar	1925
V. Busunov	(3)	CDSA, Moscow	29 Oct	1957

Testimonials

T. Ford	(3)	International XI (N. Heath)	25 Apr	1956
D. Kevan	(3)	WBA Past XI (G.Williams)	28 Apr	1965

Albion and Me …

Bob Finch

(Believed to be the oldest former Albion player alive today)

The ball came low across the goalmouth – I couldn't miss. I scored, one of only two goals I netted during my Albion career. That was in 1933, yet it seemed only yesterday that my footballing career started.

At school in Hednesford I lived for sport – athletics and football especially. I left school and started work down the mines at the 'Old Hednesford Colliery', first as a messenger boy and then as a 'rope runner' which meant that I conveyed coal from the stall to the bottom of the shaft. I started playing right-back for Hednesford Town in the Birmingham League when I was 15 and in my first season clubs like Aston Villa, Stoke and Wolves were showing interest me.

Legend has it that if Albion wanted a player a director would go to one of the mines and shout down the shaft his requirements. With the next load up would come a player to fit the bill! It didn't happen quite like that but in April 1925 I signed for the Albion. I was still only 16 at the time.

During the 1925-26 season Hubert Chamberlain had an accident and I played my first game in the Central League side, the first of many I might add, It was on 27 February when I made my senior debut against Leicester City at The Hawthorns. The reserve team regularly played in front of 5,000 fans, but to run out on to the pitch with almost 20,000 supporters cheering on their teams was an experience to savour. I never lost that thrill of first hearing and then seeing all those fans when running up the tunnel.

It all started so well in the 1925-26 season. I was only 17 and playing for the first team, one of the youngest players in the League at that time, but in the next season I contracted diphtheria and was ill for ten weeks. The season was over for me. In the 1927-28 campaign I regained my place in the first team and played in two England trial matches, one at The Hawthorns and the other at Middlesbrough. These turned out to be 'real' trials as at Middlesbrough my covering half-back was carrying an injury and on the other occasion we formed no understanding with each other whatsoever.

I always regretted this lost opportunity as I wanted to compete at the highest level.

I lost my place in 1930 through injury and the Albion bought Bert Trentham, a great player who took over my position. I didn't regain it on a regular basis until 1936. In 1939, after 14 years at The Hawthorns, I was transferred to Swansea Town, but the war broke out soon afterwards and I returned to the Midlands.

To my embarrassment I failed my medical for the army due to a burst ear drum and joined the police war reserve instead. I then played in some All-Star matches and for Hednesford and Tamworth. I was still involved with football with the police for some years but times moves on and golf became my sporting passion.

The Albion had been very good to me. I started on £3 10s per week and over the years this went up to £8 in the playing season with a win bonus of £2 and £1 for a draw. In the summer my wage was reduced to £6 a week. Not a great deal compared with today's standards but a lot more than I would have earned

Bob Finch, believed to be the oldest surviving Albion player.

The worries, the butterflies in my stomach would begin to dissolve and the long wait was over. We beat Leicester 3-1 and it was the first of more than 230 first-team appearances for the Albion.

In all I played in over 460 games for the Baggies and had a great time. I was a member of Albion's Second Division promotion-winning side in 1930-31 and was reserve full-back at Wembley in both the 1931 and 1935 FA Cup Finals.

I frequently captained the second XI and helped them win the Central League championship on four occasions.

down the pit. I was getting paid for doing something that I loved – playing football and competing.

Usually we would train in the mornings but often had to go back in the afternoon as well. Training consisted of fitness work, a five-mile run was a favourite of the coach, and team relays such as piggy-back races. We did some ball-work and several times during the week we would play practice games. Occasionally we would run, or be taken in a coach to the brine baths at Droitwich to enjoy a relaxing swim. I can remember travelling to Rhyl on several occasions. We would stay in a hotel for several days and do a lot of fitness work as well as playing tennis and golf. That was probably where I first got interested in golf.

The matches were very competitive and injuries frequent but the treatment was basic with the trainer, or his assistant, performing 'magical' massage. It was easy to aggravate an injury during a match because no substitutions were allowed in my day.

This is why the twelfth men were seen dressed in suits on the photographs which were taken when the Prince of Wales shook hands with the teams before the Cup Final.

Remember those old football boots? I certainly do. Several of mine were made by Mansfield Hotspur. They had uppers of brown moor calf with solid, firm soles that were riveted all round and don't forget those unbreakable toe-caps. I think I paid about 26 shillings for a pair and I would use either the 'Villan' or the 'United' model, depending on the playing conditions.

If a new pair were too tight I would lie in a hot bath with them firmly laced to my feet. Controlling the ball was not always easy with these boots but it was the same for everybody.

Occasionally we would play friendly matches and I can recall touring Ireland. We stayed at the Grand Hotel in Belfast and were given a civic welcome by the Lord Mayor of Belfast. The following day we played Linfield. After that it was on to Dublin for a match against Shelbourne, followed by a dinner that night, but we were given strict instructions by our manager 'to bed in good time lads.'

However, the meal did not compare with the celebration dinner following the Baggies' FA Cup Final victory over Birmingham in 1931. The reception was held at the Great Central Hotel, London and the eight courses were complimented by some excellent wine, Liebfraumlich Superior 1921 and Louis Roederer 1920. A good time was had by all.

I was fortunate to play with and against so many good players, but from the opposition I think Alex James of Arsenal was the best forward I ever faced. He could show a back the ball and then magic it away. Stan Matthews was also a wonderful player, so skilful and fast, but unfortunately he often tantalised the left-back and not me. The most gifted winger I ever faced was probably Cliff Bastin, also of Arsenal. He was superb – but when we beat the Gunners in front of almost 65,000 fans at The Hawthorns in the FA Cup in 1937, I think I did a good job on him.

In conclusion, I'm very grateful for my time with the Baggies and the opportunity to meet so many interesting and talented people. Even today as a 91 year-old there are still people who recognise me as Bob Finch, the Albion footballer.

Alan Ashman

It's easy to recall memories of the 1968 FA Cup Final, but what I also remember very clearly are some of the happenings which were not reported on during that unforgettable run-up to Wembley and after the heady celebrations which followed our victory over Everton.

Lining up your pale-faced players for a yellow fever 'jab' is not the best preparation three days before a quarter-final tie with Bill Shankly's Liverpool. On the other hand it did give me something else to think about. I wasn't happy about this interruption but Dr Rimmer had such an enviable calming influence. He smoothed away my panic and even convinced me it was really nothing at all to worry about.

I passed on this gem of medical information to the players and Bobby Hope and Jeff Astle quickly suggested what I should do with the needles.

John Kaye muttered: "Bloody stupid. I'll have two – we might get Leeds in the semi-final!" and John Osborne looked as though he was being led to the scaffold.

A previously arranged end-of-season tour to East Africa was the reason for this unwelcome distraction. The Doc, bless him, was right, of course, but I have a feeling the 'jab' would have got a mention had we not put out Liverpool after two riveting replays watched by close on 150,000 lucky people.

Forty-eight hours after the Cup Final triumph, flying high on Moet in a VC 10, we were on our way to Dar-Es-Salaam.

The players were soon to find out that it needed something more than a yellow fever injection to protect them in Kampala. We played six matches on that tour and the hospitality wherever we went was first class. The two games in Dar-Es-Salaam and two in Nairobi all went well with no real problems. The other two were in Kampala and there was nothing friendly about either of them.

I had to read the *Daily Nation*

100 YEARS AT THE HAWTHORNS

Alan Ashman, recalls the day Albion 'got the needle'.

about problems of behaviour on and off the field and the poor standard of refereeing in East African soccer. One report said: 'A free-for-all began after the referee sent off a Kisumu player. The referee was forced to call a halt to the match – especially as he lost two teeth in the mad melee that followed.'

The first of the Kampala matches was against the Uganda national team. This was a brawl from start to finish and it really opened our eyes.

We were not playing exhibition football. The prestige to be gained from beating the English Cup winners was obviously very much desired and one particular German coach was after it. We won the match with a goal from young Asa Hartford after our skipper Graham Williams had been sent off. We then moved on to Nairobi for the following match against Kenya where the local press condemned the behaviour of the Uganda team and

the lack of control by the referee in no uncertain terms.

When we flew back from Entebbe airport for the match against a combined East African XI we didn't expect it to happen again, but it did – even more so this time.

The match in Kampala's Nakivubu stadium in front of a hostile capacity crowd of 22,000 was a disgrace. Their coach must have rewritten the laws of the game. Hartford was sent off after getting tangled up with two intimidators and this self protection reaction by the youngest, smallest player was the signal for the first pitch invasion. Later the whole stadium seemed to erupt when we strongly objected to a blatant, vicious chest high challenge on Ian Collard, but this time the crowd were joined on the pitch by baton-wielding soldiers. My only concern during the next few minutes of total confusion was to find the missing Asa and drag him off the pitch for the second time.

At half-time we were losing 2-1 on goals, well behind on points and knock-downs, a player short and seated in the stand, our chairman Mr Jim Gaunt and his fellow directors were being marked man-to-man by three East African presidents – Obote, Nyerere and Kaunda. Wembley was a million miles away and so was the football.

In the noisy dressing room a decision was made. We go out for the second half and play their rules. We did just that and our ten men did it better than their 11. The hard stuff continued but we replied in kind – and with interest.

Time was running out when a spectacular 18-yard volley from Ronnie Rees had us whooping around and referee Ngaah couldn't do anything about it – despite adding on 15 minutes stoppage-time!

Phew! All that hassle for a hand-

ALBION AND ME . . .

ful of West Brom directors and a small group of British residents and diplomats.

The following day I was assured by reporters that only the assassination of Senator Robert Kennedy in America had kept what they described as 'The Battle of Kampala' off their front pages.

I wondered if it might just have found space had they won?

Yes that was a memorable year – the year the Albion rolled up its sleeves and got the needle.

Jeff Astle

If I could have written the script to the 1968 FA Cup Final, it would have read: West Bromwich Albion 1 Everton 0. Goalscorer: Jeff Astle. We were destined to win the trophy that year (after a narrow escape at Col-

Jeff Astle – "If I'd written the script..."

(chester) and I was already marked down as the scorer of the winning goal at Wembley. So what was different? The only thing wrong, really, was that it took me so long to find the net.

Looking back on that season I realise now what a fantastic feat I achieved by scoring in every round of the FA Cup competition and finished up as one of the top marksmen in Division One.

I never gave it a thought at the time but I was told that only a handful of players had scored in every round prior to me achieving the feat in '68 – and only Peter Osgood has done it since.

Of course, we were a very good side and with three or four more players I really believe we could have won the First Division championship.

The spirit in the team was tremendous. I still tell people now that we all acted like brothers. We played together, went out together and knew each others families.

But that moment when I scored the winning goal to bring the Cup back to The Hawthorns is one I shall remember for the rest of my life... it was such a fitting climax to a wonderful season for myself and the Albion.

Somehow I knew Albion's name was on the trophy that year and that's just how things worked out.

I was so excited that I never went to bed that night. I just talked and walked around London waiting to pick up the first edition of the morning newspapers.

I even found a small box of matches with a picture of my goal on the front. Amazing that. And when we got back to the Midlands it was another great feeling...the fans even decorated the outside of my house with flags, banners and rosettes with the word 'King' everywhere.

My only regret was having to give up League football through injury in 1974. I really wanted to carry on at Albion, but there was no way I was going to take money under false pretences.

But I wouldn't swap those happy memories for anything. The team we had between 1967 and 1970 was a very good one. It used to run itself most of the time.

The saying was that we would 'turn up on a Saturday and go for goals'.

Sometimes it worked, sometimes it didn't. But we had great fun.

Looking back, I often wish I was starting all over again. I could have become a millionaire in this day and age. But then what's money when you've had the times I've had in football.

I really never thought it would work out like it did when I joined Albion from Notts County for £25,000 in 1964. But everything went down so well. I made loads of friends, played alongside and against some of the world's greatest players. I represented England, played in the World Cup finals and visited many countries. They used to say you had to be a sailor to see the world – I did it playing the game I loved and with the best team in the land – West Bromwich Albion. Let's get into the Premiership and quick.

The goal that Jeff Astle would have scripted – the winner in a Wembley Cup Final.

Ray Barlow

I was spotted by former Albion centre-forward Jimmy Cookson whilst playing junior football for Gerrads FC, my local team in Swindon. I was recommended to secretary-manager Fred Everiss and after a brief discussion I signed the appropriate forms at The Hawthorns in June 1944, turning professional six months later. It was the start of a tremendous career for me with Albion which lasted for 15 years.

I played a bit during the latter stages of the War and after my national service I finally established myself in the first team during the second half of the 1948-49 which culminated in us winning promotion to the First Division under manager Jack Smith.

We had a fine set of players at the club in those days and once we had consolidated ourselves in the top flight we improved rapidly. Smith

ble. We mastered the Russians in their own backyard, gave mighty Honved and their famous Hungarian superstars, Puskas, Bozsik, Koscis and such likes, a run for their money in Brussels and we beat all the best teams in England over a period of three or four years including the Busby Babes from pre-Munich days.

I had some happy times at Albion. I made so many friends, some I'm still in contact with, and I wouldn't have swapped being a footballer for all the tea in China.

After leaving Albion in 1960 I had a brief spell with Birmingham City and then assisted Stourbridge before hanging up my boots.

I still attend matches at The Hawthorns – well I am a true Baggie – and I wish the team every success in the future...let's hope we can get into the Premiership.

Brendon Batson

Whenever people talk to me about West Bromwich Albion the thing that immediately springs to mind is one glorious season...the season we took Europe by storm in 1978-79.

I had left Arsenal without really making the grade but it was always my ambition to play at the highest level and in the highest Division I could, so when the chance came to leave Cambridge United to join Albion I jumped at it.

But I really didn't realise how well the move would turn out... thanks mainly to that wonderful season.

By the start of the 1978-79 campaign I had made my way into Ron Atkinson's first team in place of Paddy Mulligan... by the end of it I was established in the right-back position.

During that same season I had the truly magnificent experience of European football. Only now, with clubs still attempting to qualify for various European competitions, do I

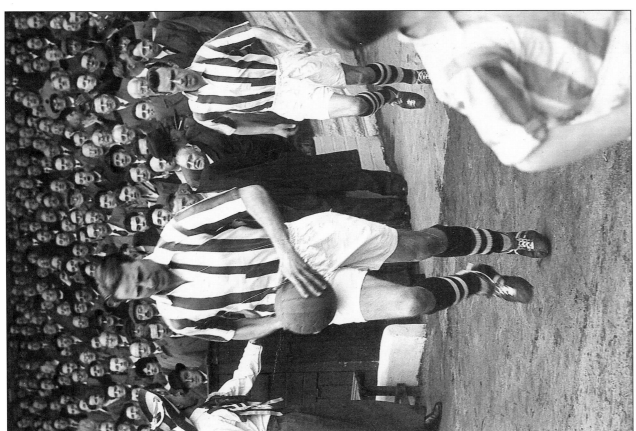

Ray Barlow (followed by Jimmy Dudley) leads out Albion for their FA Cup semi-final replay with Aston Villa at St Andrew's in 1957. Villa won 1-0.

had been replaced by Jesse Carver who in turn handed over the duties to Vic Buckingham. At that time we were a very strong team and in 1953-54 almost won the double. It was only through a crop of injuries (suffered after we had reached Wembley) plus international call-ups which stopped us from taking the League championship, but we made up for that disappointment by beating Preston in the Cup Final.

I must say that the players at Albion in the early 1950s were great – goalkeepers Norman Heath and Jimmy Sanders, full-backs Stan

Rickaby, and Len Millard, my fellow half-backs Jimmy Dudley, Joe Kennedy and Jimmy Dugdale, and a truly brilliant forward-line of Frank Griffin, Paddy Ryan, Ronnie Allen, Johnny Nicholls, George Lee – and just prior to that there was Dave Walsh. We had some quality reserves as well including Billy Brookes, Ken Hodgkisson, Wilf Carter and a few others.

We were a very consistent team; we played attractive football – we were made to by the boss – and I believe we could have won the European Cup if it had been possi-

realise just how important that was. But probably the best thing about that one season were the players around me. They were the finest bunch of lads in the land – even in the First Division.

Obviously that season had its high and low points. I remember the game at Norwich City when we went to the top of the League. It should have been a great celebration, but we only managed a draw and Norwich snatched the equalising goal while I was off the field changing my boots.

Needless to say the boss wasn't very pleased with me that day.

But the good times far outweighed the bad. I don't think I will ever forget the UEFA Cup trip to Valencia when Laurie Cunningham gave the best performance I have ever seen – but then he was just typical of the playing staff that term.

It was really exciting to go out and play alongside World Cup stars and we truly believed in our abilities.

At the back we had the strength of John Wile and Ally Robertson; Wiley was an ever-present and played over 70 matches that season. In the middle Bryan Robson and Len Cantello were fabulous. I believe it was Len who helped Robbo develop into the international player he later became.

At full-back alongside myself there was Derek Statham who, in terms of talent, was one of the best footballers I ever played with.

And up front Cyrille Regis and Laurie Cunningham were superb, but Ally Brown was the unsung hero. He used to pop in some vital goals while Tony Brown scored them regularly from midfield.

A team of all-rounders.

And we can't forget the boss – big Ron – who used to get us so wound up before a match. I recall that on the odd occasion as we left the changing rooms he asked our kitman Dave Matthews to ring a cowbell as if we were boxers going into the ring for a big fight.

Defeat against Nottingham Forest on the last day of that 1978-79 season cost us the runners-up spot in the First Division. We came so close to winning the League and UEFA Cup that season but in the end had nothing to show for our efforts. Yet the memories will linger on, and for me, well I think I just about repaid my £30,000 transfer fee.

Brendon Batson – one 'glorious season' always springs to his mind.

Martyn Bennett

The whole of my professional football career was shaped by my first few years at West Bromwich Albion – and I will be ever thankful for that.

When I joined the club as an apprentice I realised I perhaps hadn't got quite so much talent as some of the youngsters around me...so I decided from day one I was going to work my socks off to make the first team.

Remi Moses had the same attitude as myself and together we gave up our social life and worked towards that common goal of first team football. You see, it's all about attitude – there are far too many players who have talent and think there's no need to work.

At 17 years of age my time finally came – the most memorable moment in my Albion career – my League debut against Everton at The Hawthorns.

I had to mark Dave Thomas, but the whole of the team gave me such tremendous support that I had no need to feel nervous. And to crown it all we won the game 1-0.

When I look back now I will always remember the example those players set me from the day I walked into the club and I tried to follow that example for the rest of my career.

Ally Robertson would always

Martyn Bennett – "...the whole of my professional career was shaped by Albion."

Wilf Carter is beaten to the ball by Charlton goalkeeper Sam Bartram in 1954.

have a word of advice as would John Wile – but if I stepped out of line they would come down on me like a ton of bricks. Yet I learned an awful lot from both of them and copied their attitude, leadership and discipline. I wouldn't have been half the player if it wasn't for the professionals of the day – the Robertsons, Wiles, Brendon Batsons, Bryan Robsons and so on... they were so good that we hardly needed a manager.

And once I had become an experienced professional myself I tried to pass tips on to the younger Albion players as they came into the club. If kids get a good grounding and a good start like I did, then it will stay with them for the rest of their lives.

The team I played in went on to represent Britain (England if you like) in Europe and reached two FA semi-finals, one of which – the FA Cup clash with Queens Park Rangers at Highbury in 1982 – was the most disappointing day of my footballing life.

But the good times helped me through all of my injury problems and I felt the good times were just around the corner again before I was forced to quit the game with a back injury in 1990 at the age of 29. I so much wanted to be part of it – but it wasn't to be and although I still watch the team, it's nothing like the real thing, being out there on the pitch yourself.

Wilf Carter

My earliest memories of the Albion were when I was a toddler, just big enough to be able to look over the wall at the Birmingham Road End of the ground. Some of my favourite players at that time in the mid-1940s, were Billy Gripton, Jim Pemberton, Harry Kinsell, Frank Hodgetts and Ike Clarke. When I was 15 years of age (late 1948) I started work as an office boy at The

Hawthorns under the watchful eyes of Eph Smith, Alan Everiss and manager Jack Smith, who eventually signed me as a professional – that was the happiest day of my life – the fifth January 1951.

My fondest memory of my stay at The Hawthorns was being a non-playing member of the 1954 Cup-winning squad. Along with Stuart Williams, Freddie Cox and Billy Brookes, we travelled to London as part of the 'team' that almost achieved the coveted League and Cup double that season.

Another happy memory for me came the following season when Albion drew 4-4 with rivals Wolves in front of 45,000 fans at Molineux in the annual FA Charity Shield game. We had two goals disallowed

that night and with some justification you could say we were robbed. Nevertheless I have treasured the plaque I received for sharing that shield with the Wolves.

I obviously recall my debut for Albion against Fulham at Craven Cottage in September 1951 when I deputised for the injured Arthur Smith at inside-right. After scoring four goals in four pre-season friendly matches at The Hawthorns I became part of the first team set up and was over the moon when I was named in the side. Unfortunately we lost 1-0 in front of 30,000 fans, but I had made the breakthrough.

Soon afterwards I returned to London for my second senior outing and this time we beat Chelsea 3-1 and I scored my first goal.

Jim Cumbes – great pals with his rival John Osborne.

The best goal I ever scored for Albion – my own choice – was the one at Molineux in December 1955. We were 3-1 down at the time; there were just ten minutes left on the watch and suddenly we strung together a terrific move involving five or six players. The ball was being passed around sweetly and as it came across the edge of the penalty area I raced forward and fired a shot high into the top left-hand corner of the net, well away from the diving 'Cat' Bert Williams. We pressed hard for an equaliser after that but couldn't manage it.

I got along with everybody I came in contact with at The Hawthorns, from Major H. Wilson Keys to the char-lady herself Mrs. Beckett.

It was a pleasure and honour to have been associated with West Bromwich Albion Football Club. I was sorry to leave, but thereafter I had some great times with Plymouth Argyle and Exeter City and I still attend matches at The Hawthorns whenever I can, travelling up from my home in the West Country.

Jim Cumbes

My transfer to the Albion in August 1969 came right out of the blue to me, although there had apparently been several First Division clubs who had shown interest for some months.

The move came after a particularly good match for me with Tranmere Rovers at Port Vale in a League Cup-tie. We won 1-0 and I had one of those games that goalkeepers dream about.

Alan Ashman signed me for £35,000 which I think at the time was about the second highest fee ever paid for a goalkeeper.

Although the match against Port Vale was the one that clinched my move to Albion, it was also a costly one for me – Albion got to the Wembley League Cup Final that season, but I was Cup-tied and unavailable for selection right through the competition.

Those were tough early days for me...adjusting to the standards of the First Division and what was a very good Albion side, which contained legends like Jeff Astle, Bobby Hope, Tony Brown, John Kaye and captain Graham Williams.

I remember well my first morning at the training ground at Hope's. I was quietly getting my training gear on, preparing for my debut the following day against Arsenal at The Hawthorns in front of 32,000 fans and the Match of the Day cameras.

The papers had made a great play about me being a first class cricketer as well as a footballer, but I was not to know at this stage that Jeff Astle was the great joker of the team, and as I sat in the changing room doing up my boot laces, a voice opposite me declared that the club had paid £35,000 for a fast bowler.

As I bowed my head and tried to keep out of the way, Jeff then added that they could have got John Snow for £20,000.

Humour was always around in the dressing room at Albion in those days, and I have some wonderful memories of my short (two-year) spell there.

The late John Osborne was, of course, my great rival for the goalkeeping spot but he became a great buddy. In fact that group of players had a remarkable team spirit and we were all great pals.

It is not often that we get the opportunity to meet each other again, but whenever we do, it is as though we were all together only yesterday. There are hundreds of other stories regarding those good old days at The Hawthorns, but space is short...

Chuck Drury

I spent ten years at The Hawthorns and I have so many fond memories of my time with Albion. My earliest

ALBION AND ME . . .

recollections on joining the club was to witness the sheer brilliance of the 1954 FA Cup winning side. I was in awe of them watching the magic of their play, the pin-point passing, the delicate footwork and the intelligent unselfish running off the ball. The Hawthorns was certainly the place to be to learn the trade.

Despite the stress, the injuries, the tellings-off and the inevitable demotion, I quite enjoyed my stay with Albion. There were a few moments of glory, just a little bit of fame, but best of all I made lots of friends.

Chuck Drury – in awe of the 1954 FA Cup winning players.

I remember some great times I had with fellow team-mates, particularly Derek Kevan, Keith Smith, Jimmy Campbell, Alec Jackson and Chippy Clark. I used to enjoy the training and had a few laughs in the dressing room with our resident comedian Barry Hughes. He was hilarious. Probably his best story was when he portrayed the club Directors in the roles of cavalrymen which he'd seen in a western film the previous night.

There are three matches which will always stick in my mind. One

was an FA Cup-tie at The Hawthorns against Spurs in 1962. My instruction from the manager Archie Macaulay was to mark Jimmy Greaves out of the game. I failed miserably, Greaves scored twice and we lost 4-2. Although somewhat exonerated by the manager I felt very badly about allowing him so much space.

Another game was when we played Wolves at Molineux a month after that Spurs encounter. It was an evening kick-off and on the morning of the match my son, Carl, was very ill in hospital. There were complications after he had broken his leg. Obviously I was worried sick but I decided to play in order to take my mind off things. We performed brilliantly and won 5-1, and I was rewarded with my only goal for Albion – a screamer from 25 yards. Thankfully Carl recovered from his ordeal.

The third game was the last match of the 1961-62 season at White Hart Lane. We beat Spurs, the reigning League champions and FA Cup holders, 2-1 in front of 52,000 fans. Some of my family were there to see us beat the country's best team.

Jimmy Dugdale

When I signed professional forms for Albion in the summer of 1952 I was paid £12-a-week. Later on in my career I earned up to £30-a-week (including £5 appearance money) and even when I played for England 'B' in Hungary I only got 2s 6d (13p) for one day's expenses. When Albion won the Cup in 1954 all the players received a £20 bonus for that Wembley occasion. Nothing like what players receive today – then those were the days before freedom of contract that has ultimately given footballers the licence to print money.

Players like myself from the old

days aren't jealous because we all know the game can be a precarious business. It's a limited lifespan and in any case the next tackle could always be the one to put you out for good.

The game was hard but fair in my day. We always had a drink after every game and had lots of laughs. I remember the late Johnny Nicholls, a great pal of mine, coming out of manager Vic Buckingham's office at The Hawthorns one day looking gob-smacked.

He, like myself, had just played against Preston in the 1954 FA Cup Final. He had scored almost 30 goals that season and all of a sudden had found that he he had been docked ten bob (50p) a week from his wages for not scoring enough.

The expression of Nicco's face had to been seen to be believed. But it was true and furthermore there was nothing he could do about it.

I had a great time at Albion. I

Jimmy Dugdale – his pal Johnny Nicholls suffered a wage cut for not scoring enough.

played with some brilliant footballers – Ray Barlow, Joe Kennedy, Jimmy Dudley, Frank Griffin, Reg Ryan, Ronnie Allen, George Lee, Don Howe, Stuart Williams, Len Millard, Nicholls of course, and so many more. Even the goalkeepers Norman Heath and Jimmy Sanders were pretty useful. I wouldn't have swapped my time at The Hawthorns for anything else.

After Albion I played for the Villa and had the fortune to go back to Wembley and win another Cup winners' medal in 1957. I then played for Queens Park Rangers before retiring in 1963.

Despite the trauma of losing my right leg a few years ago following an accident at work, I still attend old players' reunions – I always look forward to these occasions. They bring back so many memories when we sit around chatting about the good old days – and the bad. Obviously certain people look concerned when I sit there looking rather incapacitated in a chair, unable to get around. They ask me how I am, I just them I feel legless.

Don Goodman

I will always remember my first impressions of West Bromwich Albion and The Hawthorns – for me, it was like a dream come true.

When I arrived at the club, under the guidance of manager Ron Saunders at the time, it was like landing on another planet compared with my old club, Bradford City.

I will never forget Bradford because they were my first club, but I will always be thankful to Ron Saunders for giving me the break and having the faith in my abilities.

I was surprised and flattered that such a big club should be interested in me and I remember thinking at the time 'All we need to do now is get back into the First Division and things will be perfect.'

Of course, things don't always go according to plan and the first couple of seasons we only narrowly missed relegation to Division Three – and that would have been disastrous.

But things were turned round and we did well although we never climbed back into the top flight during my time at The Hawthorns.

There were plenty of high spots for me at Albion – a gripping FA Cup-tie with Everton which went to a replay before we lost in the last minute at Goodison Park, was one of the best.

I was injured in that game at the time when I was in tip-top form and I never really recaptured it afterwards.

My first hat-trick also came in that season in another unforgettable match at home to Crystal Palace which we won 5-3. I took hold of the matchball afterwards and still

Don Goodman, for whom joining Albion was 'a dream come true'.

have it in my possession (somewhere).

There were also a few low spots but throughout my time with Albion the supporters were always good to me and that was a tremendous help. Albion fans love a trier and, even if things didn't always go right for you, I was a battler and always gave 100 per cent out on the field, no matter what.

During my time at The Hawthorns I saw a lot of changes, including three different managers – but I learnt a tremendous amount from a lot of people including players.

I was sad to leave The Hawthorns in a way but as they say time moves on. I always got a great reception when I revisited Albion territory, especially with Sunderland and with Wolves – it was marvellous when they applauded me wearing an old gold shirt.

I wish Albion all the best for the future.

Ken Hodgkisson

I first started playing serious football as a pupil at Spon Lane School. Then I turned out regularly for Erdington Albion and Church Army Social, reaching the local Shield Cup Final at The Hawthorns which we won 4-1. I was late arriving for this game and the 12th man was kitted out and ready go on when I suddenly appeared. I'm glad I got there because after the game I was asked to join the Albion groundstaff. That was quite a thrill I can tell you.

I developed slowly and reached the youth squad. Then one day after training Arthur Fitton came down the corridor at The Hawthorns and said Hodgy you're in the first team tomorrow to play at Villa Park. What, I said, you're joking. But it was true and in front of almost 50,000 spectators I made my League debut in April 1953. We drew 1-1 and I had a great time. Soon after-

team and saw some exciting players develop, among them Martyn Bennett, Mickey Lewis (one of my best finds), Carlton Palmer, David Burrows, even a young Sean Flynn (in the mid 1980s – a player we initially missed) and Gary Robson.

In later years I did a lot of scouting and although the game, the team, the ground have all changed,

football is still my game, and I would do it all over again given the opportunity.

Bobby Hope

Throughout my footballing career I always believed in entertaining the crowds – and, believe me, that's exactly what we did when I played for the Albion.

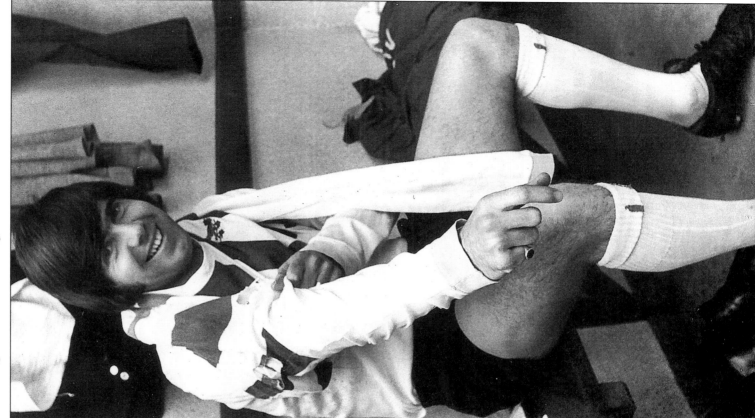

Bobby Hope "...I always tried to entertain. That's what footballers are paid for..."

Ken Hodgkisson – he thought his debut call-up was a joke.

wards I scored my first senior goal in a 2-2 draw at Old Trafford.

Trainer Arthur Fitton gave me plenty of encouragement in the dressing room before the game and out on the pitch Ronnie Allen and Ray Barlow were also so obliging.

At the start of my Albion career Billy Elliott and Jim Sanders – who always seemed to be puffing away on a cigarette – gave me great support as did the other two trainers, Arthur Fitton and 'W. G.' Richardson.

After six years at The Hawthorns I moved to Walsall in 1955, staying at Fellows Park until 1966. After that I assisted Worcester City, Dudley Town as both a player and manager before linking up with my old Walsall colleague Albert McPherson on the coaching staff at The Hawthorns in 1975. Initially I looked after the youngsters who came to the club for night training. I helped Albert 'Mac' with the youth

100 YEARS AT THE HAWTHORNS

When I joined the club at the end of the 1950s I was immediately impressed by the stock of internationals playing in the first team.

Don Howe, Bobby Robson, Ray Barlow, Stuart Williams, Ronnie Allen and Derek Kevan were all part of the set up and they shaped my thinking on how the game should be played – lessons that I remembered and tried to put into practice throughout my career.

I learnt a lot from the older players and when I made my League debut against Arsenal at The Hawthorns in April 1960 being marked by a certain Tommy Docherty, it was certainly a day I will never forget.

But not only were we an entertaining side in those days, we were also an adventurous one, sometimes too adventurous for our own good, and that's probably why we didn't do as well as we could have in the First Division.

We became known as a Cup side and we proved that to be the case in 1966, 1967, 1968 and 1970 when we reached four major Finals, although to this day I will always cherish our dramatic FA Cup quarter-final second replay victory over the favourites Liverpool at Maine Road in 1968, rather than any of those four Finals.

When people remind me of the Cup, I always think about the first game we played against Colchester United in 1968 when we were really lucky to scrape a draw. They had a goal disallowed in the closing stages and nobody to this day knows why it was ruled out.

It just goes to prove that you need luck in the Cup competitions, but you also have to know how to play a bit. And not only did we have a tremendous side but we also had a tremendous team spirit within the club.

Jeff Astle was one of the funniest

men I've ever come in contact with and even John 'Yorky' Kaye was very humorous at times, dry but humorous.

Oh yes, there were bad times when I was supposed to be leaving the club, but even the bad times were good in a strange sort of way.

During my time at Albion I managed to break into the international scene with Scotland when I will never forget playing alongside such characters as Frank McLintock and Jimmy Johnstone.

It was an enjoyable time and I am honestly pleased that I played then rather than today. I was proud to have been a player with the Albion – despite the fact that I later played for rivals Birmingham City, Sheffield Wednesday and in America.

Maarten Jol

Moving to The Hawthorns was a big thing for me. I was the first Dutch footballer to play for West Bromwich Albion and the £200,000 fee paid for my services made me think 'have I done the right thing.' The answer was yes. I had always wanted to play in England ever since Frans Thijssen and Arnold Muhren had come over to sign for Ipswich Town.

I first started to kick a ball around when I was five. I had no time for other games – I wanted to be a footballer.

As a youngster I supported Tottenham Hotspur and when I came over to England as a teenager (not very often I might add) I always tried to go and watch Spurs. I even saw Aston Villa, West Ham and Leeds all play at home, the latter against the Albion.

I was playing for Twente Enschede when Albion's manager Ronnie Allen came to see me in 1981. He wanted me to fill the position left by Bryan Robson. It didn't take me too long to say yes – and I made my English debut in the

October of that year against Southampton. The fans accepted me – I think – and I had a good first season at The Hawthorns, although I was disappointed to lose in two Cup semi-finals, one against Spurs, when I came face to face with one of my idols, Glenn Hoddle.

I was grateful in a way that Romeo Zondervan joined me at Albion. We were good mates and are still close today.

Maarten Jol, always wanted to play in England after Thijssen and Muhren came over.

I enjoyed my three years in England, especially with Albion. I made many good friends and visited some exciting places.

After a brief spell with Coventry City, I moved back to Holland to play for Den Haag and my last visit to The Hawthorns was when I came across with a band of Holland supporters for the European Championships. We were all shown round the stadium and I was amazed at the museum. That brought back some memories.

Harry Kinsell

Just lately my life seems to have been spent visiting the doctors or the hospital – who'd get old? I was 78 in May 1999.

I first joined Albion as a 14 year-old and played for the third team for two seasons then I moved into the Central League side and signed professional forms on my 17th birthday.

The signing-on fee then was just £10. Six months after my 18th birthday I was playing for Albion's reserves against Stoke and they tried to sign me for £2,000. There was no Bosman Rule in those days and on reflection I'm glad I stayed on.

Unfortunately the outbreak of World War Two interrupted my career – as it did for so many other footballers.

I joined the forces and became a PT instructor stationed in Blackpool, therefore I was able to play in some great sides up there which included Stanley Matthews, Stan Mortensen, Harry Johnston and Ronnie Dix. We reached the 1944 Wartime Cup Final but lost to Aston Villa.

My first job of the day as a junior with Albion was to clean out the cage and feed the bird (the thrush – the Black Country throstle).

On a Saturday home game it was given pride of place in its cage, hanging proudly on the front of the main Halford's Lane stand above the players' tunnel. Of course, the caging of wild birds is illegal now – so Albion have to make do with one on a badge or that ornamental 'Throstle' near the Smethwick End.

Also as a junior – after I had completed my chores for the day – I used to enjoy a game of snooker with Sammy Short, the third team trainer. He was quite a good player and if he hadn't been a professional footballer (he played inside-forward for Albion in the 1920s) he could

Harry Kinsell, tells the story of the 'green cockrel'.

well have become a Fred or even Steve Davis.

I suppose my best pals at The Hawthorns were wing-half Cliff Edwards, a local Cannock lad like myself, right-winger Billy Elliott, those two great Irish internationals Dave Walsh and Jack Vernon, and full-back Bob Finch from Hednesford, who was coming to the end of his career when I first joined the club. He's still alive now – the old codger.

I must tell you about the incident of the GREEN cockerel. We had gone on a tour to Belgium and

Luxembourg in 1946 to play three matches. At the start of the first game against a Belgium XI in Verviers, Billy Elliott was presented with a green cockerel in a lovely resplendent cage. We were all proud of our trophy and it travelled around with us, staying in our hotel rooms. One night Ray Barlow, always game for a laugh decided to put a hard boiled egg inside the cage.

The next morning when we looked into the cage there were some of us who thought the bird had laid it.

Unfortunately at the end of the tour we weren't able to bring the bird home so we gave it to the Belgian courier... but the last laugh was on us, for we heard later that the cockerel had turned white...they'd dyed it.

I was fortunate enough to play for England on two occasions, once against Wales at The Hawthorns in October 1945 when we lost 1-0 and I had a scuffle with George Lowrie and the referee ticked both of us off at length. I thought we were going to be dismissed but he let us stay on and finish the match.

In 1948-49, when Albion won promotion to the First Division, I played a game at outside-left against Fulham at home which we lost 1-0. Manager Jack Smith was struggling at the time to find a replacement for the injured Bobby Barker. He'd used Frank Hodgetts, Hugh Morrow, Ginger Wilcox, Ernie Shepherd and Arthur Smith but wasn't all that pleased, so he gave me a go. It was strange really but Bobby came back only to get injured again.

Yes I had some great times at the Albion. I later played for Bolton Wanderers and West Ham but there was something missing there; all my best football was played at The Hawthorns – and I still follow the fortunes of the Baggies to this day.

Alan Merrick

In season 1971-72 I thought I might have a chance of entering the *Guinness Book of Records* by being named as Albion's substitute most times. I must have sat on the bench for 15-20 matches and went on just once, against Arsenal. I got to know that blanket well – it certainly kept me warm. But the manager knew best.

As for me, it was terrible. I didn't like it being the twelfth man at all – not many footballers do. When you did get on you can quickly make

Alan Merrick – "...I thought I might get into the *Guinness Book of Records...*"

yourself look a right Charlie. Normally it took me about ten minutes to settle into the pace of a game and occasionally it was far too late to make much of an impact.

Still, that's football – and despite that I certainly enjoyed my time at The Hawthorns.

I got on so well with so many players – John Wile, Alistair Robertson, Asa Hartford, Lenny Cantello, Tony Brown and jovial Willie Johnston.

I was predominantly left-footed and I preferred to play in defence, even as a sweeper. But manager Don

Howe had other ideas. I played alongside John Wile a fair bit but in one season I donned six different numbered shirts, even playing as a midfield destroyer and as an orthodox full-back. I didn't mind really – it was nice to be involved on a regular basis.

There was always one hell of an atmosphere in the dressing room – win, draw or lose. Even when Albion went down in 1973 we never let our morale slip too low. I knew, as did the rest of the players, that we wouldn't stay down for too long. And so it proved, although I only

ALBION AND ME . . .

figured briefly under Johnny Giles' managment before leaving The Hawthorns for Kidderminster Harriers and then deciding to move over to the States where I am living and working right now.

Good luck to the Albion – let's hope you can make it into the Premiership to celebrate the Millennium in style.

David Mills

When I joined West Bromwich Albion in January 1979 I became Britain's costliest footballer – the fee was £516,000.

I went to The Hawthorns with a lot of optimism but an unfortunate first five months in the Midlands paved the way for things to come for me.

Albion were doing very well that season and Ron Atkinson bought me to strengthen a side that was bang on course for the First Division title.

When I joined up with Albion I was happy with my form having played well for Middlesbrough. I was ambitious and had no hesitation in making the move south.

But things began to go a little wrong shortly after my arrival at The Hawthorns.

Firstly, the weather took a turn for the worse and Albion had several matches wiped out...All of a sudden we were left without any fixtures.

Then when the games finally did continue, Ron Atkinson decided to keep faith in the side that had done well for him in the first half of the season, which meant I was on the substitute's bench.

It was difficult to assess his decision but at the time I had to see it from both points of view.

After doing do well the player who would have been left out in my favour would surely have felt hard done by. So there I was, after the biggest move of my life, still not playing football.

When I finally did get into the side, we maintained our challenge and finished third in the League, but I felt my big break would come the following season – I was to be proved wrong.

During an end-of-season testimonial match at Birmingham for defender Garry Pendrey I badly damaged a tendon and ended up with my leg in plaster throughout the summer.

That first unlucky period set a seal on the rest of my contract. I never got myself into a position where I could have a decent run in the first team – a period of concerted effort.

Had it not have been for the injury, or the bad weather, who knows what would have happened – but that's football.

I have often been asked if I regretted my move to Albion... I can honestly say I didn't then and still don't.

David Mills, once the most expensive footballer in Britain.

The fee didn't bother me – it was beaten shortly afterwards anyway when Trevor Francis went from Blues to Nottingham Forest for around £1 million.

I do know that I played with some great professionals during my short time at The Hawthorns. But I had reached a peak at Middlesbrough and I never had a chance to continue. The first four or five months set the pattern of my entire stay.

Sad – but that's how things go sometimes. Still, I had a good career in football, Albion included, and I know that I was appreciated at most clubs. I scored plenty of goals, especially for Middlesbrough – I just wished I could have done the same for Albion. Teaming up regularly with Cyrille Regis and Tony Brown would have been just great. And there were players like Bryan Robson, Len Cantello and Willie Johnston who could create chances for you.

From Albion I went to Sheffield Wednesday (after a loan spell at St James' Park) where I teamed up again with my former Middlesbrough boss, Jack Charlton. I then had an excellent spell at Newcastle United and played alongside Kevin Keegan, Chris Waddle and Peter Beardsley, helping the Magpies gain promotion in 1983. I returned to Ayresome Park in the summer of 1984 before ending my League career with Darlington where I became coach. I later became player-coach of Whitby Town and also assisted Dorman's Athletic in the over-35 League.

In 1988 I was driving my car through the Tyne Tunnel in the north east with my father in the passenger seat. The car crashed. I suffered terrible facial injuries and sadly my father died. It took me quite some time to get over that accident but my wife Sandra was brilliant and now I'm okay.

Bobby Newsome, still thrilled to enter The Hawthorns, 50 years after he first saw the ground as a player.

Bobby Newsome

I arrived at the Albion in March 1939 and I can still remember the thrill of running out on to the famous Hawthorns pitch – and I still get a thrill today when I go along to watch a game.

being welcomed by everyone all those years ago was great – captain Sandy McNab, Harry 'Popeye' Jones, 'W. G.' Richardson and my own con-temporaries. I was invited to join a group which included Billy Elliott, George Dudley, Stan Butler and Jack Screen. We relaxed after a Saturday game by going along to the T.I. ballroom in Oldbury to have some fun.

Sunday, 3 September 1939 was a momentous day for all the players as we met to listen to the radio broadcast of the declaration of war. The following day we were all told that our contracts had been cancelled but our wages would be paid for that week. We dispersed to various parts of the country, but along with several other players including Sandy, George, 'Popeye', Stan, Eddie Connolly, Tommy Bell and Larry Coen, I went to work at Accles and Pollock, doing some light training on Tuesday and Thursday evenings.

Eventually we started to play in regionalised League and Cup competitions, lining up with and against a variety of footballers, an international like Peter Doherty one week, a local amateur from works football the next. I even played in goal in one game as a guest for Albion's neighbours Wolves.

After the War was over several new faces arrived at The Hawthorns, men like Jack Vernon, Dave Walsh and Jimmy Sanders. I never really got to play with these stars because two months after being demobbed I was transferred to Coventry City (June 1947). However, I have never lost my affection for the Baggies – a great club.

Johnny Nicholls

(*written before his sudden death in April 1995*)

I played for West Bromwich Albion from 1949 to 1957...and quite simply I had the greatest time of my life.

I loved it at The Hawthorns and although we weren't paid a great deal of money, I wouldn't have swapped my time as a player then to play in this day and age.

Heath, Brierley Hill and Wolverhampton. We were all rough but a good set of lads nevertheless.

When I eventually made the breakthrough into the first team it was in the fifth round of the FA Cup away at Blackburn in 1952. More than 51,000 packed into Ewood Park that day to see Rovers win 1-0, Bill Eckersley scoring from the penalty spot with just five minutes to go.

Ronnie Allen was injured for that game – and that's how I got my chance – but I managed to keep my place when Ronnie came back, and I couldn't have done anything without him as a striking partner.

Of course, I will always remember the 1954 FA Cup Final against Preston North End at Wembley. In those days you could only play at Wembley in this competition or for England so it was something extra special for us players.

That side was one of Albion's greatest ever – managed by Vic Buckingham, the best boss I've ever played under.

Even Bryan Robson wouldn't have got into that side, and I think, with three more players to strengthen the squad, we would have achieved the double that season. As it was we won the Cup and finished second in the League behind our arch rivals the Wolves.

Other matches that spring to mind are the 7-3 win at Newcastle early in the 1953-54 season when I scored my first Albion hat-trick and we were cheered off the pitch; our Christmas encounter with Liverpool in 1953 when we won 5-2 and when I played alongside Ronnie Allen for England against Scotland at Hampden Park in April 1954 in front of 134,000 spectators. That was tremendous and we both had the pleasure of scoring in an excellent 4-2 win.

Those really were the days.

Johnny Nicholls, one of a team of 'Black Country lads'.

You see, football was a sport in my day. We had to work hard and we had to play hard, and we never took anything for granted.

We had to come up through the ranks before we had a chance of playing in the first team – and there were about seven or eight Albion sides when I was there, but you would never want to ask for a transfer.

My memories of those great years lingered on and on. We travelled first-class on the trains and stayed in top hotels all round the country. And there are many memorable matches to recall.

My first boss at The Hawthorns was Jack Smith, who had a dream to get a complete Black Country team of lads together. They came from West Bromwich, Dudley, Tipton, Oldbury, Smethwick, Cradley

James Quinn

Although I haven't been with Albion all that long, I've really enjoyed it at The Hawthorns and for my part in this book I would like to talk about the more recent players and their way of life.

Lee Hughes has by far the worst dress sense I've ever seen in a footballer. Sometimes when he wears a suit and a yellow shirt, he looks like the American gangster Al Capone. Some of his casual wear makes you wonder why shops ever put it on sale in the first place.

Hughesy also provides the videos on the team coach. *Father Ted* tapes are his favourites, but I prefer Steve Coogan, or a game of cards.

Besides there being a couple of jokers in a pack of cards, one of the biggest jokers in the Albion camp was Paul Holmes. He used to spray your clothes with perfume, attach various notices to the back of your training kit and floated anything in the bath he could find including strapping, plasters, the lot.

Matt Carbon has owned the sportiest, flashiest car I've seen for some time. His BMW M3 Evolution has a personalised number plate – and he's already had an accident in it. Driving down the motorway, a piece of metal which had come loose from a road-sign came flying towards him. It speared straight through the windscreen. Matt survived but it caused £4,000 worth of damage.

We've all seen *Who Wants To Be A Millionaire* on ITV – and Richard Sneekes is the brains at Albion. He can speak Italian, Dutch, German, French, English and Brummie. He buys the *Guardian* newspaper – but that might be just to make him look good.

Cyrille Regis

Although we never won a major trophy, the Albion side I played in during the 1977-78 and 1978-79 seasons will always provide me with lasting memories; European exploits such as in Valencia where Laurie Cunningham was magnificent; plus crowds at The Hawthorns; the romance and passion of our 1978 FA Cup run with John Wile's head streaming with blood and the sadness of the fans on the way back from Highbury. To play in a team with so much talent, flair and mental strength made it a smooth transition for myself. The humour, friendship and spirit of the squad will always be with me.

I remember the time I joined

Cyrille Regis – 'lasting memories...'

Albion. I was a qualified electrician playing for Hayes in the Isthmian League in 1976-77 and quite a few scouts had come along to watch our games. Nothing materialised until Ronnie Allen, Albion's chief scout, who had apparently watched me two or three times, persuaded the Hawthorns board to sign me on a 12-month contract by saying: "I'll buy him (Cyrille Regis) with my own money and when he makes it, you can give me the money back." I think I made it.

Yes, we had some great times. I shared rooms with Laurie – who had the best dress sense at the club – Tony Godden and the 'joker in the pack' Derek Statham (and, NO it wasn't four in a bed).

Two other jokers were Andy King and Mick Martin. I recall Paul Barron having the flashiest car – a Martini Porsche 911 and manager Ron Atkinson, who certainly knew his football – he made us tick – and he also gave me some right real rollickings. But it was all worth it.

Geoff Richards

Signing amateur forms for Albion in October 1943 at the age of 14 was a big thrill for me, as I had supported the team since I was five.

I started to play regularly in the Central League side when I was 16, lining up alongside players like Sandy McNab, Billy Gripton, Ray Barlow, Frank Hodgetts, Bobby Barker and George Dudley; I was then taken on as a full-time professional in 1946.

Billy Elliott was the first team outside-right and had always been my idol, so it was a great thrill when I made my League debut as his replacement against Luton Town at home in December 1946. I scored our goal after 32 minutes, and although we lost 2-1, it was like a dream come true.

Albion had a surplus of wingers during the time I was at the club and often the reserve team forward-line contained five players who were all really out-and-out wingers.

The next biggest moment for me arrived on Easter Tuesday 1948 when I played at inside-right against Birmingham City in front of 52,000 fans at The Hawthorns. Albion had been beaten 4-0 at St Andrew's on the Easter Monday, so it was great to

ALBION AND ME . . .

Geoff Richards (third from left) reports for training in August 1947 along with Aldridge, Hood, Elliott, assistant trainer W. G. Richardson, Tighe, Walsh, Kinsell, Hodgetts and Pemberton.

gain a 1-1 draw against the eventual Second Division champions.

That weekend in 1948 was quite amazing. I played for Albion's second team on the Saturday, their third team on the Monday and the first team on the Tuesday.

My special pals at Albion were the late Johnny Nicholls, Norman Heath and Harry Guy. Unfortunately a serious knee injury ended my professional career in 1952.

Stan Rickaby

My time at The Hawthorns was the happiest and most successful of my footballing career but the way it ended was very disappointing and, indeed, hurtful.

From August 1950 to April 1955 I must have played more games for the first team than any other player. In the spring of 1955 a few journalists were writing that I should have been back in the England team, and I felt that I was playing as well as

ever – and the player himself knows whether he is playing well or not.

My last game was against Sheffield United at The Hawthorns. We played poorly after indications during the season that we could reach the heights achieved by that great 1953-54 team.

For instance, I had two excellent games, plus many more, against the Wolves in the FA Charity Shield and Honved in Brussels. Coming off the field after the Sheffield game, Jimmy Dudley said to me: "Well played Stan, it's a good job you played well...or words to that effect. Then we were all staggered to see that my name was missing from the team-sheet for the next game, the local derby against Wolves at The Hawthorns. I had never been dropped before and I had played a couple of hundred games, missing only one through 'flu and about five or six at the end of the 1953-54 season, including the Cup Final, after taking a knock in the sixth-round tie

with Tottenham Hotspur and making it worse by playing in the semi-final against Port Vale.

I was in the England squad for the World Cup in the summer of 1954 but had to pull out with that injury.

A very annoying postscript to all this has been the often quoted 'Stan left under a cloud'. That cloud was created presumably by manager Vic Buckingham, who put me on the transfer list.

He gave no explanation, but I always thought that the mechanisations of the Albion chairman and the Wrexham chairman whose son, Stuart Williams, just happened to be a useful full back – but none would have said he was better than me – were responsible.

I always thought Vic and I had a great rapport, and right up to my last game he had never criticised me. Indeed, I was the first player he spoke to when he joined the club. We were playing Chelsea in a FA

Stan Rickaby, whose happiest days were spent at The Hawthorns.

Cup fourth round second replay at Villa Park and at half-time he came into the dressing room and was introduced to us. He walked up to me and said 'Great, I've got a foot-balling full-back. I need one for my methods.' And from then on we got on wonderfully well together.

So where did the 'cloud' come from?

Then during the following few seasons when I was with Poole Town, I was often asked to play in

benefit matches all over the country. Whenever I played other players taking part would wonder why I was not in the First Division. I played against Fulham and after the game both Johnny Haynes and Jimmy Hill said I was wasting my talent.

At Lilleshall I played against the England team which was to take on Sweden. I faced the Liverpool left-winger Alan A'Court and he said the same.

I could go on, but I will leave it at that.

I will say again that I thoroughly enjoyed my time at The Hawthorns.

Leaving Middlesbrough for the Midlands at the time took some get-

ting used to, but once I was bedded in, all went well. It was disappoint-ing to miss out on that 1954 Wembley win over Preston, but myself and Norman Heath did receive winners' medals for our efforts in the previous rounds, I still follow the fortunes of the Baggies and I wish them well in the 21st century.

Ally Robertson

I was lucky enough to spend 18 years at The Hawthorns...18 years of great memories, great players and great traditions.

But my only regret is that I was not part of an Albion side that won

Ally Robertson – "...some 18 years of great memories, great players, great matches..."

ISBN 978-0-9566222-0-4

Published by Pat McEniff and Marita Mulcahy © 2010
Cover by Monica Flanagan

Printed by Browne Printers Ltd
Letterkenny +353749121387

in the mirror, pulling on his Ulster Defence Regiment beret and tilting it to one side. He was forty-six, fairly tall and dark-haired, had brown eyes and was handsome, yet he always wished he was as tall as his brother Robert. He was four inches smaller at five foot ten, but even then he considered himself not such a bad figure of a man and his uniform was quite well filled out. He buttoned his belt and unlocked the cupboard door. His Browning glistened. He had spent half an hour cleaning, checking and oiling it just before he went to bed the previous night. He was quietly proud that his Sergeant Major always said that he was the best-turned-out and most able man in the Company. This resulted in his recently being promoted to Corporal, First Class. His new red stripe and medal said everything and compounded his feeling of pride. He enthusiasm made him take the stairs to the big bedroom two steps at a time so that he could quickly check the stock from the window there. He never resisted the urge to look out the window of that room. The view of the near field and the haggard gave him a comfortable feeling. The Charolais cattle were all there, backside into the breeze. He marvelled at how well they had adapted to Fermanagh with its drumlins as opposed to the flat fields of France. They stood tall on the ground – their bellies well up from the rushes in the low- lying area in which they grazed. He also looked fondly at his brood mare, Bobbin. She was sleek, dark brown and elegant – a direct descendant of his father's beautiful old mare, Mollie, who had won many a red ribbon at the Balmoral Show. She was fairly close to foaling and looked huge and content.

Racing downstairs and outside onto the gravel, he shoved a clip in the Browning for safety. He unlocked and opened

added to over the years so it was a bit spread about, but Olive believed that this added to its charm. The whole front of the house was covered in a purple-leaved grape vine. In good summers the grapes were edible and she thought about her daughters, Heather and Florence, leaning out of the bedroom windows to get the biggest and best bunches. Her daughters were much in her mind at that time. She hoped that Heather would do well in her 'O' levels. Her English and typing were good. There might be a chance of a job in Ormsbys. She knew that one of the girls in the office was pregnant and would be leaving soon. The Ormsbys were Albert's family solicitors and her own family had strong connections with them. (They were Protestants like the Elliots.) The pregnant girl's job could be Heather's even if her results were only average. And Olive had been good to Anna at one time, and look where she was now – senior partner in the firm. Wasn't she there when Anna's baby was born without the doubtful benefit of marriage, and it was Olive's own cousin who had adopted the child. Strange business, that – Anna having a relationship with a Fenian. Olive could never understand it.

Florence, on the other hand, could look after herself. She smiled with satisfaction as she thought of her aristocratic high forehead, fine grey eyes, wonderful colouring and the ash blonde hair, not to mention her slim, well-shaped body and endlessly long legs. Florence will get on just fine, she thought. She has a sweet nature. Her resemblance to her sister Thelma was disturbing at times but Olive kept putting it to the back of her mind. Florence had an innocence about her – not like Thelma, with her husky voice and earthiness.

4

about. A helicopter, with its rotor turning slowly, stood on the large sweep of driveway in front of the house. Three aides-de-camp, all in full attire, were tucking into sandwiches and coffee. They stood up the minute she came into the room and strode towards her offering their sympathy. She was bewildered. She looked about for Albert. Albert's sister, Winifred, came towards her, all concern. "Ah Olive! Will you go a cup of coffee?" Olive took the cup mechanically. Winifred continued, "The Colonel wants to talk to you. He's waiting in the drawing room with your sister. And the Bishop says he will be here in half and hour."

Olive wished that they would all go away but she hadn't the strength to say anything. She remembered that Albert had never met Colonel Hyde-Whyte and supposed that the helicopter had something to do with his being there. Winifred then offered Olive two pills that the doctor had left for her and she obediently put them on her tongue and swallowed them with the coffee.

"Olive" said Winifred kindly, "come upstairs with me for a moment so you can brush your hair and put on a bit of make-up. You must put your best foot forward for your visitors."

Wearily Olive allowed all this, knowing that she really had no other option. "Winifred" she said, "I don't know what's happening to me but I'm glad you're here. You're always here when you're needed." Winifred smiled acknowledgement and then hugged Olive. Suddenly Olive began to cry. Albert was always about, but from now on there would be no Albert. Not today, not tomorrow, not ever. "Fuck!" she

you feel, I doubt if you want to know about the one which came from McCaughey and the Free Staters. I put it in the bin anyway. The Royal Ulster Constabulary is convinced your husband was killed by Free Staters from Belduff. The Group will deal with them. However, the fact that a local lad has been seen by one of Captain Darcy's chappies drinking in O'Moore's in Belduff is much more sinister. He's from Donstown, Keown's his name. The RUC is anxious to get him to help them with their inquiries. Our local sleeper also reckons he did it."

The door opened, "Oh Olive, I know you said you were not to be disturbed, but some local has been stopped at the foot of the lane, says he's Patrick Maguire, has no ID and says he is the gravedigger" wailed the sister, who was no longer familiar with the area. "He says he must speak to you personally".

"He's harmless" said Olive listlessly.

"Harmless or not" responded the Major, "he must be searched thoroughly, as the place is coming down with VIPs. Check him for a handgun."

"Good God!" exploded Florence, who had just come back into the room and heard the end of the conversation, "it's Sharpening- stone! No one would give him a handgun. He might shoot himself! He only wants directions on where to dig the grave." She left and a couple of minutes later and returned with the gravedigger. Aged about forty-five, he was tall and dark-haired. While he wouldn't be considered good-looking, he had a certain air about him – as if he would be

"Oh for God's sake Patrick, give it up will you! We have more to be thinking of. How much do you charge for a grave?"

"Ah now Olive," said Patrick, "I wouldn't charge you or Albert anything. I would consider it an honour to dig his grave. He was good to me."

"Patrick, how much do people normally give you?" Olive tried again.

"Twenty pounds" he said quickly, "but I wouldn't charge you."

"Heather," called Olive, "please bring me my handbag." She opened her purse and pushed a twenty-pound note down into his breast pocket. "Now," she said, "I must ask you to leave as I have the Bishop coming and he will want to speak to me on my own."

"Your Florence is very pretty," continued Patrick Maguire doggedly, "nearly as good-looking as her aunt. Tell Thelma when she comes that I spoke kindly about her."

I will in my eye tell her, thought Olive as she waved the gravedigger towards the door.

A huge Union Jack hung limply in the drizzle.

* * *

Pray! thought Olive incredulously. The last thing I want to do is pray! I don't think God was around when all this was happening to Albert. But once again her good manners prevailed and she bowed her head as the Bishop said the words that were meant to soothe and calm her. "Amen," she said and then, "So be it." But she did not accept it at all.

The Bishop drank his tea, which was by then very cold, and next asked to see Heather and Florence. Winifred went to fetch them.

* * *

The sleek black Jaguar crunched up the gravel and stopped in front of the house. The others in the room were startled when, with a strength they thought had left her, Olive shouted, "Thelma's here!" and got up and ran to the front door.

Out of the car got Thelma looking like a model from Jaeger's window in Donegal Square. At forty-four she oozed sex from every pore, and yet there was an air of discontent about her. The soldiers stood to attention long before her husband, the Assistant Commissioner of the RUC, got out of the car. They were mesmerised by her walk, her beauty. She was something else. "Olive!" she cried, "I am devastated! Poor Albert!" and then as she flung her arms around her sister she said more softly, "Poor you." Her voice was husky and intriguing, her perfume rich and expensive and Olive, for all her reservations about her sister, loved her and sobbed into her coat. They eventually went into the house together with Thelma's arm around Olive's shoulder.

"No, please," said Olive. "I want to see Albert". The Major put his arm awkwardly around her shoulders and explained as best he could that the coffin would remain closed and that she would have to remember her husband as he was. Thelma still said nothing. Olive suddenly thought about her daughters and what they must be going through. "I'll go to the kitchen to the girls," she said, and quickly opened the door before they could stop her. She was confronted by Hammersmiths' men with the coffin. Sobbing, she rushed past them into the kitchen where she was comforted by her daughters and the women.

* * *

Winifred was greeting the Rector, Mr. Warrington, and his wife and her two sisters. The group of mourners parted to allow them access to Olive, and they murmured their condolences. Olive thanked them silently, her eyes raw from rubbing away the tears. As Mr. Warrington intimated that he wanted to speak to Olive on her own, the others backed away and left the two together.

Mr. Warrington wanted to know from Olive what hymns she thought Albert would have liked for his funeral service. As she seemed put out by his asking, he suggested kindly that perhaps he would have liked "The Lord's my Shepherd" and "Abide With Me".

"Ah Rector," said Olive sadly, finally focusing on the question she had been asked, "Albert would not have wanted those at all. He reckoned people were sad enough at funerals without choking their way through those hymns. I think

14

She wants Ken Beamish here when she arrives. Has anyone got Ken's number?"

There was pandemonium. Hoover, dishwasher, Brasso out for the two bronzes over the mantelpiece, the good Beleek Black Stamp antique china was taken from the cabinet and washed – it had been a wedding present from the Regiment. More brown bread, freshly baked by a neighbour was brought in, smoked salmon to replace the chicken and ham. God, how those women came into their own! It was as if they had been waiting for this signal to put them into overdrive. They had been waiting impatiently for something important to do, and this was it. Mrs. Whicker was on her way and they were part of it!

The helicopter arrived at exactly 16.00 hours. The women hid behind each other, wanting to see but not wanting to be seen. The uniformed men took over and respectfully showed the Prime Minister into the drawing room where she sympathised formally with Olive. Mrs. Whicker, fixing her handbag authoritatively on her forearm, checking that every hair was in place and that the left seam of the tweed skirt was straight, continued, "I am going to strengthen the security forces by moving in three hundred SAS men as soon as possible. You, Major, will deal with this by giving new instructions to the counter-terrorists. I am immediately going to instruct the Royal Engineers to build towers close to the frontier. These people must be stopped in their tracks, I say! They should be shot before they cross the Border, or even at the crossings themselves!" The watching women were held in thrall by her dominance. She added, "That's all, men! I will stand under the Union Jack for a

the large bed that had been her's and Albert's. "How will I cope with the loneliness?" she asked herself. "How will I cope with having no one to hold me and tell me he loves me? How will I manage to take all the family decisions on my own?" And so she sobbed throughout the night and finally, as the dawn light began to filter through the curtains, she fell asleep, exhausted.

* * *

Dear God! thought Patrick Maguire, but it never stops raining in this bloody country! In the summer Lough Erne is in Fermanagh. In winter Fermanagh is in the lake. He got into his ancient Datsun and had to slam the door twice before it shut to his liking. He pulled out of Monument Hill, the housing estate where he lived near the town of Enniskillen, and drove past the aerodrome. On the broad road in front of him he saw the Police and UDR patrol, so he reached to open the pocket on the dash of his car to take out his driving licence. The small UDR man signalled him to stop and ambled towards him.

"Where are you going?" he asked. Patrick replied that he was off to St. Anne's church in Kilmacowen to dig the grave for Albert Elliot. "Don't I know you from somewhere?" the little man asked and then added, remembering, "You're from Monument Hill, aren't you?"

"I am indeed," replied the gravedigger, "lived there for a good while now. You know," he said confidentially, I fancied Albert Elliot's sister-in-law but she preferred and married one of your own top buck cats."

He set to work and removed his anorak after about ten minutes when the rain reduced to a light drizzle. He worked on steadily until the grave had been dug and lined. He climbed out and, hearing his stomach rumble, he gathered his gear and went back to the car for his flask and sandwiches. With the car door open, he sat sideways in the driver's seat with his feet on the ground, and poured himself a cup of tea. Munching his sandwiches he viewed the surrounding countryside from his vantage point on the top of the hill. A weak sun filtered hesitatingly through the broken cloud and Patrick thought that perhaps it would not rain on Albert's funeral after all. Tidying up the remains of his lunch, he swung his legs into the car, slammed the door twice out of habit, and went back to Monument Hill to change his clothes. He had to get back to the church for three o'clock when the funeral was due to take place.

* * *

Thelma pranced into the drawing room where Olive sat, on her own, staring into the fire, and closed the door behind her. It was the morning of the funeral. Getting right to the point Thelma said, "Do you ever see Sharpening Stone?"

Olive was shocked into saying, "Thelma! That was an awful name you called the poor man and I always feel ashamed for you that it stuck."

"Ah yes..." said Thelma excitedly, bursting to continue. Olive stopped her flow by saying, "Anyway, if I had seen him I wouldn't tell you, but I'll let you know this much – he is digging the grave at the moment. She was shocked at the

the odd bit of sex snatched here and there and saying things she didn't mean and writhing and getting no satisfaction.

She left Olive staring into the fire again.

* * *

Patrick got back to the church in plenty of time and took up a good position by the outside of the churchyard wall. He had had a word with the security men and they let him be. He watched the funeral cortege make its way slowly up the steep hill and suddenly felt very sad. Painfully slowly, the mourners and dignitaries filled the little church to capacity, while the overflow stood silently outside in the weak sunshine as the service began.

Patrick, with head bowed a little, and looking out from under his eyebrows, had respectfully watched the first few members of the mourning family file past him – and then he saw Thelma. "Jesus Christ!" he hissed through clenched teeth. For him she had not aged one whit and on him, even after twenty odd years, she still had the same electrifying effect. He felt weak and strong all at once and the feeling excited him to an embarrassing degree. Thanks be to God, he said to himself, we are all faced the same way! His eyes followed her and, with that, she spotted him and for one split second their eyes met and he detected, on her beautiful face, the slightest blush. He was angry with his eyes then because they filled with miniscule tears, and the vision that he had conjured and re-conjured for all those years and which was now there in reality became blurred. And by

note into Patrick's breast pocket and said, "Thanks Pat. You did a good job."

"It was a pleasure," responded Patrick, and was about to say what good friends he and Albert had been, but got no chance because Hammersmith moved on.

No sooner had Hammersmith left than Robert, Albert's brother, sought him out. "I understand," he said, "that you dug Albert's grave this morning?"

"Well, I did," said Patrick, "but then Albert was a good friend…"

"Anyway," said Robert interrupting, "here's a little money for you and thank you" and he pushed a twenty-pound note into the gravedigger's hand. The crowd was beginning to disperse quickly because the rain, which had held off so valiantly for the funeral, began to fall again and the sky was darkening with the promise of more and heavier rain to follow. Patrick went to the car for his oilskins, Wellingtons and shovel. He had to fill the grave once the graveyard was empty, and he wanted to get it done fast. He had been invited to the local hotel for some food and drink – as had all those who had helped with the funeral – and the thought especially appealed to him at that moment. As he turned, Thelma swept by, leaving with him the heady smell of her Chanel No 5 and the swirl of her mink coat. And this time, he thought, there was no blush and no recognition, so I've made it all up – the way I sometimes feel I've made up everything about her. And with a sinking feeling he made his way to the pile of earth and began to shovel.

24

to see you on Monday – at your house. Is that alright? Will you give me your telephone number?"

"Sure, it's in the book, Thelma," he said quietly.

"Of course," she said, "I'm so used to everyone being ex-directory. I'll phone you on Sunday night about nine to arrange a time." And reaching up to brush her lips against his, she turned and left him standing on the top of the hill in the graveyard, his hands hanging loosely by his sides and with the night settling in.

row evening." Alexander got the gist immediately. "Leave them under the carpet on the driver's side."

"OK," replied the garage owner, "but I'll need a certificate."

"That's not a problem. The Assistant Chief can look after that. He's due at the meeting tonight," said Darcy getting back into his car. He rolled down the window and said, "Where's the Chairman, by the way?"

"Him!" snorted Alexander. "He's always at the Bank!"

"I need to talk to Billy and Robin. It's about that nasty incident in Fermanagh."

"Ah" sighed Alexander nodding, "You will only need to see the Chairman and the two lads at the moment."

"Yes, I know," said Darcy curtly, "just buzz the three of them for me and tell them I will meet them in fifteen minutes in the Dolphin Bar." He closed the window to stop the rain spitting in on him and drove out into the road.

The Dolphin Bar was a dingy spot with tartan carpets that badly needed cleaning and dark brown paint everywhere – a depressing place at the best of times, but even worse at eleven o'clock in the morning. The smell of stale cigarette smoke was sickening. Darcy ordered a gin and tonic with ice and lemon, was out of luck with the ice, and looked at the pictures of the racehorses that were hung all over the walls – along with one of the Queen, framed in royal blue.

ings but not entitled to vote. I will give you five hundred pounds each when I am happy that the car you will use has been burned."

The Chairman interrupted, "The strike must be ratified by the full Group, but I don't think there will be any dissenting voice or voices. The Chaplain even wants to go on active service on the strike! We will use him later." The men listened, smiling and nodding. They understood perfectly.

"I want those bastards finished off," said Darcy. He explained the rest of the details and added, "The car will not be reported missing until it has been dumped and burned – something to do with a Chief Constable certificate. And no drinking on the job! I will meet you at Kilboo Cross. I have marked it on this map for you in red biro. It is on the Belduff/Garridon road. Tonight I will go to London for the money and the sanction for the weaponry. Goodbye and thankyou, Chairman! Please give my regards to Thelma when next you meet her."

"Actually, I will be dining with her and her husband next Wednesday night, come to think of it," said the Chairman.

"Don't forget now!" said Darcy turning to address the two men for further emphasis. "22.00 hours, and NO drinking!" This time he took full stock of the Jackal, realising for the first time how shrunken and emaciated he looked. The cancer he had been told about was taking hold.

* * *

"Gentlemen," he began, "we are surrounded by demons! Washington, the European Union, The Papacy and the British and Irish Governments are all hell-bent on dragging Ulster into Perdition! Fascism and the Child of Rome are alive and well! There is no lie too black, no crime too washed in crimson blood, no murder too Satanic, no bank robbery too monstrous but the IRA will be in there achieving its hellish ends." He looked around at the seated men and was content to note that they were all, with the exception of Darcy, listening earnestly and in agreement with him.

So, further motivated, he went on. "They have been brainwashed by the Jesuits!" he said, his voice rising. "Neither the cries of the orphans nor the agony of widows upset them! Their activities are neither curbed by the sorrows of the bereaved nor the outrage of the people! They enjoy wading knee-deep in Protestant blood! They delight in killing!"

By this stage Glasgow could sense that the Chairman was about to stop him in his tracks so he quickly continued, "The Mass is a blasphemy and it's in the Roman Catholic Churches that this blasphemy is celebrated! The SAS must be recalled! Strengthened rings of steel must be thrown around the Roman Catholic ghettos! Internment must be re-introduced!" Knowing his time had run out he shouted, "We must overcome the heathens among us!" and sat down.

In the silence that followed the Chairman quietly pointed his finger at Glasgow, looked at him squarely and said, "There

would be after the Twelfth when the Reverend Shane Glasgow had stirred things up a little.

"I could easily muster a group of youngsters then," said a professor, another member of the Group. "They would be delighted to do as I said!" The Chairman pointed out, unnecessarily, that if this wasn't done they could be faced with another Sarne Road situation in the near future. "Swift action," he said, "would bring swift results." He thanked the professor on behalf of the Group for his co-operation.

There was no further business and so the Chaplain ended the meeting with prayer.

As the members gathered up their notes and prepared to leave, Captain Darcy sidled up to the professor and asked him for help with a new programme he was setting up. All that would be needed was for the Captain to bring himself and a ream of paper with him to Queen's University. The professor gave him directions to his rooms and then they parted company.

* * *

"Department of the Navy," it read on the giant doors looking out on Whitehall five stories up. "Graham Jamieson."

Jamieson paced up and down his office nervously. Apart from his worried look there was nothing about him that stood out particularly. He was a little portly, was small and wore the regulation grey suit. He was forty-seven but looked older and his hair was thinning. Because he was sweating

phone call from Major Henderson who would join them in the next five minutes and then he asked, "Would you like a drink?" He handed the Captain a glass and then poured him a Johnny Walker, afterwards pouring a large one for himself. Without bothering to ask whether or not Jamieson objected to smoking in his office, Darcy lit a cheroot and blew the smoke nonchalantly towards the ceiling.

"Do sit down," said Jamieson, pointing to the chair on the far side of his desk. "I want to take you though some details." Looking thoughtfully at Darcy he murmured, "First we must discuss the laundry business…the one you have set up on the Highgate Road. I have no real problems with it, as the information and surveillance have both been excellent. It has identified most of the subversives in the Highgate area. I have been looking through your files and I notice that you were educated at Ampleforth. The monks there would have difficulty with your second detail, which sits very uncomfortably in your file. Now…your whorehouse on the Causeway Road…the members of the WRAC are quite disconcerted and wish you to improve on pay structures. These women are not content with Army rates of pay but are prepared to negotiate better terms. I certainly no longer intend to fund it under its present format. I'm happy with the information it gives me, but I'm not keen on the set-up, to be honest. However, if you can renegotiate with the WRAC to its satisfaction then I will be prepared to continue with the funding."

Shifting in his chair, putting on his cross face and mustering all his courage Jamieson sat forward, stared into Darcy's face and thundered, "Who gave you permission to bomb

Lieutenant Dickson is put in charge of security at the British Embassy in Washington with promotion to Captain. Ditto for Lieutenant Davidson in Paris."

Major Henderson marched into the room in much the same fashion as Darcy had done earlier. He accepted the shot of Johnny Walker and immediately Darcy began to speak as if absolutely nothing had passed between himself and Jamieson. "You first! I want ten-thousand pounds up front," he said, and then to Major Henderson, "the Group is looking after the car. Everything will be in order. The car will not be reported stolen until after it has been destroyed. The inner circle of the RUC will make sure there is no security on the roads we are using…the clearance for weapons and bullets is being drawn up down at Thiepval and the guns will not be returned. We need ammunition clips so arrange for me to collect them with registration plates, two handguns and four smoke grenades. Keown and O'Hare did the job on Albert Elliot. They were watched leaving their caravan at 05.00 hours with wires and paraphernalia. You see, O'Hare has the know-how and Keown knows the location. Keown's car had fifty-one miles up, which was just right and he got back about forty-five minutes after the incident. They each have five hundred punts in their pockets so they have got to be hit in the next ten days for us to succeed. You see, they may leave the area after that. We know that O'Hare's knowledge of explosives, command wires and semtex is such that he will be moved to another active service unit fairly soon."

Major Henderson thanked the Captain and said, "You can pick up your money and arms tomorrow." Looking at Jamieson he said,

and the A95 and, feeling that he couldn't get out of there fast enough, took his departure. Being part of the dirty tricks brigade had its disadvantages, he thought, and the sooner I am back on my own ground the better.

* * *

Captain Darcy stood at Kilboo Cross chewing a stalk of grass that he had picked out of the ditch, and looked down on Lough Melton. He had reached a milestone in his life and, while at one stage he had thrived in his chosen career, he was now beginning to wonder just what he was doing in this violent little country. He also wondered if he really belonged anywhere. He was so deep in thought that he was startled when a big, black Ford Granada spun up behind him and stopped. A large man with close-cut hair and an incredible stink of alcohol jumped out. It was King Rat.

"Hello Billy," he said evenly, "I've got stuff for you. No need to tell you how to use the weapons. There's five hundred for each of you, as arranged. The plan is that you put two bullets into Keown and two into O'Hare. No other killings, mind! That's very important. If the Southern Police find two known subversives dead, while they may not be happy, they won't go to the funerals." He sighed. Billy wasn't listening. No one listens. That's part of it. "Let's get on with it then," he said, shrugging his shoulders tiredly.

* * *

Thomas O'Donnell was in good voice in O'Moore's bar. He threw back his head and sang,

"Got that, Billy?" asked Darcy. "Get on with it then."

As King Rat and Jackal left the car Tom pleaded to Darcy, "Captain, I can't stay here much longer."

"I know, I know Tom," said Darcy. "Don't worry. I have spoken to Jamieson. I will arrange a transfer for you. How do you feel about Washington?"

"I would go anywhere."

"I know Tom, God I do know!" said Darcy.

As Tom left the Granada he heard the shots and disappeared into the night. He could imagine the panic in the pub and the smoke from the grenades, the screaming women and the yelling children and, most horribly of all, he could visualise the smile on the Rat's face as he did the job he loved so well. He hoped that he would get away before they caught up with him. He tried not to think about it. It was better not to think about it.

* * *

"OK Billy?" asked Captain Darcy as the Granada spewed around the corner heading for Kinhest.

"Dead as last year's snow!" replied the man proudly. 'There's blood spilling out of both their heads. Dear God, but I did get great pleasure out of that!" He smiled, settling into his seat, confident that he had done the job well.

III

M onday finally arrived. Patrick had spent the previous few days in his house painting. He had even tiled the bathroom – a job that had been waiting to be done for the longest time. The tiles were black and shiny and he hoped that they would impress Thelma. Then he began to worry that the smell of paint would give her a headache. He had one himself, brought on by the nervous anticipation he felt. He'd waited twenty years to see her and now that she was about to arrive into his life again – and in a manner so totally undreamed of – he felt ill. He looked at himself in the mirror and the face that looked back at him was pale. He combed his black wavy hair for the fourth time, checked that his breath was pure, decided that it wasn't and brushed his teeth again. He wiped his mouth with the towel and put it back neatly on the towel rail.

Looking out of the window he saw a taxi pull up at his gate and watched Thelma get out and pay the driver. He took a few deep breaths and went unsteadily down the stairs to open the door to his beloved.

"Welcome to Number 12" he said awkwardly. He knew it was a silly thing to say but it came out foolishly from his mouth and he wanted to kick himself for it. He took her hand, led her inside and closed the door. He would have

body stepping out of the pool of clothes that she had hurriedly dropped around her slim ankles in the few seconds that his back was turned. He grasped her and hugged her to him kissing her passionately. She ducked out of his embrace finally and leapt into his bed, pulling the duvet around her and giggling. "Get your clothes off and come here you old goat!" she said. Patrick did not need to be asked. He plunged under the duvet beside her leaving a trail of clothes behind him.

She ran her hands over him and was thrilled by the length of him and the strength of him and the firmness of his body. She moved her exquisite frame, writhing over him, caressing her clitoris with his penis. He stroked the length of her back with the tips of his fingers and then, as she raised her body above his, he cupped her magnificent pendulous breasts in his huge hands. She yearned for him as he did for her and, in an instant, she steered his enormous size inside of her and gasped in agony because he had plumbed her depth to the utmost. Their bodies were unified in violent and rhythmic passion. As she climaxed for the first time she screamed and then she whispered savagely over and over again, "You do love me!" and he answered with more feeling than she had ever heard from any man, "Yes Thelma, I adore you! You are my beautiful, beautiful spearbhean!"

They rolled over as one and she knotted her legs around his and he thrust and thrust deeply, faster and faster until they came, together. Patrick very gently rolled off her and they lay quietly, side by side, he with his eyes closed, and he stroked her and she lay still.

He told me that you had seventy thousand pounds in a high yield investment. Where did you get it from?"

Patrick answered steadily, "I spent five years in New York working for an old uncle of mine. When he died he left me the bulk of his estate and, as you can see, I haven't much need of it. I lodged it in Cavan because I don't want the revenue to know about it and get cross with me."

"There's something else too" she went on. "I like fresh oysters. There is a man in Kildalkey who sells the best in this part of the world. As I'll be calling here most Mondays, pick up a dozen every Friday and put them in the freezer. If you take them out three hours before I get here, they'll be fine." She began to put her coat on.

"Thelma" said Patrick, "Can I ask you something?"

"Fire away" she said.

"Don't you like foreplay?"

"No" she answered with amusement, "Foreplay is for wimps. I like it just as it was today. And by the way," she said, changing the subject as if it was of no consequence, "whatever became of your brother the priest?"

"Ah" said Patrick nodding sadly, "like many priests he became frustrated with his diminishing status and ashamed of the widespread corruption within his profession, and turned to the gin. At least that's what he tells me. The Hierarchy retired him to Cork where he realised his childhood am-

* * *

Heather did a jig in the hallway while holding a letter in her hand. Suddenly she tore up the stairs and burst into her mother's bedroom. "Mum! Mum!" she cried, "Will you please wake up!" Olive shot upright in her bed looking dizzy and confused from the effect of the sleeping pills she'd been taking since Albert's death.

"What on earth is all this about Heather?" she said. "Will you please calm down!"

"Oh Mum!" screeched Heather, leaping onto the bed and bouncing up and down, "my results have come and they are terrific!" She shoved the white sheet of paper into Olive's face and sat watching her mother's reaction as she quickly scanned the results.

"Oh darling!" said Olive throwing her arms around her, "this is wonderful! Your father would have been thrilled. Oh thank God!" And she hugged Heather again and kissed the top of her head.

Heather snuggled up to Olive and said, "You know what this means? I will never, never have to go to school again! And I can get a job and a car and can go all over the place and won't have to go bothering you for lifts. I will be able to go where I want when I want, and I won't have to wait around till everyone is ready. And I can drive you places instead of you always having to drive me. And I'll be able to go to the dances in Kesh and Fivemiletown. Can we make a bonfire of my school uniform?"

regularly and when she was not worshipping God, she worshipped the sun. She went alone on package holidays to warm places, taking lots of books in her suitcase. She lived on her own and cycled to and from her office. She had a dog that she adored and walked for an hour each day. Her short affair with the Fenian had shocked the few who knew about it. She wore a tweed skirt that needed pressing and a sweater that an experienced knitter would recognise as having been knitted by herself – and not too well at that. But her welcome was warm as she stood to shake hands with Olive and show her to a chair.

"Do sit down," she said. "I have to say, Olive, you are looking well. By the way, I am hoping to have Probate taken out next week and that will free your money up."

"Actually," said Olive, "that is not the reason why I'm here. I'll come straight to the point. Heather needs a job. She has just got the results of her exams and they are pretty good. I would appreciate it if you could find some work for her to do here." She waited while Anna thought for a moment before saying, "I suppose she has suitable results in typing and English, has she?"

"Oh yes!" replied Olive confidently. "She did really well in those. She studied very hard these past two years and even had grinds for six months prior to the examinations. She actually surpassed the grades her teachers thought she'd make. And I would have to say that she's a good girl. She never gave me a moment's bother. She's modest and intelligent. And she doesn't have a boyfriend," she added.

any messages and to say that he would return the calls on the following day.

He took the information to his apartment in Maida Vale and worked on the details of his role, explaining how ill his mother was and the fact that she only had twelve months to live – or maybe even less. When the work was completed, he took the tube to Kensington Palace Gardens and walked to the embassy with the Hammer and Sickle flag leaping about gaily in the breeze. He ran up the stone steps and shoved the long brown envelope through the wide letter-box.

He was glad to get that over. Taking a quick glance over his shoulder to check that he was not being followed, he hurried to the tube station. He had to get to see his mother quickly as she got tired after six o'clock. He ran up the stairs from the platform and bought flowers for her from the flower seller at the exit onto the street.

He took a taxi to the Wimbledon Hospice and walked into the familiar, well-populated ward. His mother was thrilled to see him. She looked frail and gaunt. He remembered how she used to be – a well-rounded, pleasant-looking woman who dressed well. She was loving and caring and fun to be with. She was a great fan of Patsy Clyne and used to sing Crazy out of tune but with great gusto. Jamieson felt sad as he put his arms gently around her wasted body to embrace her. He laid her back tenderly on her pillows. Now she was ridden not only with cancer but also with guilt. She smiled wanly at her son and said, "Thank you for the lovely flowers. Sorry to be such an awful burden to you, Graham."

ly. We did receive your cheque for five hundred, and thank you. Every little helps, but the Government is reducing its subvention next month. It isn't right what's happening," she said, softening slightly.

Bloody sure it's not right, he thought angrily as he marched out onto the street.

All the way back to Maida Vale he considered that if only he had married he would have been able to share his frustrations with a wife. His mother had been right all along. He should have married. Then he could have given her the grandchildren she always wanted. No, he thought finally, I am too selfish. No woman would have put up with me. And on this note he let himself into his apartment remembering ashamedly, for he had forgotten for about ten minutes, that the doctor had told him that his mother could not live for much longer.

Three days later, Jamieson was woken early by the telephone ringing. With his heart pounding, he allowed it to ring five times before picking up the receiver. He swallowed before saying a dry hello.

"May I speak to Mr. Jamieson please?" said a well-tutored female voice. It is nothing to do with my mother, he thought with relief. The voice continued, "My name is Fiona and I am speaking on behalf of Mr. Wilmsloe of Consolidated Insurance. He invites you to Clintons in the Strand for lunch at one o'clock today."

"Thank you," replied Jamieson, "I will be there."

cooked oysters Florentine because he was told that the chef was Sardinian and that they were his forte. He then had consommé and then lobster Thermidore. He mentally patted his full stomach and then helped his digestion with more and more wine. He was quite drunk when the Martel Cordon Bleu arrived. He excused himself from the table and went to telephone his secretary. He explained that something important had come up and asked her to deal suitably with any problems. Returning to the table he smoked two good cigars and drank three brandies. Wilmsloe finally asked for the bill and paid with a gold American Express card. Jamieson accepted Wilmsloe's business card and agreed that if he had any other business he would contact him no matter what the hour. He crawled carefully into the taxi that had been ordered for him, and as he travelled home he opened the big brown envelope. He counted five thousand pounds in twenty-pound notes.

Once inside his apartment, with the stress and financial pressures suddenly lifted and his system filled with good food and wine, Jamieson went to bed and slept well.

hand he held three crucifixes, "and I will burn these myself in the marquee this evening! God Save the Queen!"

At this point, the Reverend Willie McNutt, who was marching beside Shane, took this as his cue and, pressing the microphone to his lips sang, "God save our Gracious Queen, long live our noble Queen, God save the Queen." The crowd joined in and his voice was smothered.

As the last syllable was sung, Big Shane took to his roaring again. "We will now march up the Queen's highway to the marquee and please march in step!" The crowd obeyed and proudly held their heads high, like those who know they are superior always do. Heather and Florence fell in step and joined the rear.

When it reached the marquee the crowd piled in, but already the front seats were taken up by the Ballyfia people and the VIPs. The main bulk was left to stand. Willie McNutt leapt with alacrity onto the stage and grabbed the microphone.

> *Will your anchor hold in the storms of life,*
> *When the clouds unfold their wings of strife?*
>
> *When the strong tides lift, and the cables strain.*
> *Will your anchor drift or strong remain?*

And the crowd, knowing the chorus well, joined in with volume and sincerity,

> *We have an anchor that keeps the soul*
> *Steadfast and sure while the billows roll,*

The crowd roared its compliance with all that was being said. "We have the men in mid-Ulster and here we can rely on one of our own, our singer!" he said with pride, pointing to Willie McNutt, who was beaming. "He will organise the fight from here to drive these infidels from the land of God our Beloved! The God-fearing people of north Antrim will be led by myself, and from the hinterland of east Belfast, our God-fearing George Williamson will do what is necessary! And furthermore," he added, "we will not be on our own. I have promises from Pastor Greene that our kith and kin in Scotland will not be found wanting! Let us pray to the Lord to watch over us as we go from strength to strength and finally cross our own Jordan! We must appeal to our beloved police force which is being harassed and shot in Drumree, and be thankful to our brethren from Monaghan and Donegal who gather with us in our confrontation in Portglentoo every year!"

Big Shane shook with emotion, and the effort of all this sincerity was visible in the beads of sweat that rolled down his temples. "We are proud of them," he said, "for marching down the Queen's highway in defence of our civil and religious liberties! We will never surrender to the IRA at Drumree Church, who hide behind the women and throw stones at our officers and constables! A Protestant Police Force for a Protestant People! That's what Carson set up to protect us from, heretics who we'll lock up in jail to await the Judgement Day. And what a Judgement Day that will be, my friends! The Lord will call them into eternal flames and perdition!" He threw his enormous hands to the sky and the crowd loved him. Mustering all the strength of his

Florence was transfixed to such an extent that Heather had to pull at her to get her attention. "Come on out of this," she urged. "We've heard enough of this rubbish. Next thing he'll be looking for another collection," and she pushed Florence out of the marquee in front of her. Once out on the soccer pitch, they both took deep breaths of fresh air and felt better. They had been standing for a long time and they were tired. Walking towards the gate, they met Mr. Henry, who seemed pleased to see them both, but especially Heather.

After he had shaken hands with them he said to Heather, "Miss Ormsby tells me that you have started work with her? Good girl! You made a wise choice! What I want to know is, if you would be interested in working at night with the Greenfinches?" As Heather thought for a minute he continued, "It's very easy work you know. Mostly nights and weekends. You could easily take home eighty-five pounds a week. If you did decide you could manage it, you would be keeping up a fine tradition." Heather was not sure what to say, so Mr. Henry said, "Think about it, my dear. Call me in the morning. If you decide to join the Greenfinches, I will help you to fill in the forms." Heather protested that that would be a lot of bother for him. "Not at all!" he said. "I'd be delighted. I'd simply stay on after closing time to help you. It wouldn't take long. Phone me in the morning then! Goodbye girls!"

* * *

Since beginning her job, Heather had taken out a loan and bought a perfectly serviceable Datsun. It was red and she

"Aunt Thelma gave him the name," laughed Florence. "Coming from her I am sure it has something to do with sex."

"Will you behave yourself!" said her sister.

By this time Patrick Maguire had spotted the two girls and beckoned them to come over to him. He continued playing and called to the barman. "What'll you have girls?" he asked. "I'm on the stand."

"Two glasses of cider, please," said Heather as she and her sister sat down close to the piano.

"Do you play here for money, Patrick?" asked Florence. Heather was mortified. Patrick wasn't the slightest bit put out.

"Yes, I do. Every Friday. Eight to twelve. Do you know, you are two of the prettiest girls in the county!"

"Gee thanks!" said Florence, grinning. Patrick decided she was a flirt. "You did well at Daddy's funeral?"

"I did, thanks. But it was off broad backs it was coming. I never went looking for the money. People kept pushing it at me and my father always told me never to refuse it. It was an awful day and I got a cold out of it."

He noted that Heather was not saying much and leaned towards her whispering in her ear, "Saw you going into the marquee. Your father would not have liked it."

* * *

Heather tidied up her desk in the office and went to collect her jacket and handbag. She was excited about joining the Greenfinches and was looking forward to having her forms filled in. She and the rest of the staff parted company in the car park and she drove her car to Mr. Henry's premises. He owned Henry Motors.

Archie Henry walked across the forecourt to meet her. "Good girl!" he said. "You're very punctual," and he shook her hand. "We're just finishing up. Please go right through to my office and pour yourself a cup of coffee. I'll be along in just a moment." Heather looked around his office while she sat drinking the coffee. He was obviously pretty wealthy. The office was super. She stood up to look at the framed photographs of Mr Archie Henry and his wife and children, which were all over the walls. "A good family man!" she reckoned.

When he finally came in, he was carrying a sheaf of paper, which he laid on his desk. He patted a chair and asked her to come and sit beside him. "OK," he said, we'll get all of this organised. Now for the usual questions. Date of birth? Address? Telephone number? Mother's maiden name? Have you got a current driving licence? Who are your referees? What schools did you attend? And your religion is Church of Ireland? Relatives in police regiments or prison services? Any convictions for criminal activity? Right then. That's the bulk of it. Would you please sign here, and here, and here." Obediently Heather signed and then the situation changed.

isn't it your birthday next week? I'll send you a hundred pounds. Get yourself some nice clothes. Now go home and not a word to your mother. Anyway, I'll be down next Monday. I'll tell Mr Henry never to as much as look at a family member of mine again. I'll also check to see if he's driving home sozzled after golf. It's time the bugger was caught."

Heather smiled smugly as she crossed the foyer on the way back to her car. "Aunt Thelma will stitch him up good," she smirked. The thought added two inches to her stature as she stepped lightly across the car park.

* * *

Heather, believing that she looked like a model, haughtily minced down the steps into the All Seasons Bar in Enniskillen. Now that she was well-established in her job, she felt much more sure of herself. She had decided, in the office, that a little drink before going to meet Major Benson at the local UDR headquarters would be a good idea.

Looking around and suddenly feeling self-conscious, she was relieved to see Patrick Maguire smiling at her from where he sat at the bar. She eased onto the barstool next to him, put her handbag on the counter and sat grinning at him and swinging her legs. "What'll it be, Heather?" he asked, obviously pleased to see her.

"A glass of white wine would be lovely!" she answered.

father keel over and die! I had to weigh in here then. I tried to persuade my mother to sell out the farm and move to a smaller place, but she wouldn't hear tell of it. That woman had pride in her home and the farm, she was totally upset by my father's death and had no ability whatsoever to see things in the long term. Her biggest wish was that my brother, the priest, should always have a decent place to come home to. I was, naturally, said by her. She was a great mother to us and I wanted to do what pleased her most."

Heather was nodding understandingly while Patrick told his story. "And what happened then?" she asked.

"Well," he said, smiling wanly, "my mother lived for ten years more. When she died, my brother and I had a long discussion and it transpired that what he wanted and what she had wanted for him were two totally different things. He was happy for the farm and house to be sold. He had no notion of ever coming back to it. His life was, by that time, in Cork. Do you know it took me two years to get the place sold! I had definitely put Law out of my head by that stage. I bought the house in Monument Hill then, and that's where I've been ever since."

"But are you happy Patrick?" Heather wanted to know.

"Ach, I am, I suppose," he replied. "I play a bit of golf and I have a small boat on the lake. I have no one to answer to. My only responsibility is to myself. I'd have liked to have married and had children but I suppose I'm a bit odd and no one woman wanted me."

After the barman had brought the drinks Patrick said urgently, "Heather, I want to say something to you that I said to your father fifteen years ago – and had he listened to me then, your mother would likely not be a widow now."

"Say on," she answered with interest.

"Now that you are feeling wounded, you will be approached by people asking you to join the Regiment. They're not brave enough to join themselves but they believe that you will be willing. They will point out that your family has a tradition of service. Be careful. All armies through the centuries, whether they were Assyrians, Carthaginians, Roman Crusaders, Holy Romans and, more recently, Japanese Nazis have two things in common – conquest and rape. I repeat, if you do think it necessary to join, be careful. Some of the males regard female soldiers as bed warmers and nothing more. You especially will be vulnerable. Beware of the kindest and most handsome ones. Think about it."

"Aw come on now Patrick!" Heather chided, "Don't you think I can take care of myself?"

"I mean what I say," he replied calmly, "but I am sure you think I have preached enough."

"Well I do that," she said, taking her glass from the counter and tilting it to her lips to finish off what was left in there. She was thinking, "What would this Patrick know about the Regiment! What he says is nonsense!" Looking at her watch she said, "Many thanks for the drink and the chat. It was great to meet someone I knew in here this evening. I

two cups and brought them back to his desk. He settled himself in his chair and looked Heather in the eye. She accepted this eye contact with confidence and he was impressed. "I am sure you will like it here," he said. "There is plenty of fraternising between the NCOs. I am placing you under Sergeant Whyte's tutelage. She will introduce you to your mates and see that you both learn and are happy." Heather nodded and smiled, feeling that she had made the right decision to join the Regiment. Patrick Maguire knew nothing about it.

There was a knock on the door, and in marched, saluting, the ugliest woman Heather Elliot had ever seen in her whole life. She was broad and tall and built like a Clydesdale horse, "except a Clydesdale horse would have a kinder face," Heather thought. Because Heather had been well brought up, and had had instilled in her never, ever to register shock at another human being's misfortune, her face was expressionless. All this was noted by Major Benson. Sergeant Whyte had an unfortunate nose. It was plastered all over her large face as if, during a round of boxing, Cassius Clay had met her full on with her hands dangling by her sides. And then there were her eyes. They were both staring at her nose. "This was," Heather thought, "a face that only a mother could have loved."

The Sergeant handed first the uniform and then the beret to Heather and then, saluting again, asked Heather to follow so that she could be shown her quarters. Heather became slightly confused. She jumped to her feet clutching her uniform, hurriedly said goodbye to Major Benson and raced out of the room in pursuit of the pounding horse that already

said that she was in no need of a lift, having got a car herself. The Sergeant wasn't really impressed.

Gilbert came over to their table and spoke to Heather. "Nice to have you with us!" he said warmly. "I heard about your new job. No more than myself, you obviously took this on for a top-up to the salary!" He grinned and then said, "I must be off to change because I am on manoeuvres tonight. See you around!"

"Get that coffee down you fast!" said Lily. "We must go to the locker room and get you to fit your uniform on." She leapt up, yanked at her tunic and took off. Again Heather was thrown by the speed at which she pounded away and she felt like a foal as she gambolled to keep up with her Sergeant.

When they got to the locker room, Lily assigned her locker number 315 and then said, "Get that uniform on then!" Heather looked around to see where she could go for a little privacy in which to change her clothes. She saw none and looked at Lily questioningly. "Hurry up!" Lily barked. "I haven't got all evening!" Heather opened the door of the locker and gingerly stepped out of her neat little working suit. She hated being watched but got on with the change as quickly as she could. She put the uniform on, straightened it and stood looking at Lily, waiting for her comments. Lily came towards her to straighten her beret and then, after stroking Heather's cheek with a tenderness from which the girl recoiled, she stood back to get the overall view. "That's grand!" was her pronouncement. "You're on duty now. You must call me Sergeant Whyte. Once you are in uniform

hours earlier. "At ease!" he finally bellowed and the ten Greenfinches, with no exceptions, thanked God silently. "Right girls," said Sergeant Major Hudson, becoming human, "next week will be more interesting. Weapon practice. Same time, same place. You can dismiss!"

The girls wandered off in groups, leaving Heather a little lost. Then the Sergeant Major said, "Heather! I want to talk to you." She went to him wondering what it was that he wanted to say. "Find the NCOs mess and order me a gin and tonic – and have one for yourself. Sit down and wait for me there. I'm just going to shower. I'll be along in five minutes." When he came back, the Sergeant Major pulled a stool up to Heather's table and sat down. He began, "Your father and I were best friends in the Regiment. How did you enjoy your first evening?" Heather said that she had enjoyed it very much and watched in wonder while he drank his gin in two gulps. He continued, after wiping his moustache carefully, "Many's the night I was with him on manoeuvres. He bloody well knew every nook and cranny in those bogs and mountains – and the people too! How many cups of tea and drops of poitin did we drink together! Ah yes, those were the times! He always got me a bottle of the famous stuff at Christmas for myself. Some old fellow he knew from Shraigh mountain kept a still. I miss your father. I suppose I always will. Anyway Heather, I will be a good friend of yours. You can call on my anytime. Anything I can do to help. You know. I have just one bit of advice for you and you can take it or leave it. Don't look for revenge. It will be hard for you but remember, people from the far right are preaching that there should be civil and religious liberty, while at the same time they agitate

Law degree, her thundering new Sergeant of whom she was to beware, handlebar moustaches, marching and finally she thought of dancing with Gilbert Watson and then she fell asleep.

an enormous wrestler with a grin. "My God, but you look fit! What have you been doing with yourself? I've never been in Kensington Palace Gardens before, you know. It's terrific!"

Boris agreed that he was fit and had been spending time in the gym. He also agreed that Kensington Palace Gardens was a good spot to be in and then he said, "We'll do the business when we get inside," as he ushered Sean into the building. Once inside his office, Boris wasted no time in showing Sean the reason for asking him to come immediately to London. Sean looked at the papers showing the PRSI and PAYEE details on Captain Darcy and his mates and his expression was incredulous.

"My God!" he murmured under his breath. "Where did you get this information? I can't believe it! It's sensational! Let me sit down!" and he sat carefully into the nearest chair, all the time staring at the papers he had in his hand. After a few more minutes, during which Boris watched his reaction, he continued, "These guys are nutcases. What do they think they are at? A full-time Captain and three Lieutenants – the full G7. We always knew that there was a dirty tricks team, but we had no idea it was manned by highly skilled and trained officers. It would seem that G7 are the thinkers, and the Group are the doers, with G7 passing out the guns and selecting targets – and the British taxpayer sustaining and encouraging this lot. You do know, don't you Boris, that we are bound by the decisions of our Ard Comhairle and are now non-military? We do have some renegades who stray away from civil obedience, however. We can touch base with the INLA but they are not as reli-

ephone call was made and a rendezvous set up with Olga. Drink finished, Sean and Boris went out together.

They met Olga at the Embassy and Boris introduced her as his Assistant Secretary. She had had a very active career and had seen service in Budapest and Vienna. She always carried a little Beretta. They sat down to have a drink before dinner. Rose thought her a raunchy female – strong and good-looking with fine teeth and very blue eyes. She dressed with understated good taste and was excellent company. Her English was perfect. Boris had previously explained to Sean that he and Olga would be having dinner together in the suite he had booked for them, and when he had finished his drink he left.

Not too much was eaten by either of them because Olga was very flirtatious and Sean was deeply excited by her. When he went to sit on the couch, she came and sat beside him and, taking her shoes off, she wriggled her feet underneath his backside and grinned at him. Sean put his wife Moira clean out of his mind and without a word he took Olga's hand and led her to the bed. They kissed hungrily as they removed each other's clothes and then, roughly, he took her. The sex they had was fast and cruel. It was driven by lust and it satisfied both of them.

Next morning Sean Rose left for Heathrow, where he caught the 10.30 flight to Dublin. This change from Ryanair to Aer Lingus was tactical. Moira met him and drove him to Connolly Station, where he had to wait awhile before taking the express train to Belfast. He gave his wife nine hundred pounds and told her to put it in a safe place. Putting the

Exactly thirty minutes later, the meeting convened with the two men in question present. Molloy took the chair and said firmly, "I intend to suspend standing orders and have no minutes taken. I welcome a fraternal delegate from Dublin – an ex-member of our Party and Ard Comhairle who sees matters differently from us but, at the same time, I hold him in very high esteem. He and I were imprisoned during the sixties. He comes today," he continued, "with very bad news for us. There has been a widespread breach in our security, which has to be sorted out, and he tells me that a senior civil servant in Whitehall is privy to our secrets. You will be shown the evidence of this and then we will have a discussion.

There was silence in the room while the men read what was shown them and the air was thick with disbelief. "Now," said Molloy, breaking the silence, "you have seen with your own eyes what is a breach of international law. A crowd of thugs, same as the Black-and-Tans in the twenties, funded by Whicker's government and given rank and pay as full-time officers in the service of Her Majesty, that's what they are!" It was plain that he was steaming with anger. "They obviously have no regard for us Irish – or a democratically elected Parliament. We will deal with this problem," he said icily and added, "I express our thanks to our past colleague and wish him a safe return journey to Dublin."

"You dirty ballocks! Are you trying to tell me I'm drunk?" shouted Archie.

"No Sir", replied the policeman calmly, I am a member of the traffic branch trying to enforce the Road Traffic Act".

Archie yelled, "I'll have you transferred to Crossmaglen or Beleek. The DI and I play golf together regularly".

"Is that so Sir? I must ask you to get out of your car".

"I will in my arse get out!" howled Archie, loosing the run of himself.

"Sir, if you insist on behaving like this, I will call the DI, who fortunately just happens to be here on patrol with us tonight. You can explain to him why you want me transferred to a punishment station". He called the Inspector. "Inspector, I have a man here who says he is a friend of yours. He seems to think that you can wheedle him out of taking a breathalyser test. Also, he has, in front of four officers, intimated that he would intimidate me from enforcing the Road Traffic Act...Sir".

"Archie!" said the Inspector, "will you get the fuck out of that car and blow into the bag, because if you don't you will spend the night in jail".

"Fat lot of good you are!" said Archie belligerently, "I play golf with you three times a week. I contribute to your bloody benevolent fund. I am Worshipful Grand Master of our Loyal Orange Lodge".

"I, Inspector Robinson, am appearing on behalf of the prosecution".

"I, Anna Ormsby, am here on behalf of the Defence".

"How do you plead? Guilty or not guilty?"

"Not guilty".

"Proceed"

The policeman of the night before stood and said, "On the twenty-sixth of May, this gentleman was apprehended on Golf Club Road. When asked to breathe into the breathalyser bag he refused to do so and was abusive to me personally".

"Was he wasting your time, Constable? Tell me?" the RM beseeched.

"He threatened to have me transferred to a punishment station – gave me the choice of Beleek or Crossmaglen".

"Tell me more. Were you scared?"

"I was, as I like working in the Traffic Branch".

"Tell me, Constable, why do you like Traffic?"

"My daughter was murdered by a drunken driver".

"Yes, Constable?"

"Thank you Constable O'Donnell. What did you say your first name was again?"

"Peadar".

"Thank you, Peadar. If every Constable was as dedicated as you are, we would have safer roads. Tell me by the way, what was the reading?"

"Two-hundred-and-fifty".

"Two-fifty! Are you sure?"

"Yes. The whole patrol read it!"

"Unbelievable!"

The judge, looking out over the top of his spectacles at a pale and stunned Archie Henry, said, " I have no hesitation in convicting you of the offence of failing to provide the requisite specimens when asked. Because you refused to supply a specimen of breath at the roadside I now disqualify you from driving for twelve months and fine you the sum of five-hundred pounds. I take a dim view not only of your lack of co-operation but also of your attempt to influence, prejudicially, an Officer of the Law. Those in themselves are serious offences. Any attempt to pervert the course of justice in my Court would normally be dealt a term of imprisonment – first offence or not. Consider yourself very fortunate not to be heading for Crumlin Road Gaol".

Archie stood trying to find saliva in his mouth to swallow.

the Nissan from your friend Frank? We need a light car. I have a clean licence. Make sure it's taxed and insured. The Black Bastard would hold us up all day and enjoy it".

Twenty minutes later, the Nissan was filled with diesel and was on the M1. "Do you know what", said Mick, "we'll go by Enniskillen. The road's much more scenic and we can look at the lake for twenty minutes!" The journey was going quickly enough until hunger got the better of them and they pulled up at the little Warrior Queen Hotel in Enniskillen.

They tumbled out of the Nissan and piled into the bar, which was dark after the bright sunlight they had left behind them in the street. A few wasters were scattered around, backs to the bar, eyes either on the television or staring into their black pints, saying little. They shifted their backsides into more comfortable positions on their barstools when the men came in – but that was all. They were more interested in the football on the screen than in the new arrivals. The barmaid smiled cheerfully at Dessie, Mick and Tom, obviously delighted with the little diversion their entrance had created. "Now boys!" she said brightly, "what'll it be?"

"Do you have any bar food, we're STARVING!" burst Mick, settling half of himself on a barstool while keeping one foot on the floor. The other two crowded in behind him. "Anyway, what's your name?" he continued jauntily.

"I'm Roisin!" she said, the smile lighting her face, "and we have all sorts of sandwiches – toasted if you want them that way!"

ambled restfully by, first passing under the stone bridge with the four arches and then, after several miniscule falls, they watched it disappear from their view by the old mill. There was an elegant ash tree on the opposite bank, and lots of bushes. The grass by the edge of the river had been freshly mown. Birds sang noisily while the odd van and a few cars passed over the bridge. Occasionally a salmon leapt out of the water on its way upstream. They sat there in amicable silence until Roisin reappeared with a mound of sandwiches. She set them down and then stood back, and with her hands on her hips said, "And where are you off to then?"

Dessie answered quickly, "We're off to beautiful Belduff. Do you want to come with us?"

"Ach, sure I'd love to," she answered, "but I have to stay here and earn the few bob for myself." She tossed her hair over her left shoulder with a quick jerk of her head and Dessie loved the way she did it.

"And what about joining us there tonight?" Dessie demanded. "Would you have any way of getting down?"
"I Suppose I would," she replied thoughtfully, "that's if you'd let me bring my friend with me. Sharon has a car."

"Sharon?" Mick interjected, "is Sharon a good-looker like yourself?"

Roisin blushed with pleasure as she said, "She is indeed and she has legs up to her neck! She's fierce tall!"

over again. "Not far now" said Mick to Dessie, the Fox, "You will soon be telling us your secret".

* * *

Patrick was ready and waiting on Monday. The time had come for Thelma's visit. He had done all she had asked him. Chablis in the fridge, two-dozen smiling oysters open on the kitchen table. He heard the taxi pull up, and taking the cork from the wine he poured her a glass and then went to open the door.

She marched past him, flinging her coat off on the way to the kitchen. "Leading my nieces astray, were you? You'll get jail if you touch Florence" she teased. "Bet you like her more than me!" she said coyly. Patrick went on the defensive and opened his mouth to reply but she stopped him by saying, "I'm being naughty. Give me a kiss and tell me you love me and then give me that glass of wine." She didn't get the glass of wine immediately, for he threw his arms around her, hugging and kissing her and telling her how he hadn't been able to sleep all week for thinking about her. Thelma disentangled herself and said, "Will you go easy Patrick! I'm going to have my wine and oysters before I have you! How much did he charge for the oysters?"

Patrick said, "Three pounds, fifty."

"Oh the bastard!" said Thelma indignantly. "He always charges me five."

Force, with the active connivance of the RUC. Also the raid on Cappagh. The police are known to have made the way clear for them."

Thelma was thinking. "One more thing," she said, as she seasoned her oysters with Tabasco, Yorkshire Relish and a squeeze of lemon, "how do you see Northern Ireland panning out?"

Patrick frowned and considered the many books on the shelves in his kitchen before answering. Standing up and reaching for his copy of Hansard he said, "Maybe you'd be interested in what Churchill had to say in 1922?" Thelma ate while he thumbed through the pages, laid the book on the table open at the appropriate page, and sat down to read. "This is a great quote," he murmured, nodding.

"Well read it then," she said, sucking her fingers.

He began, "'The whole map of Europe has changed. The position of countries has been violently altered. The modes of thoughts of men, the whole outlook of affairs, the grouping of parties, all have encountered violent and tremendous changes in the deluge of the world. But as the deluge subsides, and the waters fall short, we see the dreary steeples of Fermanagh and Tyrone emerging once again. The integrity of their quarrel is one of the few institutions that have been unaltered in the cataclysm that has swept the world.'"

Patrick closed the book quietly and looked at Thelma for approval. She drew up the left side of her mouth wanly and

they would have just coffee. "We're on active service so we can't have a drink".

Dessie added, "Actually we're waiting for a phone call to come here for us from the Quartermaster General."

"Enough said," nodded Big Jim understandingly. "By the way, were you watching Down play on UTV on Sunday? Did you see Mickey run in the goal and six points? Jesus, he's some tit! Didn't he show Charlie Thomond how to score!"

"McGill had a great game at midfield," said Mick joining in the conversation.

And they chatted on about the Gaelic match until the phone call came.

put his shining shoes neatly underneath his bed. I'll go to Hong Kong, he said to himself. That should be far enough away. They'll be after me for the part I played in those last two executions especially. That creepy Jamieson will look after me. He's an odious little man.

Checking that everything in his room was in order, Darcy closed his door behind him and went in search of the Sergeant. "Should my mother telephone," he said, "please tell her that I will be in Reddich in the next few days, but also say that I will return her call in the morning".

* * *

Jamieson was dreaming about big lump sums of money from the Russians when the telephone rang in his office. He absentmindedly raised the receiver to his ear and said, "Department of the Navy, Jamieson speaking!"

"Could you please hold, Mr Jamieson," said a young female voice, "for a call from Dr Williamson."

Jamieson straightened himself and took a deep breath for he knew what he was about to hear. Dr Williamson, using words that came easily to him after years of practice, told Jamieson that his mother had died twenty minutes earlier. He explained that the Chaplain had been with her at the end and that it had all been very peaceful. He consoled Jamieson by saying how fortunate it had been that the two of them had spent some hours together a few days earlier. And he consoled him further by saying that she had gone into a coma shortly after midnight and had not regained con-

yelled at to do so by a raucous female from the back of the pub.

And so the night wore on. Darcy ordered first one vodka-and-coke, then a second and then a third. Invited singers came to the piano, did their stuff and sat down. Applause waxed and waned but Darcy was not asked the second time if he would sing. He was secretly being drugged by having Rohypnol put in his drink. When he passed out, Huge Euge threw him over his shoulder and carried him outside – but few noticed and even fewer cared. (What did annoy the drinkers was that Titch decided he had entertained them enough for the evening and he left too.) Darcy was thrown into the back of a Hiace van, which had previously been parked at the emergency exit, and was driven off into the darkness.

* * *

Near Eisc River he was lifted from the van and taken to a shack with windows blacked out, and which was lit by a hurricane lamp. He came around because he was being roughly shaken and yelled at.

"Wake up Captain Darcy!" the voice kept repeating. "It's time for you to talk now!"

Darcy's head was exploding in bursts each time his heart beat. He felt dreadful. He eyes wouldn't focus for a time, but when they finally did he realised with horror that he had to be face to face with Doctor Death, the most dangerous psychotic in West Belfast. At that time he could not speak,

shot in the back of the head. If you lie, those breezeblocks beside you will be dropped on your legs and you will die roaring. You will even beg for us to finish you off telling us everything. I know! I have done this many times!"

He looked questioningly at Darcy who had glanced at the breezeblocks. When Darcy looked at Doctor Death again he went on, each syllable stressed, "Who are your sleepers? I want their names and addresses." Darcy's mouth was completely dry. "Jamieson," he thought, "is a bastard."

Rasping his dry tongue over the dry roof of his mouth he realised that everything this psychotic said was true and that only he knew his own sleepers.

He looked Doctor Death in the eye and croaked out, with difficulty, the request that he be given time to make peace with his God. He was given the time and then he began, "Jonathan Davidson is originally from Doncaster. He has served with the Royal Engineers in Cyprus and the Falklands. He was given an awareness course in Plymouth and has been a sleeper in Northern Ireland for five years. He is know here as Thomas O'Donnell and lives beside the Parochial House in Knockbrook."

At the mention of O'Donnell's name Titch interjected, "I know the hoor. I'd be delighted to give him his come-uppance!"

Darcy went on, "The other one is Barry Dickson – originally from Wakefield in Yorkshire. He has seen service with the Navy in Plymouth and has been living in the caravan park

smelt danger. It was Thursday. Footballers didn't arrive until Friday evenings. As they left by the front door, he excused himself to go to the lavatory but instead went out the back door and tore down the lane. By the time they were crossing the bridge over the river, Tom was right behind them. As they were passing the Post Office, Tom ducked into the Old Fountain Bar, ordered a pint of Guinness, took his jacket off and sat by the window to drink and watch what was happening. He knew that the alcoholic priest who was Quartermaster General lived up that end of town and he assumed that that was where the boys were going.

Half an hour went by, during which time Tom never took his eyes off the street, except to swallow a mouthful of his pint. As he saw the boys reappear, he put on his jacket and went outside. He followed them at a distance and his heart was beginning to pound. When he saw them turn in to Lowther Road he felt that he had seen enough. He went to the nearest telephone kiosk and dialled a taxi. "They're going to the caravan park," he said to himself. "Not good! Not good at all!"

His taxi arrived. The driver, Miley, was a friend of his. "Where to?" he asked when Tom opened the door.

"Enniskillen," said Tom and he quickly got in.

"Thought you could get picked up there!" said Miley.

"Sure I could," said Tom, "but my sister Theresa is sick and I'll chance it to go and see her."

is it? I hope it's not what I think it is?" and so saying he hurried off.

Tom dialled the number and Inspector Ferguson waited close by. "Hello! Can I speak to the highest officer on duty please?" He waited a moment and then said, "Major Brownlow, this is Lieutenant Davidson speaking. I am on active service in Northern Ireland and I am anxious to find out if our security has been breached. My direct superior is Captain Darcy and I am concerned that there is a dramatic increase in the numbers of active, quality subversives in our district. I believe they have now drawn down weapons and are closing in on one of our operatives. I need you to check with Captain Darcy. See if he is available to return my call. This is urgent. I am at the RUC station in Enniskillen." He hung up.

For half an hour he paced the room and talked to Inspector Ferguson. He was very agitated. Finally the telephone rang. The Inspector answered it and then passed the receiver to Tom saying, "It's Colonel Heaps!"

The Colonel told Tom that Darcy had not reported at 1900 hours, neither at 2100 hours. By 2300 hours he had not returned to base.

"I think," said Tom, "that a major breach of security has occurred and would need to be debriefed. Please send a helicopter for me to go to Thiepval and later on to Cheltenham. Thank you." He turned to Inspector Ferguson, "It looks bad for Darcy!" he said.

VIII

Heather woke up early on Saturday morning, for a change, and lay in her bed wondering why. Suddenly she grinned, remembering that she had a date with Gilbert. She yawned, stretched, pulled her pillows down and her blankets up around her chin and shoulders and, snuggling down luxuriously, she thought about what she would wear that night. She settled for her mini pleated skirt and black top and decided that she would go and get her hair done in the afternoon. She tried to go to sleep again, failed and so got up and dressed.

Gilbert phoned her at lunchtime. "Hi Heather!" he said, "everything all right for this evening?"

"Yea, grand," said Heather a little breathlessly on account of the anticipation.

"I'm going for a jar in Henshaw's before the hop. Will you meet me there?"

"That'll be fine," she said. "What time'll I meet you?"

"Say about ten?" he said.

When Heather strolled in, Gilbert, who had been watching the door, stood up and waved to her. Making her way gingerly among the tables and the waving hands holding pints, she came up to him and sat down on the stool he had been minding for her. She nodded greetings to his friends, some of whom she had known at school, and then Gilbert called a passing barmaid and ordered her a drink. "I'm just drinking Coke," he said, "but please don't let that put you off drinking whatever you want." Heather was not put off at all. She drank beer. They yelled at each other above the noise. Chiefly they yelled about how she was getting on with the Greenfinches and then it was time to go to the hop. Gilbert said, "We're as well to walk to Parklands. Sure it's only a few hundred yards. We'll leave the cars in the car park here. They'll be quite safe."

Outside the weather was nippy and Heather shivered. Gilbert did not let the chance pass and quickly put his arm around her shoulders. Heather stiffened slightly and hoped that no one she knew was watching her. Ever since the episode with Archie she had avoided, as far as possible, any close contact with men, young or old. But she wanted to get over this. She wanted to be able to discuss boys and dates and kissing – and more – just like the girls with whom she had been to school. She didn't want to be different from them. So when they got inside the dance hall and there came a slow dance and Gilbert began to dance close with her, she steeled herself and got on with it. She loved music and dancing. Henshaw's beer was going slowly and pleasantly to her head and she relaxed. Gilbert kissed her neck, nibbled her ear and then searched for her lips with his. She

but knowing that no one was there watching her she became submissive. Gilbert was gentle. She realised that. She allowed him to run the tip of his tongue around the inside of her mouth and was amazed to find it quite thrilling. Gilbert found it thrilling too. She forced Archie from her mind by thinking of what she could tell the girls, and Gilbert put his hand between her legs. She gripped her thighs tightly together so Gilbert took his hand away and also took his arm from around her shoulders. He sat and stared out the window. "Do you not want this Heather?" he asked.

Heather swallowed before saying in a small voice, "I think I do."

"Well then," said Gilbert, "can I let your seat back?" He leaned over and pulled the lever so that Heather fell back, her feet on the floor, staring up at the roof.

"Oh dear God," she thought, "now what!"

Gilbert fumbled with his jeans and she heard him undo the buttons one by one. "Take off your tights and pants!" he whispered.

Heather felt mortified but she did as she had been asked. She put them neatly on the seat behind her. He pulled his jeans down and she took a furtive look and saw the whiteness of his bum gleam in the darkness. She also saw his erection. "This," she thought, "is going to be awful."

Gilbert reached for her hand and put it gently on his penis. "Stroke me!" he begged. She did and she felt the slippery

road he took her hand. "Can I see you next Saturday?" he asked.

"Yes," said Heather thinking that she was as well. Sex, she surmised, is a queer thing, and she was puzzled that there was so much talk about it. She couldn't think why Aunt Thelma found it so necessary. But she was now, at least, one of the gang and she had a boyfriend.

She reported in. Olive was awake. "You're a bit late dear," she said doubtfully.

"I know Mum, I'm sorry. But Gilbert and I sat talking for ages. You know how it is!"

"He'd be Jim and Mary Watson's son, wouldn't he?" asked Olive. "Yes, I remember him. He's a nice lad. Good night darling. Sleep tight!"

Heather went to bed but she couldn't sleep.

* * *

Dessie, Mick and Tom walked steadily up to the mobile home in the caravan park in Belduff. Almost simultaneously they hammered on the door and burst in. The red-haired man who was sitting at the table inside was completely taken by surprise.

"Lieutenant Dickson I presume?" said Mick. "Up on your feet!" he snapped. The man pushed his chair back and did as he was told. Mick went on, "I am arresting you on behalf

for disposal. The driver asked him, "How the hell will you keep him submerged?"

"That's no problem at all," said the gillie. "I'll take him out to near Bilberry Island and then I'll put weights on him and drop him over the side. I'll fish there with my clients for the next three weeks or so. The Sonaghan and Gilaroo will feast on him and clean him up for us."

"There'll be a few others to follow. You were told, weren't you?"

The gillie nodded. "I'll be ready," he said.

* * *

Miley Cadden drove his taxi straight from Enniskillen to O'Moore's Bar and met the boys. "I dropped Tom O'Donnell off at the Coin Bar about midnight," he said. "Said his sister was ill and that he was going to visit her. He also said that he would see me tomorrow."

* * *

"Jesus!" said Dessie, suddenly remembering Roisin, the barmaid from The Warrior Queen, "What about the women and the disco!"

Mick and Tom smiled. "Yea," said Tom, "what's your hurry? There's plenty of time. We'll get to see them all right. Business comes first!"

IX

The disco, when Dessie, Mick and Tom got there, was in full swing. It was also very crowded. David, the DJ, was justifying his great reputation. His collection of discs was terrific and the way he mixed them drew the crowd. He stood up there above the gyrating mass of humankind, thin as a lathe, head shorn, swaying and mouthing to his music, his earring sparkling and the beads of sweat running down his temples. He loved his job. Now and then he took great gulps from his pint and every so often he would draw deeply from the fag he always kept smouldering in the ashtray by his right hand. He was a hit and he knew it. He'd been about the world a bit, this David, but he always spent the summer months in Belduff. He said he couldn't help coming back.

Dessie spotted Roisin fairly quickly. Her blonde head stood out in the crowd, especially under the strobe lights. She was doing the most amazing things on the floor with a fellow with dreadlocks. Dessie jerked his head in her direction and his mates followed him as he made his way through the sweaty mass, in its continuous state of flux, and tipped her on the shoulder. She shifted her concentration from her rhythmic feet to his face and beamed at him with instant recognition. "So you made it!" she yelled at him above the clamour. Dessie smiled and nodded. He then pointed at

"Oh Gawd!" she answered quickly, "I thought you were going to tell me I had legs like Tina Turner."

"I don't know who the fuck Tina Turner is!" he said belching. "I have to go for a leak," and he wandered off in search of a lavatory.

"Come on the hell out of this Mick!" said Sharon urgently, "before that git gets back," and the two of them went off towards the dance floor. An older man bumped into Sharon on the way and, full of good humour, said to her, "Sweetheart! Where have you been all my life?"

She stopped and eyed him up and down scathingly and then said with much sarcasm, "I think I wasn't born for most of it." She held out her hand to Mick who was happy to take it and the two of them went to dance.

Bridget, when introduced to Tom, looked relieved. She had had her bellyful of her drunk. As Tom squeezed between the two of them the drunk was saying confidentially to her, "I am a psych-y-atrist at the Mental Hospital in Sligo."

"Well, if that's what you say you are," Bridget said smiling sweetly, "then I am Sharon's manager and she's doing a gig in Castlebar tomorrow night."

"Tell that to the Marines!" said the youth rudely.

"Yes," said Bridget, "and you're not earning much as a psych-y-atrist in the Mental Hospital in Sligo for that hos-

He sat drumming the three middle fingers of his right hand on his desk. It sounded like a horse cantering very fast. He narrowed his eyes and thought, "Margaret Jackson? No. Not yet. But Heather Elliot seems settled enough."

* * *

Olive, Heather and Florence sat in large armchairs watching television. The library was cosy. The heavy curtains were drawn tight and the large logs burning in the grate threw up little explosions of sparks from time to time. They decided not to turn on the small lamp on the table by Olive's elbow, so the flames from the fire threw shadows on the books which lined the walls. They were watching 'Arsenic and Old Lace'. It was one of Olive's favourite films and as her daughters had never seen it, she had begged them to watch it with her. They hadn't protested. They were good girls and didn't resent spending time with their mother.

Anyway, they were enjoying the film when Florence suddenly sat up listening. "Is that the phone?" she said disbelievingly. Olive reached for the remote control and turned the volume down on the telelvision. It was indeed the telephone.

"Who on earth can that be at this hour of the night!" she said crossly.

"Stay where you are Mum. I'll get it," said Florence, struggling up out of the depths of her chair and running nimbly out of the room and into the icy cold of the hall.

"I'm not bathing again!" said Heather flatly. "It's too damn cold. Good job I have my uniform ready. I'd best go and change quickly. He says he wants me there as soon as possible."

In her bedroom, she quickly changed out of her jeans and sweater and into her uniform. She brushed her hair and deftly put on the beret with the harp on it. She took a quick look in the long mirror at her overall appearance, switched on her electric blanket in readiness for her return and then went downstairs.

"Good girl Heather!" said Olive. "That was quick!"

"I can't tell you exactly when I'll get home," said Heather, checking that all she wanted was in her handbag, "but I will probably be in time for breakfast. He did apologise for giving me such short notice but said I could have a lie-in afterwards! Big deal!"

"He's a tough one!" said Olive nodding. "By the way, I'll be going to early Communion in the morning and when I get back you'll probably be in bed, so take care, my lamb."

"I will," said Heather, going over to kiss her mother on her forehead, "and don't worry about me and church. I'll go to Evening Prayer tomorrow at eight. Bye Florence," she added, "wish I could see the end of the film. Tell me how it finishes."

Heather was puzzled but accepting nonetheless. Over coffee the Major asked her if she was happy in her work and she agreed that she was. He asked after he mother and they chatted on amicably. In was a normal, polite conversation for a boss to have with an employee but Heather felt slightly uncomfortable and didn't know why. When Major Benson left his seat and went towards the door saying, "We'll lock this for security," she definitely felt uneasy. She quickly noted that all the blinds were drawn on the windows. As the key turned in the lock she got to her feet but he was standing in front of her in an instant.

Heather was a lone private. She did not really mix with the other girls and was always at the periphery of conversations. She listened while the others chatted but never really got involved. She had been taught not to listen to idle gossip and had therefore never been included in the chat about the randy platoon leader.

"You find me handsome Heather, don't you?" he said confidently.

"I...I...don't know, Major," she stammered.

"Of course you do," he said quietly. "All you young girls do. I know you chat among yourselves. You love to be associated with power."

"No Major," said Heather in desperation and in a small voice. "I never think about power." She swallowed several times and looked down at the carpet with heart pounding.

to Heather, one foot on the floor, the other dangling. With total calm he picked up the receiver of his telephone and dialled a number. After a few seconds he said, "Hello Jill. Could you please go to the sentry box and relieve Madeline McCullough. Tell her I want her to come to my office immediately." He hung up and remained sitting on his desk. He heard Heather put the comb down behind him and he reached back, took it and put it in his pocket. Looking idly around at the girl he said, "Pull your collar up around your neck." As she did this Madeline knocked at the door.

"Come in!" said Major Benson brightly. "Ah, Private Mc-Cullough, Private Elliot fainted. The poor girl must have found it too hot in here. Would you be so kind as to take her home and put her to bed. I'm sure that a few hours' sleep will see her right as rain."

Full of concern, Madeline helped Heather to her feet and led her to the car park. "Poor wee Heather," she said. "How are you feeling now?"

"Oh I'm all right Madeline," said Heather weakly, "I'm sure it was just as Major Benson said. Too hot in there."

She's been through the mill in more ways than one, thought Madeline. There'll have to be a stop put to that bastard. And indeed, a stop was to be put on him, but not in a way that Madeline could ever have imagined.

* * *

you. And," she added, "I'll have that hideous, ghastly bastard Benson stitched up before too long. I am shocked by what you've just told me…Just be patient, angel. See you in a few hours. Dry your tears and think how your Aunt Thelma is getting to work on your behalf. That should give you a lift!"

Thelma used her telephone. She spoke to one of the ladies with whom she was due to have lunch and apologised that she could not be there. Double-checking that her husband was not about – she was sure she remembered him saying that he would be out of town that day – she retrieved, from underneath the carpet in her bedroom, the key she had had cut to his study, unlocked the door and went inside.

Well now!" breathed Thelma in the empty room with a satisfied smirk on her face. Who would have thought it! As well as all his disgusting, debauched activities with young girls, Bugger Benson has a woman! He's actually straying! Isn't it the wonder his dick hasn't dropped off! He had some fucking neck to try something on with a member of my family. He'll be sorry he did that!

She took a notebook from her handbag, wrote down a few relevant details and, having turned the computer off and left things as she had found them, she walked purposefully out of the house.

* * *

his car. He felt in his inside pocket for Thelma's envelope, reassured himself that it was there, got out and went into the shop.

He said hello to the thin, positively scrawny woman who stood behind the counter, and commented on the weather. Her eyes watched him and he felt uncomfortable. He put her in her late forties. She was fit. He could tell. "I wonder," said Patrick politely, "if I could see the boss?"

The woman shifted her weight from her right foot to her left and said with a total lack of expression, "I am the boss." Patrick was a little less composed than previously. Producing the envelope and handing it to her he said, "I was asked to give you this and to get a reply." He read the headlines on the newspapers displayed just above floor level while she read the letter.

Looking up she said to him, "I take it you are a messenger – no more?"

"That's it," said Patrick.

"Then," she said, "tell the scribe that we will deal with this in our own time."

"Is that all?"

"Yes," she said and he thanked her and left the shop.

* * *

the first big Lambeth drum swung proudly past Florence yelled into Heather's ear, "Wouldn't that put you in mind of the Salvation Army joke?"

"I don't remember it," said Heather, "but I am sure you are about to remind me!"

"Yea," said Florence. "The big, busty Salvation Army woman comes over to the group of wee girls watching the performance and says to one of them, "Which hymn would you like, dear?" and the girl says, "If you wouldn't mind, I'd like him on the big drum!" and she pointing at this fine-lookin' young fella."

Florence linked her arm through Heather's and said, "Go on, let you! You can laugh!" and Heather did because she had to. She knew then and there that she really did love Florence.

The Orangemen marched on. Band after band of colour and ribbons, sashes and bowler hats, fine male voices and pride.

Above all there was pride. And the womenfolk stood and watched their men and admired them with their manly chests all puffed out. And they too sang along.

"Oh God!" said the woman by Heather's side with much emotion, "how I love that aul' Sash," and she threw back her head and gave it her all. Heather closed one eye and winced as she bellowed out,
"It is old but it is beautiful, and the colours they are fine.

her sister, she had no hand to swipe them from her cheeks so she let them flow. Shaking her head sadly from side to side, and holding her breath for seconds at a time so that she would not sob, Heather retired into her mind. "It's so wrong. It's all wrong! This is my country and I love it. But every day I meet people who are sick with hatred. How can I stand here and be seen taking part in such an atrocious demonstration of loathing."

As children burst from the crowd and skipped into the road to dance along behind the last band until it reached the finishing spot, she freed her arms and turning to Florence said, "I will never ever go to anything Orange again, never!"

* * *

Heather lay in her bed in the dark. She had no idea what time it was. She was thinking. A dog barked in the distance and the old house creaked occasionally in the familiar way it always did. "Daddy," she whispered into the darkness, "I miss you and I wish you were here. Please forgive me for what I am thinking. I'd hate it if you thought I was letting you down. But I've tried and tried to follow in the family tradition and it's got too much for me. Patrick Maguire believes that if you'd let go of the bloody family tradition you wouldn't have died. I hate thinking about how you went. It wasn't fair. You never deserved that. Mummy and Florence didn't deserve to have you die either, but they seem to be resigned to it and I'm not. They believe you did your duty. I'm not into duty of that sort, Daddy. I'm sick to death of murders and beatings and kneecappings and of no one trusting his neighbour. And all for what? I learnt about

X

The rotor blades of the Jolly Green Giant spun and the Chinook rose slowly into the sky. The grass was flattened by the down-rush of air. Thelma waved indifferently with one hand and held onto her hair with the other, cursing because she had had an excellent re-styling job done that morning.

A major security review was taking place at a secret destination in Scotland and her husband was one of the members of the review party. He had just been promoted to Assistant Chief Constable with more money and a bigger and better Jaguar. Whatever about the money, Thelma adored the Jaguar. She felt really on top of the world when she drove it. She loved the way it wriggled its behind when she put her foot hard on the accelerator, and this was exactly what she did as she raced down the M2 on her way to Belfast. She idly switched on Downtown Radio and hummed to herself as she sped along. She admired the panoramic view of Belfast Lough as it lay spread out in front of her.

As she got to the bridge over the Lagan she slowed down. Traffic was building up and she swore at it. Suddenly the music on the radio was stopped for an announcement and the serious voice used for times like this said, "Here is a newsflash. Five minutes ago, a helicopter crashed into the

Finally, one Friday she telephoned, and Patrick's relief swamped him. He had barked his shin on the corner of the wooden box of tools he had left in the hall in his hurry to pick up the receiver. Holding onto his damaged limb with both hands and rocking backwards and forwards, he sandwiched the receiver between his shoulder and ear and crooned, "Oh Thelma, how are you! I've missed you so much! How I wish I could have been with you to hold you and comfort you. I tried to phone you but no one would give me your number – not Olive, not the girls!"

"I'm fine, Patrick," she said reassuringly. "Hope you haven't been naughty with those scrubbers!"

"Ah God Thelma!" he said in horror, "on my mother's grave I swear I've hardly left the house since you were last here."

"Right so," she said cheerfully, "I believe you. And Patrick, I'll be down on Monday at the usual time." He closed his eyes when she said this. His cup was full. "You'd better get the oysters!"

"I'll go straightaway!" he said with delight.

"There's no rush," she said, "this is only Friday. And I've decided that I don't like the carpet you have on your bedroom floor. Could you change it for a green one?"

"Of course!" he said, thrilled to do anything that she asked, "anything else?"

warriors in the world – magnificent infantry who would fight this religious war to the death, believing that to die fighting would bring the ultimate heavenly reward. Four divisions had been totally lost and the drain on hard currency severe. Then thirteen divisions of infantry and three divisions of armour were tied up continually on duty. That was no help to the worsening financial situation. As for Gorbachov and the Glasnost business! Comorov shook his head sadly.

He left his desk and paced up and down. Throughout his career he had been trusted for his straight, incorruptible stance. Information he had got that day, together with his feelings of bitterness at having reached the age of fifty-one and being as good as rouble-less, made the thought of defection to the United States very attractive. The more he thought about it the more attractive it became.

Slowly his mood changed from one of bitterness to one of almost glee. He rubbed his hands together and mouthed, "Good man Jamieson! MI5 will be amazed when they find out what you have done!" The files he had on the agents in Great Britain and France should get him all the concessions he wanted from George Lane. His spies had told him that the man was not at all happy in Moscow, so his information could be of benefit to both of them.

Now that he knew what he would do, Comorov began to think about his wife and two daughters. He felt bad that he could not tell them what he was up to. Once in America he would organise a holiday for them in Cuba. There would be a stopover in Shannon where they could seek political

* * *

George Lane was the CIA'a Head of Station, Moscow. It was the most important post of its type in the world and he was proud of himself when he was given the appointment. It meant a big hike in his salary and his expenses were enormous. Moscow was a great listening post and these were exciting times with the beginning of the collapse of the Communist system and the withdrawal by the Russians from Afghanistan. It was the first reversal the Red Army had had since its ignoble retreat in front of the Blitzkreig in the Second World War. This was a change from Langley in Virginia where he had been teaching Russian, amongst other things.

He had always kept himself fit by jogging each morning, but jogging in this infernal cold was more of a chore than a pleasure. On his way home to his apartment he trotted into Lennin Avenue and was more than surprised when a large Zil drew up beside him and two sergeants got swiftly out. George Lane halted, panting, and the men came to stand on either side of him. "You will please come with us," they said, ushering him into the car.

Comorov's office door was opened and George Lane was shown in. He looked puzzled. After the two soldiers had been dismissed Vlad Comorov turned to him and smiled. "Sorry to bring you here like this but it was necessary to avoid suspicion. Would you like a cup of coffee? Americans always drink coffee, isn't that so? We Russians prefer black tea."

them knowing that what had just passed between them was to their mutual advantage.

"Right then," said George Lane, "my man will meet your man in the tea shop on Lennin Avenue at 1500 hours on Wednesday?"

"Yes," said Vlad Comorov, "everything will be in order." They discussed their agents, how they looked and what they would be wearing, and finally they agreed on the exchange of words.

* * *

Nikita put the brown paper parcel and his newspaper under his arm and looked at his watch. Because it was twenty minutes before three o'clock and there was plenty of time, he decided to go on foot to the teashop. He easily lost himself in the crowd of depressed people who walked the streets of Moscow on that very cold day.

In the tea shop he looked around, spotted whom he believed to be his man in the left corner at the back, got his cup from the counter and walked towards him. He was reading his evening newspaper, Vechernyaya Moskva. After excusing himself and asking, in Russian, whether it would be all right to join him at the table he said in English, "What was the temperature in Miami yesterday?" to which the man replied, "How hot would you like it to have been?" Everything was, as Comorov had said, in order.

* * *

ror, patted a bit of stray hair into place and, saying goodbye to his Russian clothes and his Russian life, left the room.

The helicopter pilot was waiting for him. "We're on schedule, Sir," he said, "but we want to keep it that way so let's go!"

As Comorov hurried after him he said, "Is George Lane not coming with us?"

"No, Sir," came the reply and Comorov thought to himself, "He's wise. If I were in his position I wouldn't attempt to leave with a defector of my kind either!"

"You understand, Sir," said the pilot, "that we are flying fairly low so as to remain undetected by Russian Air Traffic Control?"

"Yes, but where are we going exactly?"

"We have big enough fuel tanks on this baby to take us all the way to Oslo, after that you will transfer to a regular flight and go to Washington – and then Langley for debriefing."

"Ah," nodded Comorov, "I see." He closed his eyes and vehemently wished himself out of Russia and into safety. He thought that he would have been sent to London first, but then London was not to be trusted any more what with Burgess, Blunt, McClean and their ilk. "MI5 is riddled with buggers like those," thought Comorov contentedly, "but my favourite is the fellow Jamieson!"

Mrs Whicker was extremely concerned by the delicate information given her by her Cabinet Secretary. The problem was, just who was she to trust? She was disillusioned at that time. "Snooty-nosed, pedantic idiots the lot of them," she sniffed. "Tons of intelligence yet no common sense. What I must do is keep a tight rein on all this information, improve on my listeners, sort out my Red-leaning civil servants and give them a good boot up the arse.

Buckingham!" she yelled through her open office door. "Get the Deputy PM on the telephone and tell him to get here fast!"

The Deputy Prime Minister arrived running and was told not to eat or even go to the lavatory, but to get himself immediately to Northolt. Being used to Mrs Whicker, he understood what he was to do pretty quickly.

The Deputy Prime Minister of Great Britain flew from Northolt to Washington. He went to collect the relevant files that Comorov had spirited from Moscow. He spent only a few hours on American soil before flying home to London with the documents under seal for Mrs Whicker. Jamieson was in deep trouble.

him and offering him a pen she said, "Just sign here, and here and, oh, here as well. I've marked the places.

Patrick did not take the pen. He straightened himself against the back of his chair, crossed his legs easily and said, "Thelma, my sweetheart, I know that what you have in mind for me is, in your opinion, for the best and thanks for all the trouble you have gone to. But now you've got to think of what I'd like. I won't have my career and future possible earnings dictated by the feelings of the sporting lady golfers of Royal Belfast. I know that a woman of your standing can't possibly have her photograph taken with a part-time gravedigger and it put in the Ulster Tatler! I'm not a complete eejit Thelma! I'll have my own method of making my way up this social ladder that worries you so much. I'll do it by investments and a bit of business. We can go into this together for all that. I've been checking the businesses for sale for the past little while. Did you know that?" He didn't wait for her to reply. "For all you found out about me off your late husband's computer, you didn't get the whole of it. The money I got for the farm is in a safe little spot just waiting to be used. It'll break my heart to sell this house, but for us I am prepared to do that. I'm told it's worth about thirty thousand. Putting all I have together, I think I could afford a small hotel in a village in west Donegal you know. That's what I have in mind now!"

Relieved to have off-loaded all his plans onto this woman, Patrick Maguire uncrossed his legs and leapt to his feet. Gathering the startled Thelma in his arms he swung her round and round, humming "The Homes of Donegal" into her ear. He then whispered wickedly, "What I have in mind

In the police station the reason for Jamieson's arrest was explained to the duty officer. "Right!" he said, "now empty your pockets!" Slowly he put his loose change, his wallet, his pen, his penknife and his handkerchief on the table. He behaved like an old, old man.

"Come on!" urged the Duty Officer. "Your watch now!" Jamieson stared at his possessions while a clerk listed them in a book and then he wrote his signature at the bottom of the page. He found it difficult to control the pen.

Before he was led away, the Duty Officer said, "You have been charged with the very serious offence of treason against the realm. You will be questioned . Do you wish this questioning to be in the presence of your solicitor?" Jamieson nodded. "You are allowed just one telephone call."

"Yes, I want to call Abraham Grundy," he said. "My solicitor."

* * *

Mrs Imelda Gillespie was flustered.

As a teenager she had been courted by John Gillespie and things had taken their usual course. They married when she was twenty-one and he twenty-two. Things were difficult at first but then John got a good job managing the local farmers' co-operative, and in the space of five years they were blessed with three sons. "That's enough," thought Imelda. "Things will be clean and decent from now on in." So she swapped the double bed for two singles and got on with

pretty and flanked by charming little houses on either side. "Cosy" was the adjective often used to describe it. The view was incredible. There was the vast Atlantic to the front and the Donegal hills to the rear. It was a veritable paradise.

Imelda had her finger on the pulse of all that was happening in tourism. Where there were grants to be had she had them. She extended the hotel to the back, put in extra bathrooms, enlarged the dining room and found herself a good chef who specialised in seafood. The rest of the staff was local, and during the school holidays her sons did their fair share of the work. She was pleased when her eldest decided that when he left school he would make a career of hotel management. Imelda's cup was full until the awful day when John came home and told her that he had been promoted. This promotion would mean moving to County Carlow.

Imelda deliberated. She tossed and turned in her single bed at night. She agonised over everything – leaving her dentist, her doctor, Donegal, her home, her hotel, her husband. John remained unmoveable. In the end she went to confession.

"No, my good woman," said Father Flanagan. "As a practicing Catholic, you must stay by the side of your husband. To expect him to come home to you at weekends is out of the question. You must go with him. For the good of your marriage and your family the two of you must stay together." He blessed her, and she went home and advertised the Lobster Bay Hotel in The Irish Times, The Irish Independent and also in the Donegal Democrat.

As Mrs Gillespie rattled on about twenty-two bedrooms with bathrooms en suite, the annual turnover, the kitchen that had been recently inspected and passed by the North Western Health Board, the fine state of the fire escapes, the six months of Saturdays which were completely booked for weddings, her orderly tax returns and her reason for selling, Patrick Maguire, who was totally disinterested in the conversation, was gazing at the sun. It was setting like an enormous half orange over the sea. He loved the place. He wanted it. He didn't care right now for the silly details. What bothered him was the price and whether or not he could afford it. He wished Thelma and Mrs Gillespie could come to the point. Suddenly he became alert as he heard the owner of the hotel say, "The price is two-hundred-thousand pounds." He looked at her steadily. He was wondering if he should say that he would have to think about it. Thelma quickly seized the moment and said sharply, "We'll give you one-hundred-and-seventy-five. Take it or leave it!"

Mrs Gillespie thought fast. It was the best offer she'd had. "I'll take it," she said. "You can have possession in sixty days."

* * *

"Well Patrick, anything to report since the last time?" said Thelma flinging her coat onto a kitchen chair in such a way that it immediately slithered off onto the floor.

Patrick bent to pick it up saying, "No Thelma. It's as boring as Churchill's 'dreary steeples'."

"No," she said coming over to put her hands on his shoulders and look into his eyes. "No, it's not that at all. There's the fact of your religion. I think it would split the family and I couldn't have that." He was about to speak but she interrupted, "Please believe me. I love things the way they are. I'm really looking forward to visiting you weekly in Paradise in Donegal. I love spending time with you. But to marry you…No!"

She stood back from him and his gaze was on the floor. He was deeply hurt. But down in his soul he knew that she was right. It wouldn't work.

"You wouldn't be thinking of telling me to fuck off or anything like that?" she said, anxious to break the silence.

Looking at her fixedly he replied, "I'm as well to tell you the rest of what wasn't in your husband's files I suppose."

"What!"

"I'm a Sleeper."

"Oh Dear God!" she cried, "and to think that I didn't know ·that! What am I to do! Jesus!"

"What are we both to do Thelma;" he said sadly.

They stood far apart, looking at each other. Now they could think of nothing to say.

* * *

100 Years at The Hawthorns

100 YEARS AT The Hawthorns

A celebration of West Bromwich Albion's home since 1900

by Tony Matthews

Express & Star

The Breedon Books
Publishing Company
Derby

Contents

Introduction

ON 3 September 2000, The Hawthorns – home of West Bromwich Albion Football Club – will celebrate its 100th birthday.

Since 1900 more than 4,000 matches (not including friendlies) have been played there involving various Albion teams. The first XI have played in over 2,000 competitive matches including 1,662 in the Football League, 131 in the FA Cup and 60 in the League Cup.

Derby County were Albion's first visitors to the ground – drawing 1-1 in a Football League match almost a century ago – and since then over 150 other different teams have ventured to West Bromwich to compete against the Baggies, including, club sides from Austria, Belgium, France, Germany, Holland, Italy, Malta, Portugal, Romania, Russia, Spain, Switzerland, Turkey and Yugoslavia as well as representative sides from Canada and China.

The Hawthorns has staged three major internationals (1922, 1924 and 1945) and played host to both FA Cup and League Cup semi-finals.

Some of the game's greatest players have performed on the Hawthorns' pitch – among them Ivor Allchurch, Gordon Banks, Cliff Bastin, Jim Baxter, George Best, Danny Blanchflower, Steve Bloomer (scorer of the first goal on the ground back in 1900), Rainer Bonhoff, Billy Bremner, Charlie Buchan, Roger Byrne, Raich Carter, John Charles, Bobby Charlton, Kenny Dalglish, Dixie Dean, Jimmy Dickinson, Peter Doherty, Ted Drake, Duncan Edwards, Tom Finney, Trevor Ford, Neil Franklin, Hughie Gallagher, Jimmy Greaves, Johnny Haynes, Glenn Hoddle, Eric Houghton, David Jack, Alex James, Pat Jennings, Bryn Jones, Kevin Keegan, Fred Keenor, Mario Kempes, Denis Law, Tommy Lawton, Jimmy McIlroy, Wilf Mannion, Stanley Matthews, Billy Meredith, Bobby Moore, Stan Mortensen, Ian Rush, Len Shackleton, Peter Shilton, Neville Southall, Ronnie Starling, Frank Swift, Tommy Taylor, and Billy Wright. And of course there have been many star players who have donned the famous navy blue and white striped shirts of Albion, including Ronnie Allen, Jeff Astle, Ray Barlow, Sid Bowser, Tony Brown, Fred Buck, Joe Carter, Clive Clark, Jimmy Cookson, Laurie Cunningham, Stan Davies, Jimmy Dudley, Jimmy Dugdale, Billy Elliott, Doug Fraser, Johnny Giles, Tommy Glidden, Frank Griffin, Asa Hartford, Bobby Hope, Don Howe, Willie Johnston, Harry 'Popeye' Jones, John Kaye, Mario Kempes, Joe Kennedy, Derek Kevan, George Lee, Bobby McNeal, Tommy Magee, Len Millard, Fred Morris, Jimmy Murphy, Johnny Nicholls, John Osborne, Bob Pailor, Harold Pearson and his father Hubert Pearson, Jesse Pennington, Cyrille Regis, Bill Richardson, Sammy Richardson, 'W. G.' Richardson, Stan Rickaby, Ally Robertson, Bobby Robson, Bryan Robson, Reg Ryan, Jimmy Sanders, Teddy Sandford, Maurice Setters, George Shaw, Chippy Simmons (scorer of Albion's first goal at The Hawthorns), Joe Smith, Derek Statham, Jack Vernon, Dave Walsh, John Wile, Billy Williams, Graham Williams and Stuart Williams…and we can't leave out strikers Don Goodman, Lee Hughes, Andy Hunt and Bob Taylor.

The Everiss family – Fred and his son Alan – have been associated with Albion and The Hawthorns for well over 100 years. Alan is now a life member and shareholder and he first set foot inside The Hawthorns back in 1933, when he worked as an office clerk under his father who was secretary-manager of Albion from 1902 to 1948 – a Football League record in terms of service with one club.

Managers have come and gone – Jack Smith, Vic Buckingham, Gordon Clark, Archie Macaulay, Jimmy Hagan, Alan Ashman, Johnny Giles, Ron Atkinson, Ron Saunders, Ron Wylie, Nobby Stiles, Ossie Ardiles, Keith Burkinshaw, Alan Buckley, Ray Harford and Denis Smith along with ex-players Don Howe, Ronnie Allen, Brian Talbot and Bobby Gould. Some did Albion proud, others failed.

Albion have won the League Championship, the FA Cup and the Football League Cup during their time at The Hawthorns. Now they want to get into the Premiership.

The ground itself, the facilities therein, the supporters are all there – let's hope Albion will soon be entertaining the likes of Manchester United, Arsenal and Liverpool and, indeed, competing with the best teams in Europe.

Tony Matthews
Summer 1999

Hawthorns Calendar

1900

Ground officially opened on Monday, 3 September 1900 for the First Division game between West Bromwich Albion and Derby County. At the time The Hawthorns could house around 35,500 fans, and there were 20,104 present on the opening day to see Steve Bloomer (Derby) score the first goal with 'Chippy' Simmons equalising to become the first player to find the net for Albion. The game ended all square at 1-1.

transferred to The Hawthorns, burned down on Guy Fawkes' Night. Reports say that the blaze was caused by a spectator leaving a lighted cigarette in the stand.

1904

The old Stoney Lane stand, known as 'Noah's Ark' which had been

1905

A half-time scoreboard was installed for the first time.

Albion players and officials pictured at the official opening of The Hawthorns on 3 September 1900. Back row (left to right): I. Whitehouse (president, Birmingham League), W. Heath (secretary, Staffordshire FA), J. C. Orr (secretary Birmingham FA), D. I. Pitt (director, WBA), T. H. Sidney (vice-president, Football League), H. Lockett (secretary, Football League). Second row: H. Powell (director, WBA), T. H. Spencer (director, WBA), H. Radford (committeeman, Football League), C. E. Sutcliffe (committeeman, Football League), D. Haigh (vice-president, Football League), J. J. Bentley (president, Football League), H. Keys (chairman, WBA), W. W. Hart ((committeeman, Football League), W. McGregor (founder, Football League), C. Perry (director, WBA), J. Lones (director, WBA). Seated: Frank Heaven (secretary, WBA), C. Keys (auditor, WBA), Pickering, Wheldon (captain), Simmons, Jones, Dunn, Adams, J. Paddock (trainer, WBA). On ground: J. M. Bayliss (director, WBA), Chadburn, Roberts, Reader, Williams, Hadley.

HAWTHORNS CALENDAR

The Halford's Lane Stand in 1954 before it was redeveloped in 1982.

1939

The wooden roof over the Halford's Lane stand was dismantled and replaced by some asbestos sheeting which rested on five giant steel stanchions. The roof was also extended outwards to the front of the terraces.

1940-46

Owing to the war very little work was carried out on the ground but in 1945 England played Wales in a Victory International which drew a 54,610 crowd.

1947

A new block of turnstiles was erected on the Handsworth side of the ground, behind the Woodman Corner.

1949

The wooden terraces in front of the main Halford's Lane stand were replaced by concrete and 750 extra seats were installed in the stand itself. The first electronic turnstile aggregator to be installed on a Football League ground in Britain was put in at The Hawthorns.

1950

A new Directors' Box was provided and the club's offices and dressing rooms were completely re-modernised.

1951

Eight new turnstiles were installed at the Smethwick End.

1957

Floodlights were erected at the ground for the first time at a cost of £18,000. The first game under the 'new' lights saw Albion draw 1-1

In 1951-52, a season ticket for the Halford's Lane end cost £5 5s (£5.25).

with Chelsea in a League Division One fixture on 18 September. Soon afterwards – on 29 October – the Russian Red Army team (CDSK from Moscow) came over to officially open the lights. Albion beat them 6-5 in a classic friendly in front of a 52,805 crowd.

1958

A wing stand at the West Bromwich/Birmingham Road End, was

The Halford's Lane Stand in 1977.

reconstructed at the Smethwick and Birmingham Road Ends with several new crush-barriers also being erected.

1979

Work started on the new £2.5 mil-

lion Halford's Lane stand which would accommodate 4,500 spectators. This was built in two phases over a three-year period:1979-82, and included some more Executive boxes.

1983

The Hawthorns Throstle Club (built next to the ground in 1964) was closed. A large electronic scoreboard was erected on the front of the stand at the Smethwick End (but this was removed in 1985).

1985

A completely new roof was fitted over the terracing at the Smethwick End of the ground and new safety measures were installed at the ground.

1986

A up-to-date, state-of-the-art crowd control video system was installed at the ground.

1988-92

Major safety work was carried out all over the ground following the

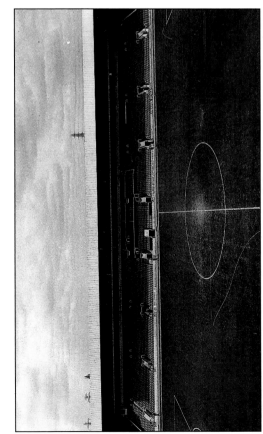

Between 1979 and 1982 the Halford's Lane Stand was rebuilt at a cost of £2.5 million.

HAWTHORNS CALENDAR

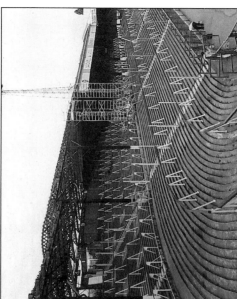

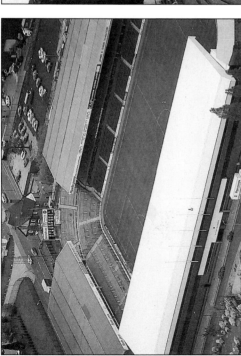

An elevated view of the same Birmingham Road end-Rainbow Stand corner in1990.

Work under way on the Smethwick end in the wake of the Taylor Report.

Aerial view of The Hawthorns in 1993-94.

1994

In the close season the pitch was relaid with enhanced drainage in the summer and the Birmingham Road terracing was dug up as work continued on the redevelopment of The Hawthorns. Albion kicked-off the 1994-95 season with five away League games as the ground was not declared ready when the League programme was due to commence.

The combined cost of refurbishing the stadium came to £4.15 million, of which the club received £2,097,000 from the Football Trust in 1995. The 'new' modernised Hawthorns was officially opened for the First Division visit of Bristol City on Boxing Day, a game Albion won 1-0.

1995

The Hawthorns Museum was officially opened by manager Alan Buckley, vice-chairman Clive Stapleton and curator Tony Matthews. The Hawthorns railway station was re-opened after 27 years and the capacity of ground was cut to 27,000.

1996

The club offices were moved from The Hawthorns to the newly erected and more substantial Tom Silk Building situated on the opposite side of Halford's Lane, some 300 yards away. A new club shop was also opened.

1997

The Hawthorns ground was now officially an all-seater stadium with a capacity of 25,296.

1998

In the summer The Hawthorns pitch was completely dug up again, and returfed for only the fourth time in 98 years, following similar exercises in 1912, 1990 and 1994. Undersoil heating was installed.

1999

Albion played their 2,000th home game in the Football League at The Hawthorns on Saturday, 17 April, drawing 2-2 with Portsmouth in front of 12,750 spectators.

2000

The Hawthorns officially celebrated its 100th birthday on 3 September.

FACTS AND FIGURES

- The 1,000th Football League game at The Hawthorns was between Albion and Leeds United on 10 October 1970 when over 37,000 fans witness the 2-2 draw. And in April 1999 Albion's 2,000th home match in the Football League attracted a crowd of 12,750 to The Hawthorns to see the 2-2 draw with Portsmouth. This fixture was marred however, when a supporter raced on to the pitch and assaulted a linesman.

- On 29 July 1977 a limited over cricket match was staged at The Hawthorns between the Indian and Pakistan Test sides. The Indians won by four wickets and 2,641 attended. The proceeds went towards a children's charity and Imran Khan's benefit.

- On 15 October 1980, the first floodlight cricket match was played at The Hawthorns when Ian Botham's XI (which included David Gower) played Warwickshire CCC in a 30 overs match, the proceeds going towards Alistair Robertson's testimonial fund.

- In November/December 1919 Wolverhampton Wanderers played two Second Division League games at The Hawthorns v Barnsley (lost 4-2) and Stockport County (2-2) because their home ground at Molineux had been closed following crowd disturbances.

- The Albion v Liverpool Coca-Cola Cup-tie at The Hawthorns on Wednesday 15 October 1997 realised record gate receipts for the club (League and Cup matches) of £264,127.50.

- Walsall played Brighton & Hove Albion in a Third Division game at The Hawthorns in February 1970 because the Saddlers' Fellows Park ground was waterlogged. Brighton won 3-0.

- Albion's average home League attendance at The Hawthorns is 19,765. The average FA Cup attendance is 31,618, and in the League Cup (under its various guises) it is 16,788. The best seasonal League average is 38,819 in 1953-54. The lowest is 4,884 in 1904-05.

- On 11 May 1931, HRH The Prince of Wales (later King Edward VIII and the Duke of Windsor) visited The Hawthorns to offer his congratulations to Albion on their unique 'double' achievement.

- On 7 August 1944, the American and Canadian armies staged a baseball match at The Hawthorns before a 5,000 crowd.

- Immediately before World War One an athletics meeting, staged over two days, took place at The Hawthorns, and there was also a boxing tournament held there featuring the great Jimmy Wilde.

FA Cup

P	W	D	L	F	A
131	76	30	25	268	123

European Fairs, UEFA & Cup-winners' Cup

P	W	D	L	F	A
11	6	1	4	21	13

Anglo-Italian Cup

P	W	D	L	F	A
10	3	3	4	16	13

Autoglass Trophy

P	W	D	L	F	A
4	3	0	1	10	2

Anglo Scottish Cup

P	W	D	L	F	A
2	1	1	0	4	2

Full Members Cup

P	W	D	L	F	A
2	1	1*	0	4	3

* lost on penalties

Watney Cup

P	W	D	L	F	A
1	0	1*	0	4	4

* Lost on penalties

Texaco Cup

P	W	D	L	F	A
5	3	1	1	8	3

Wartime Football

P	W	D	L	F	A
136	87	20	29	421	216

Totals

P	W	D	L	F	A
2024	1131	491	402	4170	2125

Albion's record at The Hawthorns (competitive level):

Football League

P	W	D	L	F	A
1661	917	419	325	3299	1678

Football League Play-off

P	W	D	L	F	A
1	1	0	0	2	0

Football League Cup (inc CCC, LC & WC)

P	W	D	L	F	A
60	33	14	13	113	68

HAWTHORNS FIRSTS

- Albion recorded their first 5-0 League win at The Hawthorns on 10 March 1906 v Blackpool (Division 2).

- On 5 October 1906 the first players' social club room was opened at The Hawthorns.

- Albion's Fred Shinton was the first four-goal hero at The Hawthorns in his side's 5-0 victory over Clapton Orient (Division 2) on 6 October 1906.

- 19 January 1907 saw the first abandonment of a competitive game at The Hawthorns when the Albion-Barnsley Second Division clash was called off after 80 minutes through failing light.

- The first representative match held at The Hawthorns was a Junior International between England and Scotland on 4 April 1908. England won 4-0.

- The first player to score a hat-trick on his debut for Albion at The Hawthorns was Billy Jordan v Gainsborough Trinity (League) on 16 February 1907. Jordan was also the first Reverend to play in a senior game at The Hawthorns.

- The first recorded own-goal at The Hawthorns was scored by Fulham's Leslie Skene v Albion in a Second Division match on 12 September 1908.

- Albion's first 7-0 League victory at The Hawthorns was against Grimsby Town (Division 2) on 2 January 1909.

- The first player to score from the penalty spot in an FA Cup-tie at The Hawthorns was Albion's

- George Harris v Bolton Wanderers on 16 January 1909.

- On 30 September 1911, the first 40,000 crowd assembled at The Hawthorns – 45,203 fans watching the League game with Aston Villa.

- Hubert Pearson became the first goalkeeper to score at The Hawthorns when he netted a penalty for Albion in a 2-0 win over Bury on 26 December 1911.

- The first wartime game at The Hawthorns was played on 24 April 1916 when Albion defeated Aston Villa 3-1 in a friendly in front of 8,221 fans.

- On 27 September 1919 Sid Bowswer became then first Albion defender to score a hat-trick in a senior game – doing so against Bradford City at The Hawthorns in a Division One match.

- Albion's first 8-0 League win at The Hawthorns was against Notts County (Division 1) on 25 October 1919. In this same game Fred Morris also became the first player to score five goals.

- A League game – not involving Albion – was staged at The Hawthorns for the first time on 29 November 1919 when Wolves were beaten 4-2 by Barnsley in a Second Division encounter. This was because Wolves were made to play two 'home' games away on a neutral ground following crowd trouble at Molineux.

- Albion won the League Division One championship for the first (and so far only) time in season 1919-20, clinching the title at

against Albion on 6 December 1902.

- This first FA Cup goal scored by an opponent at The Hawthorns was by Vivian Woodward of Tottenham Hotspur in a first-round replay on 11 February 1903 – and it this was also Albion's first Cup defeat on the ground.

- The first 3-3 League draw at the ground followed three days later when Albion were held by Sheffield United on 14 February 1903 (Division 1).

- The first FA Cup semi-final took place at The Hawthorns on 15 March 1902 when Derby County drew 1-1 with Sheffield United in front of 33,603 supporters.

- The first FA Cup draw at The Hawthorns was that between Albion and Nottingham Forest (1-1) on 10 February 1904.

- The first official *Albion News* was produced for the home League game with Burnley on 2 September 1905.

- The first opposing player to score two hat-tricks at The Hawthorns was Charlie Millington of Aston Villa – in a Birmingham Cup-tie on 4 September 1905 and in a Staffordshire Cup match on 2 October 1905.

- The first player to be sent-off at The Hawthorns was Jimmy Conlon of Bradford City in a Second Division League game v Albion on 11 November 1905.

- On 24 February 1906 Albion registered their first 6-0 League win at The Hawthorns v Glossop (Division 2).

HAWTHORNS FIRSTS

League Division One game v Stoke City.

- The first former Albion player to score a hat-trick at The Hawthorns was Derek Kevan (then of Manchester City) who netted three times for a past Baggies' XI in Graham Williams' Testimonial match on 28 April 1965.

- The first League Cup-tie at The Hawthorns saw Albion beat neighbours Walsall 3-1 in a second-round tie on 22 September 1965. Albion's Tony Brown scored the first League Cup goal on the ground while the first visitors' goal was netted by Colin Taylor.

- Gerry Howshall was the first Albion substitute to come on at The Hawthorns – replacing John Kaye in the League game with Nottingham Forest on 5 February 1966.

- The first Albion 'sub' to score at The Hawthorns was Dick Krzywicki v Manchester City in a League Cup-tie on 5 October 1966.

- The first competitive European game took place at The Hawthorns on 9 November 1966 when Albion defeated the Dutch side D.O.S. Utrecht 5-2 in a second round, second leg tie of the Fairs Cup to go through 6-3 on aggregate. Tony Brown scored Albion's first 'home' European goal in this game; he also netted Albion's first European penalty and the Baggies' first European hat-trick – all in front of a 19,170 crowd.

- Albion suffered their first 'European' home defeat when they went down 3-1 to the Italian side Bologna in a third round, second leg clash on 8 March 1967.

- The first European Cup-winners' Cup game at The Hawthorns was between Albion and the Belgium side RFC Brugge on 2 October 1968 when Albion won 2-0 with goals by Asa Hartford and Tony Brown to go through to the second round on the away goal rule.

- Albion's first home defeat in the Cup-winners' Cup came on 19 February 1969 when Dunfermline Athletic won a third round, second leg encounter 1-0 in freezing conditions.

- Albion's first home League Cup defeat occurred v Tottenham Hotspur, who won 1-0 on 8 September 1971.

- The first Hawthorns League Cup draw followed on 3 October 1972 when Albion were held 1-1 by Liverpool in round three.

- Willie Johnston (Albion) and Archie Styles (Everton) were the first two players to be sent-off in the FA Cup at The Hawthorns – dismissed for fighting in a third-round replay on 30 January 1974.

- On 19 June 1975 Albion appointed their first-ever player-manager at The Hawthorns when Johnny Giles joined the club from Leeds United.

- Willie Johnston was also the first player to be sent-off in a League Cup-tie at The Hawthorns v Brighton & Hove Albion on 22 September 1976.

- In season 1977-78 Cyrille Regis scored in his first home games for Albion in the League Cup (v Rotherham United), in the First Division (v Middlesbrough) and in the FA Cup (v Blackpool).

- The first UEFA Cup game at The Hawthorns was played on 27 September 1978 when Albion defeated the Turkish side Galatasaray 3-1 in a first round, second leg clash. Bryan Robson scored the first goal.

- Albion's first UEFA Cup home defeat was suffered at the hands of Carl Zeiss Jena on 3 October 1979, the East German side winning a second round, second leg encounter 2-1. At half-time in this match Albion's Ally Brown became the first player to be sent-off in a European game at The Hawthorns.

- John Deehan (Ipswich Town) was the first ex-Albion player to score a hat-trick in a competitive match at The Hawthorns – doing so in a Division Two League game on 13 September 1986.

- In 1988-89 defender Stacy North became the first Albion player to appear in 46 League games in a single season.

- The first former Albion player to score a 'Cup' goal at The Hawthorns was Ian Banks of Barnsley – in a Zenith Data Systems Cup encounter on 21 November 1990.

- The first Third Division match at The Hawthorns was between Albion and Exeter City on 17 August 1991. Albion won 6-3 (their first Third Division win) and Albion's Craig Shakespeare netted the first goal in this Division from the penalty spot.

Hawthorns Diary

1900-01

Unfortunately Albion's first season at The Hawthorns ended in bitter disappointment when relegation was suffered for the first time in the club's history; Albion finished bottom of the League table with only 22 points out of a possible 68.

Under secretary-manager Frank Heaven, Albion drew their opening game on 3 September with Derby County (1-1) in front of a 20,104 crowd, and after that the team's performances, at home and away, were inconsistent to say the least, and, in fact, they lost 19 of their 34 League games, nine in front of their own supporters. They failed to win two games in a row and recorded only seven victories during the whole campaign, one of them a crushing 7-2 success over mid-table Bolton Wanderers in early December.

Of the many defeats, the heaviest were those of 6-1 at home to Nottingham Forest and 5-0 at Liverpool, Bury and Derby.

Some of the more established players, including three England internationals – the legendary goalkeeper Joe Reader, right-half Tom Perry and inside-forward Fred Wheldon – were coming to their end of their respective careers, while another England star, full-back Billy Williams, was forced to quit the game through injury at the age of 24. In all 24 players were utilised during the course of the season, with only Amos Adams and Harry Hadley ever-presents. Fred Buck played the first of his 319 senior games for the club and scored the first of his 94 goals.

Despite their dismal League form Albion had a good run in the FA Cup and reached the semi-final stage before losing 4-0 to Tottenham Hotspur at Villa Park. Albion also lost in the Final of the Birmingham Charity Cup to Aston Villa.

Home League attendances in 1900-01 averaged almost 12,000, around 6,500 up on the previous season. The top crowd was that of 35,417 which saw the local derby with Aston Villa on 8 September 1900.

1901-02

During the 1901 summer break several new players were signed as Albion's directors and management

Albion line-up in 1901-02, Second Division champions. Back row (left to right, players only): J. Stevenson. A. Adams, I. Webb J. Kifford, H. Hadley. Front: A. Smith, W. Lee, D. Nurse, C. Simmons, T. Worton. On ground: J. McLean, G. Dorsett.

right-half Arthur Randle. He took the place of Dan Nurse and went on to play 143 times for the club up to 1908. Harry Brown was installed in the forward-line to accompany Simmons, but he found it hard going and scored only three goals in 21 games.

With poor performances on the field, it was no surprise to see the average attendance fall by 3,000, down to 12,651.

Fred Everiss and his directors knew that there was a lot of work to be done if Albion were to climb back into the top flight – and at the AGM in the summer, positive moves were forthcoming in this respect – although it must be said there wasn't a great deal of money around to buy new players.

1904-05

Back in the Second Division with problems mounting all the time, Albion began with Jack Manners at centre-half and a trio of new faces in the forward-line – Lawrie Bell, Walter Jack and Albert Lewis, and indeed, Lewis got off to a flying start, scoring all his side's goals in an inspired 4-1 victory at Burnley. After that Albion's on-the-field performances were rather mixed despite the introduction of more new players, such as brothers Arthur and Llewellyn Davies (a future Welsh international), Fred Haycock, tall goalkeeper Jimmy Stringer (another former Wolves man) and centre-half Tom Hayward. But for long periods the team was well below par, although occasionally they did produce the goods, beating Doncaster Rovers 6-1, Burton United 4-0, Blackpool 4-2 and Barnsley 4-1 before Christmas. To make matters worse (regarding money) the old stand ('Noah's Ark') which had been transferred from Stoney Lane, burned down on Bonfire Night (the cause being put down to a lighted cigarette being left in the stand).

More signings were made, including Ted Pheasant, a robust defender from Wolves, but his presence did not make all that much difference and as 1904 gave way to 1905, the players found themselves hovering in a mid-table position. Bumped out of the FA Cup by Leicester Fosse who won a preliminary-round tie at The Hawthorns by 5-2, Albion failed to make much headway in the League and after recording a mere seven more wins they ended up a poor tenth – a massive 28 points behind the champions Liverpool, but only three away from having to apply for re-election. Half-backs Manners and Randle were the mainstays of the team; of the forwards Jack top-scored with 13 League goals. The average attendance at The Hawthorns slumped to a disappointing 4,884 – a drop of 7,800 on the previous season… with only 2,072 bothering to turn up for the clash with Gainsborough Trinity in January.

Albion's creditors were hammer-

Albion's first-team squad in 1904-05. Back row (left to right): F. Everiss (secretary), J. Kifford, I. Webb, R. Playfair, J. Pennington, Mr G. Dempster. Middle: W. Barber (assistant trainer), A. Randle, L. Bell, H. Hadley, A. Lewis, J. Manners. On ground: W. Jack, H. Brown, H. Aston, G. Dorsett.

the middle line and Albert Evans, once of Aston Villa, who broke his leg four times in his career, was challenging Betteley and Pennington for a full-back spot. It was very competitive and despite losing to Southern League Southampton in the FA Cup, Albion continued to do the business in the Second Division, pushing Bradford City, Leicester and Oldham all the way. However, two home defeats against mid-table Gainsborough and Grimsby Town, and crucial reverses at Leicester, Hull City and lowly Chesterfield didn't help matters, and at the end of the day Albion had to settle for fifth place in the table, just seven points adrift of the champions Bradford City.

It was obviously disappointing, but there was a feeling within the camp that the good old days were not too far away.

Buck top-scored in 1907-08 with 18 League goals; Walker in his only season with Albion, netted 15 and early in the New Year Hubert Pearson made the first of 377 senior appearances in Albion's goal. He was to remain at the club until 1926 by which time he had been joined by his son, Harold, also a goalkeeper.

Albion's average League attendance this season was 11,100 – just over 1,000 down on the previous campaign. On 11 January 1908 a new record crowd for The Hawthorns of 36,727 saw the FA Cup-tie with Birmingham.

Pennington added four more England caps to his collection, playing against Ireland, Wales, Scotland and Austria, while Billy Jordan scored six goals for England's amateur side v France.

At the club's AGM Harry Keys was replaced as chairman by former player William 'Billy' Isaiah Bassett, who was to hold this office until his death in 1937.

1908-09

This season saw Albion miss promotion to the First Division by just .0056 of a goal – and the players claimed that they were robbed of that extra goal by a referee's decision at Blackpool. This match at Bloomfield Road on 28 November 1908 resulted in a 2-0 win, but it should have been 3-0 as Charlie Hewitt's effort rebounded from the net support so hard that the referee and his linesman thought that it had hit the crossbar and disallowed the goal. Billy Garraty, who could have put the ball back into the net, walked away towards the centre spot unaware of the furore to follow.

Bolton won the title from Tottenham and neither team beat Albion during the campaign, the Baggies doubling up over the Londoners.

Albion lost only two of their first 22 League games up to 2 January and looked well on course to take the title. But they stuttered with just one win in the next six, and they were also eliminated from the FA Cup by Bradford City. From their next ten fixtures they won six and drew three and required (as it transpired) just two points to gain promotion and three to take the championship. Sadly they could only take a point from a 0-0 draw at Stockport and then blew it all on the very last day by losing 2-1 at Derby.

A 7-0 win over Grimsby was Albion's best League win this term – and they were equally impressive in beating Blackpool 5-1, both at home.

Ten players each made over 25 appearances; goalkeeper Stringer, full-back Pennington, half-backs George Baddeley (who was signed from Stoke at the age of 34 and went on to play for the club until three weeks short of his 40th birthday), Sam Timmins and Jack Manners and forwards Billy Thompson (ex-

Sunderland), Welsh international Bill Davies, former Liverpool star Charlie Hewitt, Fred Buck and England international Billy Garraty, who helped Aston Villa win both the League Division One title and FA Cup before transferring to The Hawthorns from Leicester Fosse.

With promotion a strong possibility right up to the last week of the season, Albion's average home attendance went up to 17,845 – their best ever since entering the Football League in 1888. On Boxing Day a record League attendance of 38,049 attended the Albion-Birmingham local derby.

On the international front, Pennington took his total of England caps to 11 with appearances v Wales, Scotland, Hungary (2) and Austria, and winger Bill Davies played for Wales v England.

In May, 1909 Albion went on their first-ever overseas tour, playing seven games in Scandinavia, including friendlies against two English clubs, Hull City and Newcastle United. They recorded four victories, the best coming v Gefle 10-0 and a Stockholm Select XI 8-3.

1909-10

This season saw Albion finish 11th in Division Two – their lowest position in the Football League up to that time.

They started off well enough, winning eight of their first 12 matches. But six defeats from the next seven balanced things out and after that they never really threatened. Indeed, the Baggies ended on a dismal note, suffering four straight defeats as well as playing out a dull goalless draw with Derby. They did a little better in the FA Cup, losing to Barnsley in the third round after overcoming Clapton Orient and Bristol City.

A comfortable 5-0 romp over Gainsborough was Albion's best win

Albion's 1912 FA Cup Final side: Back row (left to right, players only): G. Baddeley, H. Pearson, S. Bowser, R. Pailor. Seated: A. Cook, J. Pennington, R. McNeal, F. Buck. On ground: C. Jephcott, B. Shearman and H. Wright.

extra-time after Jesse Pennington had refused to 'foul' the Barnsley forward as he broke clear of the Baggies' defence.

Secretary-manager Fred Everiss started the season with Stan Allan (ex-Newcastle United) at centre-forward in place of the injured Bob Pailor and Ben Shearman from Bristol City on the left-wing. Then halfway through the campaign he introduced the speedy Claude Jephcott to the other flank. His career was to end prematurely in 1922 with a broken leg but he went on to serve the club as a director for many years after retiring. Late on Albion debuts were given to two players who were to become vital members of the team after the War – ace goalscorer Fred Morris from Tipton and inside-left Howard Gregory from Aston Manor (Villa territory) who later became,e a star left-winger.

Albion's performances were professional rather than dashing, their

best League win coming early on when they triumphed 3-0 at Villa Park. Pailor top-scored with 13 goals and 'keeper Hubert Pearson, who missed only two League matches, netted with two penalties. The average League attendance at The Hawthorns rose by 2,400 for over 18,000 – the highest in the club's history. On 30 September The Hawthorns attendance record was broken when 45,203 fans watched the League game with Aston Villa.

Again Albion succumbed to Villa in the Final of the Birmingham Charity Cup (0-4).

Pennington's cap tally went up to 19 with games against Ireland, Scotland and Wales, while Fred Buck and Ben Shearman both played twice for the Football League, lining up together in the games against the Southern League and Irish League.

1912-13

This turned out to be a rather moderate season for Albion, who had to

settle for tenth place in the First Division, 16 points below the champions Sunderland and 15 clear of relegated Notts County. They also went out of the FA Cup in the first round,. beaten by Southern League West Ham United at the third attempt.

Albion, in fact, had a useful first-half to their programme, amassing 25 points out of 38, but after Christmas they struggled both at home and away and mustered just 13 more points from their remaining fixtures to finish up rather disappointingly in mid-table. The usual line-up (fitness and availability permitting) was: Pearson (or Moorwood); Smith, Pennington; Waterhouse, Buck, McNeal; Jephcott, Wright/Morris, Pailor/Morris, Bowser and Shearman. Full-back Arthur Cook, George Baddeley and Howard Gregory were the main reserves.

Pailor scored a smart hat-trick early on in an impressive 4-2 win at

Albion v. Liverpool on Saturday Last.

Cutting from the *Birmingham Daily Mail* covering the Baggies' First Division match against Liverpool at The Hawthorns in January 1914.

Albion registered only 49 League goals during the season, but conceded just 43, only nine of these at The Hawthorns. They ran up some impressive victories including a 4-0 win over Liverpool and 4-1 victories over Notts County and Bradford (away), but they also lost heavily at Bradford City (0-5), Manchester City (0-4) and Chelsea (1-4), the latter two late on when points were a necessity.

Fred Morris finished up as leading marksman with 11 goals; Bentley netted nine and Swift seven. Howard Gregory, who was slowly getting into his stride, grabbed a superb hat-trick in a 3-2 home win over Tottenham Hotspur.

A total of 26 players were called up for first team action with eight of

them appearing in 28 or more games.

Owing to the circumstances and uncertainty of the War, the average League attendance at The Hawthorns was down by almost half to 10,823 with the best single attendance of 19,492 watching the local derby with Aston Villa in late January. Just 4,410 saw the final League game of the season at home to Bradford City, Albion's lowest for three years.

Harold Bache, McNeal and Hubert Pearson all represented the Football League, the former and Pearson v the Irish League and the latter v the Scottish League.

The Irish League fixture, played on 7 October 1914, in front of 9,250 spectators, was the first representative match to be staged at The Hawthorns, and it was so well organised by Fred Everiss that he received a gold medal from the Football League afterwards.

1915-19

There was no competitive football played by Albion until March 1919. Prior to that the team participated in friendly matches but these were few and far between because the Midlands was a vast munitions centre.

On 15 February 1916 Albion's brilliant unorthodox centre-forward Harold Bache, a Lieutenant in the Army, was tragically killed on a Flanders battlefield. He was only 26.

Although they lost one star player, Albion gained another when 'wee' Tommy Magee was signed in the trenches' after being recommended to the club by an army colleague of his, Tom Brewer. Magee officially joined the club in January 1919 and went on to appear in more than 400 games for the Baggies, helping them win the League championship and FA Cup as well as gaining England recognition. He was to stay at The Hawthorns until May 1934 when he transferred to Crystal Palace.

After peace had been declared in 1918, Albion played in the Midland Victory League during March and April 1919 – and they duly won the title with two victories over Aston Villa, one over Derby County and a draw with Wolves, amassing a total of seven points from their six matches. Derby finished second, Wolves third and Villa fourth.

This highly competitive tournament certainly reunited the players once more and despite such a lengthy break owing to the conflict in Europe, the Albion team looked very useful in those 'Victory' games. The likes of goalkeeper Hubert Pearson, full-backs Joe Smith, Jesse Pennington and Arthur Cook, half-backs Sammy Richardson, Sid Bowser, Fred Reed, Bobby McNeal and Frank Waterhouse and forwards Claude Jephcott, Jack Crisp, Tommy Magee, Andy Smith, Alf Bentley,

HAWTHORNS DIARY

Albion, League champions 1919-20. Back row (left to right): W. Barber (trainer), Pearson, T. H. Gopsil (assistant trainer), E. Smith (assistant secretary). Second row: Mr F. Everiss (secretary), Mr D. Nurse, (director), Cook, Mr W. L. Bassett (vice-chairman), Mr H. Keys (chairman), Jephcott, Mr Seymour (director), Lieut-Col Ely (director). Seated: Crisp, A. Smith, McNeal, Pennington, Bowser, Morris, Gregory. On ground: J. Smith, Magee, Bentley, Richardson. The trophies are the League championship and the FA Charity Shield.

November, seven more victories followed in quick succession and despite an early exit from the FA Cup (beaten by Barnsley) Albion powered on with two successive five goal romps over Blackburn. They lost only two of their last 15 League matches and finished up deserving champions with a massive nine points margin over second-placed Burnley. Albion's attacking play at times was quite brilliant, inducing rave reports in various newspapers up and down the country.

The League's leading scorer Fred Morris created a new club by netting 37 goals. And between 29 November and 24 January he scored in ten consecutive League games – another record.

He was aided and abetted by Bentley (15) and Gregory (12) while Bowser weighed in with ten (eight penalties). McNeal was the only ever-present, but 11 other players each managed 24 or more League appearances. Bowser (v Ireland), Pennington (v Wales and Scotland),

Joe Smith (v Ireland) and Morris (v Scotland) all played for England, with Pennington taking his final tally of caps to 25, having gained his first in 1906-07. Smith also played in the Victory international v Wales. Wingers Jack Crisp and Claude Jephcott (both v the Irish League) and Pennington (v Scottish League) all represented the Football League.

Crisp, Pennington and Morris all took part in the England v The South international trial at The Hawthorns on 9 February, attended by 14,427 spectators.

Albion's success this term realised a record average home League attendance of 30, 532 – a rise of almost 20,000 on the 1914-15 figure.

Albion also won the FA Charity Shield by defeating Tottenham Hotspur 2-0 at White Hart Lane, Andy Smith claiming both goals.

Albion's second XI also won their respective championship – taking the Birmingham & District League title for the third time… after losing their opening game 5-1.

1920-21

As reigning League champions, Albion began the defence of their crown in unconvincing fashion, drawing their first four games and losing the fifth. In fact, they recorded just two victories in their opening 11 fixtures in their opening 11 fixtures and fell well off the pace. They never recovered and finished in 14th position with 40 points, 19 behind the champions Burnley, who had taken the runners-up spot behind the Baggies the year before.

Fielding practically the same players who had done the club proud in 1919-20, Albion never matched the performances of the previous season and they won only eight home matches, losing six times in front of their own supporters. They had several poor spells during the campaign, the worst coming in December, February and March – and they lost four games on the bounce around Easter time.

They were hammered 5-1 at Blackburn and Huddersfield, crashed 4-0 at Manchester City and 3-0 at Sunderland, Bolton and Chelsea. Arsenal won a thriller by 4-3 at The Hawthorns and perhaps Albion's best display was their 4-1 victory at Old Trafford against Manchester United.

Albion didn't last long in the FA Cup either, losing in the opening round to Second Division Notts County 3-0 at Meadow Lane.

A handful of new signings were made including centre-forward Bob Blood, who was bought from Port Vale for £4,000 in February. He went on to score 26 goals in 53 games for the Baggies before leaving in 1924. And right at the end of the campaign a player who was to become a big favourite at The Hawthorns – Aston-born Joe Carter – arrived from Westbourne Celtic.

Goalkeeper George Ashmore, who went on to win England honours, also made his first appearance

HAWTHORNS DIARY

Wing-half Sammy Richardson, a key member of the League championship side and a virtual ever-present in the first three seasons after World War One, lost his place to Tommy Magee in 1923 but returned in 1924-25 and 1925-26.

HAWTHORNS DIARY

win over Aston Villa. He topped Albion's scoring charts with 30 goals in League and Cup; Carter notched 14 and Wilson 13.

Eight players appeared in 34 or more League games this season, with ever-present Joe Smith again the inspiration. Goalkeeper George Ashmore was absent once (a 2-1 defeat at West Ham) while Magee, skipper Reed and Wilson all had 40 outings apiece.

Albion's average League attendance this term was up by 3,200 to 20,596.

Magee was capped three times by England – v Belgium, Scotland and France. The the match v Belgium was the second international to be staged at The Hawthorns and England won 4-0 on 8 December in front of 15,405 fans. Davies added two more Welsh caps to his tally, playing against Scotland and Ireland and Jimmy Spencer represented the Football League in the annual game against the Irish League.

Albion's second XI, going for a hat-trick of Central League triumphs, could only finish third this time round.

Harold Pearson, son of former goalkeeper Hubert Pearson, joined Albion as an amateur goalkeeper from Tamworth Castle. He was to remain at The Hawthorns until 1937.

In February 1925 Albion's first trainer at The Hawthorns, Jack Paddock passed away and the following month former Hawthorns defender Jim Stevenson died aged 49, following an accident at the Leven Shipyard in Scotland.

1925-26

In this season the fixture list reverted back to pre-war days in that each club no longer met the same opposition on successive Saturdays – a change instigated by Albion.

At the start of the campaign

Albion were listed as one of the favourites to win the League title. But they never responded to the call and ended up having a very moderate campaign, finishing in 13th position with 40 points, 17 behind the champions Huddersfield, who duly retained the trophy for the third successive season.

Albion won only three of their first ten matches then lost two of the next ten; from Boxing Day onwards they were totally inconsistent, conjuring up just seven more victories while suffering 11 defeats.

Practically the same set of players who had performed so well the previous season were still at The Hawthorns, although Magee, James, Byers and Adams all struggled with injury. In fact, up to Christmas, once it had settled down, the team looked very useful, especially when beating Manchester City 4-1, West Ham United 7-1, Bury 4-0, Burnley 5-3, Newcastle 4-0 and Manchester United 5-1, all at home. Messrs. Carter, Davies, Glidden and Wilson were scoring goals, but then, perhaps surprisingly after the New Year had arrived, League results everywhere began to fluctuate and Aston Villa ended Albion's hopes in the FA Cup.

Davies (with 19 goals), Wilson (17), Carter (14) and James (12) were Albion's top League scorers while Carter also netted twice in the FA Cup. Ashmore again did well in goal, making 40 League appearance. His performances between the posts led to his winning an England cap v Belgium. Joe Carter also made his international debut for England in that same match and scored to celebrate the occasion. Stan Davies won three more caps for Wales (v England, Scotland and Ireland) while Ivor Jones also appeared in that latter game.

Tommy Magee played in 15 games on the F.A's. tour of Canada between May and July 1926.

Jones was one of two internationals who left The Hawthorns this season, rejoining his former club, Swansea Town. The other was rightback Joe Smith, who signed for Birmingham after 16 years and 471 first-team games for the Baggies.

Goalkeeper Hubert Pearson, who had missed an international call in 1923 because of injury, also left The Hawthorns after 377 League and Cup appearances.

Bob Finch made his League debut at full-back against Leicester City – the first of 234 appearances for Albion – and Harry Dutton established himself in the senior side at left-half.

The supporters became disillusioned early on and only 8,287 saw the home game with Manchester City in September. After the Yuletide period attendances at The Hawthorns ranged from 10,000 to 19,500 and when the last ball was kicked Albion's average for the season stood at 18,595 – a drop of 2,000 on the previous campaign.

1926-27

In the summer of 1926, Albion recruited left-half Nelson Howarth from Bolton Wanderers and he lined up in the first team on the opening day of the League programme against Sunderland at The Hawthorns. Over 31,000 fans saw the Baggies win that game 3-0, but things didn't go too well out on the park after that.

Out of their next 25 matches, Albion registered just four victories and they they slithered down the Division, falling deep into the relegation zone. Sadly they never recovered from that disastrous spell and although the players battled out of their skins during the latter stages of the campaign, the Baggies eventually went down as wooden spoonists with Leeds United, having lost a record number of matches – 23.

1928-29

In April 1928 Albion secured the service of left-winger Stan Wood from Winsford. He was to become one of the stars of the 1930s and made his debut in the fourth game of this season at home to Notts County.

Albion began this campaign rather disappointingly, losing three of their opening four matches. They picked up and won four of the next five only to fall away again by recording just two more victories in their next ten League outings up to mid-December.

At this juncture Albion were lying nearer the relegation area than challenging for a top six place, but after an unbeaten Christmas period which saw them win three and draw one of their four matches, they commenced a useful run in the FA Cup. They knocked out Grimsby Town, Middlesbrough and Bradford Park Avenue before losing in a replay to Huddersfield Town.

During this excellent Cup campaign, Albion's League performances were poor – only one win in seven – but from 16 March onwards they roared back and collected 18 points from their last 12 matches, registering eight victories, including five in a row.

Jimmy 'Iron' Edwards had gained a regular place in the side at inside-left and Bill Richardson was now firmly established in the middle line. These two players, along with Wood, goalkeeper Harold Pearson, full-back George Shaw, right-half Tommy Magee, skipper Tommy Glidden and inside-right Joe Carter, were to become key members of the side over the next three seasons.

Albion finished the 1928-29 campaign in seventh position with 46 points, only nine fewer than champions Middlesbrough and seven behind runners-up Grimsby Town.

Cookson with 28 goals, was again leading scorer. Glidden netted 23 and Carter 13. The reliable Shaw played in every League game; Glidden missed two and right-back Bob Finch three. But a handful of players moved on – Chambers became player-manager of Oakengates, Howarth was forced to retire through injury and George James signed for Reading after scoring 57 goals in 116 games for the Baggies.

Albion's average League crowd in 1928-29 dropped by over 6,000 to 13,220 – the lowest since 1909-10.

Joe Carter appeared in two internationals for England, scoring in them both against Belgium (one goal) and Spain (2).

In this latter match England led 3-0 in Madrid, but eventually crashed 4-3 amid wild scenes of excitement, and Spain thus became the first continental side to defeat England.

Albion, 1928-29. Back row (left to right): Phil Hunt (assistant trainer), Bill Richardson, Jim Edwards, Arthur Perry, Harold Pearson, Len Darnell, George Ashmore, Joe Carter, Herbert Webster, Joe Evans, Stan Wood, Jim Hudson, Maurice Jones (ground assistant). Second row: Mr Eph Smith (assistant secretary), Mr Fred Everiss (secretary-manager), Ernie Pattison, Mr L. Nurse (director), Mr H. Keys (director), Mr W. I. Bassett (chairman), Mr J. Round (director), Mr W. Hackett (director), Tommy Glidden, Sam Guest (assistant trainer), Fred Reed (trainer). Third row: Reg Fryer, George James, Nelson Howarth, Jack Rix, Dickie Baugh, Sammy Short, Enos Bromage, Francis Corbett, Bertram Cope, Bob Finch. On ground: Fred Leedham, Frank White, Jimmy Cookson, Jimmy Murphy, Arthur Fitton, George Shaw, Griffith A. Taylor, George Bytheway, Tommy Magee.

Albion parade the FA Cup around Wembley after their 1931 victory over neighbours Birmingham.

in front of a 69,241 record crowd took Albion through to Wembley for the first time, but before the all Midland showdown with Birmingham, there were nine more League games to contest. From these Albion collected 11 vital points to keep bang on course for promotion. But it was now getting mighty close at the top.

A hard-fought but deserved 2-1

victory at Wembley over Blues at Wembley where W. G. Richardson's two goals proved decisive, earned Albion the first half of the double, but they still had it all to do.

They required maximum points from their remaining two League games to gain promotion with Everton – and they did it by beating Stoke City 1-0 at The Victoria Ground (W. G. Richardson on tar-

get) and then by narrowly defeating Charlton Athletic 3-2 in a nail-biting encounter in front of a record League attendance of 52,415 on the final day of the season. 'W. G.' headed in the deciding goal at the packed Birmingham Road End midway through the second half.

It was a truly great moment for the players and management – and indeed, the supporters.

Albion fulfilled 52 games this season (42 in the League) and they scored 99 goals. W. G. Richardson (24), Wood (17), Glidden (16), Carter (11) and Cookson (11) all reached double figures.

Nine players appeared in 32 League games or more with Pearson, Shaw and Bill Richardson a trio of ever-presents.

The average League attendance at The Hawthorns rose by 7,700 to a healthy 21,722.

For all the effort put in by the players, not one earned full international recognition in 1930-31, although Joe Carter did represent the Football League against the Scottish League.

Magee, Cookson and Shaw, however, toured Canada with the FA party between May and July 1931 with Cookson collecting 26 of the 107 goals scored on that tour.

1931-32

Back in the top flight after a four-year absence, Albion began in style, beating the reigning champions Arsenal 1-0 at Highbury in the opening match, Stan Wood scoring in front of a 55,380 crowd.

Just over five weeks later on the same ground Arsenal got revenge with a Cliff Bastin goal in the 88th minute to win the FA Charity Shield.

Albion played very well during the first half of the season, and among some impressive victories were those of 4-0 v Blackpool,

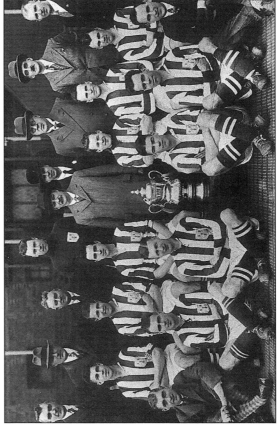

West Bromwich Albion, 1931 FA Cup winners and also promoted to Division One. Back row (left to right): Fred Everiss (secretary-manager), Mr J. Everiss (director), Mr L. Nurse (director), Harold Pearson, Mr W. I. Bassett (chairman), Mr E. Smith (assistant secretary). Mr J. Round (director), Mr H. Keys (director), Fred Reed (trainer). Middle row: Bill Richardson, Jimmy Edwards, Tommy Glidden, Tommy Magee, Joe Carter, Stan Wood. Front row: Jimmy Cookson, Bert Trentham, W. G. Richardson, Teddy Sandford, George Shaw, Bob Finch.

HAWTHORNS DIARY

Albion, 1934-35. Back row (left to right): Fred Everiss (secretary), Fred Reed (trainer), Harry Raw, Harold Pearson, Joe Carter, George Shaw, Claude Jephcott (director). Middle: W. G. Richardson, Teddy Sandford, Bill Richardson, Billy Bassett (chairman), Tommy Glidden, Jimmy Edwards, Bert Trentham. Front: Stan Wood, Jack Sankey, Wally Boyes, Harry Jones, Jimmy Murphy.

Albion never got themselves into a position to challenge for honours. They had some good spells and some indifferent ones, with their best sequence of results coming between the end of September and the end of December when they won seven and drew six of their 16 matches.

Then they started 1934 off in terrific style, beating Manchester City 7-2 at Maine Road, with the great Frank Swift in the home goal. But after an FA Cup defeat against Chelsea, Albion's League form became a bit of a mishmash from thereon in, although they did end with a flurry, collecting five wins from their last eight matches as well as drawing 4-4 at Villa Park.

Albion scored 78 League goals, with W. G. Richardson claiming 26 of them and Glidden 13. Carter and Sandford also reached double figures with ten apiece.

Two players were ever-present – skipper Glidden and Teddy Sandford.

Goal-ace Jimmy Cookson said farewell to The Hawthorns at the start of this season, leaving for Plymouth Argyle, and Tommy Magee also left the club after 15 years and 434 appearances for the Baggies. He signed for Crystal Palace.

Albion's average home League crowd in 1933-34 was 20,078 – a fall of more than 2,700.

The reserves had another excellent season and retained the Central League title with a superb record of 28 wins and 101 goals for a total of 64 points. A record crowd of 22,372 saw the home game with Aston Villa in March.

At international level, wing-half Jimmy Murphy and winger Walter Robbins helped Wales win the Home international championship for the second season in a row. Murphy added two more caps to his

Welsh collection when he lined up against Scotland and England, while Robbins scored against the Scots.

Full-backs Bert Trentham and George Shaw represented the Football League v the Irish league and the Scottish League respectively.

In August 1933, former Albion player and Director 'Jem' Bayliss died at the age of 70. And in December 1933, another former Hawthorns star, goalkeeper Jim Stringer, died at the age of 55.

In August 1933 another Everiss, Fred's son Alan, joined the Hawthorns' office staff, while in January 1934 former Baggies' winger Claude Jephcott was co-opted on to the Albion board of directors.

1934-35

For the second time in four seasons Albion marched out at Wembley Stadium – but on this occasion they ended up second best, losing 4-2 to Sheffield Wednesday in the 1935 FA Cup Final after conceding two late goals.

Equalising twice through Walter Boyes and Teddy Sandford, Albion

looked the stronger team during the latter stages, despite carrying two 'injured' players – Tommy Glidden and Joe Carter – but some slack defending allowed the Owls in for two killer strikes. Albion's 'keeper Harold Pearson and full-back George Shaw were the ones at fault, but 'W. G.' Richardson had a rare off day, and should have scored to give Albion a 3-2 lead with a quarter-of-an-hour remaining.

En route to Wembley, Albion knocked out Port Vale, Sheffield United (7-1 at home), Stockport County (5-0 away), Preston North End and Bolton Wanderers (after a replay) in the semi-final. Arthur Gale, deputising for Glidden, scored in each round up to the semi-final, but he was dropped for the Final in favour of his captain along with Harry 'Popeye' Jones, who had deputised for Carter since early March.

It was a big mistake to rely on the fitness of Glidden and Carter and had Jones (or even Jack Sankey) accompanied Gale on the right-wing at Wembley then things might well have been totally different.

HAWTHORNS DIARY

Albion staff in 1935-36. Back row (left to right): Sammy Short (trainer), Teddy Sandford, Jim Singleton, Arthur Hickman, Harold Pearson, Harry Lowery, Sid Swinden, W. G. Richardson, Bert Trentham, Bill Richardson, Bill Tudor, Norman Male, Herbert Hunt, Jack Lewis, Arthur Brookes, Jimmy Murphy, Fred Powell (groundsman). Second row: Fred Reed (trainer), Tommy Glidden, Joe Guest (assistant trainer), Harry Jones, 'Bos' Trevis, Ted Crowe, Walter Robbins, Major H. Wilson Keys (director), Jimmy Adams, Lol Coen, Jack Sankey, Jack Screen, Stan Wood, Harry Kinsell, Joe Carter, Alan Everiss (office clerk). Third row: Mr A. C. Jephcott (director), Mr L. Nurse (director), Hugh Foulkes, Alf Ridyard, Harry Raw, Mr W. I. Bassett (chairman), Bob Finch, Geoff Spencer, Harry Ashley, Mr J. Round (director). Fred Everiss (secretary-manager). Front row: Jimmy Edwards, George Shaw, Tommy Green, Syd Rawlings, Jack Rix, Jim Driscoll, Arthur Gale, Wally Boyes, Cliff Grosvenor.

in Amsterdam, Boyes helping to set up the winning goal for Worrall.

Jimmy Murphy added to his collection of Welsh caps by playing against England, Scotland and Ireland and represented a Wales/Ireland XI against the Football League. Another international trial took place at The Hawthorns on 27 February 1935 before a 12,845 crowd, England (with Albion's Sandford in the line-up) drawing 2-2 with The Rest.

November 1934 saw the death of former Albion centre-forward Billy Lee.

1935-36

'W. G.' Richardson set a new scoring record for Albion this season by claiming a total of 40 goals – 39 in the First Division and one in the FA Cup. He was in terrific form from October onwards after a rather slow start (only two goals in the first eight games). He scored four times in a crushing 7-0 win at Villa Park,

did likewise in a 5-2 Boxing Day home triumph over Middlesbrough, netted hat-tricks in successive matches against Blackburn Rovers (won 8-1) and Liverpool (won 6-1) and also weighed in with five separate braces. And still he couldn't get into the England team.

Amazingly Richardson's goals failed to inspire Albion. They finished the season in 18th position – just three points away from relegation. They lost six home matches and 14 on their travels, and there is no doubt that it was their abysmal form on opponents' grounds which let them down.

Secretary-manager Fred Everiss relied on the experience of his senior professionals for most of the season but injuries and loss of form certainly damaged his plans and, in fact, a total of 27 players were called into action during the course of the campaign – the most used at first team level since 1921-22.

'W. G.' Richardson was the main-

stay of the side, missing only one League game (a 2-1 home defeat by Chelsea) while Jack Sankey, George Shaw, Bert Trentham, Bill Richardson and new-signing Jack Mahon (from Leeds United) all managed to get into the thirties. Mahon was the main goalscoring support to 'W. G.' with a total of 17 goals.

In the FA Cup Albion went out in the fourth round, beaten at the third attempt by Bradford Park Avenue, this after they had ousted Hull City 2-0 in their opening tie.

Albion's reserve team couldn't maintain their fine record by adding a fourth successive Central League championship to the hat-trick achieved since 1932-33 and this season they had to settle for fourth place.

The average League attendance at The Hawthorns rose to 23,064, the second best since 1921.

Jimmy Murphy collected three more Welsh caps when he played

HAWTHORNS DIARY

towards the end of their Albion careers, including full-back George Shaw, centre-half Billy Richardson, wing-half Jimmy Edwards and left-winger Stan Wood.

Another Shaw, Cecil (no relation to George) was signed from Wolverhampton Wanderers, and he had the misfortune to miss a penalty in the Cup-tie at Coventry, having previously had a 100 per-cent record from the spot.

W. G. Richardson with 22 League and Cup goals, was once more Albion's leading marksman. Harry Jones, who took over the inside-right berth, netted 18, Jack Mahon obtained 14 and Walter Robbins scored 10.

Wally Boyes and 'W. G.' Richardson made most League appearances (39) and apart from Cecil Shaw, there were other club debuts for centre-half Bill Brockhurst, inside-forward Sammy Heaselgrave and wingers Jimmy Prew and Lol Coen.

At the end of the season goalkeeper Harold Pearson moved to Millwall after appearing in 303 games for Albion. Jimmy Murphy collected two full Welsh caps v Scotland and Ireland, and helped his country win the International Championship for the third time in the 1930s.

The average League attendance at The Hawthorns this season dropped to 21,707.

At the club's AGM it was announced that Mr Lou Nurse was to take over as club chairman from the late Billy Bassett. Norman Bassett followed his father on to the board in August 1937.

1937-38

This turned out to be a disastrous season for Albion. They were relegated to the Second Division as wooden spoonists, conceding a 91 goals in the process, and crashed out of the FA Cup to Third Division (North) opponents York City.

After ten League games had been played Albion had chalked up six victories and were well placed in the Division. But a run of four successive defeats saw them slip below the halfway mark and they never recovered after that. From mid-December to early March they recorded just two wins from 12 games and following their Cup exit, results got even worse with only four more victories arriving from the last 15 matches. Amazingly, Albion could and should have stayed up despite their mediocre form. There were so many other teams battling against relegation as the season drew to a close, and it transpired that three more points would have saved the Baggies from the drop. Yet they ended the campaign by losing their final three fixtures and finished up with 36 points, the same as Manchester City, but two fewer than Stoke City, Birmingham, Portsmouth and Grimsby Town, who all escaped the drop.

Albion suffered some hefty defeats, losing 4-0 at Stoke, 6-1 at home to Sunderland, 5-3 at Derby and Everton, 4-2 v Bolton, 7-1 at bottom club Manchester City (an astonishing scoreline this) and 4-1 on the last Saturday at Middlesbrough.

Their best wins were almost all at home: 4-0 v Chelsea, 5-1 v Liverpool and Huddersfield and 4-3 v Brentford and Birmingham. They also won 4-1 at Grimsby.

In an attempt to stave off relegation Albion signed two well established players, Scottish international wing-half Sandy McNab from Sunderland and England left-winger Joe Johnson from Stoke City; blond half-back Harry Lowery, goalkeeper Harry Baldwin and defenders Idris Bassett and Cyril Davies were also introduced to the team.

W. G. Richardson again topped the scoring list with 17 goals. Jack

Mahon netted 13 and Harry Jones 11, while the up-and-coming Ike Clarke from Tipton scored six times.

Cecil Shaw and Teddy Sandford, who was now playing at centre-half, were both ever-presents, and winger Jack Mahon missed just two matches.

The average League attendance at The Hawthorns rose to 23,246.

In February 1938 Wally Boyes moved to Everton (after 165 games for Albion) and at the end of the season George Shaw went to Stalybridge Celtic, having made 425 appearances for the Baggies.

Stan Wood joined Halifax Town after 280 games and 66 goals for Albion.

On the international front, Jimmy Murphy concluded his Welsh international career (15 caps) by playing against Scotland and England. In later years (1956-63) he was the Welsh international team manager.

In December 1937 Chippy Simmons, scorer of Albion's first goal at The Hawthorns in 1900, died at the age of 59.

1938-39

Back in the Second Division for the first time since 1931, Albion were marked up as one of the favourites to win promotion in what turned out be the last full League season before the outbreak of World War Two. But they never really got in a challenge after Christmas – and when the curtain came down in April they found themselves in tenth position, ten points behind champions Blackburn Rovers and nine fewer than runners-up Sheffield United.

Albion had a pretty good first half to the campaign – they won three of their opening four matches, and then recorded nine victories from 13 games between mid-September and early December. But once into the New Year their overall

An Albion reserve line-up in the wartime season of 1941-42. Back row (left to right): George Banks, Harry Kinsell, George Willetts, Cyril Davies, Harry Lowery. Front row: Frank Hodgetts, Arthur Wilkes, Bobby Newsome, Alan Parker, Arthur Griffiths, Len Millard.

Leading scorer was Billy Elliott with 128 goals; 'W. G.' Richardson netted 123, Clarke 77, Jones 60, Heaselgrave 50, Robbie Newsome 34 and Charlie Evans 33. In all Albion scored 795 goals (673 in League and Cup).

Albion's 1939-46 wartime record (League and Cup):

Season	P	W	D	L	F	A
1939-40	37	23	5	9	107	67
1940-41	32	14	5	13	92	82
1941-42	31	18	4	9	115	69
1942-43	38	17	6	15	84	83
1943-44	39	14	11	14	90	93
1944-45	40	15	11	14	75	74
1945-46	46	23	9	14	110	74
Totals	263	124	51	88	673	542

● The two Albion-Chelsea League games in 1945-46 realised 20 goals – Albion won 8-1 at home and lost 7-4 in London.

● 45 hat-tricks were scored by Albion players during World War Two. 'W. G.' Richardson netted 12, Clarke 10 and Harry Jones 8.

● In March 1942, Albion full-back Harold White was awarded the Military Medal, only the second professional footballer to be decorated during World War Two.

A junior player, J. E. Britnell, was awarded the DFC in 1946.

● Albion's best wartime wins were 10-1 v Luton (1941), 8-2 v Swansea (1941), 8-1 v Notts County (1941), 8-1 v Chelsea (1945), 8-2 v Wolves (away, 1941), 7-0 v Northampton (1941), 7-1 v Walsall (1944) and 6-0 v Northampton (1945).

Their heaviest defeat was 10-3 at Walsall in 1941, and they also lost 9-0 at Leicester in 1943, crashed 8-0 at Coventry also in 1943 and 8-2 to

Aston Villa in 1942 and Stoke (home) in 1944.

● Albion reserves beat a Smethwick League XI 17-0 in a friendly in January 1945. Tommy Bowen scored seven of the goals and a young Ray Barlow six.

● On 20 October 1945 a Victory international was staged at The Hawthorns between England and Wales. Albion's full-back Harry Kinsell played for England, but ended up a loser as the Welsh won the game 1-0 in front of an all-ticket crowd of 54,611 which paid record receipts of £8,753.

● Albion's right-winger Billy Elliott played twice for England during the war, lining up against Wales in 1943-44 and in the Victory international v Scotland in 1945-46. Kinsell also played in the Victory international v Ireland in 1945-46. Welshman Doug Witcomb played in six wartime internationals against

England, two in 1939-40, two in 1940-41 and two in 1941-42. He also played in the Victory international v Scotland in 1945-46.

Elliott and Kinsell also played regularly for Army and Combined Services XIs during the War, both in the UK and in Europe.

In June 1946, a new signing from Ireland, centre-forward Dave Walsh represented the Republic of Ireland twice v Portugal and Spain.

● On a sad note, seven former Hawthorns players died during the wartime period: 1919-20 championship-winning star Alf Bentley (in April 1940), full-back Amos Adams (1941), wing-half Harry Hadley (in September 1942), left-winger George Dorsett (in April 1943), centre-half Abe Jones (in the summer of 1943), Lance Corporal George Handley, who was a England junior international and also played for Crystal Palace (in Sicily in July 1940); and wing-half Jack Manners (in May 1946). Also Walter Wheatley, an Albion trialist, lost his life

– while Reg Ryan, Gil Williams and Billy Lunn and a few others were ready in waiting.

Albion continued to play well and pick up points and between late October and mid-December they claimed another four wins to keep in touch with the top clubs. However, the period from late December through to the end of February was a disaster with only one League win coming from nine games. And Tottenham Hotspur knocked Albion out of the FA Cup in the fourth round.

At this juncture the changes were being coming thick and fast with a certain Arthur Rowley now in the attack alongside Walsh, and goalkeeper Norman Heath establishing himself between the posts.

Albion couldn't get back on the track and although they improved late on with a flurry of goals, they again finished a disappointing seventh with 45 points, 14 less than the champions Birmingham City and 11 behind runners-up Newcastle United.

Jack Haines (signed from Leicester City in a part-exchange deal which sent Peter McKennan to Filbert Street) scored a hat-trick in Albion's best win of the season – 6-0 at home to Bradford Park Avenue – while Arthur 'Biff' Taylor from Dudley netted five times in four games at the end of the campaign.

Walsh once more topped the scoring charts with 22 goals (all in the League). Rowley netted five times, four coming in the League, which marked the beginning of his record haul of 434 in this competition gathered almost exclusively during the next 17 years – after leaving Albion.

There were two ever-presents – Pemberton and Millard – while Elliott was an absentee on three occasions.

The average League attendance at The Hawthorns in 1947-48 was the best-ever at 30,856 – a rise of more than 6,200 on the previous season. Almost 52,000 saw the game against Birmingham in March – the biggest on the ground for a League match since December 1937.

Both Vernon and Walsh were each capped three times by Ireland in the games against England, Scotland and Wales. Walsh was a scorer v England in a dramatic 2-2 draw at Liverpool and also played for the Republic of Ireland versus Portugal and Spain (one goal).

In the League game against Doncaster Rovers at The Hawthorns on 3 April Welshman Alun Evans of Albion suffered a blow to the head which resulted in his retirement and in later life caused him to lose his sight in one eye.

1948-49

On 12 July 1948, Fred Everiss, after 46 years in office, resigned as secretary-manager at The Hawthorns and in September he became a director of the club. He was replaced as secretary by his brother-in-law Ephraim Smith (a servant of the club since 1906) while Welshman Jack Smith became Albion's first-ever full-time team manager, taking over on 22 June 1948.. He arrived from Molineux where he had been a coach, having earlier played for Wolves, Bristol Rovers, Swindon Town and Chelsea in the League, and Albion as a 'guest' during the war. Within nine months Smith had guided the Baggies back to the First Division after an 11-year absence and there is no doubt that his experience as a player had a lot to do with Albion's success.

After a rather indifferent start (three wins from nine games) Albion gradually began to hit top form and from late September to Christmas they played some exciting football, winning 11 matches out of 14 to surge towards the top of the table. Three defeats in four either side of the New Year disrupted the team slightly but, aided by two hard-earned FA Cup wins against Lincoln City and Gateshead, and a 3-0 triumph over First Division Chelsea, in which Walsh grabbed a hat-trick, they picked up the momentum again; as Easter approached they

Albion skipper Jack Vernon shakes hands with West Ham captain Sam Small in the 1947-48 season.

Albion players training in 1951. Left to right: Les Horne, Reg Ryan, Glyn Hood (heading) and Jack Vernon.

for a 21-year-old winger from Port Vale by the name of Ronnie Allen. Allen was to become one of the greatest players ever to don a Baggies' shirt. He scored 234 goals in 458 games for the club and later had two spells as manager at The Hawthorns. Almost 61,000 fans turned up to see Allen make a scoring debut for Albion in the 1-1 home draw with Wolves and he netted another four goals before the season ended, helping Albion edge up to 14th position as they claimed four wins from their last six matches.

Walsh was once more leading scorer with 15 League goals to his name. Sanders was again an ever-present between the posts, while Pemberton, Millard, Kennedy, Vernon, Walsh and Reg Ryan, who was now established in the side at left-half, all appeared in 34 or more games.

Albion's average home League attendance of 38,819 was a new club record – and was 5,440 better than the previous season's figure.

Vernon added to his collection of international caps by captaining Ireland against Scotland and England, while Walsh also played against Wales as well as lining up for Eire versus Finland, Sweden and England, the latter at Goodison Park when the English lost for the first time on home soil to a 'foreign' country. Reg Ryan also played for Ireland against Wales and for Eire versus Sweden and Belgium.

In March 1950 former Albion goalkeeper Ike Webb died at the age of 75.

In the summer of 1950 veteran trainer Fred Reed was replaced at another ex-player, Arthur Fitton.

1950-51

Stan Rickaby, who had been signed from Middlesbrough towards the end of the previous season, established himself as Albion's right-back this term, in place of Jim Pem-

berton., while centre-forward Fred Richardson and inside-left Andy McCall also made their mark. Richardson was signed to replace Dave Walsh, who was surprisingly (from a supporters' point of view) transferred to Aston Villa while McCall arrived from Blackpool.

Other favourites on the move around this time included Haines (to Bradford), Bobby Barker (to Shrewsbury), Charlie Evans (to Stafford Rangers), Cyril Williams (to Bristol City).

Taking the season as a whole, it was a disappointing one for Albion, who finished 16th in the table with 37 points, only five clear of relegation. They won just 13 matches and had two long, inept spells – the first covering 15 games from 19 August to 28 October which brought them just three wins, and the second between late-December and late-March which again produced only two wins in 13 games. There were some useful performances however. The reigning League champions Portsmouth were walloped 5-0 at The Hawthorns, Everton were beaten 3-0 at Goodison Park and

Arsenal succumbed 2-0 in the Midlands. Albion also suffered some heavy defeats, among them a 5-0 thrashing at Tottenham and 3-0 hidings at Highbury, Manchester United and Sheffield Wednesday.

There was no joy in the FA Cup either as Albion went out in the third round to Derby County after a replay.

Allen, in his first full season, top-scored with ten goals, Barlow netted nine and Richardson eight.

Barlow was the only ever-present in the ranks; Rickaby missed one game as did Vernon while Allen and the dependable Millard missed two matches.

Norman Heath, a wartime signing, was now making his name in the Albion goal and star of the future, right-winger Frank Griffin, signed from Shrewsbury Town in April 1951, made his debut in the last game of the season at Sunderland.

The average League attendance at The Hawthorns fell by 7,727 to 31,082, and only 39, 066 witnessed the local derby with Wolves, the lowest for this prestigious Black Country fixture since October 1936.

HAWTHORNS DIARY

Arthur Fitton is about to be ducked by Ronnie Allen, watched by Len Millard, Frank Griffin and the rest of the Albion players, at the Droitwich Brine Baths in October 1952.

Manchester City, while Stoke City, Cardiff, Newcastle and Liverpool were beaten at The Hawthorns. Allen with seven goals was in fine form and the team as a unit was playing well.

Then came a poor run of results with only one win in seven games, but this was soon over and as the winter set in so Albion again picked up the momentum, running in five more victories by the end of the year, including a magnificent 5-4 triumph at Hillsborough.

A shock, however, at this juncture was the loss of coach Jesse Carver who returned to Italy in December.

Albion then started 1953 off with a cracking 5-3 win at Newcastle and also progressed in the FA Cup by knocking out West Ham 4-1 at Upton Park. Then, after a 5-0 defeat at Burnley and a 5-1 hammering at Stoke, Albion appointed Vic Buckingham, ex-Spurs left-back, as their new manager.

He moved down from Bradford Park Avenue (February 1953) and saw Albion quickly go out of the Cup (at the fourth attempt to Chelsea), but he realised that he had inherited a fine squad of players. He took his time regarding any alter-

ations and slowly but surely worked things out for the good, seeing Albion end the season confidently, by losing only one of their last six matches to take fourth place, their highest finish since 1932-33.

Albion rounded off the season by visiting the Irish Republic to play in two exhibition games against Select XIs of Waterford and Bohemians.

Allen netted 21 goals to head the scoring charts once more; Lee scored 11, Griffin and Ryan nine apiece and Nicholls seven. Rickaby

and Dudley were both ever-presents; Allen, Millard, Barlow and Lee missed one game each; Ryan was absent twice with Heath (36) and Griffin (35) also giving good service. A player who made his debut this season in place of the injured Joe Kennedy, was Liverpool-born centre-half Jimmy Dugdale, who was to become a real star in the middle-line.

Albion's average home League attendance went up by 1,800 to 31,527 and 54,480 fans witnessed the local derby with Wolves in October.

Reg Ryan was the only player to win senior international honours this season, lining up for the Republic of Ireland against France and Austria. Barlow won a second England 'B' cap against Scotland and he also twice represented the Football League v the League of Ireland and the Danish Combination. In the close season he toured South America and U.S.A. with the England party.

In July 1953, Buckingham made his first major signing, bringing centre-forward Derek Kevan down to The Hawthorns from his former club Bradford Park Avenue for a fee

New manager Vic Buckingham (second left) and the Albion players listen to a recording of the second-half commentary of their FA Cup game with Chelsea in 1953.

Albion skipper Len Millard with the Cup after the Baggies win over Preston.

As they progressed in the Cup so their League form began to suffer but after defeating Newcastle United 3-2 in the fifth round courtesy of another Allen treble in front of a packed house of 61,088 spectators and Spurs 3-0 in the quarter-final, the double still looked on. But then it started to go wrong.

Port Vale were beaten 2-1 in the semi-final at the cost of Rickaby and soon afterwards Heath was so badly injured at Roker Park that he never played again.

Buckingham brought in his reserves – Joe Kennedy, Wilf Carter, Fred Cox (his old Spurs team-mate) and ex-Wrexham right-back Stuart Williams – but the results went against Albion and after losing their last two matches – 6-1 at Villa Park and 3-0 at Portsmouth – they watched as the League trophy annoyingly found its way to Molineux.

Albion however, celebrated at Wembley and won the Cup for the fourth time, as goals from Allen (2, one a penalty) and Frank Griffin (the winner in the 87th minute) saw off Preston in front of a near 100,000 crowd. So it was a 'double' in the end for the West Midlands – but not as Albion had hoped it would be.

Allen top-scored with 34 League and Cup goals, and his strike partner Nicholls netted 32. Not for nothing were they known as 'The Terrible Twins.'

Right-half Jimmy Dudley was an ever-present while Lee was absent once and Millard twice.

Albion's average home League attendance went up to 38,279 – the second best in the club's history. The top League attendance was that of 53,210 for the 2-1 win over the then FA Cup holders Blackpool.

Over 134,000 fans saw Allen and Nicholls both score in England's 4-2 international win over Scotland at Hampden Park and the same two players won further caps against Yugoslavia in Belgrade. Rickaby also played for England – against Ireland, while Stuart Williams represented Wales v Austria. Ryan was capped three more times by the Republic of Ireland, twice against France (he scored in one) and once v Luxembourg (when he also found the net).

Allen and Nicholls gained England 'B' caps – the former v Switzerland and Scotland, Nicholls as 'sub' v the Swiss. Nicholls also won an England under-23 cap against Italy in Bologna.

Jimmy Dugdale also played at 'B' team level for England against Switzerland, Yugoslavia and Scotland, who had Albion's Jimmy Dudley in their side, while Ray Barlow, Dugdale and Stan Rickaby

HAWTHORNS DIARY

their next eight outings to slide down towards the bottom end of the table.

Changes were made to the team as Buckingham brought in Crowshaw, wing-half Gerry Summers, Maurice Setters (signed from Exeter) and left-winger Graham Williams from Rhyl, soon to become a Welsh international and later a Cup Final left-back.

Shortly after Christmas the tide turned and over an eight-week period Albion regained their composure, started winning again and slowly moved up the Division. But after going out of the FA Cup to neighbours Birmingham City on a snowbound Hawthorns pitch, their League form took a turn for the worse with six defeats coming in the next nine outings. Inside-right Bobby Robson was signed from Fulham for £25,000 in March, but he didn't have the greatest of baptisms, Albion suffering successive 4-0 defeats in his first two outings. Thankfully the season was all but over by now and when the final curtain came down Albion found themselves in 13th place with 41 points, six clear of relegation.

In the latter half of the season youngsters Brian Whitehouse and Roy Horobin were blooded and a record £25,000 signing from Fulham, Bobby Robson, came into the side at inside-right.

Allen (18 goals) was top-scorer again; Lee netted 12 and Nicholls eight.

There were no ever-presents, but Jim Sanders (41), Jim Dudley (41), Len Millard (40), George Lee (40), Ray Barlow (38) and Ronnie Allen (34) all made worthy contributions – as always.

Albion's average home League attendance was 26,922, the lowest since 1946-47, and a drop of over 4,000 on the previous season.

At international level Stuart

Williams earned another three caps for Wales, lining up against England, Scotland and Austria. Joe Kennedy captained England 'B' v Yugoslavia and Scotland and Don Howe won his first England under-23 cap v Scotland.

In the summer of 1956 Bobby Robson went on the FA tour of South Africa and played in four 'test' matches.

Albion's reserves had their best season since the War as they finished sixth in the Central League.

In October 1955, Hubert Pearson, Albion's goalkeeper in the 1912 FA Cup Final and 1920 League championship winning side, died at the age of 69. He was followed in June and July 1956 by two playing colleagues, Bobby McNeal (aged 65) and Joe Smith (66) who also won League championship medals.

1956-57

For the third season running Albion failed to get off to a good start, winning only three of their opening 12 League games.

Manager Buckingham was concerned and made frequent changes, bringing in Kevan at centre-forward, switching Allen to the left-

wing, re-introducing Nicholls at inside-left (in place of Brian Whitehouse), inserting Setters for Jim Dudley, and recalling the experienced Len Millard for Stuart Williams at left-back.

Things improved and four wins were registered off the reel with no goals conceded. Albion, though, stuttered their way through December and January, managing only one League win – 1-0 at home to Newcastle, this being the last Christmas Day game at The Hawthorns. They got through the opening rounds of the FA Cup, beating Doncaster Rovers in a replay and Sunderland, but their overall form left a lot to be desired. Roy Horobin was now in the side at outside-left and he did well, helping Albion through a sticky patch as they claimed four important victories to avoid being caught up in a relegation dogfight.

Progress was made to the semi-final stage of the Cup as Blackpool and then Arsenal fell by the wayside (both after replays) but Albion couldn't get to grips with the League situation. They won only two more matches (out of the last ten) and they also lost to Aston Villa in the

Jim Sanders punches clear from Aston Villa's Pace and Dixon as Brookes and Dudley cover at The Hawthorns in August 1956.

were ousted in the fifth round of the Cup, Albion's influential right-winger Frank Griffin fractured his leg. It was a body blow but the team battled on and in the quarter-final faced Manchester United only a few weeks after the Munich Air disaster. The game at The Hawthorns ended 2-2, but in the cauldron of Old Trafford the Baggies were beaten in the very last minute in front of an emotional 60,523.

Amazingly, three days later, Albion returned to the same ground for a League game and whipped United 4-0 in front of 3,000 more spectators. That Cup defeat rocked morale however, and Albion's League form deteriorated. They fell away to finish fourth after gaining just two wins in their last nine outings. Wolves won the title with 64 points, 14 more than Albion.

Three players scored 78 of Albion's 112 League and Cup goals between them: Allen 28, Robson 27 and Kevan 23.

Robson (41) and Ray Barlow (40) appeared in most League games.

Albion's average home League attendance was up by 9,200 to 32,558, and 221,253 fans witnessed the four FA Cup-ties at The Hawthorns (average 55,313). A crowd of 56,904 attended the local derby with Wolves – the best League crowd on the ground since March 1950.

Don Howe won 11 of his 23 England caps this season, appearing against Wales, Ireland and Scotland in the Home International Championship, the friendlies against France, Portugal and Yugoslavia and in the World Cup v USSR (three times), Austria and Brazil.

Derek Kevan played in ten of those internationals, missing the game against France – and he scored twice at Hampden Park v the Scots and also v USSR and Austria (once each). Bobby Robson netted twice on his England debut v France and he, too, played against the Russians (twice) Brazil and Austria in the World Cup Finals in Sweden.

Stuart Williams was also on World Cup duty with Wales and he played in ten internationals this term v England, Scotland, Israel (twice), Ireland, Hungary (twice), Mexico, Sweden and Brazil.

Howe appeared in three England under-23 games v Bulgaria, Scotland and Wales. Kevan and Maurice Setters also played against the Bulgars, with Setters also lining up versus Romania, Scotland and Wales. Ronnie Allen, Howe, Kevan and Robson all played for the Scottish Football League XI v the Scottish League at Newcastle with Kevan scoring a hat-trick, and Barlow captained the 'League' side v the League of Ireland.

Robson (3) and Allen (2) scored all England's goals v a Sheffield XI (won 5-4).

At the end of this season three 1954 FA Cup winners left the club – goalkeeper Jimmy Sanders, with 391 appearances behind him, signed for Coventry City; skipper Len Millard joined Stafford Rangers after 21 years and 625 appearances for Albion and left-winger George Lee moved to Lockheed Leamington, having scored 65 goals in 295 games during his ten years at The Hawthorns.

1958-59

This turned out to be another good season for Albion who finished a creditable fifth in the First Division with 49 points (12 fewer than champions Wolves). They also reached the fifth round of the FA Cup and scored another 93 goals.

A 6-0 win at Birmingham in pouring rain was one of the many fine away displays put on by Albion; others were at Portsmouth (won 6-2), Villa Park (won 4-1) and Preston (won 4-2). The best home performances came against Chelsea (won 4-0), and Tottenham (won 4-3). On the down side Albion lost 5-2 at Wolves, 5-0 at Tottenham, 4-2 at home to Burnley and 4-3 at Highbury, despite Derek Kevan's hat-trick.

Albion lost only one of their first nine League games; they won eight out of 12 between mid-October and the end of December and over a four-week period from the end of March they lost one in ten, gaining six more victories.

Kevan with 29 goals was top marksman. Allen scored 17 and Burnside 12.

Kevan (41), Setters (41), Hogg (40), Howe (40), Stuart Williams (40), Allen (36) and Barlow (36) played in most League games.

The average League crowd at The Hawthorns was 31,547 – a thousand down on 1957-58.

Clive Jackman, who had been signed the previous season from Aldershot, started off in goal but was badly injured at Villa Park in October and never played for Albion again. His place went to Ray Potter, a bargain buy from Crystal Palace. Chuck Drury, a local lad, who made his debut at Bolton in February 1958, had some useful outings in the half-back line, while wingers Jimmy Campbell and Derek Hogg, the latter signed from Leicester City in the summer, did well.

During the season Albion did not introduce one newcomer into their first team – the only time this has happened.

During 1958-59, Howe collected nine more England caps, playing against Ireland, USSR, Wales, Scotland, Italy, Brazil, Peru, Mexico and the U.S.A. Kevan also played against Mexico and the U.S.A. (scoring in each game). Stuart Williams added three Welsh caps to his tally, playing in the games v Scotland,

HAWTHORNS DIARY

never in with a chance of challenging for honours. They accumulated 41 points – only nine more than relegated Newcastle United, whom they crushed 6-0 at The Hawthorns with an Alec Jackson hat-trick. This was their best win of the campaign, coming immediately after five successive defeats at the start of the League programme. Manchester City were beaten 6-3 at The Hawthorns, Allen – in his last season with the club – netting a hat-trick, but Albion crashed to a 7-1 defeat at Chelsea (Jimmy Greaves doing the damage with five goals) and they also lost 4-2 at Wolves and 4-2 at home to Fulham.

Albion's best spell – 11 games which included nine wins, seven on the bounce – came right at the end of the season after Clive Clark, a flying left-winger signed from Q.P.R. for £20,000, and Jack Lovatt had joined Jackson, Burnside and Kevan in attack.

Albion's interest in the FA Cup ended at the first hurdle, beaten 3-1 at lowly Lincoln.

Kevan, with 18 goals, was chief marksman yet again; Burnside netted 13 and Jackson 12.

Howe was the only ever-present; Jackson missed one game and Robson two, and all told manager Clark used 25 players including two ex-Walsall stars, lanky wing-half Peter Billingham and centre-half Stan Jones.

Albion's average home League crowd in 1960-61 was 24,707 – their lowest since 1957.

On the international stage Derek Kevan won his 14th and last cap for an unbeaten England in an 8-0 Wembley win over Mexico. Robson also played and scored against the Mexicans as well as lining up against Northern Ireland, Luxembourg, Spain, Wales, Scotland (netting the first goal in a 9-3 win), Portugal and Italy. Graham Williams represented Wales against the Republic of Ireland, Scotland and England and his namesake Stuart played against Eire, Spain (twice), Northern Ireland and Hungary.

Robson also represented the Football League v the Italian League and captained the League XI v the Scottish League. Howe also appeared in this latter game.

Clive Clark won an England under-23 cap v Wales – his only representative honour in a fine career. Graham Williams also featured in this game. And at the season's end Don Howe toured New Zealand with the FA party.

At the end of the season Albion gave free transfers to two great players – Ronnie Allen and Joe Kennedy, who had both starred in that 1954 FA Cup win. Allen joined Crystal Palace after scoring 234 goals in 415 games for the Baggies, while Kennedy teamed up with Chester, having amassed 397 appearances for the club.

Derek Hogg was also on the move earlier this season, moving to Cardiff City. Stan Steele, signed from Port Vale in March, played one game for Albion (at Blackburn) before returning to the Potteries' club in August and trainer Dick Graham also departed for Crystal Palace (November 1960). He was replaced by Wilf Dixon.

In September 1960, former Albion winger Walter Boyes died suddenly at the age of 47 and in February 1961 Sid Bowser, an Albion player between 1908 and 1924, passed away at the age of 69. Both players won England recognition.

1961-62

In October 1961 silver-haired Archie Macaulay, the former Arsenal and Scottish international wing-half, took over as manager at The Hawthorns – taking over from Gordon Clark who joined former boss Vic Buckingham at Sheffield Wednesday.

However, for Albion this turned out to be a disappointing season. They had a disastrous set of League results during the first half of the campaign, registering only five wins, two of them emphatic 4-0 successes over Arsenal and Blackburn Rovers, both at home. They held their own between December and March before a gallant late run, when only two defeats were suffered in their last 12 League games, saw the Baggies pull themselves clear of relegation trouble to finish in ninth position with 43 points, 13 behind the champions Ipswich Town.

There is no doubt that at one stage relegation was certainly a possibility but Albion's battling performances paid off and towards the end of the season they were playing some delightful football. Indeed, they ended on a high with six wins out of eight, starting off with a terrific 5-1 scoreline at Molineux against arch rivals Wolves. Albion then ran up five victories on the trot, including a 4-0 pounding of Chelsea and a last-day slaughter of Blackpool, who crashed 7-1 at The Hawthorns with Derek Kevan slamming in four goals.

Albion's heaviest defeats of the campaign were 4-1 at Chelsea and Manchester United, and they also lost 4-2 at home to Tottenham, who also dumped them out of the FA Cup in the fifth round by the same score in front of a near 55,000 crowd – this being the last time the 50,000 barrier has been broken at The Hawthorns. Albion had accounted for Blackpool (after a replay) and Wolves in the earlier rounds.

Kevan headed the scorers with 34 goals (in League and Cup) and was joint top-scorer in the First Division with Ipswich's Ray Crawford (later

HAWTHORNS DIARY

March (this after he had said farewell to the Hawthorns fans with a blistering hat-trick in a 6-1 win over Ipswich Town), Albion's season was all but over.

Manager Macaulay departed, replaced in April 1963 by the former England international inside-forward Jimmy Hagan, and just as if to say 'welcome' things perked up a little towards the end of the campaign, Albion winning four and drawing two of their last eight matches. But it was, in truth, a very disappointing season for all concerned at the club.

Kevan with 16 goals again finished up as top scorer. Keith Smith and Alec Jackson offered support with 14 apiece.

Graham Williams and Stan Jones each made 40 League appearances in 12 years with Albion with Don Howe (38) and Clive Clark and Bobby Cram weighing in with 36. Debutants this term included midget Scottish right-winger Kenny Foggo, centre-forward Max Murray, another Scot who arrived from Rangers, but returned to his homeland (with Third Lanark) in double-quick time, inside-forward Ronnie Fenton, a £15,000 buy from Burnley and full-back Ray Fairfax, whose first outing was at Anfield in front of 44,000 fans.

Stuart Williams, after making 246 appearances in 12 years with Albion and gaining a club record 33 caps for Wales, left to join Southampton along with Davey Burnside, who scored 42 goals in his 135 outings for the club. Centre-forward Keith Smith also moved on, signing for Peterborough United after netting 34 times in just 70 outings for the Baggies.

The average League attendance nose-dived to 18,637 – the lowest since 1938-39 and the turnout of 10,759 v Bolton was the worst for six years.

Even Albion's reserves didn't do much better, finishing 12th in the

Central League – their lowest position since 1959.

Tony Millington, who had the misfortune to concede 15 goals at Molineux this season when Albion lost 7-0 to Wolves in a re-arranged First Division game and 8-0 in a reserve fixture, won his first three Welsh caps v Scotland, Hungary and England. Fellow countryman Graham Williams also played against the Hungarians as well as Northern Ireland. Millington also earned under-23 recognition for Wales v Scotland and Northern Ireland.

In September 1962 'Sandy' McNab, the former Albion and Scotland wing-half, died at the age of 50 after a short illness.

Major H. Wilson Keys was replaced as Albion chairman by 'Jim' W. Gaunt at a board meeting on 9 April 1963 with Tommy Glidden stepping up to vice-chairman.

1963-64

Albion began this season with two new players in their line-up – left-half Terry Simpson (signed from Peterborough United) and centre-forward John Kaye (bought from Scunthorpe United). They settled in well and a month or so into the League programme, two more new faces were introduced – Scotsman Doug Fraser (secured from Aberdeen) and Oldham-born teenager Tony Brown, who on his debut at Ipswich, scored the first of 313 goals for the Baggies and made the first of 826 appearances – both club records.

Albion's pre-November performances were generally good. Playing confidently they ran up some impressive victories, including those of 4-0 over Arsenal, 3-0 v Fulham, 4-3 in the local derby with Aston Villa and 3-1 against Birmingham City – all at home.

In fact, they lost only three of

their opening 13 matches but then had a run of six without a win. A transfer rebellion early in December was quickly followed by the infamous tracksuit saga when manager Hagan refused to allow the players to wear tracksuit bottoms in freezing temperatures. This was thankfully resolved and Albion quickly put together a seven-match unbeaten League sequence either side of Christmas which included a thrilling 4-4 home draw with Tottenham. Exit from the FA Cup, beaten in a fourth-round replay at Arsenal after an eventful 3-3 draw at The Hawthorns, triggered off an indifferent stretch which lasted from February onwards, and only two more victories were recorded in the last eight League fixtures.

Albion finished the season in tenth position with 43 points, 14 behind the champions Liverpool, but well clear of next-to-bottom Bolton Wanderers (28 pts).

Winger Clive Clark had a fine season, top-scoring with 17 goals. John Kaye netted 12, Kenny Foggo 11 and Ronnie Fenton 10, while a young Micky Fudge weighed in with four, including a hat-trick in a 4-2 win over Everton.

Goalkeeper Ray Potter, centre-half Stan Jones, Terry Simpson and 'Chippy' Clark were all ever-present; the average League attendance at The Hawthorns rose slightly to 20,552; Albion's second XI finished runners-up in the Central League – their highest position since 1934-35 – and skipper Graham Williams played in three internationals for Wales v England, Scotland and Northern Ireland.

In April 1964, full-back Don Howe was transferred to Arsenal for £40,000 after 379 appearances for Albion. Chuck Drury (to Bristol City) and Alec Jackson (to Birmingham City) also moved on...and the first of a number of Throstle Clubs

HAWTHORNS DIARY

There were also debuts for several other players including Graham Lovett, Ian Collard, Dick Krzywicki and Ray Crawford, the former England international centre-forward, signed from Wolves.

Departures included Tony Millington to Crystal Palace and Ronnie Fenton to Birmingham City.

The average League attendance at The Hawthorns fell by 1,100 to 19,405 and for the first time since 1935-36, Albion's best single turnout failed to top the 30,000 mark.

Graham Williams was the only player to receive international honours, playing times for Wales against Scotland, Denmark, England, Greece (twice), Northern Ireland (scoring his first goal for his country), Italy and the USSR.

During the summer of 1966 Albion went on a short Dutch tour, losing 2-1 to Alkmaar but defeating ADO The Hague 2-1 and Ajax 1-0. The latter team was managed by former Albion boss Vic Buckingham.

1965-66

Albion entered the Football League Cup for the first time this season – going on to win the trophy by beating West Ham United 5-3 in the last of the two legged Finals.

En route to the Final Albion ousted Walsall (3-1 at home), Leeds United (4-2 away), Coventry City (6-1 in a Hawthorns replay – Jeff Astle netting a hat-trick), Aston Villa (3-1 also at home) and manager Jimmy Hagan's former club, Peterborough United in the two-legged semi-final (2-1 at home and 4-2 at London Road when Tony Brown hit a treble). They then lost 2-1 at Upton Park in the first leg of the Final on 9 March but turned things round in the return leg at The Hawthorns a fortnight later to crush the Hammers 4-1 after a magnificent first-half performance in front

Albion, winners of the 1966 League Cup.

of a 32,000 plus crowd. This victory booked Albion a place in the Fairs Cup for 1966-67 – their first taste of competitive European club football.

In the League itself Albion did very well and claimed sixth position with 50 points – 11 behind the champions Liverpool. This was their highest finish for six years and was due to an excellent run of nine games without defeat from early April to when the last ball was kicked in May.

Prior to that Albion's form had been in and out. They began with six wins, two defeats and a draw from their opening nine matches. Then they fell away somewhat before losing one in seven during October and November. Only one victory was recorded over an eight-match period either side of Christmas and after crashing out of the FA Cup 3-0 at Bolton, Albion then claimed just two more victories in eight outings before ending the season with a flourish.

Their best wins were those of 6-2 v Stoke City (a hat-trick here for John Kaye and an own-goal by ex-Baggies' star Maurice Setters), 6-2 v Fulham, 5-1 at Sunderland on New Year's day, 5-3 at home to Nottingham Forest and 5-1 v Leicester.

Their heaviest defeats were suffered at Leeds and West Ham where they lost both games 4-0.

Early on in the season Jeff Astle cracked in two hat-tricks in seven days, v Sheffield Wednesday (won 4-2 at home) and Northampton Town (won 4-3 away).

Tony Brown top-scored with 27 goals (in League and Cup). Jeff Astle netted 24, John Kaye 23 and Clive Clark 12. In total Albion registered 119 goals at competitive level.

Substitutes were used for the first time this season and Graham Lovett was Albion's first No.12 to be called off the bench, replacing Kenny Foggo at Northampton in September.

Doug Fraser and John Kaye were ever-presents and the average League attendance at The Hawthorns was 19,781 – up by just 376.

Albion's second XI finished fifth in the Central League with Terry Simpson playing in all 42 games – an unusual occurrence in reserve football.

Skipper Graham Williams took his tally of Welsh caps up to 21 with appearances against Northern Ireland, Brazil (twice) and Chile while Albion's young Republic of Ireland striker Ray Treacy made his

lutely and scored telling goals to reach Wembley for the second successive season – and this time they won, beating Everton 1-0 after extra-time to lift the FA Cup for the fifth time. It was a great occasion, especially for Jeff Astle, who scored the winning goal in the 92nd minute.

Albion eventually overcame Colchester 4-0 (after a 1-1 draw), then took out Southampton (3-2 away with Graham Williams temporarily in goal, also after a replay), Portsmouth 2-1 at Fratton Park, Liverpool (at the third attempt, finally winning 2-1 at Maine Road) and Birmingham City 2-0 in the semi-final at Villa Park.

Everton were favourites to win but Albion battled on with grim determination and won with this line-up: John Osborne; Doug Fraser, Graham Williams; Tony Brown, John Talbut, John Kaye (who had been converted to a defender when Eddie Colquhoun broke a leg at Newcastle); Graham Lovett, Ian

Collard, Jeff Astle, Bobby Hope and Clive Clark. Dennis Clarke came on for Kaye at the start of extra-time to become the first 'sub' used in an FA Cup Final.

The team also did themselves justice in the First Division after a disappointing start when they had two wins, two draws and five defeats in the first nine games. But from their other 33 matches Albion registered 15 victories and ten draws to finish a creditable eighth in the table with 46 points, 12 behind the champions Manchester City, whom they defeated twice (3-2 at home and 2-0 at Maine Road) over Christmas.

Wolves 4-1, Sheffield United 4-1, Burnley 8-1 (Albion's best home League win since September 1957), Stoke City 3-0, European Cup winners-to-be Manchester United 6-3 and West Ham United 3-1 were all defeated at The Hawthorns as Albion turned on the style. But there were one or two upsets with Everton winning 6-2 on Albion soil just two months before the Cup Final (Alan

Ball scored four goals) while both Southampton (4-0 at the Dell), Coventry City (4-2) and Liverpool (4-1 at Anfield) also gave Albion a hiding.

Albion didn't do well at all in the League Cup, losing to Reading in the opening round. But it was the other Cup they which drew their interest – and what a great day out it turned out to be – especially after that Wembley disappointment a year earlier.

Jeff Astle was easily top-scorer with 35 goals, including three hat-tricks, two in three days v Manchester United and West Ham late in the season. Clive Clark and Tony Brown with 15 apiece, followed the 'King' in the scoring charts. Indeed, Astle became the only Albion player to score in every round of the FA Cup in a winning season.

John Talbut, as reliable as ever at centre-half, appeared in all 53 League and Cup games; Doug Fraser and Jeff Astle followed him home with 51 outings apiece.

This time Albion show off the FA Cup, won in 1968. Back row (left to right): Doug Fraser, John Kaye, Graham Lovett, John Osborne, Ian Collard, Jeff Astle, John Talbut. Front row: Tony Brown, Asa Hartford, Alan Ashman (manager), Bobby Hope, Graham Williams.

HAWTHORNS DIARY

with Rees also appearing on the right with Dick Krzywicki. Ray Wilson established himself in the side at left-back and Len Cantello made his debut in midfield, while Dennis Martin (signed from Carlisle United) and youngsters Lyndon Hughes and Alan Merrick all played their first games for the Baggies.

Albion won just three of their opening 11 games before registering four victories on the trot, including a 6-1 home thrashing of Coventry City. However, only three wins came from the next 15 fixtures – the best being 4-0 at Q.P.R. Then, surprisingly, after their FA Cup exit at Sheffield, Albion played exceedingly well, winning five of their last seven fixtures which included a 4-3 triumph over Tottenham and a 5-1 home success over Newcastle.

Albion's two heaviest defeats in their League programme came at Maine Road and The Hawthorns. They crashed again to Manchester City, this time by 5-1 and were hammered 5-2 by Nottingham Forest in front of their own supporters.

In the FA Cup, Norwich City 3-0, Fulham 2-1, Arsenal 1-0 and Chelsea 2-1 were all knocked out before Leicester ended the Baggies' Wembley hopes in front of 53,207 fans in the semi-final.

Jeff Astle (26) and Tony Brown (23) were the leading marksmen, and both Brown and John Talbut were League ever-presents.

The reserves again finished in third place in the Central League.

In May 1969 Albion played three matches in the Palo Alto Tournament in California. Three other matches were also played in Canada, including a 12-0 defeat of Edmonton All Stars.

Albion's Youth team – under coach Jimmy Dunn, ex-Wolves and derby County – reached the Final of the FA Youth Cup but lost 6-3 on aggregate to Sunderland. Dunn later

took over as first team trainer from Stuart Williams in February 1970.

Jeff Astle won the first of his five England caps, lining up against Wales; Doug Fraser and Bobby Hope played for Scotland against Cyprus and Denmark respectively; Ronnie Rees represented Wales against Italy and Graham Williams played in his last and 26th international match for Wales against Italy.

Eddie Colquhoun was transferred to Sheffield United in October 1968; Dennis Clarke joined Huddersfield Town in January 1969; Ronnie Rees left for Nottingham Forest the following month; 'keeper Dick Sheppard moved to Bristol Rovers in June 1969 and soon afterwards Clive Clark, after nine years at The Hawthorns, was sold to Queen's Park Rangers (in part-exchange for Allan Glover) having scored 98 goals in 353 appearances for the Baggies.

1969-70

Albion recruited their first-ever £100,000 player in June 1969, bringing Colin Suggett to The Hawthorns from Sunderland. Goalkeeper Jim Cumbes was another new face – bought from Tranmere Rovers for £30,000 – so too was inside-forward Danny Hegan, recruited from Ipswich Town in a deal which took Ian Collard to Portman Road.

Suggett made a great start to his Baggies' career, scoring twice in an opening day 2-0 League victory at Southampton.

But it was not to last – for 'Suggo' or Albion – and only two more wins were recorded in the next 15 First Division matches as the team slipped deep into relegation trouble.

John Osborne, a young Gordon Nisbet, later to become an England under-23 international right-back, and Cumbes all played in goal during the first month but it was 'Ossie' who held on to his position despite some poor League results.

In the League Cup though Albion made good progress at the expense of Aston Villa, Ipswich Town, Bradford City and Leicester City and as they tangled over two semi-final legs with Carlisle United so their First Division form improved considerably with five wins coming in the space of six weeks.

Carlisle were duly despatched from the League Cup 4-2 on aggregate as Albion reached their fourth major Cup Final in five years and although they went out of the FA Cup, beaten 2-1 by Sheffield Wednesday despite a thumping goal from Tony Brown, Albion were undefeated in four First Division games in January.

February wasn't so good and as the League Cup Final showdown with Manchester City arrived, Albion's form was somewhat mixed.

At Wembley, in front of almost 98,000 fans, Albion took an early lead thanks to Jeff Astle's looping header but on a soggy pitch, ruined by a recent horse show, City, inspired by Francis Lee, slowly got on top and went on to steal the prize with a 2-1 scoreline. If Suggett had scored when facing an open goal in the second half then Albion would probably have celebrated another famous victory. But he missed his chance and Glyn Pardoe snatched the winner to leave Albion with nothing to show for their efforts.

After this disappointment the season fizzled out. Nottingham Forest were beaten 4-0 in the last home game and Albion eventually finished 16th with 37 points – their lowest position in the top flight since 1954-55, and their lowest points total since 1950-51.

Astle, with 30 goals, finished up as top marksman and was also the First Division's leading scorer; Suggett scored 15 and Tony Brown 13. Suggett was also the only ever-present and had a fine season.

HAWTHORNS DIARY

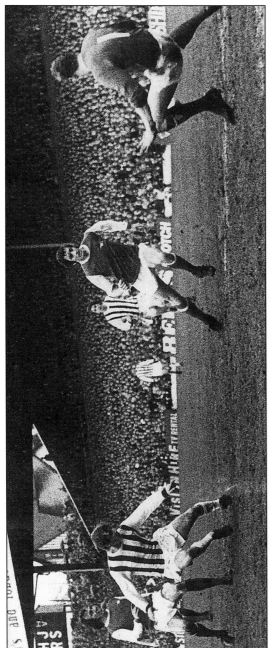

Asa Hartford scores an equaliser in the 2-2 draw with double winners Arsenal at The Hawthorns in April 1971.

those of 6-2 at double-chasing Arsenal, 4-1 at Manchester City and a 3-0 reverse at Crystal Palace.

And in the League Cup Albion suffered their heaviest defeat in the competition, losing 5-0 to Spurs at White Hart Lane.

John Wile, who was to go on and appear in 500 League games for Albion, arrived at the club in December from Peterborough United – to replace John Talbut – while right-winger George McVitie had come down from Carlisle United. Hartford was now on the left-wing and Cumbes was back in goal.

The on-field results, however, were still disappointing and only four more victories were registered before the season ended – and there was no joy in the FA Cup either, Albion going out to Ipswich Town in the fourth round.

Tony Brown with 30 goals, was Albion's leading scorer and his form this season (for he was also the only ever-present) earned him his only England cap v Wales at Wembley. Astle netted 15 times and Suggett seven.

The average League crowd at The Hawthorns was down by almost 2,200 to 25,691 and the highest attendance was that of 41,134 for the visit of Manchester United in March when a Tony Brown treble gave Albion a deserved 4-3 victory.

Elsewhere at international level Asa Hartford collected his second Scottish under-23 cap v Wales and both Jeff Astle (2 goals) and Tony Brown (1) scored in the Football League XI's victory over the Irish League; the 'Bomber' also played against the Scottish League.

George McVitie toured the Republic of Ireland and Australia with the FA party.

Albion again played in the ill-fated Anglo-Italian Cup but failed to make progress yet again after losing three and drawing one of their four matches.

Unfortunately, this was Alan Ashman's last season as manager of Albion. He was replaced by former player Don Howe in July 1971.

And defender John Talbut also left the club – signing for the Belgium side KV Mechelen after 192 games for the Baggies.

Doug Fraser also left The Hawthorns, joining Nottingham Forest in January after 325 appearances for Albion.

In September 1970 the death took place of the legendary Jesse Pennington, who died in Kidderminster at the age of 87. He joined Albion in 1903, played 495 competitive games for the club and won 25 England caps before retiring in 1922. Also laid to rest at the age of 66,

was star centre-forward Jimmy Cookson, who, between 1927 and 1933, scored 110 goals in 131 appearances for Albion.

1971-72

With former Baggies and England international Don Howe back at The Hawthorns as team manager, and supported by Brian Whitehouse and physiotherapist George Wright from Arsenal, Albion had hoped for far better things this season but instead of challenging for honours at the top they had to fight for their lives to avoid relegation.

After entering the Watney Cup and losing in the Final on penalties to Colchester United, Albion triumphed in their opening two League games (at West Ham and v Everton) but then went nine without a victory and soon afterwards had another disastrous spell when a further ten matches passed by without a single win.

By this time 17 matches had been played and only ten goals had been scored.

At this juncture they were in deep, deep trouble. Attendances had dropped to below the 20,000 mark and the goals had completely dried up. At the back Albion looked reasonably sound with Wile and Robertson starting their long associ-

HAWTHORNS DIARY

tally of 28 was their lowest since the 42 match programme was introduced in 1919-20. And the Baggies' total of 38 goals was the lowest since 1903-04.

Tony Brown netted 16 goals (including two in the Texaco Cup) to head the scoring list (no-one else reached double figures). Asa Hartford missed only one League game, John Wile was absent from two and Brown both missed three.

Among the departures this season were Bobby Gould (to Bristol City – he was later to return as Albion's manager), George McVitie (to Oldham Athletic) and Colin Suggett (to Norwich City).

Albion's average home League attendance dropped alarmingly by 4,350 to 21,438 – the lowest since 1966.

Not surprisingly not one single Albion player gained full international honours this season; Len Cantello added five England under-23 caps to his collection, playing

against Wales, the Netherlands (twice), Denmark and Czechoslovakia; Hartford represented Scotland against England and Wales also at this level.

In March 1973 the death occurred at the age of 73 of Albion's 1931 FA Cup winning full-back George Shaw. And in November 1973 former Albion goalkeeper George Ashmore died, aged 75.

1973-74

Playing in the Second Division for the first time since 1949, Albion got off to a sound start, winning their opening two matches – 3-2 at Blackpool and 1-0 at home to Crystal Palace. But then they failed to win any of their next ten League games, slipped out of the League Cup at the hands of lowly Exeter City, and saw attendances at The Hawthorns drop to under 12,000.

Peter Latchford was now in goal; former 'keeper Gordon Nisbet was playing at right-back with Alan

Merrick his partner (Ray Wilson was out injured). Wile and Robertson were the two centre-halves; Tony Brown, Cantello, Hartford and Allan Glover were manning midfield between them while Ally Brown, Shaw and Willie Johnston occupied the front positions.

A 2-0 home victory over Sheffield Wednesday in late October helped boost confidence and for a time results were favourable, with seven more victories coming before the end of the year including a 2-0 Boxing Day win over Aston Villa in front of 43,119 fans at The Hawthorns. This was the first time the clubs had ever met each other in the Second Division. Albion were now in with an outside chance of promotion, but once into 1974 Albion's form slumped again, although they did knock First Division Everton out of the FA Cup, winning 1-0 in a fourth-round replay after a goalless Sunday after-

Albion, 1974-75. Back row (left to right): Weir, Thompson, Cooper, Foulkes, Tranter, W. Hughes, Mayo, Clarke, Edwards, Bulloch, Buckham. Second row: Don Howe (manager), Geoff Wright (assistant manager), Glover, Nisbet, Robertson, Minton, Ward, Latchford, Osborne, Regan, Turner, Robson, Trewick, A. McPherson (coach), Brian Whitehouse (coach). Seated: Shaw, L. Hughes, Merrick, Johnston, Wile, A. Brown, T. Brown, Cantello, Hartford, Wilson, Davies. On ground: Donaghy, Lynex, Gregson, Rumjahn, Rushbury, Leetion, Close, Wassell.

Tony Brown's famous winner at Oldham in April 1976 which took the Baggies back to Division One.

1974, Jim Gaunt stepped down as chairman. he subsequently became president of the club while FA 'Bert' Millichip took over as chairman with Tom Silk his vice-chairman.

In April 1975 the death was announced of former Albion inside-forward of the 1930s Sammy Heaselgrave. He was 58.

1975-76

In June 1975 Republic of Ireland international midfielder Johnny Giles, formerly of Manchester United, moved to The Hawthorns from Leeds United for a fee of £45,000 to become Albion's first-ever player-manager. And what an impact the Dublin-born star had, both on the players and the supporters.

After a quick tour of Ireland and matches v Shamrock Rovers and Finn Harps, it was down to business.

After a wobbly start Albion improved dramatically with Giles dominating in centre-field where he was partnered by fellow Irishman Mick Martin (signed from Old Trafford) and Len Cantello. After being next to bottom in October they slowly but surely climbed the ladder.

Giles' international team-mate Paddy Mulligan arrived from Crystal Palace to take over at right-back. Former Walsall striker Joe Mayo replaced England's 1966 World Cup hero Geoff Hurst, who was bought as a stop-gap from Stoke City and with Ally Brown, Tony Brown, Willie Johnston, Bryan Robson, centre-backs John Wile and Ally Robertson, and veteran goal-keeper John Osborne all pulling their weight and playing out of their skins, Albion went on to win promotion after a terrific second-half to the season.

During that shaky opening period Albion won just once in ten games and went out of the League Cup to Fulham. They suffered only one defeat in their next ten outings but either side of Christmas, again went through a sticky patch, recording a solitary victory at Nottingham Forest. But into 1976 things really took off. And besides making progress in the FA Cup Albion gradually got themselves into a strong enough position from where they could mount a serious late challenge at winning promotion. They had a few hiccups here and there, which included elimination from the FA Cup (at Southampton) and the loss of a crucial home game to fellow promotion-chasers Bristol City, but with the fans behind them Giles and his players knew what was required when they travelled to Boundary Park, Oldham for their final game of the season. They HAD to win to regain their First Division status – and backed by more than 15,000 fans, Albion did the business with a goal by Tony Brown early in the second half. That 1-0 victory took the Baggies back into the top flight, along with Sunderland (the champions) and Bristol City – and the supporters celebrated long and loud.

Albion finished a point ahead of Bolton (53-52).

The Browns scored 23 goals between them, Tony 12 and Ally 11, while Joe Mayo netted eight.

John Osborne and Ally Robertson were both ever-present with Ossie keeping a club record 22 clean-sheets in the League and he conceded only 33 goals (12 at home).

Albion were promoted scoring just 50 goals, the lowest total of any promoted side since Notts County netted 46 in 1922-23.

The average League crowd at The Hawthorns rose by over 4,500 to 17,233, with four games towards the end of the season attracting audiences of more than 20,000.

Johnny Giles won his first cap with Albion, captaining Eire v Turkey. Mick Martin and Paddy Mulligan also played in that international, as well as against Poland, while Martin was also captain versus Norway.

Martin was actually sent-off in the Turkey match to become the first Albion player to be dismissed in a full international.

HAWTHORNS DIARY

Rock solid centre-backs Ally Robertson and John Wile were both ever-present, while Paddy Mulligan missed two League games and a young Derek Statham made his name at left-back.

Albion's average home League attendance was 24,523 – a rise of almost 7,300 – and 41,867 fans saw the 1-1 draw with Aston Villa, the first game between the clubs in the top flight since November 1966.

Players who moved on included Mayo and Glover (both to Orient),, Dave Rushbury (to Sheffield Wednesday), Ian Edwards (to Chester) and Gordon Nisbet (to Hull City). In March 1977 Ray Wilson announced his retirement because of injury at the age of 29.

Willie Johnston played seven times on the wing for Scotland, lining up against Sweden, Wales, Northern Ireland, England, Chile, Argentina and Brazil. Giles, Martin and Mulligan all played for Eire against England, Turkey, France (twice), Poland and Bulgaria, while Treacy was capped against the Poles and the French. Martin (v Bulgaria) and Johnston (v Argentina) were both sent-off.

Laurie Cunningham became the first black footballer to represent England in a major international when he starred in the under-21 game v Scotland at Sheffield, scoring a goal to mark the occasion. He also played against Finland and Norway (as sub) while Wayne Hughes represented Wales under-21's v both England and Scotland.

In December 1976, George James, Albion's centre-forward of the 1920s, died at the age of 77, He scored 57 goals in 116 outings for the club. And in January 1977, another two former Albion players – Joe Carter and Cecil Shaw – died in Handsworth, Birmingham. Carter, a member of Albion's unique double-winning side of

1930-31, passed away at the age of 75. He scored 155 goals in 451 games for the club between 1921 and 1936. Full-back Shaw was 65 and played for Albion between 1936 and 1947, appearing in 251 first team matches.

1977-78

On 22 June 1977 former Baggies' favourite Ronnie Allen returned to The Hawthorns as Albion's manager and shortly after the season had commenced he introduced Cyrille Regis from non-League Hayes.

And it wasn't long before the 19 year-old strapping centre-forward from French Guyana was hitting the headlines – scoring twice on his first team debut in a 4-0 League Cup win over Rotherham United and then following up with a cracking goal on his League debut against Middlesbrough.

Albion began the season well, beating Chelsea 3-0 and drawing at Leeds. And from the day Regis arrived on the scene the results got even better, Albion losing only twice in 15 League games up to December, although they did lose 1-0 to Bury at a foggy Gigg Lane in the League Cup.

There were some impressive wins – 3-0 at Newcastle, 3-1 v Birmingham, 4-0 over Manchester United (again) and 2-0 against Leicester City.

At West Ham (a 3-3 draw in November) Tony Brown became the first Albion player to make 500 League appearances.

With Regis, Cunningham, Tony Brown, Bryan Robson, Len Cantello and Willie Johnston all attack-minded Albion were a potent force but as 1977 ended so Ronnie Allen resigned as manager, choosing to reap the rewards offered to him in sunny Saudi Arabia.

Into his place stepped the charismatic former Oxford United player

Ron Atkinson from Cambridge United – and immediately Albion were on TV, in the spotlight, receiving world-wide coverage and a team going places.

Regis, like he had done earlier, scored on his FA Cup debut as Blackpool were swept aside 4-1 in the third round. Although Albion's League form went off the boil, the team made excellent progress in the Cup, seeing off Manchester United 3-2 in a splendid Hawthorns replay, winning by the same score at Derby and then ending Nottingham Forest's long unbeaten run with a competent 2-0 quarter-final victory at home.

The crowds were now flocking to The Hawthorns – almost 37,800 fans saw that Manchester United Cup replay and 36,500 witnessed the Forest tie. Right-back Brendon Batson had arrived from the manager's old club, Cambridge United, to team up with Statham and Ally Brown had been brought back in place of Cross (transferred to West Ham).

Wembley's twin towers were beckoning – but alas, it was not to be, as Albion, failing to rise to the occasion, were beaten 3-1 by Ipswich Town in the semi-final at Highbury. Besides losing the match they also lost skipper John Wile with a nasty head wound, suffered when Brian Talbot put Town in front, and had Mick Martin sent off.

It was disappointment all round, but Albion battled on in the League and finished well, winning six of their remaining nine matches to take sixth position in the table and so qualify for the UEFA Cup. Amassing 50 points, they were only seven behind runners-up Liverpool. It had been a terrific season – especially after Atkinson had arrived – and the future was certainly looking rosy.

Tony Brown with 23 goals was

Brendon Batson, Ally Brown and Bryan Robson each had 41 League outings.

England schoolboy international full-back Martyn Bennett made his Albion debut v Everton and England youth international inside-forward Kevin Summerfield was introduced as a substitute v Derby County. Of the other newcomers, Scottish international goalkeeper David Stewart from Leeds United was unable to get into Albion's first team and left for Swansea City in 1980 without making a League appearance.

The average League attendance at The Hawthorns went up by over 2,500 to 26,702 – Albion's best since 1969-70.

Before the season kicked off properly Albion enjoyed an 8-1 testimonial match success at Motherwell, then visited Syria for two prestige games. At the season's end Albion returned to Denmark for the first time in 70 years to play three friendly matches. The last of these – a 7-0 win over IHF on 31 May was Albion's 76th match – the most they have ever played in one campaign.

On the international scene, Laurie Cunningham won three England caps v Wales, Sweden and Austria. He also played for the 'B' side v Czechoslovakia with Cyrille Regis who came on as a substitute. Bryan Robson played against the Austrian 'B' team, scoring the only goal of the game.

Gary Owen joined Albion from Manchester City in May 1979 for £465,000 and immediately played in two England under-21 internationals v Bulgaria (captain) and Sweden (sub). Bryan Robson also represented his country at this level against Wales, Bulgaria (as sub) and Sweden (one goal) as did Derek Statham, while Regis collected under-21 caps against Denmark, Bulgaria and Sweden, scoring goals in the latter two matches. John Anderson

enjoyed his four more Eire under-21 appearances, playing against USSR Argentina, Hungary and Yugoslavia.

Paddy Mulligan won more Republic of Ireland honours v England (as captain), Denmark, Bulgaria (sub) and West Germany.

Both Laurie Cunningham and Willie Johnson left Albion – joining the Spanish giants Real Madrid and the Canadian club Vancouver Whitecaps respectively, with Cunningham's fee being set at a record £995,000. In his two years at The Hawthorns he had become a real superstar, scoring 30 goals in 114 outings. Johnston – a great favourite with the fans – spent seven years with Albion and netted 28 goals in 261 games. Earlier, in December 1978, Mick Martin was transferred to Newcastle United for £100,000.

In May 1979 Len Cantello was transferred to Bolton Wanderers for £400,000 – leaving immediately after his testimonial match. He scored 21 goals in 369 games for Albion, occupying a variety of positions. A month later Paddy Mulligan rejoined his old buddy Johnny Giles at Shamrock Rovers.

In February 1979, former Welsh international Walter Robbins, an Albion player during the 1930s, died at the age of 68.

1979-80

In July 1979, to replace Johnston, Albion boss Ron Atkinson signed Peter Barnes from Manchester City, paying a club record £748,000 for the England winger. He also added another striker to his squad, bringing in John Deehan from arch rivals Aston Villa for a fee of £424,000. Deehan was the first player to move from Villa Park to The Hawthorns for 70 years – George Harris being the last in 1909. And experienced defender Garry Pendrey arrived from St Andrew's – shortly after

playing for his former club Blues against Albion in his Testimonial match.

This was Albion's Centenary Season and it was celebrated with a 1-0 win over the Dutch side Ajax at The Hawthorns on 11 August.

After a very poor start to the League campaign (only one win from their opening nine matches) Albion recovered reasonably well to finish in a mid-table position of tenth with 41 points. They lost only 12 of their 42 League games but drew a club record 19, including 11 away from home. Ten of the last 15 matches were drawn – six of them 0-0 – and if some of those results had been converted into victories the Baggies would have finished much higher in the table.

Albion claimed two 4-0 home victories over Manchester City in mid-September and Southampton the following month. They also beat Coventry City 4-1 at The Hawthorns and defeated both Bristol City and Crystal Palace 3-0.

Nottingham Forest inflicted the worst defeat on the Baggies, winning 5-1 at The Hawthorns early on in the campaign. Albion also lost 4-0 to one of their bogey sides, Ipswich.

There was an eight-goal thriller on a sodden Hawthorns' pitch in March when Albion were held 4-4 by struggling Bolton Wanderers. Peter Barnes scored a hat-trick for Albion, including two penalties.

Albion failed to make progress in any of the Cup competitions this season. They went out of the League Cup to Norwich City in the fourth round (after a replay) then lost 2-1 at West Ham in the third round of the FA Cup, again in a replay when Tony Brown scored his last ever goal for the club. Albion also crashed out of the UEFA Cup at the first hurdle to the East German side Carl Zeiss Jena, losing both legs, 2-0 away and

HAWTHORNS DIARY

There were also solid 3-0 home wins over Middlesbrough and Norwich and just after Christmas Manchester United were defeated 3-1 in front of more than 30,000 fans at The Hawthorns.

Liverpool gave Albion their worst hiding of the season, winning 4-0 at Anfield while Coventry beat the Baggies 3-0 at Highfield Road.

Albion didn't do too well in Cup competitions, falling to Manchester City in the League Cup after a marathon with Preston North End and losing 1-0 at Middlesbrough in the fourth Road of the FA Cup.

Cyrille Regis top-scored with 17 goals; both Ally Brown and Bryan Robson netted 11 apiece and Peter Barnes weighed in with 10.

Like the previous season goalkeeper Godden and centre-half Wile were both ever-present and up-and-coming midfielder Remi Moses missed just one League game.

The reserves were Central League runners-up, nine points adrift of Liverpool. Goalkeeper Mark Grew played in all 42 games.

The average attendance at The Hawthorns was down considerably to 20,382 – the lowest since 1975-76.

During the season overseas trips were made to Yugoslavia for the Trofeo Marjan tournament, Italy (to Napoli), Kuwait, Sweden and Canada (a short tour of three matches). Albion also travelled to Belfast where they beat Linfield 2-0 in a friendly.

Barnes added four more England caps to his tally, playing against Brazil, Wales, Spain and Switzerland (the latter two as sub). Robson also represented his country against the same four nations as well as performing against Norway, Romania (twice), Scotland, Switzerland again and Hungary.

Four Albion players – Barnes, Brendon Batson, Cyrille Regis and Derek Statham (one goal scored) – played for England 'B' versus the U.S.A. Batson also starred against Australia and Spain and fellow full-back Statham also appeared against Spain and scored.

Moses, after a superb season, was capped by England at under-21 level against Norway (as sub), Switzerland (twice), the Republic of Ireland, Romania and Hungary, while Gary Owen captained the England under-21 side against the Swiss (one goal) and Romania.

On 9 June 1981 Ron Atkinson stunned the club and its supporters by quitting as Albion manager to fill the hot seat at Old Trafford, taking Mick Brown and Brian Whitehouse with him. Into his position – for a second spell as Baggies' boss – stepped Ronnie Allen. On the playing side, Peter Barnes moved to Leeds United for £930,000, a record fee for the Elland Road club, and John Trewick went north to Newcastle United for £234,000.

A sad loss in September 1980 was the death of vice-chairman Tom Silk who was killed with his wife Ruth while piloting his aircraft in the South of France. He was returning from a short break to watch Albion's League Cup-tie at Everton.

In June 1980, FA 'Bert' Millichip was elected chairman of the FA Council.

In July 1981, Billy Gripton, Albion's centre-half from the mid-1940s, died at the age of 61, and shortly afterwards Gripton's successor, Jack Vernon, one of Albion's finest-ever defenders, and an Irish international, who also played for Great Britain and the United Kingdom, died in Belfast. He was also 61 and appeared in 200 games for Albion between 1947 and 1952.

1981-82

Season 1981-82, from Albion's point of view, was bitterly disappointing inasmuch as they lost two Cup semi-finals, both in London and by the same scoreline of 1-0 and had to fight for their lives to stave off relegation; they also went out of the UEFA Cup in the first round and one of the club's finest post-war players – Bryan Robson – was transferred to Manchester United in October for a record £1.5 million, Remi Moses (valued at £500,000) going with him to join their former boss, Ron Atkinson, at Old Trafford.

Tony Brown also left the club – joining Torquay United after 20 years at The Hawthorns during which time he broke records galore.

As Allen sought to get a balanced team he made numerous signings and team changes (some not to the fans' liking) and introduced a new coach, the former Albion wing-half Gerry Summers.

Steve Mackenzie was acquired from Manchester City for £650,000; Andy King arrived from Everton for £445,000 and soon after Robson's departure, the Dutch international Maarten Jol was snapped up from Twente Enschede for £200,000. He was joined later in the season by fellow Dutch international, Romeo Zondervan, who also came from the Enschede club at a similar price. Clive Whitehead (from Bristol City for £100,000) was another recruit while former youth team players Mark Grew, Derek Monaghan, Mickey Lewis, Gary Childs, Alan Webb and Kevin Summerfield, along with Martyn Bennett all got first team outings.

In the First Division Albion's form was very mediocre and they finished 17th in the table, a drop of 13 places from the previous season. At one stage they were staring relegation straight in the face but did just enough towards the end of the campaign to survive the dreaded drop, amassing 44 points, just two clear of the relegation trap-door.

HAWTHORNS DIARY

ing February and March, quickly followed by six successive defeats, saw them slip down to mid-table. However, they ended the campaign well – with a sequence of three wins and a draw – but a final position of 11th could and should have been a lot better.

Occasionally the team produced some exciting football – revenge was gained over Ipswich in excellent style with a 4-1 win in March and Birmingham City were eased out 2-0 in the local derby.

But it was on the whole another disappointing season, emphasised to a certain extent by the average League attendance at The Hawthorns of 15,260 – Albion's lowest in the First Division since 1914-15.

On the overseas front, Albion travelled to the Netherlands to play Twente Enschede and also to Cyprus for a game against a Limasol Select XI.

Regis top-scored with 11 goals followed by Eastoe with 9 and Thompson with seven. Romeo Zondervan made most League appearances (40) and Gary Robson

was introduced to first team football, having two outings as a substitute.

Robson helped Albion's reserves to win the Central League Division One title. Barry Cowdrill skippered the team which lost just five out of 30 games.

Derek Statham played in three internationals for England – against Wales and Australia (twice), while Regis won his fourth cap against West Germany.

Under-21 honours went to Regis (as captain) v Denmark and Owen with two appearances v West Germany (two goals scored).

In March 1983, striker Ally Brown was transferred to Crystal Palace after spending 11 years at The Hawthorns during which time he netted 85 goals in 359 appearances.

David Mills (to Sheffield Wednesday) and Mark Grew (to Leicester City) also moved to pastures new.

In the summer of 1983 centre-half John Wile – after almost 13 years with Albion – moved back to his former club Peterborough United as player-manager. He appeared in 715 first-team games for the Baggies (500 in the Football League) and skippered the team in three Cup semi-finals as well as acting as a terrific ambassador when Albion toured China in 1978. Wile was later to return to the club as chief executive.

In March 1983, the death occurred of former Albion goalkeeper Jimmy Adams, a wartime stalwart, at the age of 75.

At the club's AGM in August 1983, Bert Millichip handed over the position of Albion chairman to Sid Lucas, Millichip himself assuming the role of president. Brian Boundy was elected as vice-chairman.

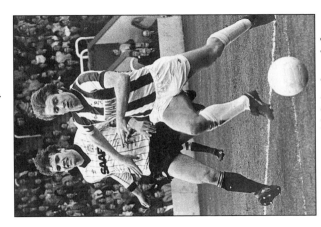

Peter Eastoe (right) signed from Everton in 1982 and in his first season, with eight goals was second-highest scorer behind Cyrille Regis.

down the road to sign Ken McNaught from his old club Aston Villa to fill the centre-half berth vacated by John Wile and the Scotsman made his debut, ironically, at Villa Park on the opening day of the season when Albion lost a seven-goal thriller by 4-3.

Another defeat quickly followed at Stoke, but a six-match unbeaten run pushed Albion up the table, only for them to fall back as they registered just three victories in their next 13 outings and went out of the Milk Cup to Aston Villa after ousting Millwall (5-4 on aggregate) and Chelsea at Stamford Bridge in the opening two rounds. This sudden reverse in fortunes led to Wylie and coach Mike Kelly leaving The Hawthorns (13 December 1983) with Johnny Giles returning to Albion as a replacement, along with coaches 'Nobby' Stiles and Norman Hunter.

But the little Irishman found it tough as Albion continued to lose matches.

Two welcome wins were obtained after Christmas (one of them a 3-1 home triumph over Aston Villa) but things didn't improve all that much on the field and after losing at home to Third Division Plymouth Argyle in the FA Cup and suffering a humiliating 5-0 defeat against Nottingham Forest at The Hawthorns soon afterwards, Giles went out and signed two midfielders – Steve Hunt from Coventry City and Tony Grealish from Brighton.

Both made their debuts in a 1-0 win at Tottenham and with ex-Aston Villa and England winger Tony Morley in good form, Albion slowly eased their way out of trouble with two wins and a couple of draws to finish 17th.

It had been a difficult season all round with chronic injury problems and as a result the average League attendance at The Hawthorns

1983-84

Manager Ron Wylie went four miles

HAWTHORNS DIARY

Albion's worst-ever season – especially at The Hawthorns. Some supporters never even saw them win a match while thousands more were so disappointed and disgruntled after the first two months of the campaign that they either threw away their season tickets or decided to stay at home instead of travelling to The Hawthorns. This resulted in the average League attendance falling yet again to a moderate 12,194.

Only 6,021 spectators turned up for the match with Sheffield Wednesday on 22 April – the lowest since April 1939.

Relegation seemed a formality as early as January.

Tony Brown was appointed first team coach in place of Norman Hunter at the start of the season.

Johnny Giles resigned as manager in September by England World Cup winner and former Manchester United star 'Nobby' Stiles, who in turn, handed over the reins to ex-Aston Villa and Blues' boss Ron Saunders in February 1986.

And Albion went out of the FA Cup in the third round and the Milk Cup (to Aston Villa) in round four, although they did reach the semi-final of the Full Members Cup (beaten by Chelsea).

Throughout the season players shuffled to and from The Hawthorns.

At the start Garth Crooks (ex-Stoke City and Tottenham Hotspur) and Imre Varadi (formerly of Sheffield Wednesday, Newcastle United and Everton) were paired up front to replace Garry Thompson, who went to Hillsborough. Then the lanky George Reilly arrived from Newcastle. He did better towards the end of the season when joined by Craig Madden from Bury. And a certain Steve Bull was also called up, along with Gerry Armstrong, formerly of Tottenham Hotspur, Watford and Real Mallorca, who had starred for Northern Ireland in the 1982 World Cup and fellow countryman Robbie Dennison from Glenavon.

In midfield Welsh international Mickey Thomas (bought from Chelsea) and Martin Dickinson (ex-Leeds United) along with Andy Thompson and Darren Bradley (signed from Aston Villa) joined the two Steves, Hunt and Mackenzie, while Paul Dyson (another former Stoke player) partnered long-serving Ally Robertson at the heart of the defence and Colin Anderson, ex-Torquay United, had a few games at left-back. Stuart Naylor, transferred for £100,000 from Lincoln City, replaced Tony Godden and Paul Bradshaw in goal and three more youth players, David Burrows, Carlton Palmer and Mark Robinson also made their debuts.

Gary Owen, Paul Bradshaw, Mickey Thomas, Jimmy Nicholl, Carl Valentine, Micky Forsyth, Steve Hunt, Garry Armstrong and Tony Godden all left The Hawthorns in the most traumatic of seasons.

Albion started off badly, deteriorated terminally and subsequently suffered relegation for the sixth time at The Hawthorns.

Several unwanted club records were created as Albion plummeted into the Second Division…

- Fewest wins (four).
- Record number of defeats (26).
- Least number of away wins (one).
- Fewest home wins (3).
- Most home defeats (10 from 21 games played), equalling the record set in 1950-51.
- Least number of home points gained (17).
- Fewest number of home goals scored (21).
- Lowest number of points gained (24 – from 42 games).
- Nine consecutive League games lost (between 20 August and 28 September 1985)
- Most players used in a season (34).

Albion, 1985-86. Back row (left to right): Micky Forsyth, Jimmy Nicholl, Martyn Bennett, Tony Godden, Paul Bradshaw, Barry Cowdrill, Carlton Palmer. Middle row: George Wright (physiotherapist), Tony Brown (coach), Gary Robson, Colin Anderson, Nicky Cross, Clive Whitehead, Derek Statham, Steve Hunt, Nobby Stiles (assistant manager). Front row: Carl Valentine, Steve MacKenzie, Johnny Giles (manager), Garth Crooks, Imre Varadi, Tony Grealish.

Wolves), Madden (to Blackpool), Robinson (to Barnsley), Whitehead (to Portsmouth), Grealish (to Manchester City), Crooks and Mackenzie (to Charlton Athletic) and Evans (to Plymouth).

Old favourite Ally Robertson also joined Wolves after 729 appearances for Albion's first team. In 569 games of all types he had played alongside John Wile, the most durable defensive partnership in Albion's history.

In September 1986, Joe Kennedy who helped Albion win promotion in 1949 and the FA Cup in 1954, died at the age of 60.

John Westmancoat left Albion in October 1986 for Birmingham City. her was replaced in office by Gordon Bennett, managing director of Bristol Rovers. Norman Bodell replaced Roy Horobin as chief scout and ex-Burnley goalkeeper Alan Stevenson took over from Tom Cardall – temporarily absconded to Aston Villa – as Commercial manager.

1987-88

Another disastrous season for Albion who finished in their lowest-ever League position – 20th in Division Two – only one point clear of relegation.

Ron Saunders remained in charge for the first month of the campaign before being replaced by Ron Atkinson who became the third manager to return to a second spell at The Hawthorns, following Ronnie Allen and Johnny Giles.

He was faced with a tall order – to refloat a sinking ship.

With coach Colin Addison he set about a difficult task with confidence but the players simply weren't good enough and the results, both at home and away, were sometimes shocking.

There was another swift turn round in players – strikers Andy Gray (ex-Dundee United, Aston

Villa, Wolves, Everton and Scotland) and Stewart Phillips (from Hereford United), winger Tony Morley (for a second time from Den Haag), midfielders Tony Kelly and Brian Talbot (both from Stoke City), defenders Simeon Hodson (from Newport County), Graeme Hogg and Kenny Swain (on loan from Manchester United and Portsmouth respectively), Stacey North (from Luton Town) and goalkeeper Peter Hucker (a loan signing from Oxford United) – all arrived at The Hawthorns, but with Martyn Bennett and Paul Dyson out with long term injuries plus the inevitable suspensions – Atkinson was never really able to field a settled side, Yet The Hawthorns' loyalists stood by their team – and the manager – and, indeed, the average attendance at home games was 10,079, around 800 up on the previous season's figure.

Among some horrible home defeats were those against Leeds United and Millwall (both by 1-4); Swindon Town (1-2, when Tony Kelly was sent off), Blackburn Rovers (0-1) and Reading (0-1), the latter being Albion's worst display of a sorry season.

Quite surprisingly, on their travels Albion should have won at Aston Villa, Middlesbrough and Ipswich – three of the better sides in the Division – and they were unlucky at Plymouth, where they fought back from 1-3 down to draw 3-3, and at Leicester, where they were beaten 3-0. But in truth the side was one of the poorest Albion supporters had seen for years.

Thirty players were used (it was 34 and 28 respectively in 1985-86 and 1986-87)… and there lay the trouble.

Atkinson knew he wanted to strengthen his squad, but money was scarce and one or two senior professionals performed well below par.

Brian Talbot's arrival (in January) certainly made a difference to the midfield, but it was far too late in the day to expect miracles.

In comparison with their League form Albion fared no better in the three Cup competitions they entered, losing in the first round of the Littlewoods Challenge Cup to neighbours Walsall, in the third round of the FA Cup to the eventual winners Wimbledon and in the Simod Cup to Ipswich Town.

One consolation was that Albion's second string gained promotion from the Central League Division Two and won the Birmingham Senior Cup for the first time since 1895.

Andy Gray top-scored this season with ten goals; Tony Morley netted eight. Carlton Palmer made most full League appearances (36) but Goodman played in 40 matches (six as a sub).

A check behind the scenes saw Bert Millichip still holding the position of president. Sid Lucas Brian Boundy, who resigned in June 1988, as vice-chairman.

In August 1988 Lucas himself stood down to be replaced by John Silk.. Other Board members in 1987-88 were Trevor Summers, Joe Brandrick and Mike McGinnity. Gordon Bennett was now Albion's secretary, having replaced John Westmancoat in December 1986.

There were no major international honours for Albion players this season.

On the move in the summer were Martin Dickinson (to Sheffield United), Bobby Williamson (to Rotherham United), Barry Cowdrill (to Bolton Wanderers), Steve Lynex (to Cardiff City) and George Reilly (to Cambridge United).

1988-89

Three newcomers – left-back Arthur Albiston (from Manchester United),

HAWTHORNS DIARY

Ronnie Robinson (to Rotherham United), Andy Gray (to Rangers), Stewart Phillips (top Swansea City), Tony Morley (to Tampa Bay Rowdies), Robert Hopkins (to Birmingham City), Tony Kelly (to Shrewsbury Town) and Paul Dyson (to Darlington).

In August 1988, the death took place in Buxton of former Albion centre-forward Bobby Blood, who scored 26 goals in 153 games between 1921 and 1924. He was 94.

Cliff Edwards, a former Albion half-back and club director, died in March 1989, aged 68.

And in July 1989, the tragic death occurred of Laurie Cunningham, who was killed in a car crash on the outskirts of Madrid. He was just 32 years of age and had scored 30 goals in 114 games for Albion (1977-79).

1989-90

This turned out to be yet another poor season for Albion who finished 20th in the Second Division, equalling their lowest ever League position and for the second time in three years they had to squeeze out of relegation trouble.

A disastrous home record was perhaps responsible for their inept campaign, Albion winning only six and losing nine of their 23 League matches at The Hawthorns, conceding 37 goals in the process, the most by any club at home in the Division.

They also lost to Bradford City 3-1 at home in the Littlewoods Cup before pulling off a miraculous 5-3 victory at Valley Parade in the second leg to go through on the away goal rule. Albion then beat Newcastle 1-0 at St James' Park before going out of the competition to Derby County, who also won 5-0 at The Hawthorns in the Zenith Data Systems Cup-tie between the clubs.

Over 30 players were used in League and Cup competitions with four different goalkeepers employed before the end of September. Manager Brian Talbot utilised five different right backs and five central defenders (No.5) and made eight changes on the left-wing.

Injuries caused a lot problems for the boss who hardly ever fielded an unchanged team. More than 20 players visited the treatment room at various times, three with broken legs. But in all honesty it was inconsistency which was the key to Albion's failure to gain results out on the park.

The team managed no more than two League wins on the trot and Third Division football looked a cast iron certainty after just one victory was recorded in eight games immediately after New Year. During this period Albion surprised their critics by knocking two First Division sides – Charlton Athletic and Wimbledon – out of the FA Cup before losing at home to neighbours Aston Villa.

Twelve vital points were gained with wins over Bradford City and Watford at home and from trips to Hull City and Brighton which lifted the Baggies to safety – but it was mighty close.

The best win of the season was a 7-0 hammering of Barnsley, a game which marked the end of Martyn Bennett's career with Albion. He retired from League action with a back injury after more than 200 outings for the club. And manager Brian Talbot quit as a player at the season's end after more than 21 years in the game.

Newcomers in the Baggies' camp included John Thomas (from Bolton Wanderers), Gary Hackett and Steve Parkin (both from Stoke City), Irish international Bernard McNally (Shrewsbury Town), former England international Mark Barham, ex-Walsall star Craig Shakespeare (from Sheffield Wednesday), Graham Harbey (Ipswich Town) and Gary Bannister (Coventry City). Among the few youngsters to emerge were defender Daryl Burgess and striker Adrian Foster.

Don Goodman was leading scorer with 21 goals; Chris Whyte (44), Tony Ford (42), and Bernard McNally (41) appeared in most League games and the average attendance at The Hawthorns was 11,313 – around 1,400 down on the previous season's figure.

In the summer The Hawthorns pitch was completely returfed.

Players on the move included Chris Whyte (to Leeds United for £550,000), Kevin Bartlett (Notts County), Martyn Bennett (Worcester City), Paul Bradshaw (Peterborough United), Gavin Ward (Cardiff City), Mark Barham (Brighton) and John Thomas (Preston North End).

In November 1989, the former Albion wing of the 1930s, Jimmy 'Spud' Murphy, a wing-half who played for Wales and managed Manchester United, died at the age of 81. He had been the Welsh international team manager for eight years: 1955-63.

1990-91

At 4.44pm on Saturday 11 May 1991, Albion were relegated to the Third Division for the first time in the club's history after what was their worst ever season of League football, even surpassing that dreadful 1985-86 campaign.

A dejected chairman John Silk admitted that it was a 'black day' for all Albion supporters, but vowed 'we'll be back.'

That was no consolation for the loyal followers, however, who had backed the team all down the line during a traumatic season in which the average home attendance rose by 688 to 12,001.

It was amazing that Albion ended

Kevin Donovan's great diving header in the 3-2 home win over Wolves in September 1993.

1993-94

Albion began the 1993-94 season without Ossie Ardiles. The friendly and likeable Argentinian quit The Hawthorns, to the obvious disappointment of the board, players and, indeed, the supporters, to take charge of his former club Tottenham Hotspur. Chairman Trevor Summers quickly promoted Keith Burkinshaw to the manager's chair, stating that it was of prime importance that continuity should be maintained.

It proved to be a difficult and at times very tense season as Albion, attempting to consolidate themselves in the First Division, scrambled to safety on the very last day of the campaign by virtue of a nail-biting 1-0 victory at Fratton Park against Portsmouth; Lee Ashcroft's header did the trick, much to the relief of the 10,000 travelling Baggies' supporters. Anything else than a win would have sent the Baggies straight back down from where they had just escaped.

Surprisingly, Albion played well during the opening two months or so, actually rising to fourth in the table. But by mid-October they were right down amongst the strugglers and although they picked up around Christmas time, moving up to 16th, thereafter it was a real battle for survival. Injuries and suspensions were frequent and only occasionally was the manager able to field an unchanged side.

Nevertheless certain players performed well below par for far too long and although Bob Taylor and Andy Hunt claimed 30 League goals between them, Albion's overall scoring record let them down badly, especially away from home where they netted less than one goal a game.

In the FA Cup Albion made an inglorious exit from the competition, losing 2-1 at non-League Halifax Town, a truly dreadful result. Albion also took part in the Coca-Cola Cup (losing to Chelsea) and played six matches in the revamped Anglo-Italian Cup.

Thirty players were called into action including newcomers Neil Parsley and Kieran O'Regan (both secured from Huddersfield Town), Ashcroft (bought from Preston North End for £225,000), defender Paul Mardon and midfielder David Smith (both from Birmingham City) and left-back Paul Edwards, signed from Wolves.

Two loan players – striker Graham Fenton (Aston Villa) and left-back Paul Williams (Coventry City) – added some impetus to the side, but despite pleas from the fans Albion failed to secure the transfer of the latter on a permanent basis.

Taylor with 21 goals was again Albion's leading scorer. Defender Daryl Burgess made the most League appearances (43) and the average League attendance at The Hawthorns was a creditable 16,868 – a rise of 1,707 on the 1992-93 figure.

And to the delight of the fans Albion beat arch rivals Wolves twice this season.

Another bonus was the reserve team's winning promotion from the Pontins League Division Two under the guidance of former player and now coach John Trewick.

Players leaving The Hawthorns included Wayne Fereday (to Cardiff City), Gary Hackett (Peterborough United), Simon Garner and Nicky Reid (Wycombe Wanderers) and Kwame Ampadu (Swansea City).

In the summer of 1994, Trevor Summers relinquished his position of chairman, handing over the seat to Tony Hale. Clive Stapleton became vice-chairman in November.

During the close season The Hawthorns pitch was re-laid with enhanced drainage.

1994-95

Like it had been in 1993-94, Albion were again involved in a battle to stave off relegation – and once more they just managed to hold on to their First Division status, avoiding the drop with two games remaining following a 0-0 home draw with Derby County.

HAWTHORNS DIARY

and Andy Hunt and defenders Paul Mardon and Paul Raven in fine form.

By the end of October with 13 games played but no longer in the Coca-Cola Cup (beaten by Reading in round 2), Albion travelled to Millwall knowing that victory would take them to the top. But they were beaten 2-1 and this reverse set the Baggies on an astonishing run of successive League defeats, with only one win coming in the next 15 games.

Manager Alan Buckley refused to panic and despite a 4-3 FA Cup defeat at Crewe, Albion slowly but surely got themselves back on track, although they did miss out on a trip to Wembley by losing to Port Vale in the area final of the Anglo-Italian Cup.

Into the camp came veteran goalkeeper Nigel Spink (from Villa Park), full-backs Paul Holmes (from Everton) and Shane Nicholson (from Derby), on-loan midfielder Peter Butler (from Notts County) and Dutchman Richard Sneekes (a £400,000 buy from Bolton). And with Sneekes in excellent goalscoring form (he netted ten times in the last 13 matches) Albion eased themselves up to a creditable 11th spot in the table after collecting 24 points out of 39 during the last third of the campaign – a campaign which was split into three, each completely different in terms of performances.

Taylor skippered the side during the second half of the season and was top marksman with 23 goals. He netted his first hat-trick for the Baggies (in a 4-4 draw with Watford) and claimed his 100th for the club in the final League game v promoted Derby County.

Daryl Burgess and Andy Hunt appeared in most League games (45 each) and the average League attendance at The Hawthorns was 15,166 – up by around 850 on the previous season.

Among the players leaving Albion were veteran goalkeeper of more than 400 senior appearances Stuart Naylor, who moved to Bristol City, Tony Rees went to Merthyr Tydfil, Paul Edwards joined Hednesford Town and Mike Phelan went to Norwich City.

At international level this season the only honour went to central defender Paul Mardon who earned a Welsh cap when he came on as a substitute against Germany.

In February 1996, former Albion goalkeeper Bill Harris died, aged 77 and another 'keeper, Jock Wallace, died in July 1996, aged 61.

1996-97

Yet another very ordinary season for Albion who struggled to finish a moderate 16th in the First Division. And they also went out of both Cup competitions in the opening rounds, losing to Third Division minnows Colchester United in the Coca-Cola Cup and to Premiership outfit Chelsea in the FA Cup. A pre-season success, however, was forthcoming when Albion won the Isle of Man Festival Trophy by winning their three games without conceding a goal.

Expectations were thus high when the League programme kicked off, especially after that splendid late surge of goals from the Dutchman Richard Sneekes at the end of the previous campaign.

But alas, Albion started off disappointingly and never recovered – pointingly and never recovered – and the fans soon started to show their disgust, more so after arch rivals Wolves came to The Hawthorns and won 4-2.

Canadian goal-ace Paul Peschisolido's outings were restricted because of international call-ups; fellow striker Bob Taylor couldn't get fully fit; defender Paul Mardon was also sidelined through injury; ex-Grimsby Town goalkeeper Paul

Crichton never endeared himself to the supporters and midfielder Peter Butler missed the first four months owing to an injury suffered in a behind doors pre-season friendly against Coventry City.

Manager Alan Buckley switched his line-up around as best he could in an effort to find a winning formula, yet with the odd exception here and there Albion failed to impress as a unit and indeed, failed to maintain any sort of consistency, except for a brief unbeaten period approaching Christmas.

After losing to Chelsea in the Cup – when Australian defender Shaun Murphy made an impressive debut – and going down again to Wolves, Buckley's job was put on the line. That line snapped soon afterwards and he was sacked; this allowed former Blackburn Rovers boss Ray Harford to take over, bringing with him ex-Baggies' favourite Cyrille Regis as coach, accompanied by John Trewick.

At this juncture (February) Albion were in relegation trouble, but the form of the teams below them didn't improve and so they survived, ending up 13 points clear of the trap door.

Among the new faces who came into The Hawthorns camp this season were Australian-born right-back Andy McDermott (secured from Q.P.R. for £400,000), midfielders Paul Groves (bought from Grimsby for £600,000) and Graham Potter (enrolled from Southampton), Peschisolido (another £600,000 buy from Birmingham City), goalkeeper Alan Miller (signed for £400,000 from Middlesbrough, who, in fact, had been on loan at Albion in 1991) and Shaun Murphy (from Notts County).

Albion's best wins were those of 5-1 at home and 4-2 away over Norwich City, Peschisolido netting a hat-trick at Carrow Road and 4-0 v

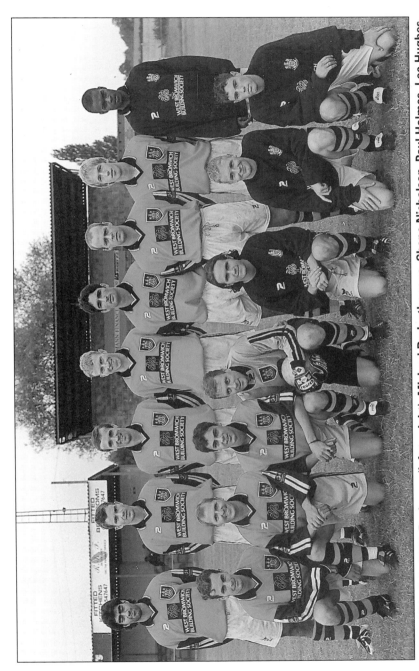

Albion XI in July 1997. Back row (left to right): Michael Rodosthenous, Shane Nicholson, Paul Holmes, Lee Hughes, Shaun Murphy, Tony Dobson, Graham Potter, Darren Cunningham. Front Row: Darren Bowman, Dave Gilbert, Dean Bennett, Paul Crichton, Dean Craven, Carl Tranter, Adam Buckley.

latter game attracting a 23,013 attendance at The Hawthorns.

Albion, in fact, topped the table in early September and were hardly out of the top four until Christmas; they had reached the third round of the Coca-Cola Cup before losing to mighty Liverpool. But once into the New Year their form went pear-shaped. Confidence seemed to drain away and although they just about kept in touch with the promotion contenders until mid-February, there was no way the team was going to make the Play-offs. And so it proved.

It must be said that Albion scrambled a series of home wins to keep them in the top bracket but their away form at times was very poor. They even crashed to arch rivals Aston Villa 4-0 in the FA Cup and were slammed 5-0 at The Valley by Premiership-bound Charlton Athletic. One consolation was that they won at Molineux and so completed the double over Wolves, both scorelines finishing 1-0.

But on the other foot, all three rele-

gated clubs took points off Albion – Manchester City did the double, Stoke managed two draws and Reading won at Elm Park.

One consolation was that Albion mastered the Potters 3-1 in an FA Cup-tie at The Hawthorns in January (Denis Smith's first win as the Baggies' manager and against his former team) and so ended a long chapter of failure against one of their bogey clubs.

Injuries to key players didn't help matters and during the course of the season 34 players were called into action by the two managers.

On the bright side a £250,000 signing from Kidderminster Harriers, Lee Hughes, did exceedingly well in his first season of League football, finishing joint top-scorer with Andy Hunt on 14 goals.

Matt Carbon and Sean Flynn, both of whom were signed from Derby County, battled hard and long in defence and midfield respectfully; Northern Ireland international James Quinn, a £500,000 capture from

Blackpool, did well as an attacking midfielder once he had settled down and record buy Kevin Kilbane, a left-winger who cost £1.25 million from Preston North End, played in 50 of Albion's 53 first team matches this term. Another Irishman, Mickey Evans, arrived from Southampton for £750,000 and loanees James Thomas (Blackburn Rovers), Paul Beesley (Manchester City) and ex-Liverpool star Steve Nicol (from Sheffield Wednesday) plus winger Franz Carr all had outings as did Australian international full-back Jason Van Blerk, also from Manchester City

Unfortunately this was to be the last time strikers Andy Hunt and Bob Taylor were to wear Baggies' shirts. They both left The Hawthorns on 'free transfers' at the end of the season – Hunt to newly-promoted Charlton Athletic and Taylor to relegated Bolton Wanderers where he had been on loan since January. Between them Hunt and Taylor scored 198 goals for Albion in a com-

sible 46 – and the average League attendance at The Hawthorns was 14,582 – a drop of more than 2,000 on the 1997-98 figure...which was a big concern to the Board.

Albion debutants this season were the two Italians – Bortolazzi and Maresca – DeFreitas and Phil Whitehead, teenagers Gabbiadon, Oliver and Justin Richards and winger Mark Angel.

And Jason Van Blerk set a new club record by collecting 13 yellow cards.

On the international scene Kevin Kilbane (Republic of Ireland) and James Quinn (Northern Ireland) both represented their country at senior level; Daniel Gabbiadon played for the Welsh under-21s, likewise Kilbane for the Republic of Ireland under-21 side while at youth team level Adam and James Chambers, besides being the first set of twins ever to play in an Albion team, also became the first twins to appear in the same England side when they came on as substitutes in the Nigeria under 20 international tournament in April 1999. Teenagers Enzo Maresca (Italy juniors and under 18) and Adam Oliver (England under 18 and under 20) were also honoured this season.

During 1998-99 five Albion players – Chris Adamson (to IK Brage in Sweden and Mansfield Town), defenders Tony Dobson (Gillingham), Paul Mardon (Oldham Athletic) and Paul Raven (Rotherham United) and striker Brian Quailey (Exeter City) – all went out on loan. Dobson later moved to Northampton Town while goalkeeper Paul Crichton was transferred to Burnley and Stacy Coldicott went to Grimsby Town for £100,000.

At Board level Paul Thompson quit in February 1999 to be replaced six weeks later by the former chairman of West Midlands Travel Don Colston.

Albion also swapped goalkeeping coaches – former Irish international Gerry Peyton (appointed October 1998 in place of Eric Steele) being replaced in February by Tony Parks,

the ex-Spurs and Falkirk custodian who was still registered as a player with Scarborough, managed by former Albion No.2 Colin Addison.

Nick Worth (from Burnley) came into the club as the new physiotherapist in place of Paul Mitchell who returned to Grimsby and Albion also employed fitness coach/dietitian Frank Nuttall, who had been a player with Celtic.

Bobby Hope, the former Albion midfield star, became the club's youth development liaison officer under youth development manager John Trewick and this meant that five 1970s playing stalwarts: John Wile, Cyrille Regis, Trewick, Hope and Ally Brown (steward of the nearby Throstles' supporters' club) were all back with Albion in one guise or another.

In the latter months of 1998 two former Albion goalkeepers died – Dick Sheppard (of a heart attack in November) and John Osborne (from cancer in December). In February 1999 Arthur Mann, former Albion assistant-manager, was tragically killed in an accident at his Birmingham place of work involving a fork lift truck. He was 51 and played for Manchester City against Albion in the 1970 League Cup Final at Wembley.

1999-2000

Soon after the 1998-99 League season had ended two established West Bromwich Albion directors - Barry Hurst (on 17 May) and Clive Stapleton (23 May) - both resigned from the board and in the aftermath of their departure leading shareholders, guided by former Albion director and millionaire businessman Paul Thompson, called an Emergency General Meeting scheduled for 8 July, whereby it was anticipated that chairman Tony Hale's position might come under threat.

Thus, at the time of going to print the immediate composition of the Albion board remained unsure.

Also behind the scenes at The

Hawthorns, manager Denis Smith's assistant, Malcolm Crosby, left Albion to take up a coaching position with Premiership club Derby County and into his place Smith was considering upgrading former player and coach Cyrille Regis.

Striker Lee Hughes, who dropped a bombshell shortly before the end of the previous campaign, was offered a substantial pay rise to stay at The Hawthorns.

Ex-Albion player and manager Bobby Gould quit his position as manager of Wales and another former Albion boss, Ossie Ardiles, became manager-coach of Croatia Zagreb.

Meanwhile Albion's playing preparations for the 1999-2000 season began with a tour of Denmark in July and the last campaign of the 20th century commenced in earnest on Saturday, 7 August when Albion entertained Norwich City at The Hawthorns prior to an intriguing Worthington League Cup encounter at Halifax.

Manager Denis Smith and his coaching staff, along with the players, were quietly confident that 1999-2000 would be a good season for Albion. However, in July, Smith left Albion and in August, Brian Little was appointed. But as far as the supporters were concerned, deep down they firmly believed that once again a lot of pressure would be placed on the shoulders of hot-shot Lee Hughes (if he stayed at The Hawthorns).

If he could come up with another 25-30 goals and his fellow strikers could weigh in with a similar number, then who knows what might transpire.

A top six finish is certainly within Albion's capabilities. Anything less would be a major disappointment - again!

So let's hope that Albion can celebrate the year 2000 in style and likewise celebrate their 100th year at The Hawthorns by playing in the Premiership for the first time ever.

Time will tell.

24 September 1904 v Doncaster Rovers won 6-1 (Division 2)

Only 5,261 spectators turned up for this game, and they had to endure a tedious first half when Albion scored once – on 20 minutes when George Dorsett's shot-cum-centre flew into the net after deflecting off Harry Aston's shoulder. After the break however, Albion were unstoppable and they gave Rovers a real walloping. In the 50th minute Bill Davies' corner was converted by Dorsett; on the hour mark another delightful Davies flag-kick led to Albert Lewis finding the net and in the 67th minute Walter Jack headed in Aston's cross for 4-0. A fine dribble and shot by in-form Dorsett made it 5-0 in the 75th minute and with ten minutes left Jack scored again from Davies' cross. Len Hyde pulled a goal back for Rovers with time running out.

11 November 1905 v Bradford City won 6-1 (Division 2)

Albion, with four straight wins under their belts, scored twice in the first ten minutes through Fred Shinton, and Adam Haywood. In the 33rd minute Andy McGeachan replied for Bradford from a corner, but two minutes later Shinton made it 3-1. It was all Albion in the second half. Simmons lashed in a rebound to make it 4-1 and after City's Jack Halliday had gone off and Jimmy Conlin was sent-off, Albion made good use of the space to score twice more through Shinton and Simmons. The attendance was 9,000.

26 December 1905 v Barnsley won 5-3 (Division 2)

An eventful encounter saw Albion, unbeaten in 11 games, twice come from behind despite playing the last 40 minutes with only ten men. Barnsley scored first in the tenth minute after a defensive mix-up but

Fred Shinton was in terrific form for Albion in the 1900s and in the games against Bradford City, Barnsley and Grimsby he especially shone.

Simmons quickly equalised. In the 22nd minute Billy Law crossed for Shinton to put Albion in front. But back came Barnsley who drew level right on half-time. After Albion had been reduced to ten men when George Young went off injured, Jack Manners sliced the ball into his own net to put visitors ahead at 3-2. But urged on by 23,021 fans, they were level through Shinton on 72 minutes and four minutes later Simmons put Albion in front at 4-3. Simmons then completed his hat-trick to give Albion a fine win.

25 December 1906 v Grimsby Town won 6-1 (Division 2)

Over 19,000 fans saw Albion make it six home wins on the trot. Tom Dilly scored the Baggies' opening goal on 15 minutes. Two minutes later Adam Haywood added a second from Dilly's pass and four minutes after that Shinton fired in number three. Grimsby's Fred Robinson reduced the deficit with a header on 50 minutes before hot-shot Shinton scored three fine goals in 12 minutes

21 December 1907 v Lincoln City won 5-2 (Division 2)

In front of 7,000 fans, Albion fell behind to a Billy Langham goal on 25 minutes. But soon afterwards Buck was tripped in the area, and the same player got up to score from the spot. Albion ran the show after and in the 77th minute David Walker gave them the lead. Two minutes later Jordan made it 3-1. Lincoln hit back and after Jesse Pennington had miskicked Langham scored his second goal. Albion were then awarded a second penalty but this time Jim Saunders saved Buck's shot. Amazingly two minutes later Albion got a third spot kick and this time Walker scored with ease. Harry Wilcox rounded things off with a fifth goal on 88 minutes. Thus in a 12 minute spell five goals (one a penalty) were netted and another penalty missed.

2 January 1909 v Grimsby Town won 7-0 (Division 2)

Albion extended their unbeaten League run to 13 matches with this crushing win over the Mariners. Kicking with the wind towards the Birmingham Road goal, Albion got off to a flying start on a heavy pitch when debutant Sid Bowser latched on to a Buck pass to score in the second minute. On 15 minutes Bill Garraty set up Bowser for goal number two and after Buck had shot wide from the penalty spot on 27 minutes Garraty swept in Albion's third goal ten minutes from half-time.

Another smart goal from Buck followed in the 48th minute and 24 minutes later Albion were 5-0 up thanks to a terrific long range shot by Jack Manners. Sixty seconds later, with Grimsby's defence in tatters, Thompson's centre was put away by

to sew up the points, the impressive Haywood assisting in all of them.

scored with a low drive to the keeper's right. Bob Pailor made it 3-1 on 52 minutes with a splendid shot from distance and the same player scored again 12 minutes later with another powerful drive. Boswer then hit the post as Albion kept up the pressure.

26 September 1914 v Liverpool won 4-0 (Division 1)

Over 18,000 fans, some of them Belgian refugees, saw Liverpool, runners-up in the FA Cup Final only five months earlier, blitzed by a keen Albion side for whom England amateur international Harold Bache played superbly well. Alf Bentley opened the scoring on 13 minutes after some fine work by Bache and Fred Morris.

Morris then nipped in with a second goal on 40 minutes following some clever play by Shearman and Bache. Nine minutes after the restart Morris netted his second and Albion's third goal from Louis Bookman's centre and with ten minutes remaining Bentley added a fourth with a 12-yard shot.

Sadly, just over 16 months later, Harold Bache, who made such a sensational impact in this match as an unorthodox centre-forward, lay dead on a Flanders battlefield.

25 October 1919 v Notts County won 8-0 (Division 1)

Albion, minus four key players but with eight wins to their credit from their first ten matches, outplayed County before a 36,086 crowd with Morris scoring five goals. His first came in the ninth minute when he blasted Howard Gregory's pass beyond Albert Iremonger in the County goal. His second – after enormous Albion pressure – arrived in the 40th minute when he netted confidently after a fine 35-yard solo run. In the 51st minute he completed his hat-trick with another well-

Fred Morris scored five goals against Notts County in October 1919.

taken shot following Gregory's adroit square ball, and then County's defender Jack Foster turned Jack Crisp's centre into his own net to make it 4-0 after 61 minutes. Morris duly added two more goals in quick succession – his fourth in 70th minute was set up by the marauding Crisp (making it 11 goals in 11 games for the striker) and two minutes later he put Albion 6-0 in front after Crisp had again manufactured an opening. Gregory sneaked in unnoticed to claim Albion's seventh goal in the 79th minute after Morris had struck the bar and with five minutes remaining Tommy Magee notched number eight, darting through a huge gap in the County defence to score with ease.

26 December 1919 v Sunderland won 4-0 (Division 1)

A crowd of 43,579 saw this Boxing Day encounter at a rain-swept Hawthorns and it was Albion who pulled all the crackers on their way to a first ever Division One champi-

onship, to record their fifth successive League victory.

Their first goal came on 14 minutes when Magee scored a disputed goal after he cashed in on a weak back pass by Bob Young. It was tit-for-tat up to the break but then it was all Albion. In the 52nd minute Morris put away a back-header from Bentley following Crisp's cross. In the 75th minute Gregory sent Morris through for his second goal and two minutes from time Bentley scored from six yards. Bobby McNeal's shot almost split the crossbar in the closing minutes and Crisp had a 'goal' ruled out for offside right at the death.

1 May 1920 v Chelsea won 4-0 (Division 1)

Before kick-off the First Division championship trophy was presented to Albion's skipper Pennington, who proudly held it aloft to the delight of the home supporters in the 35,668 crowd.

Albion had already scored 100 League goals prior to this game, needing one more to beat Sunderland's record for most in the top Division ...and they did just that on 17 minutes when McNeal, bursting into the penalty area, hammered the ball home from 12 yards after excellent work by Andy Smith, Gregory and Morris.

Albion's second goal arrived in the 46th minute. A long cross, pumped high into the air by Crisp, was headed on by Gregory. Chelsea's 'keeper Jim Molyneux palmed the ball away, but the referee and linesman agreed that it had crossed the line.

Four minutes, Smith, moving on to Morris's short pass, cracked in a beauty from 15 yards and in the 58th minute Bentley scored from close range after Gregory and Crisp and teased the Chelsea defence.

SOME MEMORABLE VICTORIES

made it 5-1 seven minutes from time with a drive from 20 yards. An attendance of 16,227 saw Albion go to the top of the table after this result.

24 October 1925 v West Ham United won 7-1 (Division 1)

After winning only three of their opening ten League games of the season Albion had the better of the first half and led 3-0 at the interval. In the 22nd minute Hammers' left-half Albert Cadwell handled, allowing Stan Davies to net the spot-kick. Six minutes later Glidden scored with a fine cross-shot from Carter's pass and two minutes before the break Davies fired home from Glidden's centre. Seven minutes into the second half 'Tug' Wilson hit Albion's fourth goal and in the 64th minute – after Glidden had struck

the bar – Carter made it 4-0. Jimmy Ruffell reduced Albion's lead in the 73rd minute with a penalty after a foul by Fred Reed on Watson. But Albion scored twice more through Davies (his hat-trick) in the 79th minute and Carter in the 81st to win in a canter. The attendance was 20,851.

12 March 1927 v Aston Villa won 6-2 (Division 1)

On a chilly but bright afternoon in front of 50,392 fans Albion won the toss and attacked the Smethwick End. After dominating the first half, they had only one goal to show for their efforts, a 21st-minute shot from Glidden. Carter put Albion 2-0 up in the 50th minute and nine minutes later Davies netted from close range. Just past the hour mark Davies slammed in Albion's fourth

goal and two minutes later Glidden made it 5-0. Villa reduced the deficit through Dicky York in the 73rd minute, but Sammy Short restored Albion's five-goal lead on 83 minutes, only for York to round off the scoring with a late strike for outplayed Villa. Remarkably, at this stage in the season, Villa were in fifth place and Albion last and doomed to relegation.

17 September 1927 v Blackpool won 6-3 (Division 2)

This game was a triumph for Albion's centre-forward Jimmy Cookson who scored a double hat-trick. A crowd of 20,203 saw him claim his first goal in the sixth minute before Blackpool drew level through Sid Tuffnell on 33. In the second half it was action all the way. In the 47th minute Peter Thorpe handled and Cookson smashed in the penalty. Ten minutes later Cookson completed his first 'hat-trick' by gliding in a Glidden pass. Tuffnell reduced the arrears, but then Cookson blasted in his second hat-trick in the space of seven min-

Jimmy Cookson, scorer of all six goals when Blackpool came under the hammer in September 1927.

SOME MEMORABLE VICTORIES

W. G. Richardson heads home Glidden's right-wing cross against Charlton at The Hawthorns in May 1931 – and Albion have achieved the unique double of FA Cup and promotion.

Glidden drilled in number three after Richardson had done the spade-work. A George Shaw penalty – awarded for a foul on Glidden – put Albion 4-0 ahead on 77 minutes and Glidden completed the rout with a fifth goal a minute from time.

2 May 1931 v Charlton Athletic won 3-2 (Division 2)

Having beaten Birmingham 2-1 at Wembley the previous Saturday and

followed up with a crucial 1-0 League win at Stoke on Thursday afternoon, Albion had to win this final game of the season to clinch that unique FA Cup and promotion double, and 52,415 fans saw them do just that. Dai Astley put the visitors ahead after eight minutes. Albion equalised in the 37th minute through Teddy Sandford only for Astley to edge Charlton back in front 45 seconds later. But Albion

stuck to their task and a minute before half-time Glidden equalised. The second half was nerve-wracking, and it was Albion who grabbed the all-important goal in the 68th minute when W. G. Richardson headed Glidden's right-wing cross beyond 'keeper Robertson to clinch victory – and the double.

3 October 1931 v Derby County 4-0 (Division 1)

In front of the biggest crowd at The Hawthorns so far this season – 33,192 – Albion, with only two defeats against them in their previous 13 League games, put on an excellent display to beat a dogged County side who gave as good as they got in the first half. All four goals were splendidly taken, even Shaw's penalty opener on two minutes. Skipper Glidden fired in number two five minutes after half-time; Sandford rattled in Albion's third from 25 yards two minutes later and right on time W. G. Richardson ran forward to slot in number four after good work by Stan Wood.

26 December 1932 v Sunderland 5-1 (Division 1)

A crowd of 26,113 attended this Boxing Day treat and those present

Joe Carter helped Albion to a fine Boxing Day win over Sunderland in 1932.

Albion's Cup winning players are introduced to the crowd before beating Charlton to take the 1931 double.

Arthur Gale laid on a goal for W. G. Richardson and then scored himself with a diving header against Middlesbrough in January 1935.

was fouled by Bert Trentham) Boyes fired Albion back in front from Richardson's neat through ball. Boyes' cross was converted by Gale's diving header on 27 minutes (3-1) and five minutes after the interval Camsell burst through to make it 3-2. The 'Boro centre-forward then had a goal disallowed before Sandford beat two defenders to slam in Albion's fourth goal, only for Ernie Coleman to reduce the score to 4-3 on 67 minutes. But Albion had the final say with two more goals – a 25-yard special fired into the top right-hand corner of the net by Sandford and an excellent over-head hook shot from Carter.

7 December 1935 v Everton won 6-1 (Division 1)

Before taking on Everton Albion had lost three games on the bounce, scoring only one goal, but in front of 17,151 fans they hit top form and ran up a convincing 6-1 scoreline

which could easily have been doubled – all this after the Merseysiders had taken a shock third-minute lead when Jimmy Cunliffe tucked away Dixie Dean's headed pass.

Albion responded quickly and within 40 seconds W. G. Richardson had equalised from Wood's inviting centre. Two minutes later Carter's through ball was hammered home by winger Mahon and on the quarter-of-an-hour mark Richardson notched his second goal and Albion's fourth when he drove home Cookson's pass. At this juncture Albion were flying. Visiting 'keeper Ted Sagar then made three fine saves before Sandford, after beating three defenders, saw his 20-yard drive saved but followed up to net the rebound on 36 minutes.

Everton were stunned again four minutes before half-time when Carter scored following a deep free-kick by Shaw and another Sandford shot. Albion continued to press in the second half but managed only one more goal – Mahon blasting home Richardson's right-wing corner in the 53rd minute.

18 January 1936 v Blackburn Rovers won 8-1 (Division 1)

After scoring ten goals in the previous two home games, Albion were unstoppable against Rovers and netted another five in the first 20 minutes.

On seven minutes two Rovers' defenders – Jimmy Gorman and Arnold Whiteside – kicked at the ball together. It flew to W. G. Richardson who netted from close range. Fifty seconds later Mahon, free on the left, fired home number two via an upright.

In the tenth minute Richardson made a goal for Walter Robbins and five minutes later Mahon, cutting inside his full-back, scored also off a post as 'keeper Cliff Binns slipped.

In the 20th minute, a stinging

drive by Sandford was spilled by Binns and Jack Sankey was on hand to fire home a half-volley.

In a rare attack Rovers pulled a goal back on 30 minutes when Jack Thompson smashed in a penalty after Trentham had handled, Thompson having put the ball in the net initially.

After the break Albion came again and in the 59th minute, Stan Wood's splendid cross was crashed home left-footed by Richardson. The same player then completed his hat-trick in the 78th minute, finding the net with a stinging 20-yard drive.

Albion's eighth and final goal was claimed by Mahon in the 89th minute, the winger scoring easily from Sandford's pass to claim his hat-trick.

1 February 1936 v Liverpool won 6-1 (Division 1)

A fortnight after that superb victory over Blackburn, Albion were back on the goal-trail with another great home win, this time over Liverpool in front of 23,080 spectators.

Albion scored first on four minutes when Wood's low centre from the left was fired in by W. G. Richardson. But Liverpool hit back and equalised on 11 minutes when Jack Balmer converted Freddie Howe's precise cross.

Four minutes later Albion regained the lead through Mahon, who found space to net Wood's low pass. Albion continued to dominate; Richardson and Carter hit the woodwork and Liverpool's giant South African goalkeeper Arthur Riley made three stunning saves in quick succession.

Seven minutes into the second half Richardson whipped in Sandford's pass to make it 3-1 and seven minutes later Albion's centre-forward drilled in Wood's centre for his hat-trick.

with an 18-yard drive. Sammy Heaslegrave made it

2-0 with a downward header in the 36th minute from Johnson's high corner and three minutes later Johnson himself cut in from the left to grab Albion's third.

Albion's 'keeper Jimmy Adams then saved Reg Halton's 50th minute penalty, awarded for a foul by Sankey on Les Hart, before Johnson whipped in an unstoppable cross shot in the 61st minute to give his side a 4-0 lead.

Johnson was on fire at this stage and on 76 minutes he completed his first Albion hat-trick following a goalmouth melee, and eight minutes from time the England left-winger notched his fourth goal and Albion's sixth, by tapping home from close range after Harry Jones had bent the crossbar with a superb right-footed shot.

23 November 1946 v Fulham won 6-1 (Division 2)

A crowd of 20,243 saw Albion's for-ward-line in sparkling form against the Cottagers, whose defenders were fully extended as they tried to stop the flood of attacks.

Albion took the lead on seven minutes when Clarke headed in full-back Shaw's deep free-kick from the left. Four minutes later it was 2-0 when Irish international Dave Walsh, taking Clarke's pass in his stride, held off two challenges to fire low past 'keeper Ted Hinton.

On 16 minutes Billy Elliott crossed from the right, Walsh's header was parried by Hinton, but Clarke was on hand to find the net.

Fulham clawed a goal back in the 35th minute when Albion's debu-tant 'keeper Tom Grimley let Ronnie Rooke's shot slip from his grasp and Bob Thomas netted from eight yards.

Ten minutes after half-time Albion made it 4-1 when Walsh set

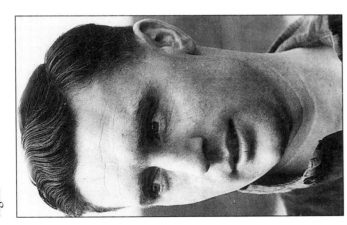

Dave Walsh held off two defenders to score in the 6-1 win over Fulham in November 1946.

up Clarke. He laid the ball off to Ray Barlow who scored to the 'keeper's right.

In the 64th minute Elliott and Clarke combined down the right, allowing Frank Hodgetts to steal in from the left to net from close range (5-1) and in the 85th minute Doug Witcomb centred for Barlow to score his second of the match and give Albion a 6-1 win.

17 April 1948 v Bradford won 6-0 (Division 2)

Having registered just two wins in their previous 12 League games and three in their last 18, this was a long overdue success for Albion, whose performance in front of 13,349 fans was one of their best for some con-siderable time. Yet surprisingly it took the Baggies over 20 minutes to score their first goal.

Following a series of attacks down the right, Arthur Taylor's per-sistence enabled Jack Haines to fire Albion in front in the 23rd minute. Just 90 seconds later Haines' pass was converted by Roy Finch (2-0). Finch then set up the hard-working

Taylor for Albion's third goal six minutes after half-time, before Arthur Rowley hit a post with a 55th minute penalty after Bradford's goalkeeper Tom Farr had brought down Taylor.

Five minutes later though, Haines scored a brilliant fourth goal for Albion from Taylor's astute pass and in the 69th minute Taylor netted himself from Rowley's through ball. With time running out Haines com-pleted his hat-trick by converting Finch's centre with aplomb.

16 April 1949 v Bradford won 7-1 (Division 2)

Twelve months on and luckless Bradford were on the receiving end of another brilliant Albion display. With the Baggies going for promo-tion, over 39,000 fans saw them rat-tle in five goals in a marvellous 17-minute spell during the first-half.

In the 15th minute Walsh tucked home Barlow's delightful pass; five minutes later Roy White handled Elliott's centre and Walsh banged home the penalty; in the 23rd minute Walsh fed Haines who net-ted superbly on the run; on 28 min-utes Walsh scored a brilliant indi-vidual goal, beating Les Horsman before tricking 'keeper Tom Farr and finishing deftly, and in the 32nd minute Haines fired home from 15 yards after Walsh had done the hard work. Hugh Morrow made it 6-0 in the 47th minute (from Haines' pass) before George Ainsley pulled a goal back for Bradford while Albion's centre-half Jack Vernon was receiv-ing treatment on the touchline. Six minutes from time Walsh grabbed his fourth goal of the game after outwitting three defenders follow-ing Elliott's quick throw-in.

9 September 1950 v Ports-mouth won 5-0 (Division 1)

A crowd of 34,460 saw Albion com-pletely annihilate the League cham-

SOME MEMORABLE VICTORIES

hat-trick goal (his third of the season) and six minutes into the second half hot-shot Allen made it 4-1 with a sweetly-struck daisy-cutter.

Allen himself laid on the pass for Nicholls to make it 5-1 in the 79th minute and seven minutes from time Nicholls confidently put away a Griffin corner.

25 September 1954 v Leicester City won 6-4 (Division 1)

Five goals were scored in each half of this ten-goal thriller – and there should and could have been many more. Over 48,000 fans saw Albion dominate the first half-hour against newly-promoted City. They took the lead in the 12th minute when Allen's 25 yarder found the net after taking a wicked deflection off Stan Milburn. Seven minutes later Griffin's high, looping right-wing cross deceived 'keeper Adam Dickson and dropped into the net behind him and in the 30th minute Griffin's low cross was smacked home by Nicholls.

In the 34th minute Leicester hit back through Derek Hines (from Jack Froggatt's cross) but five minutes from the break, Nicholls made it 4-1 with a flashing drive from just inside the area. After Allen and Lee

But the Baggies responded quickly and in the 14th minute a shot from Lee cannoned off a defender, leaving Allen unmarked in front of an empty net.

In the 28th minute Griffin raced away down the right. He fed Ryan whose pass was gleefully slammed into the net by Allen.

Seven minutes later some smart work by Ryan set up Allen for his

Another Allen goal, this time against Cardiff in November 1953.

had both hit the crossbar early in the second half, former Albion star Arthur Rowley pulled a goal back for City on the hour mark, and three minutes later Mal Griffiths made it 4-3. Albion though, moved up a gear...Lee scored with a cracking left-footer on 75 minutes and Nicholls completed his second Albion hat-trick six minutes later before Johnny Morris rounded off the scoring with a fourth goal for City on 85 minutes.

Johnny Nicholls – hat-trick hero against Leicester City in September 1954.

Derek Kevan waits for an Everton slip at The Hawthorns in March 1958. The goalkeeper is Jimmy O'Neill.

later Kevan converted another fine Whitehouse pass, driving a first time shot home from ten yards. Former Albion star Arthur Rowley pulled a goal back for City in the 25th minute from an excellent Derek Hines pass – his 300th first-class goal of his career – and a minute later the visitors drew level when future Albion winger Derek Hogg pushed the ball through to Willie Gardiner whose first shot was saved by Albion 'keeper Clive Jackman only for the one-eyed Scottish centre-forward to smack in the rebound. Six minutes from the interval Robson centred for Whitehouse to ram in Albion's third goal, City's offside appeals falling on deaf ears.

Twenty minutes into the second half Graham Williams lobbed the ball down the middle for Robson to collect and shoot home from 12 yards; six minutes later Kevan crossed for Whitehouse to net number five and in the 80th minute Allen flicked the ball over his head, allowing Robson to net his second hat-trick and 27th goal of the season... and 25,389 fans saw it.

29 November 1958 v Tottenham Hotspur won 4-3 (Division 1)

Having scored in every League game of the season, Albion continued to

made it 2-0 seconds before half-time when he burst through from the halfway line past a static Everton defence to crack his shot wide of 'keeper Albert Dunlop. Allen made it 3-0 from the penalty spot in the 80th minute after Alan Sanders had floored the rampaging Kevan and it was the 'Tank' himself who snapped up number four, smashing home Roy Horobin's pin-point pass in the 86th minute.

12 April 1958 v Leicester City won 6-2 (Division 1)

After a barren spell of just one goal in five games Albion bounced back to form with a powerful display against Leicester.

In the 11th minute Brian Whitehouse crossed for Robson to score from close range and seven minutes

Brian Whitehouse scores against Leicester City in April 1958.

SOME MEMORABLE VICTORIES

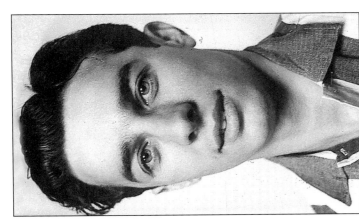

Ronnie Allen scored his final hat-trick for Albion in a 6-3 win over Manchester City in September 1960.

Alec Jackson, a thorn in the Newcastle defence when Albion romped to a 6-0 win in September 1960.

Kevan raced on to cunning Robson's pass to smash in Albion's third goal in the 20th minute, only for Joe Hayes to head home Dave Wagstaffe's corner to make it 3-2 after goalkeeper Ray Potter had saved brilliantly from Law. In the 40th minute Kevan again bulged the net with a cracking drive after Jackson had set him up and seconds before half-time Law beat Joe Kennedy to tee up Colin Barlow, who duly made it 4-3. What a half.

In the 57th minute Allen capitalised on some defensive slackness to make it 5-3 (City appealed in vain for offside) and after Kevan had been deprived of his hat-trick through another dodgy offside decision, Allen completed his seven minutes from time with a thumping drive past Bert Trautmann after a wonderful back-heeler by the influential Burnside.

28 April 1962 v Blackpool won 7-1 (Division 1)

What a way to end a season – with a block-busting performance and plenty of goals. It was a pity that only 17,462 fans turned out to see Albion completely outplay the Seasiders in all departments to record their fifth League win on the trot and their best ever over Blackpool.

which Allen scored his last hat-trick for Albion.

Burnside put the Baggies in front on ten minutes, netting easily after Jackson had bamboozled four City defenders.

Allen ran in unnoticed to steer home Jackson's pass to make it 2-0 in the 17th minute, only for City's Denis Law to sell Drury the perfect dummy, allowing George Hannah to reduce the deficit two minutes later.

the process, Albion suddenly found their form and shooting boots to outclass their opponents in front of 22,548 spectators. Newcastle, minus their 'rebel' George Eastham, had no answer to Albion's forceful attacking play and fell behind on nine minutes when Jackson scored from close range after a shrewd pass by Burnside.

Burnside then made it 2-0 in the 34th minute after some neat right-wing play by Hogg and six minutes later Jackson netted number three with a crisp finish from Hogg's measured cross.

Ten minutes into the second half Jackson completed his hat-trick with another excellent strike from 12 yards after Hogg had again out-paced the Newcastle defence. Robson scored Albion's fifth from a free-kick, given for obstruction and Kevan rounded off the scoring by heading number six in the 67th minute after Hope had chipped the ball forward.

24 September 1960 v Manchester City won 6-3 (Division 1)

A crowd of 25,163 attended this highly entertaining encounter in

One of Derek Kevan's four goals in the 7-1 win over Blackpool in April 1962.

hat-trick in front of a meagre crowd of 10,759... the lowest at The Hawthorns for eight years.

Kevan's strength and decisive finishing was too much for a frail looking Ipswich side, who ended the game with only nine men – goalkeeper Wilf Hall and forward Doug Moran leaving the action in the 14th and 65th minutes respectively, Hall with a fractured collarbone after colliding with Ronnie Fenton and Moran with a twisted knee. Kevan gave Albion the lead on 20 minutes, netting with a fine header past stand-in 'keeper Ted Phillips from Don Howe's free-kick. Ipswich fought back and equalised in the 35th minute through Ray Crawford – later to join Albion – who slammed in Jimmy Leadbetter's cross. But on the stroke of half-time Kevan met Clark's low centre to put Albion back in front.

In the 51st minute Phillips fumbled a Clark shot, leaving Alec Jackson a simple tap in, and on 68 minutes Clark cut in to send a thunderbolt shot into the net via the underside of the bar.

Cram laid on Albion's fifth goal for Smith in the 77th minute and Kevan completed his hat-trick with a close range header from Cram's lob with nine minutes remaining.

12 October 1963 v Aston Villa won 4-3 (Division 1)

Albion were missing their two international full-backs for this game – Howe and Graham Williams – and their two main strikers – Ronnie Fenton and John Kaye – and halfway through the first half it looked as though the Villa would run away with the match. They were 2-0 up with the match. They were 2-0 up and strolling after Albion's Scottish-born right-back Campbell Crawford had conceded an own-goal in the 21st minute and 45 seconds later Mike Tindall had headed home his side's second from Tony Hateley's cross. But Albion stormed back and three minutes before the break Cram, playing as an emergency centre-forward, sidefooted home Jackson's centre. In the 65th minute Nigel Sims saved Jackson's penalty after the the Albion player had been tripped by Alan Deakin, but the

'Tipton Slasher' quickly made amends for his error by equalising two minutes later with a fine right-foot shot after Deakin had failed to head clear.

Terry Simpson's excellent right-wing centre was slammed home by Tony Brown in the 69th minute for Albion's third goal and Foggo chased after Jackson's through ball, beat Charlie Aitken for speed and made it 4-2 with three minutes remaining. Tony Hateley headed a third goal for Villa in the very last minute, heading in Jimmy MacEwan's corner.

12 September 1964 v Stoke City won 5-3 (Division 1)

An exciting first-half was marred by an injury to Stoke's Calvin Palmer. The visitors, playing with pace and aggression in front of 24,505 fans, took the lead on eight minutes through John Ritchie, but Albion fought back and drew level in the 21st minute through right-winger Foggo. Two minutes later Albion went in front when full-back Cram moved forward to unleash a power-

Full-back Bobby Cram is on the way to his hat-trick against Stoke City in September 1964.

Doug Fraser (arm raised) celebrates John Kaye's goal in Albion's 4-2 win over Sheffield Wednesday in September 1965.

18th minute, diverting Brown's low cross past his own 'keeper. On 27 minutes Kaye's header from Astle's pass made it 2-0 and then Setters made a rash challenge on Clark inside the area, allowing Cram to slam in Albion's third goal from the penalty spot on 34.

Roy Vernon reduced the arrears for Stoke five minutes before half-time after a mix-up in the Albion defence but a Brown cross-shot, from Astle's pass, and a Kaye header from Clark's centre in the space of three minutes soon after the restart put Albion firmly in control. Setters made amends for his errors by setting up Peter Dobing for Stoke's second goal on the hour, only for Kaye to complete his first Albion hat-trick in the 71st minute with another fine goal after good work by Astle and Brown down the right. Brown then hit the post two minutes from time.

6 November 1965 v Fulham won 6-2 (Division 1)

A crowd of around 20,000 saw Albion claim their second 6-2 score-

line of the season with a powerful display against Fulham – and star of the show was Graham Lovett who scored two splendid goals.

It took Albion 30 minutes to achieve the breakthrough, Ray Wilson heading home Kaye's measured cross.

Two minutes after half-time Brown latched on to Bobby Hope's long through ball to fire past Tony

Graham Lovett, star of the show in another six-goal hammering of Fulham in November 1965.

Macedo for Albion's second and five minutes later Lovett, after a brilliant 40-yard dribble, made it three.

Graham Leggatt pulled a goal back for the visitors on 58 minutes after 'keeper Dick Sheppard had mishandled a Terry Dyson shot but Kaye and Wilson worked an opening for Brown to make it 4-1 ten minutes later. With 16 minutes to go Lovett scored a majestic fifth goal after another exciting 40-yard run; Clark made it 5-1 in the 83rd minute after some smart build-up play involving Hope and Brown, and a minute from time former Albion star Bobby Robson ended the scoring with a 25 yarder for Fulham.

10 September 1966 v Fulham won 5-1 (Division 1)

Fulham were well and truly thrashed and Cottagers' boss Vic Buckingham, who guided Albion to FA Cup glory in 1954, admitted afterwards: "it should have been double figures" as Astle (twice), Kaye (twice), Hope, Clark and Fraser all missed easy chances.

SOME MEMORABLE VICTORIES

Nobby Stiles had tripped Rees and Astle headed in number four in the 59th minute from Hope's free-kick awarded for a foul on Rees. Denis Law pulled a goal back for United from the penalty spot after Fraser had impeded Brian Kidd, but Albion went into overdrive and scored twice more through teenager Asa Hartford, who converted Astle's headed pass and Astle himself, who duly completed his hat-trick with a header from Lovett's centre. Two goals in the last 12 minutes by Kidd made the score more respectable. Albion went on to win the FA. Cup while United lifted the European Cup.

9 October 1968 v Coventry City won 6-1 (Division 1)

After being beaten three times in a row by Coventry during the previous year Albion completely outplayed the Sky Blues under The Hawthorns' floodlights to register a marvellous victory.

It took former City star Ronnie Rees only eight minutes to open Albion's account. The Welsh international slipped inside full-back Mick Coop to touch home Ian Collard's clever pass.

Only some brave saves by 'keeper Bill Glazier kept Coventry alive but two minutes into the second half Brown made it 2-0 when he thumped in a penalty after Brian Hill had floored Jeff Astle. Hill went off injured following this incident (replaced by John Tudor).

Five minutes later George Curtis failed to clear Rees' cross and Astle fired home the loose ball. After Hill had been replaced by John Tudor, Coventry clawed a goal back through an Ernie Hunt header but Albion responded quickly and Hartford made it 4-1 with a shot on the turn from 20 yards. Astle pounced to make 5-1 in the 75th minute after some poor defending

Asa Hartford, on target against Manchester United and Coventry in 1968 and Newcastle in 1969.

by Tudor and four minutes later a fizzing cross by Brown went into the Coventry net off Tudor's chest.

19 April 1969 v Newcastle United won 5-1 (Division 1)

A crowd of 22,481 saw Albion turn on a tremendous second half performance to humble Newcastle who at one stage looked destined to end the Baggies' six-match unbeaten run.

Newcastle dominated the first quarter of the game but then Albion got to grips in midfield and after Kaye had brilliantly headed them into a 25th-minute lead from Brown's well driven free-kick, it was no stopping Alan Ashman's marauders.

Brown also had a hand in Albion's goal in the 35th minute. United 'keeper Ian McFaul saved his cracking drive but Hartford, with his back to goal, netted with a fine overhead kick.

United got one back five minutes later when Bryan Robson, put clear by Alan Fogdon, deceived John Osborne with a cleverly placed shot.

Albion's final goal burst started half-an-hour from the end.

A push by Ollie Burton on Clark

earned Albion a 60th minute penalty which was converted by Brown. Seven minutes later Lovett sent Clark streaking through for number four and ten minutes later, following some smart play by Hartford, Astle netted number five after Brown's shot had been blocked.

6 March 1971 v Manchester United won 4-3 (Division 1)

Albion's super striker 'Bomber' Brown sent out a 'cap me' message to England boss Sir Alf Ramsey with a glorious hat-trick in this showpiece which was eventually settled in injury-time.

When Albion and United meet on the same pitch they rarely fail to let the goals fly. This was no exception as four were rattled in during a scintillating 16-minute spell early in the second half to the delight of 41,134 excited fans

George Best put United in front in the 18th minute, scoring low past 'keeper Jim Cumbes after outwitting John Wile.

Cumbes then saved brilliantly from Kidd before Brown equalised in the 32nd minute. Alex Stepney, under pressure, dropped Kaye's right wing cross and the Bomber pounced to net from close range.

This proved only an appetiser for the main feast and with just 35 seconds gone in the second half Brown netted again. Hartford sent George McVitie away down the right and was there to meet the winger's cross. His shot was blocked by a defender but Brown nipped in smartly to fire Albion ahead.

In the 55th minute United drew level when John Aston dived in bravely to head home Willie Morgan's cross.

Albion hit back strongly and within four minutes had taken the lead again. Brown, charging in from the right, held off Tony Dunne's challenge and let rip a terrific drive

SOME MEMORABLE VICTORIES

made it 2-0 in the 60th minute, drilling in Cantello's short free-kick from 18 yards.

Then after Mick Lyons had taken over between the posts Dave Shaw made it 3-0 in the 63rd minute when he raced on to Alan Merrick's long pass to fire home from 12 yards.

A goal by Mick Bernard on 73 minutes pegged Albion back but three minutes later Shaw made it 4-1 when he netted with a spectacular overhead kick after Wile had nodded down Willie Johnston's left-wing corner.

● The *Daily Telegraph* headed its report: 'Albion head for safety.' How wrong that was. Albion lost their closing four matches and went down to the Second Division.

8 March 1975 v Sheffield Wednesday won 4-0 (Division 2)

Albion had won just two of their previous eight League games before

Ian Edwards, a debut goal against Sheffield Wednesday in March 1975.

formed well as Albion strolled to victory after a dull first half.

Albion's first goal arrived on 47 minutes. Johnston outpaced Peter Rodriguez and from his cross Wednesday's Alan Thompson fouled Edwards. Tony Brown thumped in the penalty.

It was 2-0 in the 74th minute when Johnston fed a short corner to Allan Glover whose cross was volleyed home in a spectacular style by skipper Wile from ten yards. In the 83rd minute Edwards crowned his debut with a terrific goal. Picking the ball up five yards over the halfway line he raced clear of his markers before netting with a delightful ground shot.

Three minutes from time – after Rodrigues had gone off injured – Edwards set up Brown for goal number four.

20 March 1976 v Bolton Wanderers won 2-0 (Division 2)

This was a game Albion had to win as they endeavoured to gain promo-

taking on the Owls in front of 10,330 fans at The Hawthorns. Manager Howe handed senior debuts to goalkeeper Bob Ward and striker Ian Edwards and both per-

A goal for Joe Mayo (No.9) in the vital promotion win over Bolton in March 1976.

After an even opening period Albion took the lead in the 27th minute when Stepney saved David Cross's initial effort only for the striker to blast home Bryan Robson's return pass from the edge of the area.

In the 36th minute Johnston's left-wing corner curled away from goal towards Wile who leapt to steer a fine header into the United net via an upright.

Three minutes later Derek Statham surged forward and after his shot cannoned off Martin Buchan Cross was on hand to steer the ball past Stepney.

It was game over in the 56th minute when Laurie Cunningham stole in at the far post side-foot home Mulligan's fine cross after the Irishman had been set free by Johnston.

Cyrille Regis missed this game through tonsillitis.

21 October 1978 v Coventry City won 7-1 (Division 1)

Coventry – wearing a chocolate-coloured strip – were well and truly licked by a highly confident and very efficient Albion side in front of 27,409 spectators.

Cantello scored the opening goal in the 14th minute, finishing off Tony Brown's pin-point pass in style, the ball flying high into the net off diving 'keeper Les Sealey's outstretched arms.

Cunningham made it 2-0 in the 28th minute, tucking home a fine cross from the overlapping Brendon Batson. Seven minutes later Regis added number three with a powerful header after some excellent work by Cantello and Brown.

The impressive Cunningham grabbed his second goal and Albion's fourth in the 62nd minute, heading home Wile's flick-on from Brown's left-wing corner. And after Mick Ferguson had pulled one back

Len Cantello scored Albion's opening goal when Coventry were hammered 7-1 in October 1978.

for Coventry on 70 minutes when he headed in Tony Green's left-wing centre, Brown rammed in Albion's fifth goal on 76 minutes from Robson's pass. Regis claimed number six in the 82nd minute, storming through the middle of the Coventry defence before hammering his shot beyond Sealey, and Statham rounded things off with a seventh goal a minute from time, picking up the pieces after Terry Yorath had lost possession just outside the penalty area.

1 January 1979 v Bristol City won 3-1 (Division 1)

A dozen or so groundsmen, 50 stewards, 100 supporters and even a handful of Albion players helped shovel snow off the Hawthorns pitch to enable this vital League Division One game to go ahead. And after recording an excellent 3-1 victory over Bristol City in front of

31,738 frozen spectators, Albion leap-frogged over Everton to join Liverpool at the top of the First Division table – the last time they had enjoyed such a high placing since 1954.

On a skating rink of a pitch Albion played carpet football and got off to a perfect start, Ally Brown scoring in the 11th minute after City's 'keeper John Shaw had pushed out Robson's low drive.

John Wile powered Albion back in front against Bristol City in January 1979.

City then survived four close shaves before grabbing an equaliser on 21 minutes. Batson conceded a penalty when he handled Tom Ritchie's header on the line. Ritchie's spot-kick hit a post but Barnsley referee Keith Styles ordered it to be retaken after Ally Brown had thrown a snowball at the ball. This time Peter Cormack netted comfortably.

Albion went back in front when Wile powered in Cantello's corner kick in the 44th minute but after dominating the whole of the second half they had to wait until nine minutes from time to clinch victory, Ally Brown making amends for his 'penalty' misdemeanour by netting a beauty following the best move of the match.

SOME MEMORABLE VICTORIES

increased their lead with a superb goal from Statham. Romeo Zondervan started the move and after playing a neat one-two with Thompson Statham side-stepped Russell Osman to net from eight yards.

John Wark made it 2-1 ten minutes after the interval, heading Kevin O'Callaghan's cross past a flat-footed Paul Barron. But Albion upped the pace and when Regis pulled the ball back across goal in the 72nd minute Ipswich's Irvin Gernon glided the ball into his own goal. Three minutes later Thompson ended the scoring by lashing in Statham's long pass.

14 January 1984 v Aston Villa won 3-1 (Division 1)

Just 20,399 hardy supporters braved the chilling weather to watch this local derby which burst into life inside the last ten minutes.

After a dour first half Gary Shaw fired the visitors ahead in the 46th minute when he pounced on a loose ball inside the area.

Albion battled to get back on terms but found Nigel Spink in excellent form. Then a blizzard arrived and with fast time running out the game suddenly turned. On 84 minutes a mistake by Villa defender Allan Evans allowed Thompson to race in and equalise. Three minutes later Thompson rose, unmarked, to power home a great header from Clive Whitehead's high cross and with the snow swirling under the floodlights, Regis scored Albion's third goal after racing clear from the halfway line before netting past Spink with a fierce right-foot shot.

13 October 1984 v Nottingham Forest won 4-1 (Division 1)

Without a League win in six outings, Albion – and Garry Thompson in particular – suddenly found their shooting boots to out-gun a resilient Forest side in front of 12,991 fans.

Albion scored first in the 22nd minute when Steve Mackenzie's 25-yard special zipped past Steve Sutton.

Ten minutes later Nicky Cross got free down the left and his centre was headed home by Thompson.

After Ian Bowyer's shot had been deflected past Tony Godden following Bryn Gunn's free-kick in the 52nd minute, Albion went 3-1 ahead when Thompson was on hand to slam the ball home after Sutton could only touch on Clive Whitehead's centre. And with six minutes remaining Thompson claimed his hat-trick goal when he flicked the ball home following Gary Robson's cross from the left.

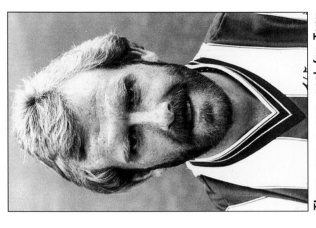

There was a rare goal for Tony Grealish in Albion's 5-1 win over West Ham in May 1985.

4 May 1985 v West Ham United won 5-1 (Division 1)

Albion rounded off their home League programme this season with a crushing victory over the Hammers – but only 8,878 spectators bothered to turn up to see it.

The deadlock was broken in the 25th minute when Steve Hunt rose at the far post to head Mackenzie's free-kick past Phil Parkes.

Ten minutes into the second half Ray Stewart equalised with a penalty after a dubious trip by Gary Owen on Clive Allen. Two minutes later Mackenzie scored a brilliant solo goal, netting from 20 yards and 12 minutes later the same player made it 3-1 after beating the offside trap to knock home Thompson's pass.

Albion's Republic of Ireland international midfielder Tony Grealish then scored a rare goal in the 76th minute, getting on the end of Hunt's long cross from the left, and the Canadian Carl Valentine created Albion's final goal eight minutes from time when gave Nicky Cross the opportunity he couldn't miss to complete the rout of the Hammers.

14 February 1987 v Stoke City won 4-1 (Division 2)

Two players, one long (George Reilly) and one short (Garth Crooks), helped Albion trounce promotion-chasing Stoke City out of sight.

Albion's emphatic victory was down to the lethal partnership up front of Reilly and former Potters' star Crooks, who led the visitors' defence a merry dance.

Garth Crooks scored twice against his former club when Albion beat Stoke City in February 1987.

pletly over-run the Potters, scoring further goals through South African striker Paskin (70 and 76 minutes), Goodman again on 85 and Robson with his second of the match 90 seconds from time. Brian Talbot, Anderson and Wayne Dobbins were outstanding in midfield and between them contributed to all six goals. Tony Ford. Stoke's talented winger who was soon to move to The Hawthorns was so unnerved by Albion's onslaught that he was sent-off for the only time in his long career for a bad tackle on Colin Anderson in the 67th minute.

11 November 1989 v Barnsley won 7-0 (Division 2)

This one-sided encounter was marred by the sending-off of Tykes' substitute Sean Dunphy with a quarter-of-an-hour left following two fouls on the menacing Goodman. He was on the pitch for just 19 minutes. And it was Goodman who opened the scoring on three minutes, heading home Ford's splendid cross.

Ford himself nodded home McNally's centre for Albion's number two four minutes later. Brittle Barnsley stemmed the tide for the next 35 minutes but then hot-shot Goodman netted twice in the 43rd and 46th minutes to complete his only Albion hat-trick. First he slotted in McNally's pass and then brilliantly lobbed 'keeper Ian Wardle for his third goal.

Kevin Bartlett followed up with Albion's fifth goal in the 49th minute, prodding home the loose ball after Wardle had mishandled Ford's cross and then the same player side-footed home Goodman's pass for number six two minutes later.

McNally rounded things off with goal number seven in the 53rd minute, netting with a penalty after Carl Tiler had handled Ford's teasing cross.

Martyn Bennett made his last appearance for Albion in the 7-0 thrashing of Barnsley in November 1989.

This was Martyn Bennett's 217th and last game for Albion – and a crowd of 9,317 saw his farewell performance.

17 August 1991 v Exeter City won 6-3 (Division Three)

This was Albion's first game in the Third Division and 12,892 saw them record their first opening day victory for 18 years. Craig Shakespeare gave Albion a 30th-minute lead with a penalty. Mark Cooper equalised a minute before half-time, defeating

Don Goodman and Craig Shakespeare, two goals apiece against Exeter City in August 1991.

on loan 'keeper Alan Miller but straight from the kick-off Goodman was pulled down and Shakespeare netted his second spot kick. On 62 minutes Goodman made it 3-1 and two minutes later the same player headed Gary Bannister's cross against the crossbar before slotting in the rebound. Foster got on the scoresheet in the 76th minute and Paul Williams added a sixth goal 45 seconds later. Exeter rallied and Steve Moran and Gary Marshall scored consolation goals in the 82nd and 85th minutes as Albion eased up.

19 May 1993 v Swansea City won 2-0 (Division 2 Play-off semi-final second leg)

A full-house of 26,045 celebrated as Albion overturned a 2-1 first leg deficit to win through to the Second Division Play-off Final at Wembley. Both goals came in the opening period – the first from Andy Hunt in the tenth minute (from some neat build up play down the left) and the second from Ian Hamilton nine minutes later, again following some smart passing down Swansea;s right flank. Skipper Darren Bradley should have sewed it up at 3-0 in the

ing in Hunt's low cross in a break-away. Two minutes later Hunt capitalised on some poor marking in the visitors' defence to push Albion 5-0 in front when he stroked the ball home following Paul Agnew's left-wing run and centre. In the 81st minute Norwich defender Danny Mills was sent-off for a foul but Hamilton squandered his hat-trick by blasting the resulting penalty high over the bar.

Norwich salvaged some pride with a late consolation from Keith O'Neill in the 88th minute.

15 August 1998 v Sheffield United won 4-1 (Division 1)

Albion were always in control of this game and recorded their first win of the season in emphatic style. Matt Carbon headed in at the far post following a corner for Albion's first goal on 24 minutes, and five minutes later Kevin Kilbane volleyed in James Quinn's cross from 16 yards to make it 2-0. Welsh international Dean Saunders reduced the arrears on 38 minutes, but two close range strikes from Lee Hughes in the 49th and 50th minutes put Albion back in control. Goalkeeper Alan Miller kept Albion in charge with a couple of excellent saves towards the end. The attendance was 16,901.

FA Cup

9 February 1901 v Manchester City won 1-0

Around 10,000 spectators saw Albion have two early 'goals' ruled out for offside in this first ever Hawthorns FA Cup-tie which was re-arranged due to the death of Queen Victoria. The only goal of the game came in the 30th minute when Simmons and Dick Roberts combined to set up Ben Garfield who scored from close range. In the second half Albion's goalkeeper Joe

Reader made two fine saves from Welsh wizard Billy Meredith.

9 March 1912 v Fulham won 3-0

Heavy morning rain made the pitch very heavy. An excellent crowd of 41,440 saw Albion adapt to the wet and windy conditions far better than Fulham to run out convincing winners of this fourth-round tie. Amazingly there was a London referee in charge – Mr C. W. Gillett – but that didn't effect Albion's polished display and two first half goals by Bowser in the 30th and 32nd minutes, both at the Smethwick End, and both well-taken after neat approach work involving four players on each occasion, set the Baggies on their way. Wright added a third goal in the 78th minute to settle the outcome. Winger Claude Jephcott's electrifying runs as well as Bowser's marksmanship were the key factors in a rousing tie.

Sid Bowser, scorer of two FA Cup goals against Fulham in March 1912.

3 February 1923 v Sunderland won 2-1

This was a great second-round FA Cup-tie, witnessed by 56,474 spectators. Both sets of players wore black

armbands following the death of Lord Kinnaird, president of the Football Association.

Albion had a chance to take the lead on 15 minutes but Morris blasted his penalty kick against the crossbar. Twelve minutes later, however, Morris made amends by putting his side ahead. Jimmy Spencer fired across the face of the goal; Gregory returned the ball for Morris to head home from eight yards.

Howard Gregory who laid on a goal against Sunderland in a famous FA Cup victory in February 1923.

Sunderland stormed back and after twice going close to the equaliser, they drew level in the 37th minute when Charlie Buchan, lurking near the touchline, turned to send a stunning 35-yard drive high into the Albion net past a bewildered Hubert Pearson in the Albion goal.

It was nip and tuck until the 63rd minute when Davies created space to set up fellow countryman Ivor Jones for the winning goal.

2 February 1924 v Corinthians won 5-0

Over 49,000 fans saw Albion easily beat the amateurs in this second

Dave Walsh, a hat-trick hero against Chelsea in February 1949.

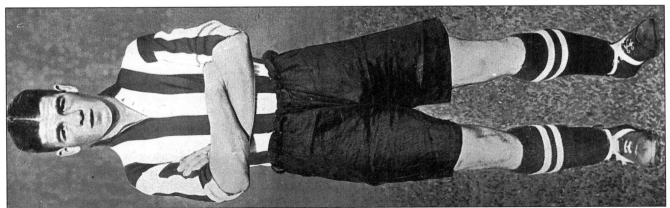

Teddy Sandford scored in Albion's big FA Cup wins over Sheffield United and Spennymoor and then skippered the side from centre-half in the famous Cup win Arsenal in 1937.

tialled by Sandford now playing at centre-half, was an important factor in a pulsating Cup-tie.

12 February 1949 v Chelsea won 3-0

Dave Walsh was a hat-trick hero of this fifth round victory by Second Division Albion over their First Division opponents. In front of a bumper 57,843 crowd – the best at The Hawthorns for 12 years – Albion held their own in the first half but then took the initiative to outwit and at times outplay the Londoners.

On 49 minutes Irish international Walsh hooked in a cross from Cyril Williams. He then had another 'goal' disallowed before John Harris misjudged the bounce of the ball to allow the Baggies' centre-forward to plunder number two halfway through the half.

Walsh completed his hat-trick with a terrific header from Elliott's angled cross ten minutes from time.

the 89th minute. But right from the kick-off City's burly defender Dave Ewing sent his back pass wide of his own 'keeper to give Albion an impressive 5-1 scoreline.

19 February 1958 v Sheffield United won 4-1

United defended doggedly in the first half of this fourth-round replay, restricting Albion to just three attempts on goal. Indeed, it was 0-0 at the break, but then Albion slipped into overdrive and finished off the Blades with three goals in three minutes just past the hour mark. Robson opened the scoring from Kevan's pass; Kevan himself then thumped home Griffin's centre for number two and after Horobin had been sandwiched inside the area, Allen added a third from the penalty spot.

Soon after Albion's third goal in-form Griffin, who was on the fringe of the England team at the time, was crash-tackled by United's centre-half Joe Shaw and received a fractured right leg.

Albion, obviously shaken by this, conceded a goal with nine minutes left, Jimmy Dudley putting the ball past his own 'keeper but a late Kevan goal secured victory to send the majority of the 57,503 crowd home happy.

31 January 1968 v Colchester United won 4-0

After surviving the first game at Layer Road by the skin of their teeth Albion easily accounted for plucky Colchester United in this third-round replay, scoring three times in the opening half-hour.

Kaye put the Baggies on the road to victory in the tenth minute with a smashing goal. Running from the centre circle, he went past two United defenders before beating goalkeeper Ernie Adams with a 20-yard special.

and-a-half months earlier, Albion once again went goal-crazy. scoring another five and missing at least four more.

Despite a lot of early pressure and possession it took Albion 34 minutes to break through, Allen stabbing the ball home after Robson had miskicked at Horobin's low centre.

Ray Barlow, playing as a 'sixth forward', scored a superb goal against Manchester City in January 1958.

In a dim and misty second half, and with Barlow playing as a sixth forward, Albion attacked in force and in the 55th minute Barlow netted a superb second goal in off the foot of a post from Setters' free-kick. Three minutes later Horobin freed Griffin down the middle and the winger scored sweetly from ten yards. Four minutes later Kevan was fouled, but the referee played the advantage rule allowing Allen to curl in a fourth goal past the stranded Trautmann. City responded and after Fionan Fagan had struck an upright and Howe had cleared off the line, Joe Hayes found the net in

Roy Horobin (above) and Wilf Carter were both on song against Sunderland in January 1957.

settled the match with a deft finish to take Albion into the next round and an away tie at Blackpool

4 January 1958 v Manchester City won 5-1

Despite the fog, almost 50,000 fans attended this third round Cup-tie and having smashed City 9-2 in a First Division match only three-

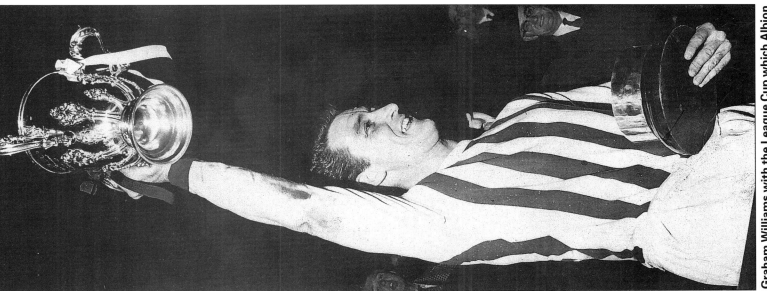

Graham Williams with the League Cup which Albion won in 1966.

some sloppy defensive play gave Albion their seventh goal in the 82nd minute. Four minutes from time Donovan completed his hat-trick with a right foot lob from just outside the area.

Football League Cup

22 September 1965 v Walsall won 3-1

Albion's first-ever League Cup-tie attracted a record crowd of 41,188 to The Hawthorns. In fact, it was the first time the teams had met each other at competitive level since 1900 and all credit to the Saddlers for making a fight of it. Brown put Albion in front just before half-time against the ruin of play, but after Colin Taylor had fired in a brilliant equaliser in the 65th minute Albion's defence came under considerable pressure. Then just after Nick Atthey's effort had been disallowed for offside, Walsall's centre-half Stan Bennett, who had played magnificently against the twin threat of Astle and Kaye, lobbed his own goalkeeper Terry Carling to concede an 80th minute own-goal and so hand the initiative back to Albion. Brown duly clinched matters three minutes later with the sort of goal he specialised in.

10 November 1965 v Coventry City won 6-1

Albion got off to a flier in this fourth-round replay, Astle firing Ray Fairfax's cross past City goalkeeper Bob Wesson after just 40 seconds play. But Coventry fought back and were level in the 28th minute when Alfie Hale and George Hudson set up Ernie Machin who finished with a well-directed ground shot.

Albion regained the lead on 40 minutes when Brown fired in a terrific shot through a crowd of players.

Albion then took the game by the scruff of the neck and stunned City with three decisive goals soon after half-time.

In the 58th minute Astle glanced in a header from Clark's centre; four minutes later Fraser burst down the middle to hammer in number four and 55 seconds after that the same player netted Albion's fifth goal with a tremendous right foot shot.

Astle duly completed his hat-trick by heading in number six from Kaye's cross with 15 minutes remaining.

23 February 1966 v West Ham United won 4-1

The second-leg of the 1966 League Cup Final saw Albion overturn a one-goal deficit against a Hammers' side which included Bobby Moore, Geoff Hurst and Martin Peters. In front of 32,013 fans, Albion started off like a house on fire, Kaye smashing home Cram's cross after only ten minutes. Nine minutes later Brown made it 2-0 and in the 28th minute Albion went 3-1 up (4-3 on aggregate) when Clark headed the ball practically out of 'keeper Jim Standen's hands. Left-half Williams made it 4-0 in the 35th minute with a crisp

drive from 30 yards. West Ham rallied in the second half and Peters reduced the arrears in the 75th minute. But it was Albion's night and skipper Williams lifted the club's first trophy in 12 years and with it came a place in the Fairs Cup for 1966-67.

25 October 1983 v Millwall won 5-1

Albion, trailing 3-0 from the first leg of this second round Milk Cup-tie against George Graham's Millwall, played exceedingly well in the return fixture and completely out-fought and outwitted the Lions to go through 5-4 on aggregate.

Albion managed only one goal in a tight first half, scored by Garry Thompson after 42 minutes, who clipped home Gary Owen's delicate chip over the Millwall defence.

Crowd trouble caused a ten minute delay to the start of the second half, but once they were back on the field Albion went for broke. In the 48th minute Regis headed in Albion's second goal from Barry Cowdrill's. Six minutes later, after David Cusack had dragged down Thompson, Owen fired in a penalty to bring the aggregate scores level and on 70 minutes Thompson scored his second of the night with a brave diving header from Owen's pass. Regis made it 5-0 with 15 minutes left after Zondervan had opened up the Lions' defence, and right on time substitute David Martin pulled one back for the Lions, who by this time had completely lost their roar and the match. The attendance was 13,331 – around 3,300 supporting Millwall.

European Competitions

9 November 1966 v DOS Utrecht won 5-2 (Fairs Cup)

A crowd of 19,692 witnessed Albion's first-ever European home game and the Baggies made hard work of it at times before overcoming the Dutch side in this Fairs Cup encounter. Albion had drawn the first leg in Holland 1-1 and were firm favourites to win the return

game at The Hawthorns – but they had fit-again hat-trick hero Tony Brown to thank for their 6-3 aggregate victory.

Bomber's and Albion's first goal came from a 13th minute penalty after defender Eddy Achterberg had foolishly handled Hope's cross and four minutes into the second half Astle headed on for Clark to nod in number two. Utrecht pulled a goal back on 58 minutes when Leo de Vroet scored from a corner but 11 minutes later Brown got on the end of Hope's measured cross to head Albion into a 3-1 lead. That was increased to 4-1 in the 75th minute when Kaye cracked in Astle's downward header and almost immediately Arie de Kuyper's shot was deflected in by Fraser for 4-2. Brown duly completed his hat-trick with a smart finish with two minutes remaining.

27 November 1968 v Dinamo Bucharest won 4-0 (European Cup-winners' Cup)

Slowly almost gently Albion ushered aside Dinamo Bucharest to enter the quarter-finals of the European Cup-winners' Cup. After a battling 1-1 draw in Romania Albion easily won this second round, second leg encounter in front of 33,059 spectators.

Surprisingly it took the Baggies 35 minutes to breach the visitors' defence. Clark, back in the side for the suspended Ronnie Rees (sent-off in the first leg), had an effort saved but Graham Lovett was on hand to drill in the loose ball.

Eight minutes later Fraser centred into the packed goalmouth; Lovett missed the ball but Brown, lurking behind him, crashed it high into the net off the underside of the bar (2-0).

Six minutes after the interval Albion scored again. Rugged defender Mircea Stoenescu floored Clark inside the area and Brown smashed in the penalty past the

'keeper's right arm. And to round off the victory the unmarked Astle stroked in goal number four in the 72nd minute after the ball broke kindly for him following Cornel Popa's strong tackle on the impressive Clark.

6 December 1978 v Valencia won 2-0 (UEFA Cup)

After holding the Spanish club with their World Cup stars to a 1-1 draw in Valencia, Albion were quietly confident of making progress into the quarter-finals of the UEFA Cup when the teams met in the second leg at The Hawthorns. In front of an excited 35,118 crowd Albion took the game to the Spaniards from the first whistle and always look the more likely side to score – and so it proved. Brown rapped in the opening goal in the fifth minute from the penalty spot after Luis Cordero had handled and then the same player sewed things up late in the second half with a stunning right foot volley on 79 minutes. In between times Cunningham headed against a post, Regis fired inches wide and Brown had a 20-yard effort saved by Fernandez Manzanedo. Valencia's World Cup stars Mario Kempes and Rainer Bonhof were both kept at bay by the efficient marking and tackling of Wile, Ally Robertson and Robson. Brown and Statham both had goals disallowed by fussy referee Robert Wurtz.

8 May 1970 v AS Roma won 4-0 (Anglo-Italian Tournament)

Albion scored four times in the last half-hour of this highly-charged but entertaining Anglo-Italian match. Victory took the Baggies to the top of their group with seven points.

Hope finally opened the floodgates in the 61st minute with a soft goal as goalkeeper De Min allowed the ball to slip under his body.

Brown added a second in the

Howe to level things up on 28 minutes with a sizzling 20-yard drive. Encouraged by this Albion swarmed forward and seven minutes before half-time another vicious 20-yard strike, this time from Robson, put them 2-1 in front.

Albion's delight however, was short-lived as the Army side equalised two minutes later when Vladimir Emishev crossed low for Valentin Babukin to fire past Jim Sanders.

On 44 minutes winger Griffin made it 3-2. Shooting low towards goal, he saw the ball squeeze in at the far post after taking a slight deflection off Kevan – but 'Frank' claimed it.

Immediately after the restart a sharp movement split the Russian defence wide open. Kevan raced into the area, was felled by a clumsy challenge and Allen scored from the spot.

Soon afterwards Kevan was brought down again but this time Allen, changing from right foot to his left, sent his spot-kick a fraction wide of goalkeeper Yuriy Beljoev's right-hand post (a rare miss).

Busunov scored a third goal for the Army side in the 62nd minute and it looked as though Allen's 12-yard miss might prove crucial, but Kevan put the centre-forward's mind at rest with two fine goals in the 64th and 82nd minutes to push Albion 6-3 ahead. But the resolute Russians had other ideas and they netted twice more through Busunov on 83 minutes (his hat-trick goal) and Emishev (88) to make it 6-5 on the night. Great stuff.

FA Youth Cup Final

3 May 1976 v Wolverhampton Wanderers won 3-0

Having won 2-0 at Molineux in the first leg of this FA Youth Cup Final, it came as no surprise when Albion again outclassed their arch rivals to win the return clash at The Hawthorns by a bigger margin and so lift the trophy 5-0 on aggregate.

In front of a 15,558 crowd Albion scored their first goal in the 20th minute when George Berry, pressurised by Mark Trenter and Derek Monaghan, lost his bearings and steered the ball past his own keeper, Tony Walker.

Six minutes later John Loveridge centred from the right but Walker lost the ball completely and it fell behind him for Albion's second goal.

After Wayne Hughes had rattled the Wolves crossbar Monaghan raced in to net goal number three in the 68th minute following Trenter's deft header.

Albion's victorious youngsters with the FA Youth Cup in May 1976.

Hawthorns Hat-tricks

Scored by Albion Players

George Dorsett, hat-tricks against Doncaster Rovers and Burton United in 1904.

Howard Gregory scored three times against Spurs in 1915.

Football League

1	R. Roberts	(3)	v	Bolton Wanderers	8 Dec 1900
2	C. Simmons	(3)	v	Blackpool	22 Feb 1902
3	T. Worton	(3)	v	Newton Heath	8 Mar 1902
4	G. Dorsett	(3)	v	Doncaster Rovers	24 Sep 1904
5	G. Dorsett	(3)	v	Burton United	8 Oct 1904
6	F. Shinton	(3)	v	Bradford City	11 Nov 1905
7	C. Simmons	(3)	v	Barnsley	26 Dec 1905
8	F. Shinton	(4)	v	Clapton Orient	6 Oct 1906
9	F. Shinton	(4)	v	Glossop North End	3 Nov 1906
10	F. Buck	(3)	v	Bradford City	17 Nov 1906
11	T. Dilly	(3)	v	Chesterfield	24 Nov 1906
12	F. Shinton	(4)	v	Grimsby Town	25 Dec 1906
13	W. Jordan	(3)	v	Gainsborough Trinity	16 Feb 1907
14	R. Pailor	(3)	v	Newcastle United	10 Feb 1912
15	A. Bentley	(4)	v	Burnley	6 Sep 1913
16	H. Gregory	(3)	v	Tottenham Hotspur	6 Apr 1915
17	S. Bowser	(3)	v	Bradford City	27 Sep 1919
18	F. Morris	(5)	v	Notts County	25 Oct 1919
19	F. Morris	(4)	v	Arsenal	14 Oct 1922
20	S. Davies	(3)	v	Sheffield United	31 Mar 1923
21	R. Blood	(3)	v	Everton	24 Nov 1923
22	J. Carter	(4)	v	Tottenham Hotspur	8 Dec 1923
23	R. Blood	(3)	v	Sheffield United	3 May 1924
24	C. Wilson	(3)	v	West Ham United	15 Nov 1924
25	G. James	(4)	v	Nottingham Forest	13 Dec 1924
26	G. James	(3)	v	Aston Villa	28 Feb 1925
27	S. Davies	(3)	v	West Ham United	24 Oct 1925
28	C. Wilson	(3)	v	Birmingham	6 Feb 1926
29	J. Cookson	(6)	v	Blackpool	17 Sep 1927
30	J. Cookson	(4)	v	Reading	21 Jan 1928
31	J. Cookson	(3)	v	Bradford	7 Sep 1929
32	T. Glidden	(4)	v	Swansea Town	26 Oct 1929
33	J. Cookson	(4)	v	Hull City	19 Apr 1930
34	J. Cookson	(4)	v	Southampton	3 May 1930
35	W. G. Richardson	(3)	v	Leicester City	24 Dec 1932
36	W. G. Richardson	(3)	v	Sunderland	26 Dec 1932
37	J. Carter	(3)	v	Manchester City	17 Apr 1933
38	W. G. Richardson	(4)	v	Derby County	30 Sep 1933
39	W. G. Richardson	(4)	v	Leeds United	6 Oct 1934

HAWTHORNS HAT-TRICKS

Ronnie Allen scored five League hat-tricks at The Hawthorns.

Derek Kevan scored six League hat-tricks at The Hawthorns, including a five-timer against Everton in March 1960.

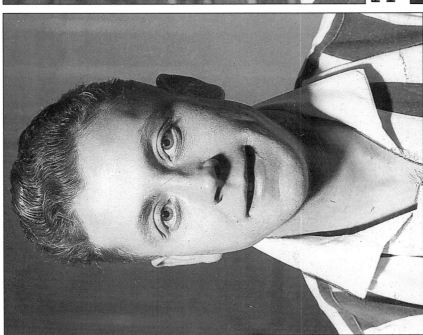

Joe Johnson netted four goals in a 6-0 win over Bury in March 1939.

Bobby Robson – four goals in the 5-1 win over Burnley in December 1957.

HAWTHORNS HAT-TRICKS

Lee Hughes scored two League hat-tricks at The Hawthorns in 1998.

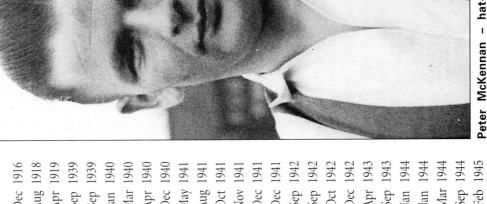

Peter McKennan – hat-trick hero against Northampton Town in 1941.

92	R. Taylor	(3)	v	Watford	12 Mar 1996
93	A. Hunt	(3)	v	Reading	10 Sep 1996
94	L. Hughes	(3)	v	Crystal Palace	5 Sep 1998
95	L. Hughes	(3)	v	Huddersfield Town	14 Nov 1998

FA Cup

1	G. James	(3)	v	Luton Town	10 Jan 1925
2	J. Cookson	(4)	v	Bradford	16 Feb 1929
3	W. G. Richardson	(3)	v	Sheffield United	26 Jan 1935
4	W. G. Richardson	(3)	v	Darlington	30 Jan 1937
5	D. Walsh	(3)	v	Chelsea	12 Feb 1949
6	R. Allen	(3)	v	Newcastle United	20 Feb 1954
7	D. Kevan	(3)	v	Plymouth Argyle	9 Jan 1960
8	T. Brown	(3)	v	Notts County	5 Jan 1974
9	K. Donovan	(3)	v	Aylesbury	14 Nov 1993

League Cup

1	J. Astle	(3)	v	Coventry City	10 Nov 1965
2	R. Hope	(3)	v	Aston Villa	14 Sep 1966
3	J. Astle	(3)	v	West Ham United	18 Jan 1967

Fairs Cup

1	T. Brown	(3)	v	DOS Utrecht	9 Nov 1966

Wartime

1	J. Mann	(3)	v	Aston Villa	26 Dec 1916
2	J. Roberts	(3)	v	Wolverhampton W	23 Aug 1918
3	T. Magee	(3)	v	RAF	22 Apr 1919
4	E. Jones	(3)	v	Tottenham Hotspur	2 Sep 1939
5	H. Jones	(3)	v	Stoke City	30 Sep 1939
6	H. Jones	(3)	v	Walsall	20 Jan 1940
7	H. Jones	(3)	v	Birmingham	25 Mar 1940
8	H. Jones	(3)	v	Luton Town	13 Apr 1940
9	W. G. Richardson	(3)	v	Leicester City	21 Dec 1940
10	W. G. Richardson	(6)	v	RAF	24 May 1941
11	H. Jones	(4)	v	Cardiff City	30 Aug 1941
12	W. G. Richardson	(5)	v	Swansea Town	18 Oct 1941
13	W. G. Richardson	(6)	v	Luton Town	22 Nov 1941
14	P. McKennan	(3)	v	Northampton Town	6 Dec 1941
15	W. G. Richardson	(3)	v	Birmingham	20 Dec 1941
16	W. Elliott	(3)	v	Northampton Town	5 Sep 1942
17	L. Millard	(3)	v	Leicester City	12 Sep 1942
18	L. Millard	(3)	v	Wolverhampton W	3 Oct 1942
19	W. Elliott	(3)	v	Leicester City	26 Dec 1942
20	W. G. Richardson	(3)	v	Northampton Town	26 Apr 1943
21	W. Elliott	(4)	v	Derby County	11 Sep 1943
22	H. Ball	(3)	v	Walsall	15 Jan 1944
23	W. Elliott	(3)	v	Walsall	15 Jan 1944
24	W. Elliott	(3)	v	Wolverhampton W	18 Mar 1944
25	I. Clarke	(3)	v	Coventry City	30 Sep 1944
26	I. Clarke	(3)	v	Birmingham City	17 Feb 1945
27	I. Clarke	(3)	v	Northampton Town	17 Mar 1945

Former Walsall centre-forward Gilbert Alsop scored four goals against a Football League XI in 1935.

Zenith Data Systems Cup

D. Saunders	(3)	Derby County	29 Nov	1989
I. Banks	(3)	Barnsley	21 Nov	1990

Birmingham Cup

C. Millington	(3)	Aston Villa	4 Sep	1905

Birmingham Charity Cup

S. Doncaster	(3)	Aston Villa	2 Oct	1912

Staffordshire Cup

C. Millington	(3)	Aston Villa	2 Oct	1905

King George V Jubilee Trust

R. Dix	(3)	Football League XI	8 May	1935
G Alsop	(4)	Football League XI	8 May	1935

Wartime

J. Morrison	(3)	Tottenham Hotspur	2 Sep	1939
J. Mullen	(3)	Leicester City	21 Dec	1940
F. Broome	(3)	Aston Villa	25 May	1942
G. Hinsley	(3)	Walsall	27 Nov	1943
F. Steele	(4)	Stoke City	19 Feb	1944
T. Sale	(3)	Stoke City	19 Feb	1944
G. Edwards	(3)	Aston Villa	2 Apr	1945
D. Massart	(3)	Birmingham City	12 May	1945
M. Tadman	(3)	Charlton Athletic	15 Apr	1946

Friendlies

F. Creek	(3)	Corinthians	28 Mar	1925
V. Busunov	(3)	CDSA, Moscow	29 Oct	1957

Testimonials

T. Ford	(3)	International XI (N. Heath)	25 Apr	1956
D. Kevan	(3)	WBA Past XI (G.Williams)	28 Apr	1965

down the pit. I was getting paid for doing something that I loved – playing football and competing.

Usually we would train in the mornings but often had to go back in the afternoon as well. Training consisted of fitness work, a five-mile run was a favourite of the coach, and team relays such as piggy-back races. We did some ball-work and several times during the week we would play practice games. Occasionally we would run, or be taken in a coach to the brine baths at Droitwich to enjoy a relaxing swim. I can remember travelling to Rhyl on several occasions. We would stay in a hotel for several days and do a lot of fitness work as well as playing tennis and golf. That was probably where I first got interested in golf.

The matches were very competitive and injuries frequent but the treatment was basic with the trainer, or his assistant, performing 'magical' massage. It was easy to aggravate an injury during a match because no substitutions were allowed in my day.

This is why the twelfth men were seen dressed in suits on the photographs which were taken when the Prince of Wales shook hands with the teams before the Cup Final.

Remember those old football boots? I certainly do. Several of mine were made by Mansfield Hotspur. They had uppers of brown moor calf with solid, firm soles that were riveted all round and don't forget those unbreakable toe-caps. I think I paid about 26 shillings for a pair and I would use either the 'Villan' or the 'United' model, depending on the playing conditions.

If a new pair were too tight I would lie in a hot bath with them firmly laced to my feet. Controlling the ball was not always easy with these boots but it was the same for everybody.

Occasionally we would play friendly matches and I can recall touring Ireland. We stayed at the Grand Hotel in Belfast and were given a civic welcome by the Lord Mayor of Belfast. The following day we played Linfield. After that it was on to Dublin for a match against Shelbourne, followed by a dinner that night, but we were given strict instructions by our manager 'to bed in good time lads.'

However, the meal did not compare with the celebration dinner following the Baggies' FA Cup Final victory over Birmingham in 1931. The reception was held at the Great Central Hotel, London and the eight courses were complimented by some excellent wine, Liebfraumlich Superior 1921 and Louis Roederer 1920. A good time was had by all.

I was fortunate to play with and against so many good players, but from the opposition I think Alex James of Arsenal was the best forward I ever faced. He could show a back the ball and then magic it away. Stan Matthews was also a wonderful player, so skilful and fast, but unfortunately he often tantalised the left-back and not me. The most gifted winger I ever faced was probably Cliff Bastin, also of Arsenal. He was superb – but when we beat the Gunners in front of almost 65,000 fans at The Hawthorns in the FA Cup in 1937, I think I did a good job on him.

In conclusion, I'm very grateful for my time with the Baggies and the opportunity to meet so many interesting and talented people. Even today as a 91 year-old there are still people who recognise me as Bob Finch, the Albion footballer.

reported on during that unforgettable run-up to Wembley and after the heady celebrations which followed our victory over Everton.

Lining up your pale-faced players for a yellow fever 'jab' is not the best preparation three days before a quarter-final tie with Bill Shankly's Liverpool. On the other hand it did give me something else to think about. I wasn't happy about this interruption but Dr Rimmer had such an enviable calming influence. He smoothed away my panic and even convinced me it was really nothing at all to worry about.

I passed on this gem of medical information to the players and Bobby Hope and Jeff Astle quickly suggested what I should do with the needles.

John Kaye muttered: "Bloody stupid. I'll have two – we might get Leeds in the semi-final!" and John Osborne looked as though he was being led to the scaffold.

A previously arranged end-of-season tour to East Africa was the reason for this unwelcome distraction. The Doc, bless him, was right, of course, but I have a feeling the 'jab' would have got a mention had we not put out Liverpool after two riveting replays watched by close on 150,000 lucky people.

Forty-eight hours after the Cup Final triumph, flying high on Moet in a VC 10, we were on our way to Dar-Es-Salaam.

The players were soon to find out that it needed something more than a yellow fever injection to protect them in Kampala. We played six matches on that tour and the hospitality wherever we went was first class. The two games in Dar-Es-Salaam and two in Nairobi all went well with no real problems. The other two were in Kampala and there was nothing friendly about either of them.

I had to read the *Daily Nation*

Alan Ashman

It's easy to recall memories of the 1968 FA Cup Final, but what I also remember very clearly are some of the happenings which were not

ful of West Brom directors and a small group of British residents and diplomats.

The following day I was assured by reporters that only the assassination of Senator Robert Kennedy in America had kept what they described as 'The Battle of Kampala' off their front pages.

I wondered if it might just have found space had they won?

Yes that was a memorable year – the year the Albion rolled up its sleeves and got the needle.

Jeff Astle

If I could have written the script to the 1968 FA Cup Final, it would have read: West Bromwich Albion 1 Everton 0. Goalscorer: Jeff Astle. We were destined to win the trophy that year (after a narrow escape at Col-

Jeff Astle – "If I'd written the script..."

ble. We mastered the Russians in their own backyard, gave mighty Honved and their famous Hungarian superstars, Puskas, Bozsik, Koscis and such likes, a run for their money in Brussels and we beat all the best teams in England over a period of three or four years including the Busby Babes from pre-Munich days.

I had some happy times at Albion. I made so many friends, some I'm still in contact with, and I wouldn't have swapped being a footballer for all the tea in China.

After leaving Albion in 1960 I had a brief spell with Birmingham City and then assisted Stourbridge before hanging up my boots.

I still attend matches at The Hawthorns – well I am a true Baggie – and I wish the team every success in the future...let's hope we can get into the Premiership.

Brendon Batson

Whenever people talk to me about West Bromwich Albion the thing that immediately springs to mind is one glorious season...the season we took Europe by storm in 1978-79.

I had left Arsenal without really making the grade but it was always my ambition to play at the highest level and in the highest Division I could, so when the chance came to leave Cambridge United to join Albion I jumped at it.

But I really didn't realise how well the move would turn out... thanks mainly to that wonderful season.

By the start of the 1978-79 campaign I had made my way into Ron Atkinson's first team in place of Paddy Mulligan... by the end of it I was established in the right-back position.

During that same season I had the truly magnificent experience of European football. Only now, with clubs still attempting to qualify for various European competitions, do I

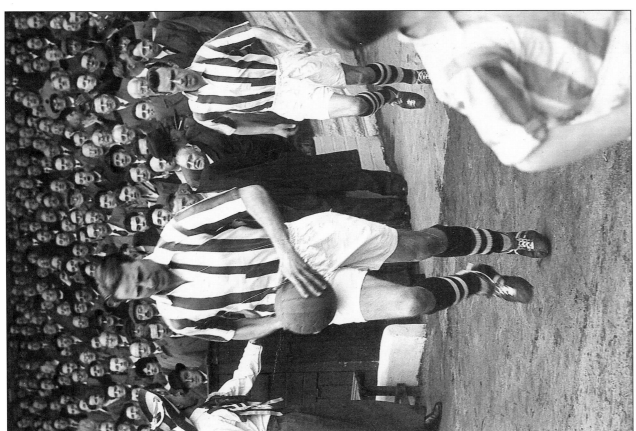

Ray Barlow (followed by Jimmy Dudley) leads out Albion for their FA Cup semi-final replay with Aston Villa at St Andrew's in 1957. Villa won 1-0.

had been replaced by Jesse Carver who in turn handed over the duties to Vic Buckingham. At that time we were a very strong team and in 1953-54 almost won the double. It was only through a crop of injuries (suffered after we had reached Wembley) plus international call-ups which stopped us from taking the League championship, but we made up for that disappointment by beating Preston in the Cup Final.

I must say that the players at Albion in the early 1950s were great – goalkeepers Norman Heath and Jimmy Sanders, full-backs Stan

Rickaby, and Len Millard, my fellow half-backs Jimmy Dudley, Joe Kennedy and Jimmy Dugdale, and a truly brilliant forward-line of Frank Griffin, Paddy Ryan, Ronnie Allen, Johnny Nicholls, George Lee – and just prior to that there was Dave Walsh. We had some quality reserves as well including Billy Brookes, Ken Hodgkisson, Wilf Carter and a few others.

We were a very consistent team; we played attractive football – we were made to by the boss – and I believe we could have won the European Cup if it had been possi-

have a word of advice as would John Wile – but if I stepped out of line they would come down on me like a ton of bricks. Yet I learned an awful lot from both of them and copied their attitude, leadership and discipline. I wouldn't have been half the player if it wasn't for the professionals of the day – the Robertsons, Wiles, Brendon Batsons, Bryan Robsons and so on... they were so good that we hardly needed a manager.

And once I had become an experienced professional myself I tried to pass tips on to the younger Albion players as they came into the club. If kids get a good grounding and a good start like I did, then it will stay with them for the rest of their lives.

The team I played in went on to represent Britain (England if you like) in Europe and reached two FA semi-finals, one of which – the FA Cup clash with Queens Park Rangers at Highbury in 1982 – was the most disappointing day of my footballing life.

But the good times helped me through all of my injury problems and I felt the good times were just around the corner again before I was forced to quit the game with a back injury in 1990 at the age of 29. I so much wanted to be part of it – but it wasn't to be and although I still watch the team, it's nothing like the real thing, being out there on the pitch yourself.

Wilf Carter

My earliest memories of the Albion were when I was a toddler, just big enough to be able to look over the wall at the Birmingham Road End of the ground. Some of my favourite players at that time in the mid-1940s, were Billy Gripton, Jim Pemberton, Harry Kinsell, Frank Hodgetts and Ike Clarke. When I was 15 years of age (late 1948) I started work as an office boy at The

Wilf Carter is beaten to the ball by Charlton goalkeeper Sam Bartram in 1954.

Hawthorns under the watchful eyes of Eph Smith, Alan Everiss and manager Jack Smith, who eventually signed me as a professional – that was the happiest day of my life – the fifth January 1951.

My fondest memory of my stay at The Hawthorns was being a non-playing member of the 1954 Cup-winning squad. Along with Stuart Williams, Freddie Cox and Billy Brookes, we travelled to London as part of the 'team' that almost achieved the coveted League and Cup double that season.

Another happy memory for me came the following season when Albion drew 4-4 with rivals Wolves in front of 45,000 fans at Molineux in the annual FA Charity Shield game. We had two goals disallowed

that night and with some justification you could say we were robbed. Nevertheless I have treasured the plaque I received for sharing that shield with the Wolves.

I obviously recall my debut for Albion against Fulham at Craven Cottage in September 1951 when I deputised for the injured Arthur Smith at inside-right. After scoring four goals in four pre-season friendly matches at The Hawthorns I became part of the first team set up and was over the moon when I was named in the side. Unfortunately we lost 1-0 in front of 30,000 fans, but I had made the breakthrough.

Soon afterwards I returned to London for my second senior outing and this time we beat Chelsea 3-1 and I scored my first goal.

recollections on joining the club was to witness the sheer brilliance of the 1954 FA Cup winning side. I was in awe of them watching the magic of their play, the pin-point passing, the delicate footwork and the intelligent unselfish running off the ball. The Hawthorns was certainly the place to be to learn the trade.

Despite the stress, the injuries, the tellings-off and the inevitable demotion, I quite enjoyed my stay with Albion. There were a few moments of glory, just a little bit of fame, but best of all I made lots of friends.

Chuck Drury – in awe of the 1954 FA Cup winning players.

I remember some great times I had with fellow team-mates, particularly Derek Kevan, Keith Smith, Jimmy Campbell, Alec Jackson and Chippy Clark. I used to enjoy the training and had a few laughs in the dressing room with our resident comedian Barry Hughes. He was hilarious. Probably his best story was when he portrayed the club Directors in the roles of cavalrymen which he'd seen in a western film the previous night.

There are three matches which will always stick in my mind. One

was an FA Cup-tie at The Hawthorns against Spurs in 1962. My instruction from the manager Archie Macaulay was to mark Jimmy Greaves out of the game. I failed miserably, Greaves scored twice and we lost 4-2. Although somewhat exonerated by the manager I felt very badly about allowing him so much space.

Another game was when we played Wolves at Molineux a month after that Spurs encounter. It was an evening kick-off and on the morning of the match my son, Carl, was very ill in hospital. There were complications after he had broken his leg. Obviously I was worried sick but I decided to play in order to take my mind off things. We performed brilliantly and won 5-1, and I was rewarded with my only goal for Albion – a screamer from 25 yards. Thankfully Carl recovered from his ordeal.

The third game was the last match of the 1961-62 season at White Hart Lane. We beat Spurs, the reigning League champions and FA Cup holders, 2-1 in front of 52,000 fans. Some of my family were there to see us beat the country's best team.

Jimmy Dugdale

When I signed professional forms for Albion in the summer of 1952 I was paid £12-a-week. Later on in my career I earned up to £30-a-week (including £5 appearance money) and even when I played for England 'B' in Hungary I only got 2s 6d (13p) for one day's expenses. When Albion won the Cup in 1954 all the players received a £20 bonus for that Wembley occasion. Nothing like what players receive today – then those were the days before freedom of contract that has ultimately given footballers the licence to print money.

Players like myself from the old

days aren't jealous because we all know the game can be a precarious business. It's a limited lifespan and in any case the next tackle could always be the one to put you out for good.

The game was hard but fair in my day. We always had a drink after every game and had lots of laughs. I remember the late Johnny Nicholls, a great pal of mine, coming out of manager Vic Buckingham's office at The Hawthorns one day looking gob-smacked.

He, like myself, had just played against Preston in the 1954 FA Cup Final. He had scored almost 30 goals that season and all of a sudden had found that he he had been docked ten bob (50p) a week from his wages for not scoring enough.

The expression of Nicco's face had to been seen to be believed. But it was true and furthermore there was nothing he could do about it.

I had a great time at Albion. I

Jimmy Dugdale – his pal Johnny Nicholls suffered a wage cut for not scoring enough.

team and saw some exciting players develop, among them Martyn Bennett, Mickey Lewis (one of my best finds), Carlton Palmer, David Burrows, even a young Sean Flynn (in the mid 1980s – a player we initially missed) and Gary Robson.

In later years I did a lot of scouting and although the game, the team, the ground have all changed,

football is still my game, and I would do it all over again given the opportunity.

Bobby Hope

Throughout my footballing career I always believed in entertaining the crowds – and, believe me, that's exactly what we did when I played for the Albion.

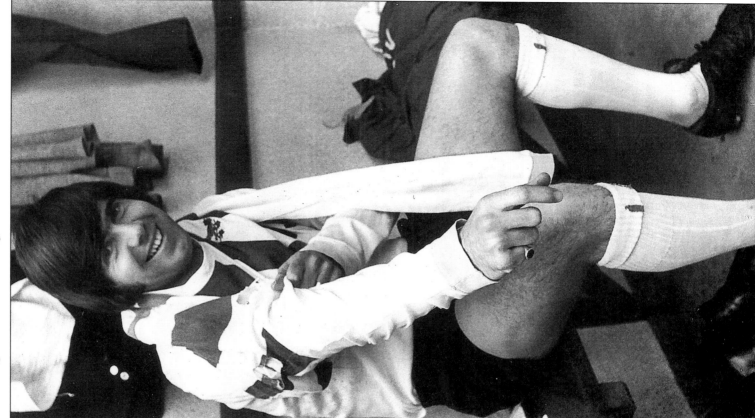

Bobby Hope "...I always tried to entertain. That's what footballers are paid for..."

Ken Hodgkisson – he thought his debut call-up was a joke.

wards I scored my first senior goal in a 2-2 draw at Old Trafford.

Trainer Arthur Fitton gave me plenty of encouragement in the dressing room before the game and out on the pitch Ronnie Allen and Ray Barlow were also so obliging.

At the start of my Albion career Billy Elliott and Jim Sanders – who always seemed to be puffing away on a cigarette – gave me great support as did the other two trainers, Arthur Fitton and 'W. G.' Richardson.

After six years at The Hawthorns I moved to Walsall in 1955, staying at Fellows Park until 1966. After that I assisted Worcester City, Dudley Town as both a player and manager before linking up with my old Walsall colleague Albert McPherson on the coaching staff at The Hawthorns in 1975. Initially I looked after the youngsters who came to the club for night training. I helped Albert 'Mac' with the youth

Harry Kinsell

Just lately my life seems to have been spent visiting the doctors or the hospital – who'd get old? I was 78 in May 1999.

I first joined Albion as a 14 year-old and played for the third team for two seasons then I moved into the Central League side and signed professional forms on my 17th birthday.

The signing-on fee then was just £10. Six months after my 18th birthday I was playing for Albion's reserves against Stoke and they tried to sign me for £2,000. There was no Bosman Rule in those days and on reflection I'm glad I stayed on.

Unfortunately the outbreak of World War Two interrupted my career – as it did for so many other footballers.

I joined the forces and became a PT instructor stationed in Blackpool, therefore I was able to play in some great sides up there which included Stanley Matthews, Stan Mortensen, Harry Johnston and Ronnie Dix. We reached the 1944 Wartime Cup Final but lost to Aston Villa.

My first job of the day as a junior with Albion was to clean out the cage and feed the bird (the thrush – the Black Country throstle).

On a Saturday home game it was given pride of place in its cage, hanging proudly on the front of the main Halford's Lane stand above the players' tunnel. Of course, the caging of wild birds is illegal now – so Albion have to make do with one on a badge or that ornamental 'Throstle' near the Smethwick End.

Also as a junior – after I had completed my chores for the day – I used to enjoy a game of snooker with Sammy Short, the third team trainer. He was quite a good player and if he hadn't been a professional footballer (he played inside-forward for Albion in the 1920s) he could well have become a Fred or even Steve Davis.

I suppose my best pals at The Hawthorns were wing-half Cliff Edwards, a local Cannock lad like myself, right-winger Billy Elliott, those two great Irish internationals Dave Walsh and Jack Vernon, and full-back Bob Finch from Hednesford, who was coming to the end of his career when I first joined the club. He's still alive now – the old codger.

I must tell you about the incident of the GREEN cockerel. We had gone on a tour to Belgium and Luxembourg in 1946 to play three matches. At the start of the first game against a Belgium XI in Verviers, Billy Elliott was presented with a green cockerel in a lovely resplendent cage. We were all proud of our trophy and it travelled around with us, staying in our hotel rooms. One night Ray Barlow, always game for a laugh decided to put a hard boiled egg inside the cage.

The next morning when we looked into the cage there were some of us who thought the bird had laid it.

Harry Kinsell, tells the story of the 'green cockrel'.

figured briefly under Johnny Giles' management before leaving The Hawthorns for Kidderminster Harriers and then deciding to move over to the States where I am living and working right now.

Good luck to the Albion – let's hope you can make it into the Premiership to celebrate the Millennium in style.

David Mills

When I joined West Bromwich Albion in January 1979 I became Britain's costliest footballer – the fee was £516,000.

I went to The Hawthorns with a lot of optimism but an unfortunate first five months in the Midlands paved the way for things to come for me.

Albion were doing very well that season and Ron Atkinson bought me to strengthen a side that was bang on course for the First Division title.

When I joined up with Albion I was happy with my form having played well for Middlesbrough. I was ambitious and had no hesitation in making the move south.

But things began to go a little wrong shortly after my arrival at The Hawthorns.

Firstly, the weather took a turn for the worse and Albion had several matches wiped out...All of a sudden we were left without any fixtures.

Then when the games finally did continue, Ron Atkinson decided to keep faith in the side that had done well for him in the first half of the season, which meant I was on the substitute's bench.

It was difficult to assess his decision but at the time I had to see it from both points of view.

After doing do well the player who would have been left out in my favour would surely have felt hard done by. So there I was, after the biggest move of my life, still not playing football.

When I finally did get into the side, we maintained our challenge and finished third in the League, but I felt my big break would come the following season – I was to be proved wrong.

During an end-of-season testimonial match at Birmingham for defender Garry Pendrey I badly damaged a tendon and ended up with my leg in plaster throughout the summer.

That first unlucky period set a seal on the rest of my contract. I never got myself into a position where I could have a decent run in the first team – a period of concerted effort.

Had it not have been for the injury, or the bad weather, who knows what would have happened – but that's football.

I have often been asked if I regretted my move to Albion... I can honestly say I didn't then and still don't.

David Mills, once the most expensive footballer in Britain.

Heath, Brierley Hill and Wolverhampton. We were all rough but a good set of lads nevertheless.

When I eventually made the breakthrough into the first team it was in the fifth round of the FA Cup away at Blackburn in 1952. More than 51,000 packed into Ewood Park that day to see Rovers win 1-0, Bill Eckersley scoring from the penalty spot with just five minutes to go.

Ronnie Allen was injured for that game – and that's how I got my chance – but I managed to keep my place when Ronnie came back, and I couldn't have done anything without him as a striking partner.

Of course, I will always remember the 1954 FA Cup Final against Preston North End at Wembley. In those days you could only play at Wembley in this competition or for England so it was something extra special for us players.

That side was one of Albion's greatest ever – managed by Vic Buckingham, the best boss I've ever played under.

Even Bryan Robson wouldn't have got into that side, and I think, with three more players to strengthen the squad, we would have achieved the double that season. As it was we won the Cup and finished second in the League behind our arch rivals the Wolves.

Other matches that spring to mind are the 7-3 win at Newcastle early in the 1953-54 season when I scored my first Albion hat-trick and we were cheered off the pitch; our Christmas encounter with Liverpool in 1953 when we won 5-2 and when I played alongside Ronnie Allen for England against Scotland at Hampden Park in April 1954 in front of 134,000 spectators. That was tremendous and we both had the pleasure of scoring in an excellent 4-2 win.

Those really were the days.

Johnny Nicholls, one of a team of 'Black Country lads'.

You see, football was a sport in my day. We had to work hard and we had to play hard, and we never took anything for granted.

We had to come up through the ranks before we had a chance of playing in the first team – and there were about seven or eight Albion sides when I was there, but you would never want to ask for a transfer.

My memories of those great years lingered on and on. We travelled first-class on the trains and stayed in top hotels all round the country. And there are many memorable matches to recall.

My first boss at The Hawthorns was Jack Smith, who had a dream to get a complete Black Country team of lads together. They came from West Bromwich, Dudley, Tipton, Oldbury, Smethwick, Cradley

ALBION AND ME . . .

Geoff Richards (third from left) reports for training in August 1947 along with Aldridge, Hood, Elliott, assistant trainer W. G. Richardson, Tighe, Walsh, Kinsell, Hodgetts and Pemberton.

gain a 1-1 draw against the eventual Second Division champions.

That weekend in 1948 was quite amazing. I played for Albion's second team on the Saturday, their third team on the Monday and the first team on the Tuesday.

My special pals at Albion were the late Johnny Nicholls, Norman Heath and Harry Guy. Unfortunately a serious knee injury ended my professional career in 1952.

Stan Rickaby

My time at The Hawthorns was the happiest and most successful of my footballing career but the way it ended was very disappointing and, indeed, hurtful.

From August 1950 to April 1955 I must have played more games for the first team than any other player. In the spring of 1955 a few journalists were writing that I should have been back in the England team, and I felt that I was playing as well as

ever – and the player himself knows whether he is playing well or not.

My last game was against Sheffield United at The Hawthorns. We played poorly after indications during the season that we could reach the heights achieved by that great 1953-54 team.

For instance, I had two excellent games, plus many more, against the Wolves in the FA Charity Shield and Honved in Brussels. Coming off the field after the Sheffield game, Jimmy Dudley said to me: "Well played Stan, it's a good job you played well...or words to that effect. Then we were all staggered to see that my name was missing from the team-sheet for the next game, the local derby against Wolves at The Hawthorns. I had never been dropped before and I had played a couple of hundred games, missing only one through 'flu and about five or six at the end of the 1953-54 season, including the Cup Final, after taking a knock in the sixth-round tie

with Tottenham Hotspur and making it worse by playing in the semi-final against Port Vale.

I was in the England squad for the World Cup in the summer of 1954 but had to pull out with that injury.

A very annoying postscript to all this has been the often quoted 'Stan left under a cloud'. That cloud was created presumably by manager Vic Buckingham, who put me on the transfer list.

He gave no explanation, but I always thought that the mechanisations of the Albion chairman and the Wrexham chairman whose son, Stuart Williams, just happened to be a useful full back – but none would have said he was better than me – were responsible.

I always thought Vic and I had a great rapport, and right up to my last game he had never criticised me. Indeed, I was the first player he spoke to when he joined the club. We were playing Chelsea in a FA

anything for their tremendous supporters.

I had many special moments but the time that really sticks out is that great day in 1976 when we needed to beat Oldham Athletic to gain promotion to the First Division.

Getting off the team coach, all you could see was a sea of navy blue and white and yellow and green.

On the down side, my great disappointments were losing in three FA Cup semi-finals – twice in the FA Cup and once in the League Cup as it was then known.

But throughout the years I lost my heart to the club – and I still have a very soft spot (and a shareholding) at The Hawthorns.

I played alongside some great characters too.

One of the greatest was John Kaye – a player I really looked up to when I was a youngster at Albion.

Although I was after John's place, he taught me everything he knew and gave me as much help as he could – and that stood me in good stead for the rest of my career.

Willie Johnston was another tremendous character and one of the biggest practical jokers in the game.

I remember when we were playing badly under Don Howe and he came out for one match wearing a mask.

Managers, too, came and went, yet I learned different things from each of them.

Don Howe was one of the best coaches in British football and I was lucky to serve under him in my early days. But I will never forget the professionalism of Johnny Giles and the flamboyancy of Ron Atkinson.

They all helped to shape the great players of the 1970s including Bryan Robson – just ask him.

I feel if we could have kept a settled side in the late 1970s we could have won many honours.

But that's football and I wouldn't have swapped my time at Albion for anything.

From my debut against Manchester United as a 17-year-old when I played against George Best, Dennis Law and Bobby Charlton – right up until the later times, Albion was always special to me – and always will be.

Bobby Robson

I always think back to my time at The Hawthorns as being an extremely good and lucky period of my career as a professional footballer. While I was there the place was best with great players: Ray Barlow, Ronnie Allen, Joe Kennedy, Frank Griffin, Jimmy Dudley, Maurice Setters, Alec Jackson, Davey Burnside, Len Millard, Don Howe, Derek Kevan, Stuart and Graham Williams and goalkeepers Jim Sanders and Jock Wallace – the list goes on and on. I was fortunate enough to be selected for England when I was with the Albion and being in the company of players of that calibre had certainly enhanced my chances of being considered for the international side. They had all helped me and brought me on.

The Hawthorns was a special

Bobby Robson – "My time at The Hawthorns was a lucky period in my career..."

with my good and bad times in the 13 years I spent at The Hawthorns.

Both Bill and his wife Ivy were very close friends, even after our playing days had ended.

We were preparing to commence our activities in the Second Division at the time I arrived, following World War Two, but with shrewd transfers we were building a great team and by 1948-49 we had won promotion to the top flight.

That season meant a lot to me. I passed out as a grade 'A' football coach under Walter Winterbottom, the then England manager and I also saved nine out of 11 penalties, which I believe is still a record for one season.

When travelling to away matches we (Billy Elliott, Jack Vernon, Dave Walsh and myself) always stuck to the same card school. And Bill and I always shared rooms.

Our trips abroad were pretty good as well and we gained some tremendous results, being the first English club side to win in Russia and returning unbeaten.

All the time I was with the Albion we had a first class team spirit, both on and off the field.

As regards nerves, I can only recollect having that sensation once – that was waiting in the tunnel at Wembley before we played Preston in the 1954 FA Cup Final. I was nervous when Ronnie Allen was about to take that vital penalty – I just turned my back and said: 'Come on Ron, do the business.'

But as Sir Stanley Matthews said "… any player that says he didn't have butterflies was not speaking the truth."

I could go on for ages, but all I can say is that I was fortunate to play behind three of the greatest centre-halves I have ever seen – namely Jack Vernon, Joe Kennedy and Jimmy Dugdale – and one of the finest left-halves in Ray Barlow.

I only hope all those lads enjoyed their years with the Albion like I did.

Certainly when Len Millard, George Lee and myself were all given free transfers in 1958 for services rendered, we were all very sad to say goodbye to a great club.

David Shaw

I jumped at the chance of joining Albion from Oldham Athletic in March 1973. Coming from the Third to the First Division was a big step for me. It was almost like going from a foreman to managing director in just 24 hours.

The atmosphere at The Hawthorns was completely different. At Boundary Park our play had enterprising promise but we missed pro-

motion. At Albion I went into a team that was desperately searching for points in a relegation battle which we lost. But that was not my fault. Indeed, there can't be too many players who have gone from the Third Division to the First and then into the Second in such a short period of time.

Relegation didn't hit me as hard as it did my team-mates. Jeff Astle, Tony Brown, Willie Johnston, Asa Hartford, Len Cantello and Ally Robertson and John Osborne were stunned. They couldn't believe it. But that's football…you're on a high one minute and at a low ebb the next.

Our manager Don Howe, however, was determined to get us all in

David Shaw – "I jumped at the chance of joining Albion…"

stay there and play football. Then Johnny Hartery, a player with Limerick, persuaded me to join his club. This was in 1943 when I was just 19. After that things went from strength to strength. I moved to Shelbourne (Dublin) and during a Cup game I was spotted by Linfield. Overlooking the fact that I was a Catholic, I signed for the Protestant club. In 1945-46 I scored over 60 goals – a record that still stands in Irish football – and this sort of form enticed several scouts to sail across the Irish Sea, including two from the Albion. After some talking I agreed to join Albion for £3,000 and the next four years were terrific for me. I scored 100 goals, helped the Baggies win promotion to the First Division in 1949 and made so many friends, some of whom I still see. I moved to Villa Park for £23,000 in 1950 and later played for Walsall. But it was at The Hawthorns where I enjoyed my football and saw it blossom. I played regularly at international level (I won over 25 caps all told) and my proudest moment

in the green jersey of Ireland was when we beat England 2-0 at Goodison Park, becoming the first overseas country to win on English soil.

One of my fondest memories in an Albion shirt was to score a hat-trick against Chelsea in a fifth-round FA Cup-tie at The Hawthorns. I was told afterwards that the commentator, Raymond Glendenning, who was covering the match on the radio for the BBC, said it was a 'red letter day' and one of the finest performances he had ever seen from a centre-forward. I was proud of that but it wasn't just down to me that day – my team-mates were brilliant.

I also recall the day we won 3-0 at Leicester to clinch a place in the First Division and when we beat the League champions Portsmouth at The Hawthorns in successive seasons without conceding a goal.

Albion had some great players immediately after the war – Jack Vernon, Ray Barlow, Billy Elliott, Jack Haines and Ike Clarke among

them. But I suppose everyone who played with these stars said the same thing. They were brilliant. Yet I also thought that Jimmy Duggan, Glyn Hood, Billy Gripton, Reg Ryan, Frank Hodgetts and Arthur Rowley were all very good footballers. Paddy Ryan and I were great mates and Arthur Rowley went on to become a magnificent goalscorer. Albion should have never sold him when they did.

I now live in Thurlestone, Devon but I never fail to visit The Hawthorns to watch Albion in action when I'm visiting the Midlands. I had such a great time there that I will forever be in debt to the club.

Brian Whitehouse

I had some great years at The Hawthorns, playing with some terrific footballers and making so many friends including Derek Kevan, Don Howe, Johnny Nicholls and Maurice Setters.

A couple of memorable moments from my Albion days were naturally when I scored two goals against

Brian Whitehouse – memorable moments include two goals against Villa in an FA Cup semi-final, and the trip to the USSR in 1957. This picture shows Whitehouse scoring against Blackpool in 1959.

John Trewick – former Albion player, now coach

I always wanted to be a footballer. I never considered anything else. In fact if I hadn't made the grade I don't know what I would have taken up.

I was playing in a local game in Northumberland when I was spotted by Albion's North-East scout, the late Bill Emery, when I was about 12. He invited me – and my parents – to visit The Hawthorns in the school holidays. He sold the club very well and I signed schoolboy forms, later becoming an apprentice (1972) and then being upgraded to professionalism.

I had some great times with Albion. There was that tremendous period under Johnny Giles when we won promotion from the Second Division in 1976. Then we played in the UEFA Cup against the likes of Red Star Belgrade and Valencia. We reached the semi-final of the FA Cup in 1978, finished third in the First Division behind Liverpool and Nottingham Forest and visited China. But I shall never forget my first-team debut in 1974 – a lasting memory that.

There were some great guys at the club and I roomed, on away trips, with Bryan Robson, Derek Statham, Brendon Batson and John Wile. Mick Martin was the joker in the pack – always up to something, like all the Irish folk I know. And David Cross often entertained us with his antics, likewise Willie Johnston.

Laurie Cunningham, Cyrille Regis and Brendon Batson – the Three Degrees – certainly had the style and the dress sense!

And most of us – if not all – had cars. Not flashy ones – we weren't paid enough – but some of the lads used to add flared wheel arches and sporty wheels to their models as well as go-faster stripes. We players always got rollickings from the various managers in our time – it was routine in football and still is I believe! Even the gentlest of them all – Johnny Giles – gave me a few tickings off. But it was all worthwhile. I learnt a lot from so many people and now I'm enjoying working at the club again, hoping to encourage younger players to come forward and wear the navy blue and white stripes of West Bromwich Albion Football Club.

John Evans (Albion secretary)

My most dramatic memories of The Hawthorns are of the impressions it made on me as a boy growing up in the Black Country in the 1950s. It formed part of what modern writers would term my 'rites of passage'.

I remember that at first I wanted to come because I knew that here was where the big boys and their dads came on Saturdays. A week after my eighth birthday I was deemed big enough to watch Albion play Derby County. It was February 1951.

The remember the crowds, the bustle, the noise; being parted from dad to go through the boys' turnstile; the relief at finding him again waiting for me on the other side.

Being squeezed tightly to the front and then the roar as the players appeared, being frightened and exhilarated all at the same time, then going home to tell my mum all about it.

I remember my first Black Country derby, getting soaked so badly in a thunderstorm that dad had to take me out. We won 2-1 but I missed all of the real action. I was not allowed to go to see the return game at Molineux next day – but Albion won 4-1 without me anyway!

I also recall when my dad was working away, begging my mum to let me come on my own. Alec Jackson had just got into the team and he was from Tipton, too, so he needed my support, didn't he?

Eventually she gave in and I ran to catch the No.74 bus from Great Bridge – just in time.

I still remember wonderful days and wonderful nights, triumphs and despair.

The fifth-round FA Cup defeat at the hands of Birmingham City in 1956, the hammering of Manchester City 9-2 in 1957 and beating the Busby Babes 4-3 only a few months before the tragic Munich air crash.

Oh yes – I remember The Hawthorns.

Denis Sunley (*Express & Star*)

I have very warm memories of West Bromwich Albion – literally.

One of my earlier assignments for the *Express & Star* was to go away with Albion for a pre-season tournament to Yugoslavia in 1980-81. No problems, I thought. A nice little trip this, watch a few football matches and then back home. What I didn't reckon on was the weather.

Having spent most of my life shivering on touchlines up and down the country watching matches being played in freezing cold conditions with rain coming down like stair-rods, I flew out to Yugoslavia well prepared. Wife, Linda, God bless her, had packed all my usual footballing clothes – overcoat, rain-coat, three woolly jumpers, thermal underwear, gloves, scarf, hat...the lot.

So you can imagine how I felt when we finally arrived at our destination – a boiling hot holiday resort on the Adriatic coast. 'That'll teach me to spend a bit more time swotting up on these matters' I thought as I made my way off the plane at sweltering Split airport.

And as the temperature soared up to melting point over the next few days, I was to learn what a friendly,

Subscribers

The Abraham Family
David Adams
Roger, Kim and Matthew Adams
Robert Aiken
Mike Allen
William H Allen
Geoff Allman
T W Angell
Mr M D Anstis
Nick Archer
Michael J Argent
Peter J Arnold
Sid Ashfield
Royston Atkin
Scott Baggott
Adam Bailey
John Albert Bailey
Steven Bailey
Brian Baker
Daniel Paul Baker
Harry Allan Baker
Ken Baker
Mr Phillip Ballard
Craig Ballinger
Len Ballinger
Kenny Banks
Martin Banner
Cyril Banyard
Vince Barber
Steve Barber
John Barlow
Gillian Barker
Paul Barker
Thomas Wilson Barrett
Jeremy Bate
John Bateman
Colin Baulch
Dave and Peter Baxendale
Michael Baxter
Peter Baxter

Michael Beard
Paul and Alistair Beard
Steve Beard
Ron Beards
Roy Belcher
Joe Davis James Bell
Neil Benbow
Trevor Bickley
Mr Lee Biddle
Mark W Bifield
Fred Birch
Daniel Bird
Lyndon Bird
R J Bird
Mr P K Birdi
Brian Bishop
Stuart Bishop
Mr S J Bissell
George Blackham
Ian Blackham
Anthony Blogg
Daniel Bloomer
Christopher Blunt
W Blunt
Gilbert Board
Sue Board
A A Boffy
Paul Bolton
Edward Bone
Peter Bone
Richard Boucher
G A Bowen
Neil R Boxley
Carl Bradford
Richard Bradford
Robert S Bradley
Neil Brealey
Paul Andrew Brindley
Peter J Broadist
The Brothwood Family

SUBSCRIBERS

J W Lloyd
J W Lovell
John Loveridge
Ryan Peter Lugg
Dave Lyons
Timothy McCarthy
Marcus McDermott
Chris McDonald
S G McNeil
Cathy and John Maddox
Mr Ashok Mal
Mr T B Mallin
Manchester Branch of WBASC:
　Ade Brandwood
　Hayden James Cooper
　Martin Dunn
　Steve Dunn
　Chris Foxall
　John, Chris & Eithne Hackett
　Malcolm Jones
　Paul Iain Morgan
　Haydn Thompson
　Richard Wagner
　Paul Wagner
　Justin Wilkes
Lee Manning
R Mantle
John Marsh
Adrian Marshall
Kevin Martin
Alan Masefield
Bobby Mason
David Mason
Luke Jonathan Mason
Tom Mason
Freda Matthews
Melvyn Meacham
Steve Finn and Linda Millard
Mark T Miller
Gemma Millinchip
K D Millington
Michael John Mills
Paul J Mills
Robert L Mills
Robert Whitelaw Mills

Stephen Mole
David and Christopher Moore
Harpreet Moore
Helen Moore
John Moore
June Moore
Jamie Moren
Mike Moren
P A Moren
John Morgan
Chas Morris
David Morris
Geoff A Morris
Huw Morris
R G Morris
Ryan Morris
Kevin Mortiboys
Craig Moseley
Martin Moseley
Paul James Moss
Francis James Moy
Stuart James Moy
Roy Mytton
Anthony Nash
Geoff Nevey
Tom Newton
John R Nicholls
Ricky Thomas Nicholls
Roy Nicholls
Kevin Nichols
Andy Nickless
Christopher Nickless
Michael James Nicklin
David Nixon
John Noon
Mick and Tom Northall
Eric Offley
Stephen Offley
Mark Oliver
Chris O'Neill
Tim Osborne
Steven Paul Owen
Douglas Parish
Barry Parker
A S Parkes

SUBSCRIBERS

Paul, Kath, Emma, Amy and Laura Shaw
Philip Shaw
Richard Shaw
Robert Shelswell
Kenneth Shutt
Keith Siggins
Tom Silk
Michael Silvester
Daniel Silwood
G A Simcox
Judy Simcox
Bernard and Michael Simmonite
G M Simmons
Colin Simpson
Gareth D Sims
Paul Siviter
Bob Skelding
Neil and Luke Skett
Craig Skidmore
John Skidmore
Mr S Skidmore
Reg Smallwood
Christopher Smith
Darryl Smith
Denys A Smith
Graham Smith
Jonathan Smith
Lee Smith
Neil Smith
Philip Smith
Rhys Smith
Stuart Smith
Dale A B Smyth
Paul W B Smyth
Stephen Smytheman
Michael Snell
Ross Snell
Will Spencer
David Spicer
Michael Spink
Leigh Sprules
Steven Sorrill
Lee A Southall
Paul Spence
Martyn Spink

Glyn D Stacey
Craig Stanton
Andrew and David Stevens
David Stokes
Joseph Stubbs
Michelle Styles
David John Sutton
Laura, Jack and Sarah Swallow
Peter Swanick
Alfred W Swann
Russell Swingell
Pat Talbot
Andrew Taylor
David Taylor
Kenneth Taylor
Laurie Taylor
Mark Garry Taylor
Peter Taylor
Brian Terence
Phil Terry
Eric Thomas
Michael Thomas
Paul Thomas
Jayne Thompson
Roger Thompson
David Thorpe
Dennis Thorpe
Ivan I Tibbetts
Paul Tilley
W Timmington
Mrs B M Timmins
Ben Thorne
D Thornhill
Malcolm Tolley
Stephen Tongue
Barbara A Tout
James S Tranter
Jonathan Tranter
Paul Trattles
G W Treadwell
R K Trentham
Andrew Trumper
Nicholas Trumper
Ian J Tubby
Mr Adrian Turley

anything for their tremendous supporters.

I had many special moments but the time that really sticks out is that great day in 1976 when we needed to beat Oldham Athletic to gain promotion to the First Division.

Getting off the team coach, all you could see was a sea of navy blue and white and yellow and green.

On the down side, my great disappointments were losing in three FA Cup semi-finals – twice in the FA Cup and once in the League Cup as it was then known.

But throughout the years I lost my heart to the club – and I still have a very soft spot (and a shareholding) at The Hawthorns.

I played alongside some great characters too.

One of the greatest was John Kaye – a player I really looked up to when I was a youngster at Albion.

Although I was after John's place, he taught me everything he knew and gave me as much help as he could – and that stood me in good stead for the rest of my career.

Willie Johnston was another tremendous character and one of the biggest practical jokers in the game.

I remember when we were playing badly under Don Howe and he came out for one match wearing a mask.

Managers, too, came and went, yet I learned different things from each of them.

Don Howe was one of the best coaches in British football and I was lucky to serve under him in my early days. But I will never forget the professionalism of Johnny Giles and the flamboyancy of Ron Atkinson.

They all helped to shape the great players of the 1970s including Bryan Robson – just ask him.

I feel if we could have kept a settled side in the late 1970s we could have won many honours.

But that's football and I wouldn't have swapped my time at Albion for anything.

From my debut against Manchester United as a 17-year-old when I played against George Best, Dennis Law and Bobby Charlton – right up until the later times, Albion was always special to me – and always will be.

Bobby Robson

I always think back to my time at The Hawthorns as being an extremely good and lucky period of my career as a professional footballer. While I was there the place was best with great players: Ray Barlow, Ronnie Allen, Joe Kennedy, Frank Griffin, Jimmy Dudley, Maurice Setters, Alec Jackson, Davey Burnside, Len Millard, Don Howe, Derek Kevan, Stuart and Graham Williams and goalkeepers Jim Sanders and Jock Wallace – the list goes on and on. I was fortunate enough to be selected for England when I was with the Albion and being in the company of players of that calibre had certainly enhanced my chances of being considered for the international side. They had all helped me and brought me on.

The Hawthorns was a special

Bobby Robson – "My time at The Hawthorns was a lucky period in my career..."

Jim Sanders in action in the 1954 FA Cup Final against Preston. "I turned my back when Ronnie Allen took that penalty…"

place to be at that time. We've all come across the expression 'total football' and I've often heard it used at international level, though it's still a relatively modern concept. But at the Albion we had defenders who could pass like inside-forwards and half-backs who could shoot like forwards. These players showed me what 'total football' was.

Vic Buckingham, our manager, was a man of flair and imagination who personified the club at that time. I went to The Hawthorns to replace Reg Ryan in 1956, two years after Albion had won the FA Cup. The club didn't get to Wembley while I was there, though we got mighty close on a couple of times, losing to Aston Villa in the 1957 semi-final and to the post Munich Manchester United side in the quarter-final a year later.

We had some cracking matches – some against Manchester United – that will always stay in my memory.

Just before the Munich air disaster we beat the brilliant Busby Babes 4-3 in a classic encounter at The Hawthorns and then after losing that cup game in 1958, we returned to Old Trafford a few days later and won 4-0 in front of 63,000 fans.

We had Maurice Setters carried off after 20 minutes of our Cup replay at Nottingham Forest but with ten men (there were no substitutes in those days) we went on to win 5-1, playing some brilliant football.

Then there was that tour to Russia which saw us play games inside packed stadiums in Moscow, Leningrad and Tbilisi. We came back from behind the Iron Curtain undefeated, having beaten the famous Russian Red Army team 4-2. And when they came over for a return game in 1957 to officially switch on The Hawthorns floodlights, over 52,000 fans saw us beat them again, this time by 6-5, a win which earned each player a £4

bonus. And our ball-juggling expert Davey Burnside was paid £50 to thrill the crowd at half-time by keeping the ball in the air for ten minutes for the benefit of the TV cameras. He was still juggling four days later.

I also recall going on tour to Canada and North America in 1959 when we scored goals galore. I netted six in one game – but that apart I had some great times at Albion and I never regretted moving to the Midlands from Fulham. The time I spent at The Hawthorns was the finest of my entire playing career.

Jim Sanders

When I joined Albion in 1945, I met two of the most respected gentlemen in football – the chairman Major H. Wilson Keys and Mr Fred Everiss, the club's secretary-manager – and also the joker himself, Billy Elliott.

These three people had a lot to do

David Shaw – "I jumped at the chance of joining Albion..."

with my good and bad times in the 13 years I spent at The Hawthorns.

Both Bill and his wife Ivy were very close friends, even after our playing days had ended.

We were preparing to commence our activities in the Second Division at the time I arrived, following World War Two, but with shrewd transfers we were building a great team and by 1948-49 we had won promotion to the top flight.

That season meant a lot to me. I passed out as a grade 'A' football coach under Walter Winterbottom, the then England manager and I also saved nine out of 11 penalties, which I believe is still a record for one season.

When travelling to away matches we (Billy Elliott, Jack Vernon, Dave Walsh and myself) always stuck to the same card school. And Bill and I always shared rooms.

Our trips abroad were pretty good as well and we gained some tremendous results, being the first English club side to win in Russia and returning unbeaten.

All the time I was with the Albion we had a first class team spirit, both on and off the field.

As regards nerves, I can only recollect having that sensation once – that was waiting in the tunnel at Wembley before we played Preston in the 1954 FA Cup Final. I was nervous when Ronnie Allen was about to take that vital penalty – I just turned my back and said: 'Come on Ron, do the business.'

But as Sir Stanley Matthews said "... any player that says he didn't have butterflies was not speaking the truth."

I could go on for ages, but all I can say is that I was fortunate to play behind three of the greatest centre-halves I have ever seen – namely Jack Vernon, Joe Kennedy and Jimmy Dugdale – and one of the finest left-halves in Ray Barlow.

I only hope all those lads enjoyed their years with the Albion like I did.

Certainly when Len Millard, George Lee and myself were all given free transfers in 1958 for services rendered, we were all very sad to say goodbye to a great club.

David Shaw

I jumped at the chance of joining Albion from Oldham Athletic in March 1973. Coming from the Third to the First Division was a big step for me. It was almost like going from a foreman to managing director in just 24 hours.

The atmosphere at The Hawthorns was completely different. At Boundary Park our play had enterprising promise but we missed promotion. At Albion I went into a team that was desperately searching for points in a relegation battle which we lost. But that was not my fault. Indeed, there can't be too many players who have gone from the Third Division to the First and then into the Second in such a short period of time.

Relegation didn't hit me as hard as it did my team-mates. Jeff Astle, Tony Brown, Willie Johnston, Asa Hartford, Len Cantello and Ally Robertson and John Osborne were stunned. They couldn't believe it. But that's football...you're on a high one minute and at a low ebb the next.

Our manager Don Howe, however, was determined to get us all in the right frame of mind for the start of the next season. But things didn't go according to plan. We started well enough but then had a poor spell which saw us slither towards the bottom end of the table. We picked up form but in the end had to settle in eighth position. The following season was another frustrating one and again we missed out on promotion by taking sixth place.

Then we had a change of manager. Howe left to be replaced by Johnny Giles and that marked the end of my Albion career. I returned to Oldham in the October and as you all know Albion went on to win promotion at the end of that season, clinching a place in the First Division with a 1-0 win at Boundary Park on the last day of the campaign. I was so pleased for Ally, John Wile, Jeff, Bomber and Ossie – Albion were the best footballing team in the Division that season and deserved to go up.

Gerry Summers

I was associated with the Albion for eight years. I first signed for the club as a 14 year-old schoolboy in 1947 and was transferred to Sheffield United in 1956.

I made my first-team debut against Manchester United on Christmas Eve 1955 when I took over the left-half position from Ray Barlow who was pushed up into the forward-line. Although we lost 4-1 in front of 25,000 spectators, it was a great occasion. And then a few weeks later I made my FA Cup debut against Wolves at Molineux. This time we won 2-1 and there were over 55,000 inside the ground.

I had some terrific times at The Hawthorns and it was a privilege to play alongside some splendid footballers like Barlow, Ronnie Allen and Johnny Nicholls. And there was George Lee, a direct left-winger who was so easy to play with.

from two of Albion's star players from the 1930s, W. G. Richardson and Teddy Sandford, and from Freddie Cox, the former Arsenal and Spurs winger who was player-coach of Albion's reserve team. And I must not forget Jesse Carver. He influenced me a great deal with his advanced coaching. He actually spent more time with the ball than running without it.

I was privileged to have been brought up as a youngster with a great reputation – a real footballing team. This benefited me for the rest of my career at Sheffield United, Hull City and Walsall and

then as manager of Oxford United, Gillingham and as a coach at Wolves, Albion and Leicester City.

• Gerry retired in 1998 after spending 12 years as Youth Development Officer at Derby County.

Dave Walsh

I was born in Barrack Street, Waterford and was educated at Mount Sion school. I never had the chance to play football for my home town team Waterford because the club went bust. With massive unemployment I was faced with the prospect of emigrating, but I didn't want to leave Ireland – I wanted to

I received a lot of encouragement

Dave Walsh – one of his favourite memories is his hat-trick against Chelsea in the FA Cup.

stay there and play football. Then Johnny Hartery, a player with Limerick, persuaded me to join his club. This was in 1943 when I was just 19. After that things went from strength to strength. I moved to Shelbourne (Dublin) and during a Cup game I was spotted by Linfield. Overlooking the fact that I was a Catholic, I signed for the Protestant club. In 1945-46 I scored over 60 goals – a record that still stands in Irish football – and this sort of form enticed several scouts to sail across the Irish Sea, including two from the Albion. After some talking I agreed to join Albion for £3,000 and the next four years were terrific for me. I scored 100 goals, helped the Baggies win promotion to the First Division in 1949 and made so many friends, some of whom I still see. I moved to Villa Park for £23,000 in 1950 and later played for Walsall. But it was at The Hawthorns where I enjoyed my football and saw it blossom. I played regularly at international level (I won over 25 caps all told) and my proudest moment

in the green jersey of Ireland was when we beat England 2-0 at Goodison Park, becoming the first overseas country to win on English soil.

One of my fondest memories in an Albion shirt was to score a hat-trick against Chelsea in a fifth-round FA Cup-tie at The Hawthorns. I was told afterwards that the commentator, Raymond Glendenning, who was covering the match on the radio for the BBC, said it was a 'red letter day' and one of the finest performances he had ever seen from a centre-forward. I was proud of that but it wasn't just down to me that day – my team-mates were brilliant.

I also recall the day we won 3-0 at Leicester to clinch a place in the First Division and when we beat the League champions Portsmouth at The Hawthorns in successive seasons without conceding a goal.

Albion had some great players immediately after the war – Jack Vernon, Ray Barlow, Billy Elliott, Jack Haines and Ike Clarke among

them. But I suppose everyone who played with these stars said the same thing. They were brilliant. Yet I also thought that Jimmy Duggan, Glyn Hood, Billy Gripton, Reg Ryan, Frank Hodgetts and Arthur Rowley were all very good footballers. Paddy Ryan and I were great mates and Arthur Rowley went on to become a magnificent goalscorer. Albion should have never sold him when they did.

I now live in Thurlestone, Devon but I never fail to visit The Hawthorns to watch Albion in action when I'm visiting the Midlands. I had such a great time there that I will forever be in debt to the club.

Brian Whitehouse

I had some great years at The Hawthorns, playing with some terrific footballers and making so many friends including Derek Kevan, Don Howe, Johnny Nicholls and Maurice Setters.

A couple of memorable moments from my Albion days were naturally when I scored two goals against

Brian Whitehouse – memorable moments include two goals against Villa in an FA Cup semi-final, and the trip to the USSR in 1957. This picture shows Whitehouse scoring against Blackpool in 1959.

Aston Villa in the FA Cup semi-final at Molineux in 1957 and when I toured Russia with the club shortly afterwards.

In that semi-final we were leading 2-1 with only a few minutes remaining. Wembley here we come I thought but the Villa scored a late equaliser and then beat us 1-0 in the replay at St Andrew's. We were all disappointed, I can tell you that for nothing.

The trip behind the Iron Curtain was tremendous and Albion became the first British professional team to win in Russia. I certainly enjoyed that trip.

One of the funniest incidents I came across during my Albion career was when we went on the S.S. Sylvania over to Canada for an end-of-season tour. Maurice Setters entered a fancy dress do whilst we were on board – what a joker.

John Wile

During my 13 years as a player at The Hawthorns there were many moments which will live with me forever.

Travelling to Boundary Park in 1976 with every car and coach decked out in blue and white and yellow and green as we travelled north on the M6 for that vital end-of-season encounter with Oldham Athletic – a game we had to win to gain promotion.

Playing in the UEFA Cup against Valencia and their World Cup stars – what a great occasion.

There were also some sad memories – losing in three Cup semi-finals when we were so close to Wembley and relegation under Don Howe in 1973.

I owe a lot to the late Reg Ryan for bringing me to Albion. It was he who spotted me when I was playing for Peterborough United. His recommendation was obviously taken seriously and I joined the club in

John Wile – travelling to Oldham for the 1976 promotion clincher is a special memory.

1970 when Alan Ashman was in charge.

He was a fine manager, but so too were Ron Atkinson – who gave me several tickings off for trying to play 'football' instead of giving the ball some welly – and Johnny Giles.

I got on well with so many players, sharing rooms with Tony Brown, laughing at Willie Johnston's wise-cracks and admiring Laurie Cunningham's dress sense, but most

If I hadn't become a professional football I would have taken a job as an electrical engineer. In fact at one point in my career I actually considered packing up the game. I'm glad I didn't.

I had many great tussles in my time with some of the game's finest strikers, Joe Jordan and Malcolm McDonald to name just two, with the latter perhaps the one I feared most.

ignoring John Osborne's.

ALBION AND ME...

John Trewick – former Albion player, now coach

I always wanted to be a footballer. I never considered anything else. In fact if I hadn't made the grade I don't know what I would have taken up.

I was playing in a local game in Northumberland when I was spotted by Albion's North-East scout, the late Bill Emery, when I was about 12. He invited me – and my parents – to visit The Hawthorns in the school holidays. He sold the club very well and I signed schoolboy forms, later becoming an apprentice (1972) and then being upgraded to professionalism.

I had some great times with Albion. There was that tremendous period under Johnny Giles when we won promotion from the Second Division in 1976. Then we played in the UEFA Cup against the likes of Red Star Belgrade and Valencia. We reached the semi-final of the FA Cup in 1978, finished third in the First Division behind Liverpool and Nottingham Forest and visited China. But I shall never forget my first-team debut in 1974 – a lasting memory that.

There were some great guys at the club and I roomed, on away trips, with Bryan Robson, Derek Statham, Brendon Batson and John Wile. Mick Martin was the joker in the pack – always up to something, like all the Irish folk I know. And David Cross often entertained us with his antics, likewise Willie Johnston.

Laurie Cunningham, Cyrille Regis and Brendon Batson – the Three Degrees – certainly had the style and the dress sense!

And most of us – if not all – had cars. Not flashy ones – we weren't paid enough – but some of the lads used to add flared wheel arches and sporty wheels to their models as well as go-faster stripes.

We players always got rollickings from the various managers in our time – it was routine in football and still is I believe! Even the gentlest of them all – Johnny Giles – gave me a few tickings off. But it was all worthwhile. I learnt a lot from so many people and now I'm enjoying working at the club again, hoping to encourage younger players to come forward and wear the navy blue and white stripes of West Bromwich Albion Football Club.

John Evans (Albion secretary)

My most dramatic memories of The Hawthorns are of the impressions it made on me as a boy growing up in the Black Country in the 1950s. It formed part of what modern writers would term my 'rites of passage.'

I remember that at first I wanted to come because I knew that here was where the big boys and their dads came on Saturdays. A week after my eighth birthday I was deemed big enough to watch Albion play Derby County. It was February 1951.

The remember the crowds, the bustle, the noise; being parted from dad to go through the boys' turnstile; the relief at finding him again waiting for me on the other side.

Being squeezed tightly to the front and then the roar as the players appeared, being frightened and exhilarated all at the same time, then going home to tell my mum all about it.

I remember my first Black Country derby, getting soaked so badly in a thunderstorm that dad had to take me out. We won 2-1 but I missed all of the real action. I was not allowed to go to see the return game at Molineux next day – but Albion won 4-1 without me anyway!

I also recall when my dad was working away, begging my mum to let me come on my own. Alec Jackson had just got into the team and he was from Tipton, too, so he needed my support, didn't he?

Eventually she gave in and I ran to catch the No.74 bus from Great Bridge – just in time.

I still remember wonderful days and wonderful nights, triumphs and despair.

The fifth-round FA Cup defeat at the hands of Birmingham City in 1956, the hammering of Manchester City 9-2 in 1957 and beating the Busby Babes 4-3 only a few months before the tragic Munich air crash.

Oh yes – I remember The Hawthorns.

Denis Sunley (*Express & Star*)

I have very warm memories of West Bromwich Albion – literally.

One of my earlier assignments for the *Express & Star* was to go away with Albion for a pre-season tournament to Yugoslavia in 1980-81. No problems, I thought. A nice little trip this, watch a few football matches and then back home. What I didn't reckon on was the weather.

Having spent most of my life shivering on touchlines up and down the country watching matches being played in freezing cold conditions with rain coming down like stair-rods, I flew out to Yugoslavia well prepared. Wife, Linda, God bless her, had packed all my usual footballing clothes – overcoat, raincoat, three woolly jumpers, thermal underwear, gloves, scarf, hat...the lot.

So you can imagine how I felt when we finally arrived at our destination – a boiling hot holiday resort on the Adriatic coast. 'That'll teach me to spend a bit more time swotting up on these matters' I thought as I made my way off the plane at sweltering Split airport.

And as the temperature soared up to melting point over the next few days, I was to learn what a friendly, helpful lot they are at Albion. The offers of help came flooding in...John Deehan loaned me a pair of shorts, Peter Barnes chipped in with a T-shirt and Gary Owen hand-ed over a natty pair of swimming trunks. By the time I had finished accepting these 'gifts' I looked like a sports fashion show; I felt really cool – in more ways than one.

Helpful Albion came to my rescue again on another trip abroad that went desperately close to going wrong.

This was back in the 1978-79 season when Albion travelled to Belgrade to play Red Star in the fifth round of the UEFA Cup. And, believe it or not, I very nearly missed the game because my press pass had blown out of the hotel window.

It was an hour or so before we were due to leave the hotel and travel to the stadium. There I was, taking things easy in my hotel room, lying on my bed with the French windows wide open, giving a superb view of the River Danube. Then, tap, tap on the door and in walked a waiter carrying a tray of drinks just as a gust of wind swept my ticket off the table and out of the window into the river. Panic.

We had made all sorts of arrangements for the match – telephones had been installed in the press box, a team of printers were standing by at our Wolverhampton offices, ready to bring out a special edition late that afternoon – and my ticket had been blown away.

I needn't have panicked, though. Enter Albion's own Mr Fixit, former secretary Alan Everiss. 'Lost your ticket Denis. No problem. Stick with us. We'll get you in' said the super-calm secretary. And they did. I sim-

ply mingled with the players and went through check-point after check-point. At one stage I even expected then-manager Ron Atkinson to hand me a pair of boots and tell me I was playing. He didn't though. Perhaps he should have – Albion lost 1-0.

Great memories of a great club.

Alfrede Vassallo (West Bromwich Albion Supporters Club, Malta)

My first experience of attending The Hawthorns came as recent as 1990. I had been a supporter of the Baggies for 30 years but I never had the opportunity to make my dream come true.

As Albion were favoured with a home fixture in the fifth round of the FA Cup against their staunch rivals Aston Villa, three members of the Malta branch seized the opportunity to go and watch their favourite team in action. We succeeded in making the long journey to the Midlands which lasted some nine hours. But before our first day in England was over we had the opportunity to wear off our fatigue by socialising with a few of our UK friends at a local pub.

The long awaited matchday finally arrived. On a heavily overcast Saturday morning, and with the rain menacing from one moment to another, together with a group of our UK colleagues, we made our way to The Hawthorns. Halford's Lane was already buzzing with activity at the time of our arrival, though it was some two hours before kick-off. Our first stop was at the club shop where we had the chance to buy some Albion souvenirs and the matchday programme. We were sur-

prised, though very pleased, to notice the Malta branch supporters club sticker fixed to the glass door of the club shop. After a brief visit to one of the executive boxes inside the ground which offered a majestic view of the Hawthorns pitch, we proceeded to the shareholder's lounge where we had the opportunity to make new acquaintances, including a first meeting with club statistician Tony Matthews.

However, not before long we made our way to our seats in the Halford's Lane stand. A crowd of over 26,000 packed inside and the atmosphere was electrifying. With Villa doing exceptionally well in the top sphere and Albion labouring in the bottom half of the Second Division, Graham Taylor's men were favourites to oust the Baggies from what was being described as the Midlands Cup Final.

Albion were out of luck on the day when as early as the fourth minute Gary Robson was carried off injured. Neither side created many chances yet Albion had more possession. Sadly from my point of view Villa went on to win the game 2-0.

After the match we met several personalities both from the Albion administration side and also from the playing staff, with Bernard McNally generously sharing his birthday cake with us. We had our photograph taken with the players and had the chance to talk to the chairman and to the teenager Daryl Burgess.

While everyone was obviously disappointed with the result, we all had a great time at The Hawthorns and I for one will never forget my first visit to see the team I support and love – West Bromwich Albion.

Subscribers

The Abraham Family
David Adams
Roger, Kim and Matthew Adams
Robert Aiken
Mike Allen
William H Allen
Geoff Allman
T W Angell
Mr M D Anstis
Nick Archer
Michael J Argent
Peter J Arnold
Sid Ashfield
Royston Atkin
Scott Baggott
Adam Bailey
John Albert Bailey
Steven Bailey
Brian Baker
Daniel Paul Baker
Harry Allan Baker
Ken Baker
Mr Phillip Ballard
Craig Ballinger
Len Ballinger
Kenny Banks
Martin Banner
Cyril Banyard
Vince Barber
Steve Barber
John Barlow
Gillian Barker
Paul Barker
Thomas Wilson Barrett
Jeremy Bate
John Bateman
Colin Baulch
Dave and Peter Baxendale
Michael Baxter
Peter Baxter

Michael Beard
Paul and Alistair Beard
Steve Beard
Ron Beards
Roy Belcher
Joe Davis James Bell
Neil Benbow
Trevor Bickley
Mr Lee Biddle
Mark W Bifield
Fred Birch
Daniel Bird
Lyndon Bird
R J Bird
Mr P K Birdi
Brian Bishop
Stuart Bishop
Mr S J Bissell
George Blackham
Ian Blackham
Anthony Blogg
Daniel Bloomer
Christopher Blunt
W Blunt
Gilbert Board
Sue Board
A A Boffy
Paul Bolton
Edward Bone
Peter Bone
Richard Boucher
G A Bowen
Neil R Boxley
Carl Bradford
Richard Bradford
Robert S Bradley
Neil Brealey
Paul Andrew Brindley
Peter J Broadist
The Brothwood Family

John George Brown
Richard Brown
Mick Bryan
Stuart Bullock
Michael Bunn
Philip David Burgess
Andrew Burton
John Burton
David Butler
Nick Byrne
Bryan Caddick
Malcolm G Calder (Happy 60th Birthday)
Arthur Campbell
Steve Cannon
Martyn Capewell
Stuart Capewell
P Carpenter
Stephen Carr
Fred Carter
Arthur Sidney Cartwright
Barry Cartwright
James Robert Cartwright
Bradley Caswell
Lindsay M Cave
Mark and Robert Challis
Ashley Hayden Chambers
Stephen Chance
Alex Chapman
John Charles
F H Chater
Graham Chilton
Philip Clements
Susan Clarke
Nichola and Laura Clynes
Richard Coles
Stewart Coller
Gordon Collins
Ian Collins
Paul Collins
Philip Collins
Mick Colsey
Robert Cooksey
Darren Cooper

John Barry Cooper
Philip Cooper
Gordon Corbett
Joe Cottam
Bob and Dave Cox
Gilbert Cox
Marc Cox
W A Cripps
John Elliot Crowe
Patrick A Crowley
Andy Crump
Andrew Curl
Andrew Cutler
Anthony Cutler
Mr Stanley Dalloway
James Dalton
Gordon L Dangerfield
Mr Joseph Dangerfield
Adam Darby
Trevor M Davenport
Colin Davies
Norman Davies
Mike Davis
Tracy Davis
Mr Chris Dawson
Mark Philip Denning
Aaron Dent
Elsie May Derry
Geoffrey Dicken
David J Dimmock
Mrs Ada Dixon
R G Dixon
Peter Dodson
Philip Doherty
T A Donohue
Geoff Dore
Jennie Anne Doswell
Ivan and Matthew Downing
Peter James Driver
Rob Drury
Mark Dudley
Michael Duffield
John Dunn
Nathan East
Paul East

SUBSCRIBERS

Verity Olivia Eden
Tony Edgington
Matthew Edwards
Michael John Edwards
David Elcock
Mark Eley
David Elliott
Ian D Ellis
Jeremy Elwell
Clive Evans
David Evans
William E Evans
Andrew Farrier
John Farrington
David Fenton
Jan and Ashley Few
Darron Field
Kayte Fieldhouse
Terence Firmstone
Keith and Robert Fisher
Tony Fisher
Iain Flaherty
Gary Flavell
Colin Fletcher
Paul Fletcher
Katie Flower
Stephen J Flower
Paul Floyd
John Martin Fordham
Eric Foster
John N Fox
C A Fraser
Joan Freeman
Dave Fryer
Mr Eric Garner
Glynne Garratt
Stan Garrett
Terence Gibbons
Sally Gibson
Craig Gilder
Richard Gilder
Mr Brian Gilman
Robert Godwin
Mr G I F Godby
Mr I P F Godby

Arthur Goodall
Barrie Gooding
Ted Gould
Tony Goule
Terence Grainger
G J Greenhough
Stephen Greenwood
Stephen Gregory
Graham Grice
John Griffin
A W Griffiths
Stuart Griffiths
David Grigg
Wayne Grigg
Nathan Gulliver
William Gurmin
Stuart Hackett
Tony Hackett
Steve Hadabora
Nicolas Hadley
Ben Hall
The Hall Family
Peter Hall
Bernard Hanson
Robin Harman
Lindsay Harpin
Paul Harris
Roger P Harris
L H Harrison
William H Harrison
Paul Hart
Matthew Hartill
David Raymond Harvey
Percy W Harvey
Martin Hassell
Vincent Haughey
John Hawker
John H Hawkesford
R A Haycock
Gavin Haynes
William Hayward
Matthew Hennefer
R Hennefer
Pete Henry
Mr Kenneth Alan Hewitt

Mr Richard William Hewitt
David M Hibbert
Michelle C Hibbert
W Hickman
Craig W Hill
Frederick Keith Hill
Martyn J Hill
Steve Hill
Rob Hindley
Jim Hingley
Christopher Hinks
Brian Hiscox
Ivor J Hodgetts
Carl Holden
A M Holland
James Holmes
Stuart Holmes
David Homans
John Joseph Homer
Paul Homer
Paul Hoper
Christopher Horton
Frederick Hill
Shaun Hipkiss
David Hollingmode
Ian Robert Homer
Gareth Hopkins
Mark V Horton
Paul Horton
Colin Houghton
Ian Hoult
F H Howell
Andrew Hughes
W Hughes
Jonathan Hunt
Lawson Hunt
Garry Jackson
Jeff Jackson
David George James
Gary L James
Martin Luke James
Ron Jarratt
Mike Jarvis
S M and L M Jeens
Frank Jeffs

Richard Jenkins
Alan Jennings
Alan K Jones
Bob Jones BSc
Ian A Jones
John Jones
John R Jones
Malcolm Jones
Mark Anthony Jones
Michael, Ian, Christopher and Andrew Jones
Peter Jones
Peter J Jones
Stephen Jones
Steve, Liam and David Jones
Jason Keady
Andrew G Kemshall
Ashley J Kemshall
Sean Kendle
Simon Kendrick
Tony Kendrick
Leslie Kenny
Michael E Kerry
John Kilkenny
Brian Kirkham
Mr Mark Kite
Mr Martin Kite
Lewis Knight
Adrian Knowles
Harold, Andrew and Oliver Knowles
Stephen Knott
Bert Lamb
Derek Latham
Robert S Lawley
Simon John Lee
Dermot Leonard
Ian Lester
Roy Lester
A Letterese
Nicky Letzer
Anthony Lewis
Mervyn Lewis
Tim Lewis
Tom Lewis
John Llewellyn
D J Lloyd

SUBSCRIBERS

J W Lloyd
J W Lovell
John Loveridge
Ryan Peter Lugg
Dave Lyons
Timothy McCarthy
Marcus McDermott
Chris McDonald
S G McNeil
Cathy and John Maddox
Mr Ashok Mal
Mr T B Mallin
Manchester Branch of WBASC:
  Ade Brandwood
  Hayden James Cooper
  Martin Dunn
  Steve Dunn
  Chris Foxall
  John, Chris & Eithne Hackett
  Malcolm Jones
  Paul Iain Morgan
  Haydn Thompson
  Richard Wagner
  Paul Wagner
  Justin Wilkes
Lee Manning
R Mantle
John Marsh
Adrian Marshall
Kevin Martin
Alan Masefield
Bobby Mason
David Mason
Luke Jonathan Mason
Tom Mason
Freda Matthews
Melvyn Meacham
Steve Finn and Linda Millard
Mark T Miller
Gemma Millinchip
K D Millington
Michael John Mills
Paul J Mills
Robert L Mills
Robert Whitelaw Mills

Stephen Mole
David and Christopher Moore
Harpreet Moore
Helen Moore
John Moore
June Moore
Jamie Moren
Mike Moren
P A Moren
John Morgan
Chas Morris
David Morris
Geoff A Morris
Huw Morris
R G Morris
Ryan Morris
Kevin Mortiboys
Craig Moseley
Martin Moseley
Paul James Moss
Francis James Moy
Stuart James Moy
Roy Mytton
Anthony Nash
Geoff Nevey
Tom Newton
John R Nicholls
Ricky Thomas Nicholls
Roy Nicholls
Kevin Nichols
Andy Nickless
Christopher Nickless
Michael James Nicklin
David Nixon
John Noon
Mick and Tom Northall
Eric Offley
Stephen Offley
Mark Oliver
Chris O'Neill
Tim Osborne
Steven Paul Owen
Douglas Parish
Barry Parker
A S Parkes

Andrew Parkes
Nigel Parkes
Ray Parkes
Kevin R Parr
Kevin Parsons
Ian Paterson
David Payne
John Payton
Daniel Peace
Dennis Pearce
Garth Pearce
Terry Pearce
Nick Peach
Derek Tudor Steve Peake
Jonathon Andrew Pearson
Malcolm Pearson
Graham Peplow
Mr Arthur Perry
Mike Phipps
Wayne Pickett
Ronald K Piddock
Mark Pilsbury
Andrew A Piper
Brian Anthony Pitt
David John Plant
B F A Poole
Jay Poole
John Edward Poole
Nick Poole
Matthew Potter
Michael Poultney
Malcolm John Powell
Mr G M Powers
John Wesley Pratt
Kevin Pratt
Dennis John Preston
Jeff Prestridge
Matthew Prestridge
Alan John Price
Ian C Price
John Price
Lee Price
T J H Price
Steve 'Priesty' Priest
Chris Prinn

Clive Proctor
Bob Proffitt
Mr M A Prosser
Alan Pugh
Ben Pugh
Matthew A Punnett
Kim Randall
Stephen Randall
Ron Randle
Paul Ratcliffe
Mr Lee Raven
Joanne Reader
Mark Andrew Reed
James Reynolds
Nathan Reynolds
Neil Reynolds
Paul Rich
Ian Riddell
Ian C Rivers
Stephen D Rivers
Alan Roberts
Andrew Mark Roberts
Kenneth Roberts
Oliver M Roberts
Michael Robins
Ben Rodgers
Mr D N Rogers
Will Rogers
M J Rolinson
Jason Rose
Michael Ross
Mr David Leslie Round
Jonathan Clive Round
Julian Rowe
David A Rowley
Gerard Ryan
Brian Sambrookes
Brenda Sanderson
Andrew Saunders
Carol Savage
Martin Scott
Michael A Seedhosue
Mr Satnam Shakham
Jonathan Keith Sharman
Alex Shaw

SUBSCRIBERS

Paul, Kath, Emma, Amy and Laura Shaw
Philip Shaw
Richard Shaw
Robert Shelswell
Kenneth Shutt
Keith Siggins
Tom Silk
Michael Silvester
Daniel Silwood
G A Simcox
Judy Simcox
Bernard and Michael Simmonite
G M Simmons
Colin Simpson
Gareth D Sims
Paul Siviter
Bob Skelding
Neil and Luke Skett
Craig Skidmore
John Skidmore
Mr S Skidmore
Reg Smallwood
Christopher Smith
Darryl Smith
Denys A Smith
Graham Smith
Jonathan Smith
Lee Smith
Neil Smith
Philip Smith
Rhys Smith
Stuart Smith
Dale A B Smyth
Paul W B Smyth
Stephen Smytheman
Michael Snell
Ross Snell
Will Spencer
David Spicer
Michael Spink
Leigh Sprules
Steven Sorrill
Lee A Southall
Paul Spence
Martyn Spink

Glyn D Stacey
Craig Stanton
Andrew and David Stevens
David Stokes
Joseph Stubbs
Michelle Styles
David John Sutton
Laura, Jack and Sarah Swallow
Peter Swanick
Alfred W Swann
Russell Swingell
Pat Talbot
Andrew Taylor
David Taylor
Kenneth Taylor
Laurie Taylor
Mark Garry Taylor
Peter Taylor
Brian Terence
Phil Terry
Eric Thomas
Michael Thomas
Paul Thomas
Jayne Thompson
Roger Thompson
David Thorpe
Dennis Thorpe
Ivan I Tibbetts
Paul Tilley
W Timmington
Mrs B M Timmins
Ben Thorne
D Thornhill
Malcolm Tolley
Stephen Tongue
Barbara A Tout
James S Tranter
Jonathan Tranter
Paul Trattles
G W Treadwell
R K Trentham
Andrew Trumper
Nicholas Trumper
Ian J Tubby
Mr Adrian Turley

Barry Turner
Bill Turner
Carl A Turner
Chris Turner
David Turner
J R Turner
Mr Paul Barry Turner
Pete Turner
Peter Turner
Ryan Turner
Tony Turner
Nigel Underhill
Darren Underwood
Allan Unwin
Mike Vass
Paul Arthur Veness
Callum James Vine
Brett Andrew Wain
Malcolm Waite
David Walker
James G Walker
Morris Walker
N Geoff Walker
Stephen Walsh
Mr B Walters
Stephen Walters
Dean Walton
Gary Allan Ward
Ian Ward
Matthew Ward
Brian Warner
Paul Wassell
David J Watkin
Robert Watkins
Stephen Watson
David Watton
Terence Neil Wall
R F Weaver
Julian Denise Welsh
Neil Wetherall
George Wheatley
Andrew White
Aaron Whitehead
Adam Mark Whitehouse
Craig Andrew Whitehouse

Geoff and Andrew Whitehouse
Mark Whitehouse
Anthony Whittingham
Kevin Whyley
Keith Wibberley
J W D Wilkes
David and James Willetts
John Williams
Mick (Baggie) Williams
Ray Williams
Russell Williams
Ryan James Williams
Stella Williams
Stephen Williams
Mark Willitts
Terry Wills
Robert Wilson
Ian Withers
L H Woodhall
David Raymond Woodward
Robert Worley
Geoff Wright
Matthew Wright
Paul Wright
Martin Worley
Derek John Wyke
Jean Zoeller